A FARM IN MARIN

PORTRAITS IN TIME FROM PANGAEA TO POINT REYES

A Deep History

SHERI RITCHLIN

To Betty Goerke,
with deep admiration and gratitude
for all you have done to make this
book possible!
Sheri

POINTER OAK

Pointer Oak / Tri S Foundation

Distributed by Millichap Books

First printing

Book and jacket design by Carl Brune

Printed in USA

ISBN 978-1-937462-37-6

millichapbooks.com

TO BARBARA BAYLEY CROSS
BELOVED TEACHER, MENTOR, FRIEND

Great valor has due honor; they weep here for how the world goes, and our life that passes touches their hearts. Throw off your fear. This fame insures some kind of refuge.

— Virgil
The Aeneid, circa 25 BC
(trans. Robert Fitzgerald)

At the right hand of the Indies there is an island called California, very close to that part of the Terrestrial Paradise, which was inhabited by black women without a single man among them, and they lived in the manner of Amazons. They were robust of body with strong passionate hearts and great virtue. The island itself is one of the wildest in the world on account of the bold and craggy rocks. . . . The island everywhere abounds with gold and precious stones . . .

There ruled over that island of California a queen of majestic proportions, Calafia, more beautiful than all others, and in the very vigor of her womanhood.

— Garcia Rodríguez de Montalvo
The Adventures of Esplandián
A Spanish novel, circa 1500

Table of Contents

That a person is made of more than cells and sinew,
more than genes and a personal history,
but also of the deep earth fires and tides and the movements of distant stars;
of galaxies and earthly plates colliding; of early ancestors, names unknown,
who trod the paths worn smooth with human exploration, longing and despair;
of the debris of fallen civilizations; tales of their heroes and their villains,
who warp the shape of psychic cells with whorls and furrows;
of luminous souls who have kept a lamp burning in the galactic dark
to signal our presence and our project . . . We, the unique creatures of Earth,
this living blue and green garden sailing about the Sun.

That we are each made of all this and so much more, spun in the web of
a cosmic whole and holiness . . .

I call this Deep History.

INTRODUCTION

IN THE INTEREST OF FULL DISCLOSURE, I should tell you this up front: The farm in Marin—that's pronounced Ma-RIN—is not a farm, it is a ranch. In New York State, where I grew up, every place with some acreage that was being cultivated was called a farm. Wheat, corn, some chickens, some pigs and a horse or two . . . That was a farm. "Some acreage" might be a hundred acres or so. To my child's eye—city-reared, apartment-dwelling—farms began where the buildings and the sidewalks stopped and there was suddenly green. Farms began where there were cows. And in my child's heart, I wanted there to be a creek where I could wade and fish and watch for frogs. Build a raft and sail down it like Huckleberry Finn. It was always the dairy farms that provided the welcome and pungent announcement that we had crossed that invisible line, which I seem to have been seeking to cross all of my life. A coming home to a place I had never been. A soul's home in nature.

I only grasped the meaning of *ranch* in my twenties on my first trip west. I was in Nevada City, Montana walking through a museum there with a family I had just met. We fell into conversation and I asked where they were from. The father explained that they had a "little ranch" nearby. How little is a little ranch? I asked. Five thousand acres he replied. This was a number, a space, which I could not hold in my apartment-size head. And this was *small*?

Several years ago I was driving through Wyoming with a friend on the way down to Mexico. In one of the small towns, I went into a local salon to have my hair cut and my eyes opened. I'm always curious about small town life and the hairdresser, like the barber, is a reliable source of information. "Many ranches around here?" I asked. "Oh not so many as before." "Are there *big* ranches?" (aging had not subdued my obsession). Her voice took on a funereal tone. "Oh hardly at all you know. They've been divided or sold off so you only have a few of your bigger ones left." "How big are we talking about?" "Well *you* know. The million acre ones." A *million*! I love to be dazzled with these kinds of numbers. I would have died for my one acre as a kid, assuming it was big enough for a creek to go through and a horse.

I went west at 21 and I've been a westerner ever since, although many Montanans and their ranching brethren would dispute the idea that California is The West. There are bumper stickers that read "Don't Californicate in Montana" or Washington or Oregon or Idaho. They have them for each state. And I admit that the Southern California coast where I spent much of my adult life is further removed from the spirit of the West than New York State. I lived in Leucadia and Del Mar—beach towns where land was measured in square feet and a quarter of an acre would cost you an arm and a leg. I saw land values soar to dizzying levels. Small houses on small lots, part vertical cliff, would go for a million dollars and be torn down to be replaced by somebody else's dream house. This wasn't just prime

American real estate. It was prime *world* real estate, with some of the most beautiful views on the planet.

This was even more true of Northern California, which I only came to know when I moved to San Francisco to attend graduate school at the California Institute of Integral Studies. I had loved the Mediterranean warmth and beauty of Southern California with its masses of bougainvillea, flowering trees like the acacia and jacaranda; its sea lavender and vividly colored ice plant and nasturtium tumbling down the sandstone cliffs along the ocean. It was another world to me after the harsh winters of Rochester, which brought icy roads, streets lined with dirty slush, snow to be scraped off the windshield in the frigid winter mornings. Snow is beautiful in the country but in cities, it turns quickly gray and the urban landscape is monochromatic through the long winter months.

The San Francisco Bay Area was another experience altogether. Beautiful in a different way. A more dramatic landscape. And there at the center of it is San Francisco, surely one of the world's most beautiful cities. So filled with light. Set on its seven hills, like Rome, with water on three sides of it, from the blue Pacific to the gleaming waters of San Francisco and San Pablo bays. And to crown this jewel, the rich and graceful red lines of the Golden Gate Bridge. A giant soaring harp singing to the sea and land. It is one of the seven wonders of the modern world with views so fine you want to stop right in the middle and join the tourists taking in the white cityscape to the east, the sailboats scattered like a flock of white birds, the Pacific opening out toward China on the west . . . The first crossing of that bridge is an experience you will never forget, and all the crossings that follow will remain fresh and stirring.

Where does the Golden Gate Bridge go? Not many people who haven't been to San Francisco know that. It is just this beautiful arching of the heart towards possibility—the quintessential archetype of crossing. Beyond, one sees green headlands and trees and a beckoning to beauty. The Golden Gate Bridge, in fact, goes to Marin—in the year 2000, the wealthiest county in the United States, measured in per household income. Sausalito, Tiburon, Mill Valley, Ross, Belvedere . . . World class places. It has the highest living costs to match, exceeding even the pricey Southern California beach towns.

The San Francisco Bay Area is one of the foremost research areas in the world, including the vast resources of UC Berkeley, UC San Francisco, Stanford and Silicon Valley. Not surprisingly, the natural and cultural milieu attracts people from all over the world. Many of the best, the brightest and the most well-heeled live in Marin. The creative and unorthodox live in houseboats in Sausalito. The high rollers live in mansions in Belvedere. When you cross the Golden Gate Bridge, you have entered a world of natural and human elegance.

Now we come back to the farm that is a ranch. The dictionary definition of "ranch" is "a farm where cattle, sheep, horses, or other livestock are raised on large tracts of open land, especially in North and South America and Australia." Texas, the vast lands of Australia, the spacious *pampas* of Argentina . . . Sure. That I can see. But Marin? You would hardly expect a farm in Marin, let alone a *ranch* of that description. It was something I just couldn't imagine when I first came here. So I will now share with you the eighth wonder of my world—a ranch in Marin—and a good deal more.

◆ ◆ ◆

My farm is in Sonoma County, an hour north of the Golden Gate bridge in a wide valley to the west of Sonoma Mountain; a peaceful fold of countryside where cows and horses still graze in open fields beside the vineyards and acres of farmland. California's main artery, Highway 101, bears its tide of automobiles north and south less than five miles away. On the other side of Sonoma mountain, the town of Sonoma goes about its business of wine in relative isolation, protected by its range of low hills, thick with vineyards and elegant wineries of international fame— Sebastiani, St. Francis, Buena Vista . . . It's a long list for a small place.

I too can walk a few steps on a golden summer evening into our own small vineyard to pick grapes for my dessert, crisp early muscats eaten right there in the fading sun, watched by the neighbor's robust cows across the creek bed, their glossy backs reddened by the slanting light.

It's not really my farm in the proprietary sense. I'm just another wild creature, enjoying its blessings under the shade of the eucalyptus trees with Mr. Fields, my 1972 camper. I share the space with a family of great horned owls and a family of red tail hawks who have penthouse apartments high up in the eucalyptus tips, with a view of the whole neighborhood. Of course they have been here much longer than I. The long flat top of Mr. Fields serves as a lower terrace to a variety of smaller birds, and once—to my amazement—a wild turkey mother, whose family had a *pied a terre* near the creek bed. By far the most numerous of the locals are the California quail who pour over the rocks, old tires and discarded odds and ends like great waves splashing in from the sea.

My farm, in fact, belongs to Ed and Susie Grossi. Ed has clarified for me that a ranch is where animals are raised and a farm is where crops of some kind are raised. Grossi Farms raises organically grown vegetables. It is 50 acres, with 37 under cultivation. Vegetables, fortunately, don't need to graze and take up so much space. They just sit tight and grow.

A dirt road cuts down between the fields from Petaluma Hill Road to the cluster of buildings that includes the Grossis' house, the office for their nursery business, the vegetable stand, and just beyond that to the left, a huge yellow metal structure that is variously called "the barn," "the shop" and "the lunch room," depending on who is using it. To Susie, who keeps the chicken feed in there, it is the barn. To Ed, who repairs his tractors and forklifts in there, it is the shop. His pride and joy, an old 1941 Chevrolet super-deluxe sedan, which he is lovingly restoring for Susie, rests in various corners in various stages of eternal repair. A lunchroom has been petitioned off for the workers, with a lazy fluorescent light that makes food look blue, if it can sustain itself long enough. The fellows usually prefer to light a lamp that sits on a table in the rear and provides token illumination. It's atmospheric for a lunchroom. Maybe it reminds them of a cantina back home.

For me, of course, it is "a barn"—as the realization of my childhood fantasies and the fact that I feed the chickens when the Grossis are gone. The chicken coop is next to the barn and it houses a variety of exotic creatures that immediately elevated my view of the species from the big, white dizzy birds I had seen waddling around a barnyard or two back east. These are a multicolored mix of French Silkies, Polish, Frizzles and a few interesting interactions of the above. One description of Frizzles reads, "Now, this is truly a unique bird. Unlike all other chickens, the feathers on the frizzle curve outward and forward giving it the appearance of having walked through a wind storm backwards." The Polish have soft white pom-poms on their heads and walk like ladies off to tea. The frizzle roosters are gorgeously arrayed in deep gold, teal, rust and black. Their back-swept feathers always remind me of a woman who has just had her hair done in a glamorous do and is all dressed up for the opera. No scrawny red legs for these breeds. They have feathered legs and feet that look like formal oriental pantaloons. These are *not* your typical barnyard fowl on the way to the dinner table. They are pampered pets, much cherished (and harassed) by the farm stand customers under ten years old.

When I first came to the farm, we had a goat that was equally coveted by the younger set. One child, after meeting it through the wire fence of its enclosure, ran back to her mother and exclaimed, "Oh *look* Mommy, they've got a reindeer!" We never corrected this impression. It seemed good for business. One summer a great barbecue was held for all of the workers and their families. Delfino, who not only manages the irrigation of the nursery but works as a cook and caterer on the side, had offered to do the barbecuing to show off some of the finer points of this Mexican cuisine. The specialty of the day? Barbecued goat. The event was a great success, but the aftermath, less so. When little Stephanie returned she went straight to the goat pen and was distraught to find it empty. "*Where?* Where is the reindeer?" I had to think fast here. "Well . . . you see . . . Santa came and had to take him back to the North Pole. It happens sometimes. There's so much to do up there to get ready for Christmas." The word Christmas did the trick. This was something worthy of her sacrifice.

The dirt road snakes left around the barn-shop-cantina and runs between the creek to the left and the vineyards to the right. The creek is invisible but its line is drawn by the eucalyptus trees along its banks. We are passing Mr. Fields' domain. At the back of the property, Hector has his bee houses. That's his business, "Hector's bees." And what happier life can a bee have than on a vegetable farm and nursery? Not to mention Susie Grossi's magnificent gardens, lush with lavender, roses, rare tulips, and dahlias. Beyond the bee houses, the road continues into the adjacent property belonging to San Giacomo Vineyards, which raises grapes for sale to Sonoma wineries.

At the center of the farm are the rows and rows of beautiful trees and shrubs which are grown by Ed and Susie's Sweetlane Wholesale Nursery. This is a specimen nursery that Ed and Susie started together a few years ago. It has grown by leaps and bounds in that time. They do high end jobs for customers like Lucasfilm in San Francisco and the mansions in Belvedere, Tiburon and the East Bay.

On the south side of the property lie the vegetable fields. The crops are rotated every year so these may be melons or pumpkins, tomatoes or peppers and beans, garlic, squash, strawberries . . . In the winter, Ed plants a cover crop of oats or barley.

When I first discovered Grossi Farms, Ed had been running it for about fifteen years. Originally he had grown hay, continuing the farming that his father had done up here as an extension of his own place down in Marin. And that was a *ranch*, not a farm. It is the one for which I have so inaccurately (according to western standards) named this book, "A Farm in Marin."

Now that we are clear about farms and ranches, I come to the second caveat. This book, as you will soon discover, is not really about a farm *or* a ranch, in Marin *or* Sonoma. It is about how my experience of those places and my search for their story opened me up to both a larger seeing and to larger questions. Questions about "those who go" and "those who stay." About movements and migrations. About things that change and things that endure. I have combined memoir and history because our smallest, most personal moments in the present are ripples on the wave that has gone before and is moving so swiftly toward what is to be. The next moment. Personal. Global. Cosmic.

The people and places I have chosen are purely arbitrary but you will see that over time they *are* connected. This story begins with a farm in Sonoma, which begins with the story of a ranch in Marin, and before that, with a plot of land in the foothills of the Italian Swiss Alps. Each is a story, enmeshed in another story. It is stories, all the way down. And where there are discontinuities—like Ticino (pronounced Ti-CHEE-no), Switzerland to Marin, well those are stories too. Sometimes the best of all because they are filled with exotica, the fantastic, for people at one end or the other. Are the streets really lined with gold as they say? Is it true that farmers in their alpine vineyards wear special shoes to work in the steep places? Tell us! The stories scatter like seeds, spread as much by tragedy as good fortune. Pine cones burst open with fire and fly before the hot winds. They take root quickly in the charred earth where the rodents have perished.

There is no place on earth where you can tear a piece of it off, hold it apart and say "There! That's *that!*" It is always, as John Donne said, "a piece of the continent, a part of the main." It is always enmeshed in larger systems connected by countless visible and invisible threads. Fine filaments of stories that form their own wide ecosystems, whispered, sung, broadcast, carved in stone, spun across cyberspace.

You can begin the story anywhere and it will touch everywhere. I begin with Dominic Grossi. And you will see how far that leads! Backwards and forwards through eons, north and south across the globe. So fasten your seatbelts!

No, on second thought, I begin with Mr. Fields. At the beginning of the story (I'm picking an arbitrary point of course), I am standing with Susie Grossi at the edge of a dry creek bed as she tells me the story of one fish.

A FISH STORY

And when the white moths were on the wing,
And moth-like stars were flickering out,
I dropped the berry in a stream
And caught a little silver trout.

— W.B. YEATS

Susie Sweet Grossi is intrepid. There's no other way to put it. This was clear to me the first time she offered to give me a ride home in the golf cart. I was living two blocks away from the farm at the time so I thought she was joking. "You can't take the golf cart on Petaluma Road," I laughed. Petaluma Hill Road is a main thoroughfare. "No problem," she said. "I'll take you the back way across the fields."

It's not as if there *was* a Back Way or even a beaten path. The thick adobe soil had been churned up beneath the tractor, preparing it for tomatoes. But Susie is a born trailblazer. We roared along the edge of this, bucketing about in a way I was sure would upend the golf cart.

"I don't think these are made for this terrain," I gasped, grabbing for anything I could hold onto to keep from being planted among the tomatoes. Golf carts were created for a serene and sedate retirement to transport often delicate bones across smooth, manicured greens. "They're plenty sturdy," she assured me. "No problem."

Today she is plunging through tall thistle and fallen branches behind Mr. Fields with the same gusto. I step carefully in her wake until we are standing on the edge of a dry creek bed. "Eddie found a steelhead trout here in the Spring," she explains.

"Here? Here among these rocks and dry sticks?"

"In the winter this is full of water running down from Sonoma Mountain during the rainy season. I guess when it started to dry up in the summer, the steelhead got trapped in a pool of water over there. Everybody was pretty excited. They thought the steelhead was extinct in this area. So now there's a creek restoration plan going on."

A city person like me never thinks about those things. I'm the kid who used to hang a worm on a curtain hook over a puddle in front of our apartment complex on rainy days. Funny thing: I never got a nibble. My dreams of growing up along a creek came back to me, so I stared in appreciation of a dream *almost* realized. Just the wrong season. Summer. I would later discover that Sonoma County is veined like a dowager's skin with a fine network of streams and I was fortunate to miss the close-up view of the creek in the winter that Mr. Fields was almost carried away by floods. There are two major watersheds in the county and we are sitting right on the edge of one of them. Here the streams puzzle their wet heads over the fastest way to San Pablo Bay or the Pacific. The flat land where the vineyards now sit at the base of Sonoma Mountain is carved with old channels where the water once ran off in an alluvial fan. "I've cut right across them with the tractor," Ed told me once.

I stare down into the dry, warm creek bed. It is a verified 95 degree day. There are rumors it may hit 100. The banks look parched. The plants and fallen eucalyptus branches are dry and stiff. I try to imagine a shimmering fish—brother to the rainbow, cousin to the salmon—hidden in any corner of it. I see it coming to life in a gravel bed up Sonoma Mountain somewhere, where it would have lain in its silvery gel in a cool, oxygenated stream with an ideal daily temperature of 44 to 50 degrees for a month or so. If the temperatures were warmer, it would have hatched in less time, but then the fish are smaller, with less chance of survival. This fish was a survivor for sure. Like its salmon cousin, its destiny was a seafaring one. It left home after a year to three years in the relative protection of the freshwater streams. I imagine this one leaping ecstatically in a surge of winter waters swelling this same creek bed, dreaming mysteriously of the Pacific. A head full of fish lore—delicate invertebrate memory of rivers running to the sea. Does this steelhead get marooned on the way up or on the way back? Were his seafaring days (they spend one to four years there) ending or beginning? Was it on its way home in an ancient rite of return to spawn new life where its own began? Unlike the salmon, the steelhead doesn't necessarily die just after spawning. They may spawn several times.

On that afternoon, I looked into the dry creek bed and just saw questions there. Whatever the answers were, this fish could never have imagined the impact it would make. How the crisis of its isolation in a cranny of water would be observed and acted upon by humans. First Ed Grossi. Then the Fish and Game folks. Then the Water Resource Board. Then the Sonoma State Environmental Studies class. The High School class, the Elementary School class . . . Never have imagined that a state-wide army had been mustered in its behalf. Wouldn't it have been surprised to know that it had already inspired its own state act: The Salmon, Steelhead Trout and Anadromous Fisheries Act of 1988. And pursuant to that become the subject of a 242 page "Steelhead Restoration and Management Plan for California"?

All this because we have learned to count things we used to take for granted. To count our blessings you might say. In 1996, when the Plan was written, the statewide population of adult steelheads was an estimated at 250,000 adults, less than half the population thirty years before. The Restoration was aimed at stopping this precipitous decline.

The major strategies of the plan are to restore the fishes' damaged habitat and to create access to historic habitat that is presently blocked; ensure through angling regulations that steelhead are not over-harvested; maintain and improve hatchery runs when necessary, and facilitate research into freshwater and ocean life history, behavior, habitat requirements and other aspects of steelhead biology.

This is a fine example of what cosmologist Brian Swimme has called "the universe becoming aware of itself. Reflecting upon itself through the human." Or through the human reflecting on the fish. Counting them.

◆ ◆ ◆

Long before we began counting, long before we began even *being*, the fish were swelling and retreating with the waters in a symbiotic rhythm of heat and cold, flood and drought. My fish's relatives have been doing this for over 300 million years. Since the late afternoon of the Paleozoic—a period known as the Upper Devonian. There is the tantalizing footprint of a salamander-like creature that lingers in Pennsylvania from that time. A creature poised in a single step, held like Keats's lovers on the Grecian urn, down through tens of millions of years.

> *Bold Lover, never, never canst thou kiss,*
> *Though winning near the goal—yet, do not grieve;*
> *She cannot fade, though thou hast not thy bliss,*
> *For ever wilt thou love, and she be fair!*

Might the salamander not also have been heading for his love, yea those many eons ago?

There were some remarkable fish ancestors in those times. Great great great great et cetera Uncle Dunkleosteus from Arizona, for example. Uncle Dunkle was a hefty lad some thirty feet long with sturdy jaws, sharp teeth and body armor whom you wouldn't want to meet in a pond on a dark night. Yet ferocious as he no doubt was, he was no match for the weather. It remains the most daunting of adversaries. The Earth was an anthology of Just-So stories long before Kipling. Temperatures have to be just-so for intricate varieties of earth-life to survive, just as the steelhead must develop in temperatures between 44 and 51, or the human body must maintain a temperature of 98.6 to be healthy. Everything has to be just so. When those conditions are no longer met, like Uncle Dunkle, the family dies off.

◆ ◆ ◆

Susie and I are still standing there at the edge of the dry creek bed. It has taken her only three or four minutes to tell me the fish story and inadvertently to teach me to see. She has made her way through the thistle to "take a look at what's going on with the creek." If anything is changed. If there is water. I was hardly even aware that it was there. Much less, that anything might be going on. Even when Ed had told me there was a wild turkey "nesting down by the creek" or that he'd heard wild coyotes there. That a deer had been seen there, although he had never been able to catch sight of it. All I saw when I looked was a ditch full of debris. In a nebulous way, like fog, I sensed all these things around me and had heard them in the night in Mr. Fields. I loved the place for its "presences." But I had never picked them out. I was getting better though. I told Susie about the orioles I had seen, sure they had a nest nearby. About the goldfinches I had watched among the nursery trees. She said they often found nests in the huge redwood planters.

It was on this afternoon, staring out at the water and the fish that were no longer there, that Susie first mentioned the farm in Marin. "You should take a walk someday down at Eddie's dad's place. It's so peaceful, you can walk for hours and forget the outside world altogether." "How big is it," I asked, trying to imagine how you could walk for hours on anybody's land this close to San Francisco and the Pacific.

"Close to a thousand acres," she said.

"*A thousand acres.*" I was stupefied. I had watched little handkerchiefs of land sold off in Southern California for astronomical prices. "Where on earth is it? Death Valley?"

"No it's in Novato. Down in Marin."

That's how it all started.

When Susie leaves, I climb into Mr. Fields and open windows in five directions to let in the late afternoon light, sounds and scents. The kitchen window, the dining room windows—there are three (this is also the office). The bedroom windows—there are four (this is also the loft, library and music room). The two skylights are opened, one above the bedroom and one above the kitchen-dining room. The front (and only) door is opened, leaving the screen door, which allows a full view of Ed's fields and vineyard. You see how spacious Mr. Fields is and open to the world in all directions except one. And who wants to look at the bottom of a pick-up truck?

Space, like time, is relative. It never crosses my mind that my world is limited to the space of a pick-up truck. It just doesn't *feel* that way. Who else can rise up in the middle of a clear night through a hatch above the bed and watch Venus, bright as a cruise ship, sailing through Orion or a late moonrise over Sonoma vineyards. Who else gets to come out in the dark when the creatures do—so close I can almost touch them, even when I can't see them in the tall weeds or among the foliage of trees. I have heard coyotes speaking to one another in their hoarse and melancholy voices. The light, quick, busy sound of quail in early morning. The heavy crackle of brush as Ed's elusive deer follows some ancient and invisible path along the creek bed. I can watch the whole world waking up around me from my perch, coffee in hand. Dew glistening across the tips of every stalk of weed and grass from here to the shadow of Sonoma Mountain. The thick tapestry of birdsong that rises in praise of each new day. My world in Mr. Fields is huge. *Huge!*

And it is about to get much larger. Curiosity will do that. It was a simple puzzlement at first that lingered in the back of my mind after my conversation with Susie about the fish. How could there be a thousand acre anything in a place like Marin? As you will see, a subsequent conversation with Ed will bring my curiosity to the fore. Even then, I didn't imagine that following a single thread could lead me deeper and deeper in time and farther and farther in space. I would soon be inviting all sorts of people into Mr. Fields' world. The stories coalesced over time as small portraits of people in the present and people in the past—sometimes very far in the past—hence my subtitle, Portraits in time from Pangaea to Point Reyes. Those portraits are fictionalized moments based on actual people. They appear in italics, unless otherwise noted. At times a letter or an actual account by a person tells the story best.

In the beginning, the thread I am following may remain invisible to you, but as you read, it will emerge more clearly. I will give you a clue in advance: I am following the principle of Six Degrees of Separation, which entered into popular culture through a play of that name by John Guare. According to this principle, everyone is approximately six steps away, by way of introduction, from any other person on Earth, so that a chain of "a friend of a friend" statements can be made to connect any two people in six steps or fewer. I have included times and places as legitimate degrees of separation, rather like a three-dimensional chess game. I do this because, as you will see, certain places and landscapes are main characters of the book. Imagine that you are entering a gallery and the rooms contain portraits, each room from a different period or place. The places may be far apart but the moment in time is the same. Or . . . The moments may be far distant in time, but the place is the same: Lombardy or North Africa or the East Coast or the West Coast of America. Ticino or Marin. As you pass through the rooms, you will begin to see the common themes unfold and the thread that leads from Dominic Grossi in Ticino, looping backward and forward but always returning to the present, to Mr. Fields and eventually to the farm in Marin that is really a ranch.

PART I

BEGINNINGS

*. . . He sang how the seeds of earth and air and sea and liquid fire
were brought together through the great void:
how from these first beginnings all things . . . took shape:
then began to harden as land, . . .
to gradually take on the form of things:
and then the earth is awed by the new sun shining,
and rain falls from the clouds borne on high:
and woods first begin to rise, and here and there,
creatures roam over the unknown hills.*

—VIRGIL. "The Song of Silenus"
Eclogues VI
(A.S. Kline translation)

*"Look about you," answered Sótuknang [to Spider Woman].
Here is this earth we have created.
It has shape and substance, direction and time,
a beginning and an end. But there is no life upon it.
We see no joyful movement. We hear no joyful sound.
What is life without sound and movement?
So you have been given the power to help us create this life.
You have been given the knowledge, wisdom, and love
to bless all the beings you create.*

—WHITE BEAR FREDERICKS to
FRANK WATERS
The Book of the Hopi

11

EARTH TIME

SUSIE GROSSI'S FISH STORY, wandering down the convolutions of my mind in a stream of consciousness, sends me off on thoughts about time, in which the fish's long story, along with the story of all things, unwinds. Time is the one thing we take for granted yet don't really understand, any more than the fish understands the water from which it is never apart. Units of time, measurements of time, depictions of units and measures of time, we have aplenty. Just walk into any house in the United States and you will quickly find dozens. What you can't see, you will hear. The microwave beeps, the dryer buzzes, the radio turns on at its appointed hour, someone's watch goes off as a reminder to make a telephone call. You can find the exact minute of our measured day by looking at your watch, your cell phone, your computer, your laptop, your microwave and even one of those old-fashioned things, a clock. It is hard to believe that the first portable clocks that could be used to determine longitude were only invented in the 17th century. Up until then, only a location's latitude could be given. A determined Englishman named John Harrison* spent his entire adult 18th century life trying to invent an accurate time-piece that could operate aboard a ship and be used to pinpoint its longitude.

None of these brilliant gadgets give us a remote sense of what time really is, any more than a yardstick can tell us about distance or a day at the beach tell us about the nature of the sea. Time, in fact, is more like the sea than the digits on the microwave or the friendly faces on our wrist. It is a vast unfathomable medium through which we swim across the small distance of our lives. Or even the lives of our species. A clock cannot tell us about duration. We can get a birds-eye perspective of space from an airplane, a satellite or a spacecraft. But we can't get a bird's-eye view of time, measured in hundreds of millions of years. Not the *experience* of it. Yet we are made of time. Not centuries. Not millennia. But long unwinding eons of time.

In his book *The Dragons of Eden*, Carl Sagan used one of our common measures of time—the calendar—to impress this point on his readers. The universe is around 15 billion years old, he notes in 1977. And based on the known calculations of that time (these estimates are constantly shifting and refining, but what is a few hundred million years difference to *us?*), the Earth is around 4.5 billion years old. To help us imagine this, he compressed the entire duration into the scale of a calendar year. The Big Bang, that colossal burst of fireworks, occurs on January 1st. Our local neighborhood, the Milky Way, doesn't come into being until May 1st. The long hot summer is almost past before the solar system takes shape on September 9th, my nephew's birthday. The Earth forms on September 14th.

I prefer to make a small change in Sagan's calendar and use it as a metaphor for the Earth's year, rather than a cosmic year. Either scenario is humbling. In the

* Do read Dava Sobel's book *Longitude: The True Story of Longitude: The True Story of a Lone Genius Who Solved the Greatest Scientific Problem of His Time.*

Earth calendar, loosely based for numeric convenience on a 4.4 billion year lifespan, each day is 12,000,000 years, each week is 84,000,000 years, each month is around 372,000,000 years. Sometime after lunch on the last day, human history as we know it comes into faint shape. We can actually take a nap and not miss much.

The first signs of life—what we would give our eye-teeth now to find on Mars or any other planet—comes forth on Earth some 4 billion years ago in February: organic carbon in small oval masses. Hooray! (You are not enthused? NASA would be popping champagne corks if the Mars Rover turned up the tiniest bit of this.) And just think, a billion years ago we have algae, bacteria, tubeworms, sponges and radiolarians. (I can see you are still not impressed.) How about *jellyfish*. Perhaps you have visited the Monterey Aquarium and been mesmerized by their magical jellyfish world. If so, you have found a time telescope, a chronoscope, that can see far into the past. If you have not, drop everything and go *now*.

These are the fruit of the long, hot summer. July's children. They have been in gestation for a billion years. That is one million millennia. A patient craftsman is at work.

THE EARTH CALENDAR PERIODS

1 Year = 4.4 billion Earth years

1 Month = 372,000,000 Earth years

1 Week = 84,000,000 Earth years

1 Day = 12,000,000 Earth years

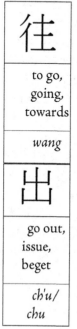

to go, going, towards

wang

go out, issue, beget

ch'u/ chu

I love Chinese characters for their elegant and economic imagery, some of which has been preserved over millennia and tell their own story. In one description of the character for *wang*, meaning "going," it depicts "luxuriant vegetation which springs up from the earth, rambling in tufts, here and there". Then there is the character for *chu*, also meaning *go, go out* as well as *to spring from, to issue, to beget*.* It is described as depicting a small plant that has grown another pair of leaves. The distinction between the images and their meaning offers a subtle, yet significant metaphor for our story: For two hundred million years—beginning in the time of those delicate, transparent creatures—the jellyfish and the one-celled gem-like radiolaria—plant life is unrooted, aquatic, floating, governed by the rhythm of the waters. Long-tendrilled blue-green algae anticipate their seaweed descendants. Plants without leaves, stems or roots drift aimlessly in their fluid home. There are inland seas over California's present eastern deserts and southern California. In the Silurian Period, these surge over what are now the Mt. Shasta and Inyo regions.

* From *Analysis of Chinese Chracters* by G.D. Wilder and J.H. Ingram.

THE EARTH CALENDAR

JANUARY	FEBRUARY	MARCH
4,464,000,000–4,092,000,000 Gaia is being born: The Earth's crust is forming	4,092,000,000–3,720,000,000 Oldest known rocks on Earth Late month: Earliest evidence of life; "organic carbon in small, oval masses." The atmosphere and the oceans form.	3,720,000,000–3,348,000,000 Early bacteria

APRIL	MAY	JUNE
3,348,000,000–2,976,000,000 Oxygen levels are rising in the atmosphere. Iron ore is produced. Heavy spring winds and high tides. (The moon is still very close to the earth.) Blue-green algae using photosynthesis, produce oxygen. *BRAVO!*	2,976,000,000–2,604,000,000 High winds and high tides continue. (Surf at your own risk.)	2,604,000,000–2,232,000,000 The Great Oxidation Event, initiated by photosynthesis. The rise of oxygen in the atmosphere proves fatal to all forms of life not dependent upon it. One of the first major extinctions. The beginning of plate tectonics.

JULY	AUGUST	SEPTEMBER
2,232,000,000–1,860,000,000 Life is flourishing in mid-summer. Cells are developing with a membrane and a nucleus, which can hold genetic material in its bountiful basket.	1,860,000,000–1,488,000,000 The new cells (eukaryotes) are frolicking in earth's summer, enjoying their nucleus from inside out	1,488,000,000–1,116,000,000 A surge of passion at summer's end: Sexual reproduction appears and the game is on! Life is developing at an increasing rate, with many-celled organisms clustering in cell colonies. *GO TEAM GO!*

OCTOBER	NOVEMBER	DECEMBER
1,116,000,000–744,000,000 Plankton, more advanced bacteria, tubeworms, sponges and radiolarians.	744,000,000–372,000,000 NOV. 18: The Cambrian Age begins. Radiolaria, jellyfish, insects, fish. Water plants move on to land, mountains in Europe are rising; the Appalachians. Lichens, the first forests. *OPEN THE GATES, THEY'RE COMING!*	372,000,000–THE PRESENT DEC.14: Pangaea forms; (17th) Pangaea breaks apart; (17th) Red-woods; Rocky Mountains, dino-saurs, (26) extinction of dino-saurs, flowers, bees; (31st) Noon: First hominids; lions, dogs, horses, armadillo, hummingbirds, 11:20PM Homo sapiens; 11:59 Human history begins. *STRIKE UP THE BAND THEY'RE HERE!*

Plants slowly develop their roots and leaves only after they are forced ashore in periods of warming, as the water evaporates in places, leaving them literally high and dry. From now on, through hundreds of millions more years, they will become increasingly centered, focused, self-organizing, localized like the small plant that issues from its center, begets. Instead of floating and rambling, they dig in deep and begin to ascend upward, in search of sunlight. They begin on land as the soft mosses and ferns, growing higher and higher until they form trees and forests.

The equator, in relation to the landmasses of this time, stretches across North America from Southern California through Ungava Bay, in northeastern Canada, crossing the north tip of Greenland. It is December on the Earth calendar. The month when it all happens. But not as fast as you might think.

Through early December (the end of the Devonian and beginning of the Carboniferous) most of California is covered by sea, except for a small land area in the Klamath region. The warm, clear waters host tropical reefs of coral and stone lilies of the sea, which are animals with flowerlike heads and stalks made of circular disks, forerunners of the starfish and sea urchin. The Southern Hemisphere is about to be invaded by successive sheets of ice.

It is during this time, to the east and Europe, for example, that the great coal forests emerge. *Coal forests? Coal that grows on trees?* No, coal *is* trees. Or was. One forgets this. They appeared in the early Devonian period (late November, early December) as grotesquely-shaped seed-fern trees that reach their climax in the carboniferous period. It is during this period that trees of larger variety emerged, some of which develop thick woody tissues around the central pith. Real trees! It is a landscape of lush vegetation. The plants use the sun's energy to combine the carbon dioxide gas of the atmosphere with water in the leaves of the plants. In this way, each green leaf, in its own encounter with the sun, is able to transform light into food, and then to create the woody, cell walls of plant tissue. Over time, dead plant tissues pile up in ancient swamps and after being covered with mud and limestone, they are slowly compressed, altered and preserved as coal. Coal, and also petroleum, contain this stored-up energy from the sun that has been transformed by plants through their magic of photosynthesis. It is still energizing *us*, millions of years later.*

It is December 28th on the Earth calendar and the first version of my fish is gliding along a stream bed, cool fresh water purling through its gills. No, it has not reached my creek, or I should say they haven't met up in time. It is still a million or so years off. The likes of great, great, great etc Uncle Dunkle, those monstrous creatures of the Silurian and Devonian waters, are long gone. His most recent ancestor, Uncle Driftwood (Eosalmo Driftwoodensis is his proper name), is a more direct progenitor of the Salmonid family. The great supercontinent of Laurasia is breaking up into the landmasses of North America, Greenland, Europe and Asia.

---

* I am indebted to Charles Camp for this material and highly recommend his fine book
Earth Song.

Huge rivers pour down into the Pacific from a high plateau to the northwest. Sturgeon in the rivers have reached as much as two tons, an angler's dream. Or nightmare. Some of the old families have completely died out, like Great Uncle Smilo (*smilodoithicus*), a formidable-looking saber-toothed salmon.

Shortly after midmonth, the Sierra Nevada mountains slowly begin to rise out of the Jurassic seas and the great reptiles whose miniature reproductions will so entrance children millions of years in the future, dominate the landscape for four long days, from December 17th through the 20th. What will become the Rocky Mountains are still swamp beds. They will not begin their uplift for six more days, around mid-day on December 26th, give or take a few million years. Still no sign of California.

North America is a place of lush rain forests—warm and tropical. From the first pines of the Permian Age, through the Araucarian forests, the cycads and ginkos, life has been abounding in continuously more complex and intricate forms. Until one day—a day I have marked in rainbow colors on my calendar—the flowers appear. What a day that is! December 21st.

My fish swims through the Paleocene among palm trees and magnolias. The first placental mammals are appearing. Then on into the Eocene among horses and camels, the first of their kind. The mighty Miocene rivers, descending from their great northern heights, deliver gravel into the low-lying country where one day (late December 31st) the Sierras will reach their heights, and finally empty their cargo into the Farallon Ocean, where the best California real estate lies estivating in the mud of the continental shelf, some twenty miles out to sea. These rivers carve deep canyons through the Great Valley which is still covered by a saltwater bay. There is an upwelling of cold water within the bay, which has its outlet in Monterey. The plains are opening up now, filled with tall grasses. Shell fish have reached a peak. Eighteen inch oysters with shells an inch thick! There are abalone, crab, sand dollars, cockles, mussels and even pearl oysters abounding, just after Christmas—on this 28th day of December, 20 or 30 million years ago. The seas are teeming with life.

Camel and antelope horses wander the young plains of Barstow and the Mohave. They browse the tough grasses, finding new sources of nourishment. Rabbits, huge land tortoises, ancestral cattle, antelopes with horns on their noses, peccaries . . . More and more creatures find their way from the forest to the newly opened plains, leaving behind beavers, tapirs, rhinos, mastodons, pig deer and other ancient creatures of the swamps and forests. To the plains too come newer creatures—the wolves and cats, perfectly designed as hunters who can move swiftly across the grasslands.

Into the Miocene he swims at year's end, my fish, among horses and giraffes and camels, hyena-like dogs and saber-toothed cats, bear-dogs and deer with fine antlers. At the edge of his stream, the elephantine mastodon dips his long ivory tusks "like chopsticks," as naturalist Charles Camp puts it, to pluck the succulent vegetation that grows there. It is a massive, wild world filled with abundant life. The land is still flat where Mt. Diablo rises today, dotted with groves of manzanita, oaks and sycamore, except for the volcanoes and lava flows on the distant Sierras. From now on, volcanoes are widespread in northern and central California. At the head of Napa Valley, near Calistoga, they will bury the great redwoods, preserving their trunks among the other trees. The ash-buried trunks of northern Nevada will turn to precious opals.* The world is a wonder!

On the very last day of the long Earth year, the world as we know it today slowly comes into being over the closing 12 million years. Coyotes, bears, cats, raccoons, horses and camels—much as they look today—will begin to populate the landscape, even as the rhinos become extinct in our hemisphere, and the pig-deer give way to the graceful deer of modern forests.

The cold is coming in. It creeps across the landscape—frost, snow, ice. A long winter's day of perpetual snow that will slowly form ice caps over Canada, the Great Lakes and the Sierra Nevada. As night comes, Yosemite Valley is a river of ice that lies 2000 feet deep; a massive white glacier that extends to El Capitan, slowly carving long ridges of rock that extend along its sides as it carries Sierra granite from the height to the foothills.

* When volcanic activity destroyed trees and they began to disintegrate, their fragments sank to the bottom of an ancient lake. There, water and silica — a chemical compound found in nature — traveled through the lake bed sediment and filled in the space once occupied by the wood fragments, creating the opals for which Nevada is famous.

NEW YEAR'S EVE

THERE IS ALWAYS EXCITEMENT ON THE LAST DAY OF THE YEAR. A little exhaustion too. December is a busy, challenging, happy, sad and frustrating month. New Year's Eve brings a moment to look back on the events of the year and to look ahead. To hope for better things in the uncharted future. A lot has been going on through the evening. The hubbub has risen to that frenetic key that parties reach at the climax of their numbers and sociability. The continents have settled down a bit and seem to be more or less staying in place. The last Ice Age ended in the early hours of the morning, about 11 million years ago. Through the day there have been floods and droughts, as there always are. Lakes have appeared and disappeared and reappeared again. As of dinner time, the mammoths and camels, the saber cats and dire wolves, are still lively members of the party. They won't die off until literally the last minute (about 8000 years). Yesterday there was a big pile-up in Los Angeles at Wilshire and La Brea. Typical L.A., right? It seems as if all of that wildlife that teemed in the forest, swamps and grasslands for eons, all got it into their scaly, wooly, feathery heads to migrate to the movie capital of the world. They learned what many a young starlet and movie mogul has learned since. It's not always as good as it looks. Only for them it was much worse. Hollywood is only a twinkle in time, but this black hole lasted for thousands of years. In those times, (it would be yesterday), a part of Wilshire Boulevard was the site of springs of petroleum and gas that bubbled together to the surface from deep in the rocks. As the fluid spread, it formed small ponds of tar. Perhaps the creatures were deceived by the film of water that covers the pool in an otherwise welcome landscape of trees and a grassy plain between the hills. Over time, unsuspecting, they come, caught in a lasting emulsion like human images in a photograph. Toads, beetles, owls. Wild horses, camels, mammoths, bison, wolves—all covered in a dark, sticky film of tar where now the asphalt of our modern roads is densely covered with automobiles and the 3:00 to 5:00 sensation that the tar has seized a new generation of hominid commuters eventually turns out to be an illusion.

Five minutes to midnight and the chatter quiets. People begin to gather for the toast, as our own family enters the scene. Homo sapiens sapiens—oh wise wise human!

One minute to midnight. This is a solemn moment. Human history is about to begin. Someone announces the news to the party and calls for the champagne to be brought. In the time it took to utter those words, half a millennium has passed. People fall silent as the champagne glasses are distributed. Another millennium goes by. Half a minute later a cork is popped and a murmur of anticipation ripples through the crowd. Egypt is rising. Sumeria. The toasts begin. "To the Earth!" someone says. "To God," says another. "To the goddess!" a woman amends. "To all the creatures and all our relations!" "To the beauty of the Earth, long may she live!" is chorused. Some misgivings are heard. All this, as civilizations rise and fall, cities blinking in and out like stars. Small sounds becoming rhythmic, singing, music, symphonies, synthesizers, blaring electronic amplifiers, a diverse cacophony tangled round the world in a thick mesh of sound, for the last second has come and the glasses are raised, poised to drink in the new. Twelve million undreamt of years of jostling landscapes and unimaginable creations.

In the time it takes to lift glasses to lips, the North and South will count their dead, trains will cross the land, planes will lift into the sky, telephones and television will appear. Two world wars will be fought and the hydrogen bomb will burst into the sky like a lethal flower. Millions of years of our ancient past will be discovered, the Earth charted, the DNA structure unraveled, miracle cures beyond number will be found. Rockets are taking off into the heavens, men are walking on the moon, people are talking round the world, sending a billion instant messages, images, songs, threats, sports scores, stock quotes . . . Ah! Here's looking at you . . .

✳ ✳ ✳ ✳

Summer 2001 ~ Grossi Farms

FARM BEGINNINGS

I can still remember walking down the long dirt road to Grossi Farms for the first time, the earth giving off its summer heat through the rows of ripened fruits and vegetables. The landscape was rimmed with ochre hills like the ones I had come to love in the mountains of the south. In this season they rise above the flat foreground like the dusty backs of sleeping camels. Directly behind the farm lies Sonoma Mountain, part of the low coastal range that runs the length of California—eleven hundred miles, if measured along its coast.

It was the summer of 2001. At that time I was living in my camper less than a mile away, working on my Ph.D. dissertation. If all went well, I would celebrate my graduation on the cusp of my sixtieth birthday. My landlady, Laurie-Ann Barbour, had recommended Grossi Farms as a great place to buy organic vegetables. It was within easy walking or biking distance. One day a handwritten sign appeared on the wooden post of the vegetable stand that said HELP WANTED. Laurie-Ann saw it first and was considering applying for the job. When she decided against it, it occurred to me that I might apply for it myself. I could use some extra money and a low-key physical job outdoors would balance out the intense mental efforts of writing my dissertation. After about a two minute conversation with Ed Grossi, I was hired. The job didn't require very strenuous capacities and I loved the short walk to work along Petaluma Hill Road, then the turn east along the dirt drive—the heart lifting, the light spreading across the fields, Sonoma Mountain rising like a distant Oz.

The vegetable stand is a simple wooden structure with a dirt floor, which sits at the edge of the fields near the nursery office. It is covered by green net shade cloth that filters the sunlight into a soft haze of light and shadows. Along the perimeter are the bins of vegetables that are replenished throughout the day by the Mexican workers as they bring them in from the fields. Closest to the entrance are the coveted seascape strawberries in green plastic baskets, plump, red and sweet. Customers also have the option of going into the fields to pick for themselves: our U-Pick strawberries at a special price. People often come to Grossi's simply for the experience of being outdoors on a farm, stepping out of the frantic stream into a world where nature is still going about her business— our business—of harvesting her fruits.

The farm also supplies the local grocery stores with organic vegetables, so part of the men's workday is spent sorting through the fresh pick and loading boxes to fill the orders. I take the phone calls from the stores and make out the slips that are stapled to a wooden board near the men's work bench. This is just behind my check-out table, in a separate area that opens onto the fields and is bordered by the old reefer truck that keeps the vegetables cool.

Alfonso Ramirez is the field foreman and a very conscientious one. The mustachioed face beneath the straw sombrero looks deceptively serious. In the early days I was fooled by that and took everything he said seriously. I only discovered my mistake when his face would suddenly open up into a wide grin and I knew that he had been pulling my leg. It was Alfonso who made the deliveries of vegetables to the stores, including the Whole Foods, Safeway and Oliver's supermarkets in Cotati, Rohnert Park, Santa Rosa, Petaluma and Sebastopol as well as the smaller specialty markets. On those days he wore with pride the green shirt with the word "Manager" on it which Ed had given him. It represented the culmination of his journey to find a new life in the United States, thanks in part to Ed's support and sponsorship through the long citizenship process. He had come with his wife Salome from Texas de Morelos, a small village two hours from the city of Oaxaca in southeast Mexico. It is a village of about a thousand people created as part of the land redistribution program after the Mexican revolution in 1920. Its diminishing population has matched the seasons of diminishing rains and it narrowly survives off its crops of corn and sugar cane. It has no hotel, no post office, no restaurant. Now, one in four Latinos living in nearby Petaluma is from this village.

The other workers at the farm—usually two—change from year to year. I would ask Ed in the autumn who would be working the following spring and he would answer, "Whoever turns up." Often workers will go from the summer seasonal jobs to what turns out to be a full-time job in a restaurant or in construction. Although Ed pays his workers well, the employment is only for four or five months and can't match the pay of construction jobs. Field work in temperatures that can rise to a hundred degrees is back-breaking, although I have never heard a single complaint out of any of them. Now and then a Sonoma State student comes by thinking that he or she would like to work outdoors "in the earth." Once they see what it is really like, they quickly change their minds. On the hottest days, Ed will have the workers come in at dawn and leave before the heat of the day.

One of the workers who has returned several times is Otùn. Otùn is also from Texas de Morelos, obviously inspired or encouraged by Alfonso to come north and apply for work at the farm. I'm guessing that, like people from many of the small towns in Mexico, they are all related in one way or another. Uncles or cousins or cousins-once-removed. Otùn has an open and expansive personality, a little less reserved than Alfonso but with the same mischievous humor. He is quick to take up other odd jobs that come up on the farm, displaying a surprising number of skills.

Then there is his young nephew Lazaro, who has also worked more than one summer at the farm. Lazaro is a broad-shouldered, sturdy, good-looking young man with soulful eyes and a bright smile that opens onto a perfect set of white teeth. He was born in the same Oaxaca town but later moved to Mexico City, where his family is now living.

As the season gets busier, Ed takes on another worker. This year it is Ángel. I can tell from his face that he is a recent arrival. I have spent time in the mountains of Mexico in native villages, protected by an invisible wall that holds them within their own ways and language. Faces that look out at strangers impassively, often with traces of suspicion, curiosity or even a mild hostility. Some, the older ones, know that they are looking into their future and they don't like it. Yet they are also drawn toward it, the younger ones especially. An undertow that pulls them inexorably toward their only hope for a better life. Ángel's face holds no hostility, but it is cautious, wary, inscrutable.

My conversation with the men is usually a light bi-lingual banter but we treat each other thoughtfully and respectfully. I have the advantage that I am the one non-Mexican person on the farm who can speak to them in Spanish. They appreciate that I am not an aloof gringa but genuinely interested in their lives. I have told them a little about mine because I know they are curious. I have declared proudly that I have a *Comadre* and my *ahijada*, my god-daughter, living in Mexico City. Being a comadre or co-mother in Mexico is more valuable even than being a citizen. And as to being a Godmother or Godfather—well Hollywood has given a broad hint of this, if you just subtract the criminal element.

I have also described to them my work as a writer, my experience of living in Mexico and my studies of its ancient cultures. We speak of the ancient cities in their own state of Oaxaca—Monte Alban and Mitla—seats of the former Zapotec and Mixtec civilizations. They listen intently and nod to confirm the wisdom of their *antepasados*—their ancestors.

Lazaro seems such a tender and innocent young man that I can hardly believe he has a wife and two children living in the capital, Mexico City. Sometimes he will pass me by with a box of vegetables and say, "Estas triste Señora?" "Are you sad? Don't be sad." I am never sad, but he interprets any expression on my face other than a smile as sadness. "No Lazaro, estoy pensativa. I'm thinking. Thinking where to put the lemon cucumbers that you have just brought in from the field." He nods in relieved approval and passes on. Another time he will say, "Don't you think it's better to be happy than sad, Señora?" "Absolutely Lazaro. It's much better to be happy."

One day the fellows were teasing me about lettering a box TORPEDO

ONIONS which was actually RED ONIONS. They had asked me to label it but I had labeled the wrong box. Picking up their spirit, I replied, in mock indignation, "Well! Lazaro and Otùn watched me write that and never said a word!" A little later, I went to the back of the stand and saw Lazaro sitting, looking very disconsolate in front of the fridge. I couldn't resist saying "Estas triste, Lazaro?" "No, Señora, pensativo."

Alfonso, looking on, explained "He's sad because he thinks you are angry at him for not telling you it was the wrong box. No Lazaro," I reassured him, "I was only kidding. I'm not mad." I smiled and laughed and he was reassured. Yesterday he passed me by again in the stand with a load of corn and said to me very earnestly in Spanish, "Señora, do you know what *amiga* means?" I nodded yes. "Are you my *amiga*?" he asked. "Yes Lazaro. Of course I am." A bright smile filled his handsome face as he replenished the bin of white corn.

I was beginning to grasp the isolation and loneliness of the young men who have left their wives and family behind to improve their lives by finding work in a distant land. It is an age-old tradition everywhere; one of the things that marks "those who go." Poor farmers go to a city to find work. Men with dreams go to another country or they go West—wherever west may be. On the outer fringes of Mexico City is a place called Ciudad Nezahuacoyotl, after the great 14th century king whose palace once lay nearby. It is a vast community of make-shift shacks where the poor who didn't find jobs end up living. Arguably their lives are worse, not better. But hope is a thing that sets people on the road and often they can't turn back.

Many years ago I took a trip by bus from Mexico City to Chupícuaro, in the state of Guanajuato, to do some research into the ancient Chupícuaro culture of the region.* My research efforts yielded little but there were two other small events that have remained in my memory of that day.

The first happened on the bus trip. During my first months in Mexico, I had been like Alfonso, Otún and Lazaro, adrift in a sea of gibberish. I had never studied Spanish. My friends were trying to help me but progress was slow and comprehension was nil beyond Hola, Buenos dias and other obvious phrases. My ignorance had the peculiar advantage of offering a different kind of silence in which human voices were just so much white noise and didn't intrude or distract. As I sat on that bus watching the landscape of Michoacan pass by, I caught myself doing an amazing thing: I was listening to the conversation behind me. I understood what they were saying! I can only compare it to the first time I stayed upright and sailed into the wind on a two-wheel bicycle.

The second thing happened on arrival in the town of Chupícuaro. The bus let me off in the central plaza and I headed toward the largest building I saw, which turned out to be the school. Once inside, I heard voices in a hallway nearby and sought them out. Several women were chatting together. Using my simple phrases of Spanish, I managed to introduce myself. It was a quiet little town so they seemed pleased by the diversion I provided. They said tourists didn't usually come to Chupícuaro. Where was I from? California, I told them and they

* (800 BC–200 AD)

all burst into laughter. Why is that funny? I asked. "Because all of our husbands are in California and you have come all the way from California to Chupícuaro!" It was clearly a first. I soon discovered that the town was emptied out of its menfolk, much like Texas de Morelos I imagine.

Later in that same day, the stand got very busy and I was only vaguely aware that all three of the men were in the stand by the melons. They had just returned from picking and they were loading them onto the table. In the morning, I had cut up a cardboard box and laid it on the melon table as a way of separating the cranes and ambrosias. "What do you think, Otún? Is that too *feo*? Ugly?" The others had come to weigh in on the matter. "Si Señora. Es muy feo." I looked at it again dubiously. They were right. My look of dismay alarmed them. Heaven forbid I should be pensativa in this place. "No no, Señora. It's fine. It's fine."

I didn't pay much attention later when Otún called over and said he needed the staple gun. I went to get it, slightly surprised at the peremptory order. There were no orders among us, just a prevailing politesse. Orders came from Farmer Ed. The patrón, as they called him. Still, I didn't think much about it and was happy to deliver the staple gun. With great flourish, Otún proudly stapled the "Ambrosia Melon" sign, which he had removed from its position above the melon table, over a new place that they had just constructed on the adjacent counter to separate them from the Crane Melons. I had been so busy that I had never even heard the nails being driven in to make the frame. They all beamed at me proudly.

After the morning picking was completed, they worked quietly behind me sorting through the day's harvest to make up the boxes for the stores or for special orders called in by customers.

"When is your birthday Señora?" Lazaro piped up one afternoon as they were working.

"October 17th."

"What do you want for your birthday?" they all chorused.

"Can we give you a fiesta?" Lazaro asked. "Would you like that?"

I was so overwhelmed I was speechless.

At the end of each day, the vegetable bins were loaded into the refrigerated reefer truck for the night. The fellows were finished at 4:30 and they could have gone home then. But we kept the stand open until 5 and they generally drifted in from the fields and stood around talking quietly in the back until closing time so that they could help me put things away. I welcomed the daily exercise and would rather have done it myself, but they took pride in this gentlemanly act and I didn't want to spoil it. I am a middle-aged woman pushing 60 and they are treating me like their mother. Should I feel honored or insulted? *Amiga*, I remind myself. I am their friend.

It must be strange to be in a place where everything around you that people are saying sounds like gibberish, just as it had been for me when I first went down to Mexico. Watching people moving their lips and having no idea what is coming out is like being hermetically sealed inside a clear plastic container. You try to learn some words in their language as a way of breaking through but absurd mistakes and poor pronunciation only bring laughter. Better to stay sealed in silence. When you suddenly find someone whose words you understand and who understands yours, believe me—they are instantly your friend. Your *amiga*.

Sometimes there were customers who lingered late or were still out in the fields picking strawberries so I encouraged them all to leave and assured them that I would be just fine. On one such day it was close to 6 when I finally started to close up, loading the boxes on the dolly and rolling them over to the reefer. Farmer Ed appeared and quietly began helping me, standing inside the truck as I passed up the bins. It had been a hot, clear day and the afternoon seemed to linger on in a golden light over the fields. We fell into conversation and Ed began to tell me more about his Dad's ranch down in Novato. "I was born on that ranch and so was my Dad," he said. That was another rare occurrence in my California experience: Not just a native Californian, but a second generation born in the same place. The saying was that if you had been in California for five years, you were a native.

"It was my grandfather's place," he said. "My grandfather, Dominic—over there they'd say Domin-I-co—came over from Switzerland. The Italian part. Ticino. A little town called Monte Carasso. He married my grandmother over here and they had ten children. Well eleven, but one died real young. So there were five boys and five girls. He bought a ranch for each of the boys. They had to work it and take over payments of course. And the girls married into ranching families."

"But were they all such big ranches?"

"Pretty much."

"So how many acres came out of that family?"

"Well let's see." He counted out names and places and acres on his fingers and came up with, "Probably about seventeen thousand."

"In *Marin*?"

"Some were in Sonoma, but mostly in Marin. Over there on Point Reyes."

* * * *

CANTON TICINO, SWITZERLAND

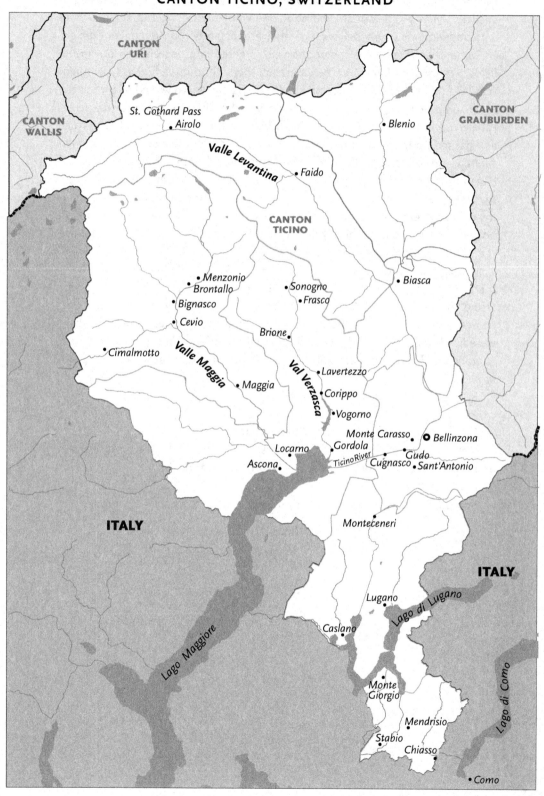

SUMMER 1776

July 4, 1776 ~ Ticino Switzerland

FATHER GALLI

FATHER MARCO ANTONIO GALLI PICKED HIS WAY carefully along a rougher part of the stony hillside path that ran high above the steep gorge of the Verzasca River in Ticino toward the village of Lavertezzo. Although he walked at a leisurely pace, he was about an important business: the Status Animarum or "Counting of Souls" in the parish of St. Mary of the Angels. He passed villagers carrying their valuable wares to market—women carrying cheese, butter and handmade cloth. The men following behind, leading their goats or heifers, the more prosperous with donkeys carrying their possessions. He stopped to greet each of them, inquiring after their health, exchanging news, offering his blessing. It was a clear, warm day and the people were cheerful. Happy to have made it through another hard winter, thanks be to God.

The Versazca valley rises several thousand feet from Gordola—where the Versazca and Ticino rivers meet—to Sonogno, the highest of the ten villages in the valley. It is a fifteen mile, narrow stretch of land, little of which can be used for farming. The highest peak is Mt. Barone at 9300 feet. The valley seems to have been formed by one of those violent shrugs of nature that rearranges the landscape for eons to come: a huge landslide that sent enormous boulders tumbling down to block the river, so that over time it was forced to carve a new path, throwing up rocks as it went through and leaving in its wake a rough and jagged landscape. Perhaps, as he walks, Father Galli is remembering the comment of a recent visitor to his parish: "A horrible valley in a savage wilderness." Too bad that he could not see the beauty of it or know the people as Father Galli did. But his parishioners never minded the criticisms of outsiders. They would have been more alarmed if the stranger had liked the place and decided to stay.

His next stop was the Dodini family. The widow Caterina Barbettini was from an ancient family in the nearby village of Cugnasco. Many of the people in Lavertezzo spent their winters in Cugnasco where the climate was warmer.

On the completion of his task, Father Galli takes a shepherd's satisfaction in counting his flock, even if it was one more headache stirred up by that heretic Luther and his 95 theses nailed to the door in Wittenberg in 1517*. While Luther's rebellious act did not impress itself forcibly on their remote village, certain of its effects had seeped into their lives in significant ways through the Catholic church's response at the Council of Trent in 1563, laying down new guidelines for the faithful and their church. It was decided then that every family must have a surname, though it hardly seemed a necessary thing at the time. The surname, the church in its wisdom had decided, must be passed down from generation to generation. Well so be it, he thought. Not such a bad thing after all. Come right down to it, these decrees had truly formed the people into a village. A sturdy thing with records and vital statistics

---

* Martin Luther was a German friar who rebelled against the Catholic Church and launched the Protestant Reformation in 16th century Europe.

which the church ordered to be recorded and preserved. The changeless present of the Versazca Valley was subtly transformed into a changing history, a record to be kept, a memory to be preserved, a future to be anticipated. Parishes were established which took in several hamlets to form a village where no village had been before. Every parish had a priest and every priest was required to record births, marriages, weddings and deaths according to a strict formula. Taxes were levied on the basis of this count. St. Peter himself was not invested with such a weighty task.

When he had finished the tally, Father Galli was pleased to note that his parish of St. Mary of the Angels in Lavertezzo contained 147 families made up of 387 men and 356 women. Had he been more attentive to the children, he might have noticed that the widow Dodini's son Giuseppe was missing. But the Ticino families had large broods and no one could be expected to keep up with their plentiful offspring. It was summer, after all, and a time when girls and boys found their relief in the cool meadows high above the river. And there were tasks enough up there for them to do from milking cows to cutting hay.

The sun was high overhead now and Father Galli sought out a favorite spot, just a short climb upward for his old bones, where he could eat a small repast, and sip a bit of the wine that Sra. Dodini had given him. They made very good wine and it was one of the treats of his job. He had a nice view of Lavertezzo's graceful old bridge. He wondered how Father Damiano was doing, high up in the Val Maggia. He was a young man, almost a child to Father Galli's eye. He had recently been sent out from Lugano to serve the remote parishes up in the Val Lavizzara. He spoke Latin poorly and stumbled through the Mass. He blushed if someone spoke to him. Not a very good candidate for the priesthood one would think. But he was a great climber and a tireless walker, so his superiors must have known what they were doing.

In his younger days, Father Galli had served up there too. So many lovely spots. It was real alpine country, with the peaks of Mt. Barone and Mt. Zuccheri soaring straight up nearby. Menzonio and Brontallo, perched on their terraces above the river. He never ceased to wonder what had brought the first settlers to so remote a place—hewing stone to build the first house. It was probably a Grandi. They were an old family. He smiled to think of Father Damiano trying to sort out all of those Grandis in Menzonio or the Giacominis in Brontallo.

◆ ◆ ◆

By late afternoon of the following day, Father Galli had reached the upper villages of Brione, Frasco and Sonogno. Although it was a stretch for him to include these villages in his count, the parishes were presently without a priest, due to the death of Father Rinaldo Fabretti and Father Galli had volunteered to do it. When he had come from his native Italy, Brione was his first parish and he had spent many years there. He could still scale the paths to the upper villages like a mountain goat, even in his old age. Perhaps just a little more slowly. He knew all of the old families in the region and looked forward to catching up with old friends there, especially the Pinanas. They say old Matteo Pinana, who had lived over a century ago, had nine children. Nobody knows how many brothers and sisters Matteo had, but the Lord has blessed the Pinana family abundantly, that is for sure. Father Galli had been dubious about the marriage of Antonio Pinana's son Bernardo to a woman twenty-five years younger than himself. But, God be praised, here was Caterina with a lovely nine month old boy Felice, testifying to his name—Happiness. And Caterina confided that there was another bun in the oven. Age was not slowing Bernardo down.

In Frasco, the next village, there was a heavenly host of young Ferrinis. Such an old family there. They said that they could trace their family back to the 1500s.

Arriving in Brione, Father Galli greeted old friends among the Bisis, the Gnesas, the Mocettinis and Buzzinis. He counted forty families in the village and even the Marcaccis of Castello Marcacci were in residence for the summer season. The village would empty out again when winter came, as people took their cattle down to the Magadino Plain. He paid a visit to the Church of Beata Vergine Assunta, where he had served so many Masses in his youth. He greeted the holy figures in the beautiful frescoes there as if they were his own family. The church had been built on the remains of a chapel from 1295. It had been expanded two centuries ago. He would stay with friends overnight and say Mass there tomorrow.*

◆ ◆ ◆

While Father Galli is making his rounds through the Val Verzasca, at the foot of the next valley to the east children from the Grossi and Morisoli families of the Poncetta hamlet of Monte Carasso were erupting into the joyous call of "Uncle Pietro!" as Pietro Grossi appeared leading a heavily-laden donkey. The eldest member of the Morisoli family, Auntie Guilietta as she was known to everyone, awoke from a doze where she had been sitting against the stone wall of her house in a cool patch of shade. Auntie Guilietta was now "somewhere north of 80" as one of her nephews put it. She was still sharp of mind and the fiber of her thinning body remained sturdy. "Uncle Pietro," she smiled to herself, and a memory rose up almost as old as she was.

Her own Uncle Pietro Grossi was well into his middle years as she remembered him. A bear of a man, whom the children loved. Her mother, Giovanna Grossi, was his younger sister and had married Pietro Morisoli. The two Pietros—so different, yet the best of friends. Pietro was big and fair and jolly like his father before him. Pietro Morisolo was dark-haired and dark complected like his own father. It had been a natural thing, when the priest had explained that they would start using a family name in their church records, that the family of Pietro Grosso, "Big Pietro," would be known as Grossi (the plural of grosso, "big"). And the family of Pietro Morisoli— dark complected, "morisolo"—took that name for his family. Giulietta was NOT dark complected, leaning more toward her mother's Grossi line. She was small and fair and generally considered good-natured. No one in Monte Carasso, living so close together in their stone houses, needed a second name to know who everybody was. One way or another, they were all related anyway.

* I am indebted to T. Anthony Quinn who wrote the original anecdote about Father Galli in his excellent work *On Wings of Gold: The Journey to America of the Salmina, Morosoli and Dodini Families of Switzerland*, which provided the foundation of my understanding of Ticino's history. I have adapted this material with his permission.

What Giulietta remembered about her own Uncle Pietro was just this—the joyous cries of children, she being one of them, whenever he appeared. Like this Pietro Grossi, now aged 22, returning from a trip to Bellinzona. Her mother Giovanna often spoke of a gift Pietro had once brought them from a chocolate shop there: the figure of a beautiful chocolate lady with wide frilled skirts and dainty slippers. Much as Giovanna had loved the rare treat of chocolate as a child, she could not bring herself to deface so beautiful a lady. Her brothers and sisters had no such qualms. They had been permitted by their mother to have one tiny piece each after the Sunday meal. The chocolate lady of Bellinzona had remained in their family for a whole month. She remembered now that on that trip he was returning from his service in the militia and her mother said he looked very handsome in his uniform.

Now another handsome young man, Bernardo Rambosio, is striding out to meet his friend Pietro. Bernardo is also 22. They are talking in earnest together as they walk and Giulietta can guess what they are talking about. Like so many before them, they are laying plans for their fall trip south to work through the winter months and earn some money for their families. Bellinzona is the place to make those contacts, get news, and of course buy the necessities that they can't make or grow. Both boys have followed the local tradition of carrying their loads of local chestnuts to sell in the streets of Milano in late fall and winter. But Bernardo has it in his mind to look for jobs as chimney sweeps, as plenty of their men have also done in the past. The pay is better and they get to be inside. There are Grossis in Como who will help them out. Families that had decided to move south year round in harder times. The two boys will leave at dawn to go into the mountains to take their turn watching over the cows and goats pasturing in the high meadows.

"Here! Stop Nardo! You stay here. You're too small to run out there with the men. They'll be here soon enough. Just you wait, I said."

"No, I'm big Auntie Giulietta. Look at me. I'm not a baby. I'm big!" The old lady laughed her dry chuckle at her incorrigible, five-year-old grandnephew Bernardo Antonio. He would grow up to be smart, like his father Giovanni Morisoli, who had gone in with his brother Bernardo to lease land from the parish of San Bernardo and San Bernardino. Now they could grow their own corn on land near the plain. Not a place she would ever like to live, with the humid summers and infernal mosquitos. But good for crops, as the high meadows were good for grazing. The only thing they could plant in this rocky soil, terracing the hillside, were the vineyards which provided them at least with their own wine.

The children and Pietro have collided now in a mass of happiness as he plays the familiar game: "Gifts? For you? Why would I have gifts for such useless girls and boys?" Then he magically produces a candy and a trinket for each one.

One of the DePrati wives sits down next to her and begins breast-feeding her new baby as she watches the arrival.

"What have you named her?" Giulietta asks. She remembers the christening at San Bernardo Church but not the name. There was a well-worn path up to the old church, what with so many births and marriages and, yes, funerals too. All part of the pattern of life in Monte Carasso. As to funerals, she had been the next in line for a long time. But she was still here. Still the Grossi-Morisoli matriarch, even without having married or had children.

"She is named Guiseppa, Auntie Giulietta."

"A very nice name that is, child."

Giacomo Guidotti unloads the donkey which is a shared community possession. Wives and older children appear from the houses to claim their goods. Giacomo and Pietro can always be relied on to get everything on everyone's list. Not that there was much. Salt, coffee, sugar, a tool repaired by the blacksmith . . .

In the boisterous excitement of Uncle Pietro's arrival and the crowd gathering around Giacomo, Giulietta hadn't noticed the stately approach of Pietro's younger brother Bernardo Grossi with a pretty young woman on his arm. He processed toward them as if a band were playing a ceremonial march that only he could hear. The lift of his head said "significant" and the firm hold on the girl's arm said "Mine" and the solemn expression on his face, interrupted by fleeting smiles when he glanced at her said, "Be ready everyone! This is important! I have news!" So THAT'S how it is, thought Giulietta. Everyone knew that Bernardo had a new girlfriend from the next village but no one had taken it quite seriously. They hadn't set eyes on the girl, Angelina, whose name had become as commonplace as polenta in their household. One had to stop and realize that she had never been present in her actual person. But here she was and her person was definitely enough to turn a young man's eye. It remained to be seen if she had the makings of a good wife and mother, but she would be thoroughly vetted by the local women before she made the march back on Bernardo's arm and the inaudible band played its triumphant or gloomy recessional. In moments, they were before her: "Auntie Giulietta, meet mi divina Angelina!"

When they had gone inside the Grossi house, Auntie Giulietta leaned back and closed her eyes. It was a good and peaceful summer and it was a good place to live. After the noise and congestion of the Italian cities where they went to work in the winter, most of the men were happy to return. The air was clear and they were free in their own place, unbothered by the countless officials and rules and intrigues of Bellinzona and Milano. All they wanted was to be left alone to their simple lives. But regular as clockwork, some new ruler somewhere would get the idea into his head that they needed to protect the people of Ticino and come to enlist their boys and get money for their armies. What did they have in Monte Carasso that anyone would want anyway? It was silly. It always made their lives difficult. Taking away their men, and what little money they had. For what?

♦ ♦ ♦

Ticino is the southernmost canton of Switzerland. Cut off from the rest of the country by the Alps at its back, it faces toward Italy and the Mediterranean climates of the south. It is mostly rugged, mountainous country deeply grooved by the three rivers which rise out of the northern peaks and converge in Lake Maggiore on the Swiss-Italian border: the Maggia, the Versazca, and the Ticino. The three rivers have carved steep valleys in their vertical countryside where, for centuries, hardy Celts and, later, Lombards sought refuge from the political intrigues and battles which continuously plagued Europe. The canton takes its name from the easternmost river, which rises near the St. Gottard Pass and flows southwest across the Magadino Plain into Lake Maggiore and then continues south in Italy as the Po River.

Celts migrated down from the passes around 400 years before Christ, settling into the areas that are now southern Switzerland and northern Italy. They were soon absorbed into the Roman Empire, which named the Celtic tribes south of the passes the Helvetii—a name that is preserved in the official name of Switzerland today: Confederatio Helvetica. They were regarded as an important part of the empire, protecting it from invasion from the north. An impossible task it would seem, yet Hannibal managed to pass along the banks of the Ticino River leading elephants and horses over the Alps.

By the fifth century, the feared barbarian invasions happened in earnest as waves of war-like tribes from northern Europe swept down and eventually over-ran Rome itself. One of these tribes, the Lombards from the Elbe Valley in modern Germany, established a powerful kingdom in northern Italy. Some of those people followed the Po river northward into Switzerland, settling in the remote crevices of Ticino's valleys. Their nomadic agrarian lifestyle continues to this day in parts of Switzerland, following the patterns of the seasons, of warmth and cold, to farm the rolling hills and valleys made fertile by the Alpine snow melt. They still graze their animals in the high mountains in summer, and then bring them down into the protected valleys when the cold comes.

Giuseppe Dodini, who was absent from Lavertezzo during Father Galli's official visit, was 16 years old in that summer of 1776, endowed with the Verzascan's gift for slipping through the most strict and rigid mesh of rules, records and requirements that would seek to grasp them. Twenty years later, after Napoleon had captured the Swiss Federation, a French general arrived in the valley to deliver his news with great fanfare: The canton of Ticino was granted immediate liberty and the right of self-government. In return for this generous act, the illustrious general asked the small favor in return of being allowed to conscript for compulsory military service all unmarried Ticinesi men between 20 and 45 years old. In the month of March 1799, in all the Val Verzasca, there was not a single unmarried man to be found without an adoring wife. No one appeared at the French headquarters in Bellinzona to comply with the conscription edict. The villagers were assessed 300-400 lire each for their failure, to be collected by representatives of the French rulers stationed in Locarno.

On May 3rd, 1799, the villagers gave their response with the clamor of church bells in every village, calling some 400 Verzascans to arms with battle axes, guns, swords, spears and sickles. This determined band marched on Locarno where the offending official had miraculously evaporated into thin air. In the words of the local parish priest, Don Leopoldo Cerri, "Peace has been achieved, but the town of Locarno was never to experience so much pure terror as it did on the 3rd of May in 1799."

It should not surprise us that Giuseppe Dodini, missing on the day that Fr.

Galli came for his count of souls in Lavertezzo, was missing again in 1808 when Napoleon's soldiers came to count the Ticino males for war with Russia. He does not appear in any records except as the father of several children born in the 1790s after he marries his first cousin, Maria Domenica Dodini. As T. Anthony Quinn remarks, "This is a family that never stays put; that wanders first throughout the canton of Ticino, then throughout northern Italy, then to America."

Nevertheless, the records that Giuseppe had safely eluded would eventually inscribe the runes of change that were already shaping themselves in that summer of his 16th year, 1776. "One day there would be no Dodinis left in Lavertezzo or even Ticino," Quinn tells us, "but hundreds of descendants dotting the American plains and valleys."*

In Monte Carasso, the young Bernardo Grossi would indeed marry the "divina Angelina," although in reality we don't know the name of his wife. We do know the name of one of his children, Domenico Grossi, and we shall hear more of him later. The young people we met with the fictional Auntie Giulietta were real people in those times, as were the first Pietro Grossi and Pietro Morisoli. They will grow up, marry, and become part of the tapestry of history that is being woven here. The Grossis, the Rambosios, the Morisolis, the Guidottis . . . Their families will continue to entwine themselves with one another into new branches, even as they become caught up in the shifting of the ground beneath them, which will carry them in new directions.

❖ ❖ ❖

In contrast to the timelessness of this Ticino afternoon—while Father Galli sips his home-made wine under Lavertezzo's bridge and Auntie Giulietta dozes in the summer sun of Monte Carasso—history is in the making far across the sea in a place that most Ticinesi hardly know exists. It has been hot and sultry there in the last few days, while temperatures in the highlands of Ticino have rarely reached 80 in these summer months, with little humidity. Of course neither Father Galli nor Giulietta would have thought in terms of temperature. Like longitude, this was a fact that simply had not existed over the thousands of years of human occupation on the planet. Who needed to know such a thing? But that is about to change too.

---

* Their descendants will also settle in the San Francisco Bay Area, although not in Marin County, which is why we will not meet them there in our stories.

July 4, 1776 ~Philadelphia

THE GENTLEMAN LODGER

THE HOUSE ON 7TH AND MARKET STREET resembles a portly man who has been run through a wringer and emerges wide in the front and narrow on the sides. The street side has four ample windows across each of the three floors. The narrow sides have two. But it is a fine, sturdily built house, the handiwork of its owner, Jacob Krafft, who built the house for himself and his new wife. They have taken in a lodger, at 35 shillings a week, who occupies the second floor with his manservant. The lodger is a courteous, soft-spoken man from Virginia. The perfect lodger in fact: quiet, amiable, and clearly a man of breeding and importance. He is 33 years old, tall, with patrician features and sandy hair.

The arrangement is as satisfactory for the gentleman lodger as it is for the Krafft family. On his arrival in Philadelphia, he had first moved into a place in the center of town. He found it an admirable city but it was still a city. The noise and crowdedness, the stench of garbage and closely packed humans perspiring in the heat was overwhelming to him after his tranquil hillside in Virginia. He felt suffocated by it and immediately set about looking for a place closer to the country where he could go for walks and clear his mind. Particularly as he had an important task at hand that had been assigned to him. The Krafft house was just at the edge of the town, with easy access to the countryside or to the town center. Across the street was a stable. The smells of a stable were familiar and welcome to him.

At 6 a.m. on this morning, the gentleman lodger is seated at this desk with a ledger opened in front of him, his quill pen scratching with careful strokes across the page. He has just finished peering through the glass at the silver column of mercury in his prize possession—a handsome thermometer which he had purchased in London. He has his eye on another thermometer that he intends to buy today from John Sparhawk. It is a fine instrument for 3£15. One of the latest of its kind, considered to be more accurate than its predecessors. He admits to himself that he collects thermometers the way some people collect snuff boxes. How much more useful, a thermometer!

Even when he is away from his beloved home in Virginia, where he has set up his weather observation station, he keeps his ledger up faithfully, recording the temperature twice a day—the first at dawn when the temperature is the coldest and then between 3 and 4, when it is warmest. "I wish you would keep a diary," he wrote to his friend James Madison, "under the following heads or columns," which he enumerated thusly:

1. day of the month
2. thermometer at sunrise
3. barometer at sunrise
6. thermometer at 4 pm
7. barometer at 4 pm
5. the weather viz. rain, snow, fair at sunrise, etc.
9. weather at 4 P.M.

10. shooting or falling of the leaves of trees, of flours, and
   other remarkable plants.
11. appearance and disappearance of birds, their emigrations, etc.
12. Miscellanea.
[The odd numbering is his.]

"It will be an amusement to you and may become useful. I do not know whether you have a thermometer or barometer. If you have not, those columns will be unfilled till you can supply yourself."

This is not an idle pastime for the gentleman lodger. He will continue it throughout his life. When finding a permanent house to live in in Philadelphia during his term as Secretary of State, one of his main concerns will be to find a location adequate for the placement of his thermometer in order to attain the most accurate reading. He will carry it on during his time in the White House as third president of the new country. (Of course at present he has no thoughts of such a thing.) The more we observe nature, he is sure, the more we understand ourselves. God's ways are apparent in nature and can often be seen more clearly there than in human life. The task is to reconcile the two, applying the fundamental laws of nature to the laws of human life. Surely humans have the same right to freedom as the birds of the air and the fish of the sea. There is no divine right of kings to take those freedoms away and contravene God's laws. "All men are created equal," he has written. They are entitled to "the separate and equal station to which the Laws of Nature and Nature's God entitle."

The temperature, he notes in his ledger, is 68 degrees. It will be a warm day again, but not as sultry as the previous days. One can feel the lifting of the heavy humidity. It doesn't take a ledger to recall those first hot stuffy days of July when the members of the Continental Congress had all been pent up in the State House, windows closed to preserve the secrecy of their discussions. And heated discussions they were. The storm that had broken out on the outside, on July 2nd, seemed to come as the natural combustion of the storms that were raging on the inside, shaking the firmament with their resounding thunder. And those in turn were raging inside of him as he felt the language of his precious document torn to pieces and some of his best, and to him most important prose rejected.

While he expected that changes would be made, the deletion of certain lines still rankle and had caused heated debate. The King "has waged cruel war against human nature itself, violating the most sacred rights of life and liberty in the persons of a distant people who never offended him, captivating and carrying them into slavery . . . Determined to keep open a market where Men would be bought and sold." But his own Monticello is run with slave labor that is as built into the fabric of life there as the banking system. It will take some larger, major act—like the one they were about to sign—to begin the huge project of eradicating it. His friend John Dickinson, from Pennsylvania, had argued adamantly that they could not take on two such weighty issues without losing both. South Carolina was dependent on the sale of indigo and rice and their major market was Great Britain. Edward Rutledge feared for his state's economy and the people's livelihood if independence were declared. He had opposed Richard Henry Lee's proposal for a declaration but *he had helped draft the Articles of Confederation, once South Carolina had taken the step to statehood.*

On Monday, Rutledge had been part of the storm that had raged, filibustering against the sections of the declaration which criticized slavery and he had succeeded in forcing their removal. How far could a state go to write its own death warrant? Losing their only customer for their main products, England, was one thing. Taking the people out of the fields who were so essential to production and thus to the state's survival would be fatal. The state would never agree to that. Three days later, when that obstacle was removed, and against the instructions of the South Carolina delegation and his own inclinations, Dickinson would persuade the South Carolina delegation to vote for the Declaration. The state had been just as angry as the northern states over the taxation issues and took up arms to join the rebellion.

July 4, 1776 ~Philadelphia

CITIZEN BEN

ONLY A FEW BLOCKS DOWN FROM THE KRAFFT HOUSE, set off in a quiet, spacious courtyard off Market Street between Third and Fourth Streets, sits a large, elegant mansion that shows clearly the hand of its owner at work, although built by the prominent Philadelphia carpenter Robert Smit under the supervision of carpenter, builder, and merchant Samuel Rhoads. It is also a three story brick home embellished with wainscoting, columns and pilasters, pediments, dentil work, frets and cornices. Its ten rooms are filled with the remarkable inventiveness and cosmopolitan taste of the man who conceived it—Benjamin Franklin. Much of the building of it took place while he was in France, sending detailed instructions by mail to be carried out by his wife, Deborah.

The house has been both a sadness and a comfort to him on his return home from his seven years in France and England. After having formed so many friendships and achieved so many diplomatic successes, he had departed in humiliation after being unfairly accused before the Privy Council of trying to provoke colonial riots against the Crown. His wife Deborah died before his return. But the house he had watched grow only in his mind's eye now embraced him with a true sense of home.

A sulfurous light from the rising July sun was beginning to color the room, the tea cup that rested on the desk before him, the notes and papers. This was the single quiet moment between the night and the day that Franklin savored. A pause between duties and worries in which he could let his mind wander briefly where it would. This morning it strayed from the dramas of the Congress to some of the sweeter moments in Paris, walking in the Moulin Joly garden with Mme. Brillon and other friends. Someone had drawn his attention to the tiny skeletons of flies—a species called ephemera or mayflies—who were born, lived and died in a single day. First light was slipping across notes he had written about them on his return, perhaps for an essay . . . No, something lighter. A letter to Mme. Brillon perhaps. She would appreciate it. He smiled to think that such grave and momentous affairs could go on in the human world, side by side with creatures whose world would last no more than a single day. Yes, he would write of the ephemera in a letter to Mme. Brillon. When things had settled a bit.

It is now over a year since he landed with his grandson Temple after the three month journey by ship. Temple had been good company and they had made the best of their trip together, taking water measurements with his homemade thermometer. His cousin Timothy Folger, a Nantucket whaler, had told him about the stream of warm water that wove through the sea like an ocean river. He had discussed it with several other American captains who explained that they made better times than British captains because they understood how to use the Gulf Stream's current when they were sailing with it and avoided it when they were sailing in the other direction. The existence of the Gulf Stream was known but not well understood or uniformly used to advantage in navigation. Franklin tested samples of the water and discovered that they were much less phosphorescent than the rest of the sea. He concluded from his discoveries that the best way to find and navigate the waters of the Gulf Stream was to equip the ships with thermometers. His sketches of the stream's course lay still in shadow on a table nearby.

Like Jefferson, Franklin has a keen interest in weather phenomena. "Some are weatherwise, some are otherwise," he quipped. Fourteen years earlier he had taken part in discussions about the effects of deforestation on local climate. Forests had to be cleared for farming in the colonies, and it was obvious to him that the cleared land was absorbing more heat and melting the snow more quickly. But he knew that many more years of systematic observations would be required before they could draw accurate conclusions about the effects of deforestation on the local climate.

It is not such a coincidence that he shares this interest with his Philadelphia neighbor, Thomas Jefferson. Both men are "natural philosophers"—(the term "scientist" won't be coined until the 19th century, or come into popular use until the 20th century when it is fully established as a separate field). Franklin and Jefferson are eager to put to use the new scientific instruments that are becoming increasingly available and to test theories of their own. Now that Fahrenheit, in Holland, has come up with a universal measurement for the mercury thermometer, new horizons have opened up for the study of weather. Both men see these studies as a piece in understanding and defining the future of this new nation.

Franklin is well aware that people have misunderstood his silence at meetings in the first period of his return. He speaks very little, even when he joins the group at their informal after-meeting gatherings at the City Tavern. He smiles to himself, aware that some see it as a sign of the wisdom of his age—he is 70 after all—while others see it as a sign that he is not in favor of independence from England. "He has just spent seven years there, hasn't he?" But his silence is for William. His son. He has been waiting. Biding his time until the reunion when he can test the waters. Make his case slowly for this move toward independence. But he has failed. He sighs at the thought of it. And of the more painful fact that William's actions as a Loyalist governor of New Jersey—a position he himself had helped to secure for William while they had been in England together—has led to his arrest by colonial militiamen. He is still under house arrest.

Now even more pressing matters are adding to Franklin's burdens. Five days ago a massive British war fleet arrived in New York Harbor consisting of 30 battleships with 1200 cannon, 30,000 soldiers, 10,000 sailors, and 300 supply ships under the command of General William Howe and his brother Admiral Lord Richard Howe. This is the greatest army that England has ever sent overseas. How are they to match a force of this size, so well equipped and highly trained? Washington has sent a brigade of six regiments to New York under Brig. Gen. Sullivan and is preparing to engage them with their full force of 10,000 volunteers, under an inexperienced, although clearly competent leader, with the British having the huge advantage of control of the open sea.

Fortunately, time does not allow him to dwell on such worries. There is always something immediately at hand to do. In spite of his seventy years he has a daunting schedule. Not only is he Postmaster General and a member of the Continental Congress, but also a member of several important and active committees.

The Committee charged with developing a declaration has its meetings at 6 am, before the opening of the Congress at 9 am. Over the last few days, he has been meeting with Thomas Jefferson and John Adams in Jefferson's lodging to go over the draft that Jefferson has written of a Declaration of Independence from England.

The morning is full upon him now and the ephemera are swept aside. He looks forward to the walk down to the Krafft house with John Adams. It is a change of scenery, with the countryside opening up before them, that lifts the heart.

Events are moving swiftly and Franklin sometimes feels that he is at the center of a cyclone. But it is not such a new feeling.

July 4, 1776 ~ Philadelphia

LETTER HOME

THE MASSACHUSETTS DELEGATION to the Second Continental Congress is housed in the Sarah Yard house at the center of town, across the street from the City Tavern. John Adams is filled with ardor for his task and enthusiasm for the experience, even as he misses his wife and family on the farm in Massachusetts. There is so much to see in Philadelphia and the days are filled with activity. The Congress meets six days a week and on Sunday there are church services to attend. Even these are filled with novelty for the out-of-town delegates. He has been among the Anglicans, the Methodists, the Baptists, the Presbyterians, the Quakers, the German Moravians and even the Roman Catholics. The Mass he attended at St. Mary's, with its music, bells, candles, gold, silver and Latin chanting, was a startling contrast to the simple and quiet services at the plain First Church in Braintree that he attends with his family.

Adams had often been told that Philadelphia is the fairest city in the colonies, and that is indeed true. It is certainly the largest and wealthiest city in British America with a population nearing thirty thousand people, nearly twice the size of Boston and larger than New York. It is the busiest of the ports, though it is more than a hundred miles from the open sea. Ships and the sea trade are its livelihood. Unlike the narrow, twisting streets of Boston, the streets of Philadelphia are wide and straight and Adams finds this pleasing. He finds the buildings "handsome and substantial" from the churches to the prison and he admires the public services, like the volunteer fire company, inspired by Benjamin Franklin.

The manufacturers and artisans of Philadelphia produce more goods than any city in America, from Franklin stoves to pianos. All of this, Adams takes in on his walks around town, savoring especially the quantity of books available. With twenty-three printing establishments and seven newspapers (more even than London!) there is always something new to discover in the thirty or so bookstores in town. And the food! The wealthy families of Philadelphia live opulently and have opened their doors to the members of the new Congress with lavish hospitality, surpassing even the wealth of New York, which the delegation had passed through on their way from Boston. Even the Quakers, he wrote to his wife Abigail, served ducks, hams, chickens, beef, creams and custards. "I shall be killed with kindness in this place. We go to Congress at nine and there we stay most earnestly engaged until three in the afternoon, then we adjourn and go to dinner with some of the nobles of Pennsylvania at four o'clock and feast on ten thousand delicacies, and sit drinking Madeira, claret and burgundy 'til six or seven."

As much as his explorations of the city, he enjoys the occasional walk into the countryside beyond Eighth Street. The fields of wild strawberries, the ponds and woods that open up before him give him a brief experience of home. But there is no doubt that his greatest satisfaction is in the drama of the meetings themselves, both the formal ones in the state house and the informal gatherings later at the City Tavern. He is one of the most ardent spokesmen of the revolution that is taking place, right at the heart of this city. If Franklin and Jefferson are on the quiet side during these meetings, Adams is lively on his feet, speaking his mind. He is not one for laboriously putting things into written words, but amazes himself with the things that just come out of his mouth, truly inspired at times. Although at other times, perhaps less felicitous. But he is writing now, saving his best prose for the letters to his wife back in Braintree. Even in her absence, theirs is a partnership of kindred spirits and he values her counsel and insight, even as she values this proximity to history being made by her husband and his colleagues.

"But the Day is past," he writes to her. "The Second Day of July 1776, will be the most memorable Epoch in the History of America. I am apt to believe that it will be celebrated, by succeeding Generations, as the great anniversary Festival. It ought to be commemorated, as the Day of Deliverance by solemn Acts of Devotion to God Almighty. It ought to be solemnized with Pomp and Parade, with Shows, Games, Sports, Guns, Bells, Bonfires and Illuminations from one End of this Continent to the other from this Time forward forever more.

You will think me transported with Enthusiasm but I am not.—I am well aware of the Toil and Blood and Treasure, that it will cost Us to maintain this Declaration, and support and defend these States.—Yet through all the Gloom I can see the Rays of ravishing Light and Glory. I can see that the End is more than worth all the Means. And that Posterity will triumph in that Day's Transaction, even altho We should rue it, which I trust in God We shall not."

He was only two days off in his prophecy.

✦ ✦ ✦

Revisiting the founding fathers after so many years, I realize how incomplete my view of them has been. They are almost too familiar to see clearly, since we meet them first in childhood every Fourth of July—celebrated much as John Adams envisioned—as a passing footnote to parades, fireworks and summer barbecues. David McCullough's excellent book on John Adams and the HBO television series that grew out of it, produced by Tom Hanks, have done a great deal to revive the full dimensions of this period and its people.

We tend to think of Jefferson, Franklin, Adams and Washington post-July 4th, 1776 as if all along they had been pressing for this independent nation, forgetting that they were Englishmen and that is how they saw themselves. When Franklin served as Postmaster, he did so as a servant of His Majesty's government. They were loyal subjects of the crown. Even in the months leading up to the declaration, the Continental Congress was solely dedicated to securing their rights *as Englishmen*. Franklin's mission in England had been related to the affairs of his own state, Pennsylvania. He had been sent by the Pennsylvania assembly to persuade parliament to replace the onerous Proprietorship of the Penns with a Royal Charter that would put them directly under the government of the king and parliament.

Franklin was a great lover of England and had distinguished friends there—like the scientist Joseph Priestley and Dr. Erasmus Darwin, grandfather of Charles Darwin. Also in Scotland, where he was given an honorary degree by St. Andrews. In France, he counted some of its most distinguished men (and women!) among his friends. He was in England on his mission for Pennsylvania when the Stamp Act was passed, which so infuriated the colonists that Franklin soon became embroiled in the diplomatic efforts to forestall it. The grievances felt against England throughout the colonies were over being treated like second rate citizens by their mother country, while being milked for their available resources.

The disdain shown by the British government in its policies toward the colonists rankled the people of talent and ability like Jefferson, Adams and Franklin. George Washington's ambition as a young man was to rise in the ranks of the British Army, but he soon discovered that such advancement would never be available to him. It is no less than remarkable that events took the course they did and that such men were present to meet them. Out of that convergence in time would come the presidency for Washington, Adams, Jefferson and later Adams' son John Quincy. The scientific and cultural contributions of Jefferson and Franklin would leave their marks all across the landscape. Jefferson's meteorological station at Monticello will become one of twelve thousand weather stations under the National Weather Service, which claims him as "the father of weather." His passionate interest in meteorology gained additional impetus from his desire to refute the claims of French scientist Georges-Louis Leclerc, the Comte de Buffon, that the climates of the colonies in America were degenerative; "that nature is less active, less energetic on one side of the globe than she is on the other" (Jefferson's translation), and therefore produced smaller and less diverse plant and animal life in the New World as compared to Europe. In 1787, Jefferson sent Buffon the skeleton of a moose along with written descriptions of the massive antlers such animals often possessed, expressing the hope that it "may have the merit of adding anything new to the treasures of nature which have so fortunately come under your observation."

We can imagine how eagerly Jefferson dispatched Lewis and Clark, as president, to explore the lands gained through his purchase of the Louisiana Territory. He sent them off in 1803 with specific instructions to observe "climate as characterized by the thermometer, by the proportion of rainy, cloudy & clear days, by lightening, hail, snow, ice, by the access & recess of frost, by the winds prevailing at different seasons, the dates at which particular plants put forth or lose their flowers, or leaf, times of appearance of particular birds, reptiles or insects."

Even before Independence is declared, we can see these men defining themselves to their European counterparts. It is in this activity that the sense of themselves as separate, distinct and *equal* grows almost unconsciously, yet ready to flare up quickly into the fight for independence when kindled by oppressive British policies.

A patriot is defined as "a supporter of one's country and its way of life." Even before the United States was a country or had a flag to wave, these men were patriots in the truest sense. They gave expression to what was unique and loveable about their native land and in this they did great service to their fellow citizens, then and now. What began as the desire to gain recognition as good citizens of Great Britain, ended in the recognition that they had something even better, although it would be a hard road ahead for all of them. Their real grit would not begin to show until they were each called into their roles of leadership. And as with the modern presidents, each left office tarnished and exhausted by the job, even as each played a vital role in holding the country together and solidifying its purpose.

We might take note here too of a young man, almost exactly the age of Giuseppe Dodini of Lavertezzo who is absent for Fr. Galli's Status Animarum. Giuseppe is probably up in one of the high meadows of Ticino watching over the family's cow and goats in an idle, dream-like summer afternoon of his sixteenth year. James Shafter, if the records are correct, will not actually turn 16 until September of this year of 1776 but he is definitely out there to be counted and to take up arms with his neighbors in what will become Vermont. In fact he fought in the Battle of Bunker Hill in 1775 at the age of 15, and ahead of him lie the battles of Bennington and Saratoga in 1777. He is decidedly in the thick of things, and if Giuseppe manages to elude conscription into Napoleon's wars and events on the European stage, James Shafter continually finds himself where the action is. This is apparently a family trait, as we will discover later. He will also do service on the Canadian frontier. For twenty-five years he will serve as a member of the Vermont Legislature.

When the next war comes along, the War of 1812, his son William will be born. James is too old to become active in this conflict but he has definitely done his national service by producing William, who will be right there at the center of things when the Vermont Constitutional Convention is convened in 1836.

The New England Shafters have a lot in common with John Adams and his family. James is born in Dudley, Massachusetts, about 70 miles west of Quincy, where John and Abigail had their farm. Both men are farmers. But they are also patriots and the times they live in call upon their services in political venues. They are also sires of important dynasties. William Shafter will go on to become a county judge and later a member of the Vermont State Legislature, like his father.

Two of William's sons, Oscar and James, will play significant parts in our story. Keep them in mind.

June 29, 1776 ~ California

ARRIVAL BY LAND

NOTHING WOULD SEEM TO BE FARTHER from the remote ancient villages of Ticino or the bustling city of Philadelphia than the land along the wide bay and the Pacific, still unknown to most Europeans and to the colonists on the opposite seaboard, engaged in their struggle for independence from England. Yet it shares one feature in common with the steep mountain villages above the alpine valleys: its protected "hiddenness" from the daring adventurers who sailed along the coast under the flags of several countries eager to discover and to claim its treasures. Again and again, some of the world's greatest sailors and navigators failed to descry the narrow gap that opened onto what legend said was the greatest harbor in the world. Cabrillo, following his successful discovery of the harbor of San Diego, sailed as far north as another bay, which may have been Monterey or Drake's Bay, but he was forced south by storms. Neither did Sebastian Cermeno or Sebastian Vizcaino discover it as they sailed along the Pacific coast at the turn of the seventeenth century.

Four decades later, Sir Francis Drake, sailing the Golden Hind from England, spent a month on the northern California coast, taking possession of what he called New Albion. Probably due to fog, he missed the narrow gate to San Francisco Bay, but found another "convenient and fit harbor" which may have been the bay which presently bears his name: Drake's Bay.*

But at last the hidden became known and the golden treasures of the mythic land of California were about to be exposed to the European world. A gold that was, and still is, to take many forms. It was not by sea that the bay was finally to be discovered—the gateway remained hidden, like the threshold of Shangri-La or Shambhala—but by land.** In 1775, adventurers of a different sort from the sea-faring explorers and conquistadors, were toiling northward from Monterey. Among them was Fr. Palou, whose account brings to life this event taking place

---

* Drake's Bay is just north of San Francisco on the shore of what will become known as Punta de los Reyes or Point Reyes.

** Spanish explorer Gaspar de Portalá first sighted the Bay in 1760 from the peak of Sweeney Ridge near Pacifica, but he mistook it for Drake's Bay.

unseen in an unknown corner of the world. Just imagine the media frenzy if such an expedition were to set out today from Monterey with little to no knowledge of what lay ahead of them and no amenities along the way; an expedition that had begun many months before in Baja California.

FATHER PALOU'S ACCOUNT

ON THE 17TH DAY OF JUNE, 1776, *about two in the afternoon, we set out from Monterey with a company of soldiers and families who had traveled there from Sonora. The company was composed of its commander, Lieutenant Don José Joaquin Moraga, a sergeant, two corporals, and ten soldiers, all with their wives and families, except for the commander, who had left his in Sonora. There were seven families of settlers, rationed and provisioned by the king; other persons attached to the soldiers and their families; five servant boys, muleteers and vaqueros, who conducted about two hundred of the king's cattle and some belonging to individuals, and the mule train which carried the provisions and utensils necessary for the road. All belonged to the new presidio. And for the founding of the first mission, we two ministers, Padre Fray Pedro Benito Cambon and I, went with two servants who conducted the loads, and three unmarried Indian neophytes, two of them from Baja California and the other from the mission of Carmelo, who drove the cattle for the mission, numbering eighty-six head, which were incorporated with those for the presidio.*

The officers of the vessels, with their pilots and chaplains, wished to accompany the expedition, and they all did so for about half a league. From this point the captain of the Principe and all the pilots turned back; but Don Fernando Quiros continued for the first day's march with the two father chaplains as far as the Monterey River, where the expedition halted and camped.

On the following day, after having watched all the people cross the river and seen the line formed on that broad plain by all those people, the pack trains, cattle, and the horse herd, they returned to Monterey after taking farewell in the hope that we would soon meet in the port of Our Father San Francisco. The expedition continued by the same road which was traveled in the exploration of that harbor in the year 1774. But the day's marches were shorter, in order not to fatigue the little children and the women, especially those who were pregnant, and for this reason it was even necessary to make several stops. On the whole way there was not a single mishap, thanks to God.

We were well received by all the heathen whom we met on the road, who were surprised to see so many people of both sexes and all ages, for up to that time they had not seen more than some few soldiers on the occasions when they went to make explorations. And they were astonished at the cattle, which they had never seen before.

On the 27th day of June the expedition arrived in the neighborhood of the harbor, and the commander ordered the camp halted on the bank of a lagoon called by Señor Anza "Nuestra Señora de los Dolores," which is in sight of the bay of Los Llorones and the beach of the bay or arm of the sea which runs to the southeast, *with the intention of waiting here for the bark in order to select the spot for the founding of the fort and presidio, and in the meantime to explore the land. On the following day he ordered a shelter of branches built to serve as a chapel in which to celebrate the holy sacrifice of the Mass. In it the first Mass was said on the 29th, the feast of the great, holy apostles, San Pedro and San Pablo, and we continued to celebrate in it every day until the camp was moved to the site which it occupies near the landing place, when the ground and the convenience of water permitted it.* *

◆ ◆ ◆

Father Palou, like his famous friend and countryman Fr. Junipero Serra, was born in Palma, on the island of Majorca. He entered the Franciscan order there and studied philosophy under Fr. Serra. Together they volunteered for the American Indian missions, joining the missionary College of San Fernando de Mexico in 1740. There they were assigned to the Indian missions of Sierra Gorda, north of Queretaro. In 1767, he was sent with Father Serra and fourteen other Franciscan Friars to Baja California. In 1769, when Father Serra set forth to establish the missions of Alta (Upper) California, Fr. Palou became superior of the lower missions. In 1773, these missions were turned over to the Dominican Fathers and Fr. Palou was sent north to serve as acting superior there while Fr. Serra was in Mexico. (He returned in 1774.) In November of that year, Fr. Palou was part of Capt. Rivera's expedition to explore the Bay of San Francisco, and on December 4 he planted the cross on Point Lobos, just south of present-day Carmel-by-the-Sea. It was in June 1776 that he joined Lt. Moraga's expedition described above where, a few weeks later, he would found the Mission Dolores. Twenty-one missions were established in California under Fr. Serra's leadership. He chose to walk almost the entire distance from one site to another, in spite of suffering from a lasting leg injury. In the last three years of his life, he revisited the missions from San Diego to San Francisco, a distance of more than 600 miles, to confirm all of those he had baptized. He died at age 70 of a snake bite at the Mission Carmel and was buried under the sanctuary floor.

According to Fr. Palou's account, we can imagine him saying Mass on the afternoon of July 4th, under branches from an oak tree, with views of the sea and the wide expanse of bay that had finally been revealed to them. They called the bay San Francisco, after the founder of their order, St. Francis of Assisi. Just one more event on that summer afternoon, although it was unlikely to have been as warm on that day of the year as it was in Ticino and Philadelphia.

* From Fr. Palou's biography of Junipero Serra, published in 1787.

CALIFORNIA 1775
(ONE YEAR EARLIER)
ARRIVAL BY SEA: THE LITTLE SHIP THAT COULD

After neglecting California for nearly 170 years, Spain was finally compelled in 1765 to turn its attention once again to the region, as it suddenly had two foreign competitors with which to contend. Great Britain, victorious two years earlier in the Seven Years' War, had seized Florida from Spain and now controlled the entire east coast of North America. . . . And word spread through Europe that Russia . . . was looking to extend its fur-trading business down the Pacific toward Monterey Bay.

— JOSHUA PADDISON, *A World Transformed*

THUS BEGAN THE SACRED EXPEDITION that would bring Fr. Palou a decade later to the site of the future San Francisco. The project was conceived by the clever but mentally unstable José de Gálvez, visitador-general of New Spain. To this end, he established a port and ship-building center at San Blas, Mexico on the northwest coast to supply the new settlements. The plan was to send three ships and two overland parties up the Pacific coast to establish missions and presidios—military forts—at California's two known harbors, San Diego and Monterey. (There were some who considered this idea as far-fetched as an idea he had once espoused of training 600 Guatemalan apes as soldiers to deal with rebellious Indians.)

The names of the Niña, the Pinta and the Santa Maria are well-known to all American school children who are reminded of them every Columbus Day, like the Mayflower celebrated each Thanksgiving with more enthusiasm than the original passengers felt toward it. But the San Antonio, the San Carlos and the San Jose are a less-remembered and less-celebrated trio of ships, hastily constructed at San Blas and dispatched on their mission to Alta California.* Looking back, the whole thing seems ill-conceived and unfortuitous. Two land parties "outfitted with priests, furniture, vestments, and livestock from the Baja missions" set out, completing an expedition of 300 soldiers, sailors, carpenters, cooks, Christianized Indians and a huge herd of horses, cattle, and mules, all headed toward San Diego Bay under the leadership of the fifty-five year old Governor Gaspar de Portolá and Franciscan Father Junipero Serra. These were both intelligent and dedicated men, but Portolá was not experienced as an explorer and not comfortable in wilderness conditions. Father Serra undertook this journey with a swollen and ulcerated foot, which required them to proceed at a slow pace and periodically carry him on a stretcher.

The three ships didn't even make it to the Baja peninsula in one piece, and that was their official starting point. They had to undergo repairs before setting out for San Diego in early 1769. The San Carlos, which had not been completed when it left San Blas, was unloaded, finished, then reloaded again at La Paz. On

---

* The present state of California was known to the Spanish of this time as Alta or "Upper" California. Baja, or "lower" California is today the most northwest region of Mexico, bordered by the Sea of Cortez and the Pacific.

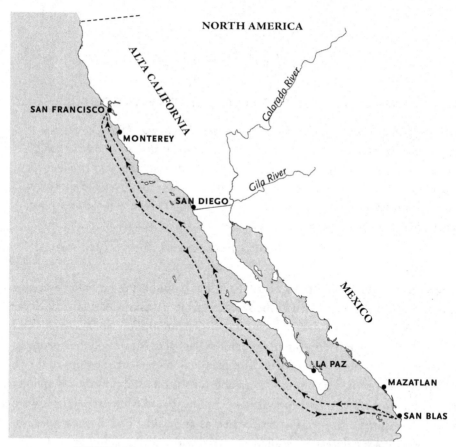

VOYAGE OF THE SAN CARLOS, WITH STOPS AT LA PAZ AND SAN DIEGO

the morning of January 9, 1769, Father Serra said a Mass for those on board and prayed for their safe journey. Gálvez was in high humor as he saw them off for La Paz, and accompanied them in another ship as far as Cabo San Lucas.

Prayers and a cheerful send-off notwithstanding, the San Carlos quickly ran into difficulties, with leaking water casks and many of the sailors already afflicted with scurvy. They encountered severe storms, and missed their destination due to a 1 degree error in the previous calculations of Vizcaino in 1602 (others attribute the error to Cabrillo). This took them too far north and added 200 miles to their journey as well as exposure to colder weather. They were rescued after four months at sea. Two dozen of the 62 man crew were dead and only four of the remaining men were able to stand. The San Jose never arrived and was never heard of again.

For those traveling by land, the journey took fifty-one days over treacherous desert terrain, attacked by hostile Indians along the way. On what was supposed to be the easy leg of the journey, the Sacred Expedition had already lost half of its members when it reached San Diego.

Undaunted, Portolá made the decision at this point to send the San Antonio back to San Blas for provisions, while Father Serra remained to begin the work of building a mission and Portolá himself led a party of sixty of the fittest men and Father Crespí on the expedition north to Monterey Bay. This entailed four months of strenuous hiking along the rugged California coast. All along the way, the Indians they encountered were friendly and helpful. Many of the areas they passed through were heavily populated. Nevertheless, they reached their destination half-starved. They had expected a more welcoming landscape, given the descriptions of Vizcaíno. In place of forests of pines and oaks and quantities of drinkable water, they found a harsh, rocky and windy beach.

Certain that they were mistaken in their calculations, the expedition pressed on with the hope of finding Monterey Bay to the north. They knew nothing yet of the sheltered and abundant San Francisco Bay that lay ahead. From a hillside to the east, (Sweeney Ridge) they caught their first sight of the bay but the view was partially obstructed by the mountains of San Bruno and Mt. Tamalpais, so they could not get a full view of the expanse of it. They mistakenly identified it at the time as an arm of Drake's Bay to the north, discovered by earlier explorers, and called it Bahia de San Francisco. It did not match the description of Monterey Bay, which by now they determined they had missed. Portolá and his company "limped back to San Diego," as Paddison put it, to find that the San Antonio had not yet returned with supplies. In six months, Serra had managed to construct some crude stick-and-mud huts which he had very optimistically christened "Mission San Diego de Alcalá." Accounts have described the remaining men as "sick, starving and wounded from the Indian attacks."

I find it impossible to imagine how despondent these people must have been at this point. The novelty of strangers had obviously worn off and the native Kumeyaay now realized clearly their intention to settle in their lands. The conflicts would only get worse. Portolá made the decision to wait until March 20th for the ship to arrive, and failing that, they would all return to Mexico, with the exception of Father Serra and Father Crespí who would stay behind on the San Carlos, which lay deserted on the beach. But history had other plans in mind for the dauntless little ship, which had endured such hardship on this first leg of the journey.

The San Antonio arrived on March 19th and delivered the much-needed provisions. Portolá once again set his men on the march to Monterey. Bear in mind that this is a distance of almost 500 miles, often over rugged terrain. He left eight soldiers behind to continue working in San Diego and divided the rest of the force between a land group marching under his command and the other half with Serra on the San Antonio. This time Portolá and his men looked more carefully at the barren beach that lay at the latitude given by Vizcaino and described as "the best port that could be desired." They began construction of the Mission San Carlos de Borromeo and a presidio nearby.

Exhausted at this point, but satisfied that the destination had been reached, Portolá sailed back to Mexico, where he took up the post of governor of Puebla and later returned to his native Spain. In his place, a fellow Catalan, Pedro Fages, took charge of the Sacred Expedition.

Early in 1775, the San Carlos was once again tapped for a mission north, this time under a naval officer, Capt. Juan de Ayala, trained in navigation, chart-making and coastal surveying with the mission to survey the waters of San Francisco Bay, which had now been definitively identified by a return of the land party to the east of it. No one had yet penetrated it from the west by sea. Once again, the ship had misfortunes to overcome in San Blas. Ship-Lieutenant Miguel Manriquez began suffering violent delusions of persecution, took ten loaded pistols onto the afterdeck and ordered his pilots at gunpoint to turn the ship around. (Given the ship's history to date I would have done the same thing.) Then he climbed into the ship's longboat, pistols in hand and rowed ashore without explanation. Captain Ayala took command of the San Carlos but accidentally shot himself in the foot with one of the pistols that Manriquez had left behind. Although the ship set sail successfully, Ayala wasn't able to leave his bunk until the middle of May.

On the morning of August 5th, the San Carlos reached San Francisco Bay, only to be faced with a dangerously strong current with whirling eddies that pushed them back out to sea. Taking advantage of a tailwind, they still managed to make excruciatingly slow progress against the tide. Unfortunately, night came on before they had made it into the safety of the bay and there was no choice but to press on. This meant navigating the dangers of uncharted waters by the dim light of a half moon. The San Carlos slipped through the narrow entrance to the bay at 10:30 pm and dropped anchor behind Angel Island.

As morning dawned on the 6th, the sight for which the San Carlos and its crew had struggled so long was finally before him. One can feel in Capt. Ayala's account the relief and optimism he must have felt when the breaking light revealed the true nature of the bay he had entered in darkness. "It is true that this port is good, not only for the beautiful harmony that it offers to the view, but because it does not lack very good fresh water, wood, and ballast in abundance. Its climate, though cold, is healthful and free from those troublesome fogs which we had daily in Monterey." Captain Ayala, selected in part for his training in mapping and surveying, was still prevented by his foot injury from embarking on the project of exploring the bay, so that fell to Pilot José Cañizares, who took the longboat out first thing to begin his explorations.

The chaplain of the expedition was Father Vicente Santa Maria, a Spanish-born Franciscan educated in Mexico at the Colegio San Fernando. He wrote a very detailed account of his encounter with the native people of the region. I cannot help but think while reading it that this is the closest we have come to what the experience of meeting people from another planet would be like, for both parties (although I would have loved an account through native eyes as well). At this moment he is 33 years old, young and open to his new experience. The San Carlos is anchored in what is now Richardson Bay near Angel Island, and the place they go ashore was then the Coast Miwok territory of Huimen, on the southernmost part of the Marin Peninsula. Here is Fr. Santa Maria's account.

August 9, 1775
FR. SANTA MARIA

SHORTLY BEFORE THE LONGBOAT, *returning from this venture reached the ship, we saw on the slope of a hill that was in front of us a number of Indians coming down unhurriedly and in a quiet manner, making their way gradually to the edge of the shore. . . . The captain came aboard and with his permission, I went in the longboat with the two sailing masters and the surgeon to communicate at close quarters with those poor unfortunates who so persistently desired us to do so, and by easy steps to bring them into close terms with us and make them the readier when the time should come for attracting them to our holy faith.*

As we came near the shore, we wondered much to see Indians, lords of these coasts, quite weaponless and obedient to our least sign to them to sit down, doing just as they were bid. There remained standing only one of the eldest, who mutely made clear to us with what entire confidence we should come ashore to receive a new offering, which they had prepared for us at the shore's edge.

Keeping watch all 'round to see if among the hills any treachery were afoot, we came in slowly, and when we thought ourselves safe we went ashore, the first sailing master in the lead. There came forward to greet him the oldest Indian, offering him at the end of a stick a string of beads like a rosary, made up of white shells interspersed with black knots in the thread on which they were strung.

Then the rest of us who went in the longboat landed, and at once the Indian mentioned above (who came as leader among them) showed us the way to the place where they had made ready for us a number of baskets, some filled with pinole and others with loaves made with a distinctly sulfurous material that seemed to have been kneaded with some sort of oil, though its odor was so slight that we could not decide what it might be. The sailing master accepted everything and at once returned the favor with earrings, glass beads, and other trinkets. The Indians who came on this occasion were nine in number, three being old men, two of them with sight impaired by cataracts of some sort. The six others were young men of good presence and fine stature. Their coloring was not so weak as we have seen in Indians at Carmel. They were by no means filthy, and the best favored were models of perfection; among them was a boy whose exceeding beauty stole my heart. One alone of the young men had several dark blue lines painted from the lower lip to the waist and from the left shoulder to the right, in such a way as to form a perfect cross. God grant that we may see them worshipping so sovereign an emblem.

Besides comely elegance of figure and quite faultless countenance there was also— as their chief adornment—the way they did up their long hair. After smoothing it well, they stuck in it a four-toothed wooden comb and bound up the end in a net of cord and very small feathers that were dyed a deep red; and in the middle of the coiffure was tied a sort of ribbon, sometimes black, sometimes blue. Those Indians who did not arrange their hair in this fashion did it up in a club so as to keep it in a closely-woven, small net that seemed to be of hemp-like fibers dyed a dark blue.

It would have seemed natural that these Indians, in their astonishment at our clothes, should have expressed a particular surprise and no less curiosity—but they gave no sign of it. Only one of the older Indians showed himself a little unmannerly toward me; seeing that I was a thick-bearded man, he began touching the whiskers as if in surprise that I had not shaved long since. We noticed an unusual thing about the young men: none of them ventured to speak and only their elders replied to us. They were so obedient that, notwithstanding we pressed them to do so, they dared not stir a step unless one of the old men told them to; so meek that, even though curiosity prompted them, they did not raise their eyes from the ground; so docile that when my companions did me reverence by touching their lips to my sleeve and then by signs told them to do the same thing, they at once and with good grace did as they were bid.

The time we were with them seemed to us short, but it was enjoyable, all the more when, upon my pronouncing the most sweet names of Jesus and Mary Most Holy, they repeated them clearly, a great satisfaction and pleasure to me and to my companions. . . . We urged them to come on board the ship, but with long speeches they avoided doing so, and by signs they invited us to come with them, pointing out the way to their rancherias. We took leave of them, however, setting out in the longboat for the ship, and they went home.

Rash, seemingly, was what I did with five sailors and the surgeon on the afternoon of the 9th of August: we decided to go as far as an Indian rancheria that was about a league from the shore and with a poor approach. We were sustained only by our Catholic faith and were impelled by godly zeal lest our gains be lost. It so happened that the Indians had assembled with their usual daily present, but we could not go over to get it because the dugout, inadequate though it was as a conveyance, was not available, being in immediate need of repair. About midday, twelve Indians appeared with the new supply. Though they called repeatedly to us, it was not feasible for us to respond to them; we lacked the means, since the longboat had not yet returned from its first expedition. Tired, at last, of pressing us and seeing that we did not comply with their requests, they all began putting on a dance. When they were done, they returned to calling us over to where they were waiting for us; and then, as we could not give them that pleasure for want of a boat, they went away as if with hurt feelings, showing by the speed of their departure that they had begun to feel worried at so decided a change in our behavior.

When we had about given up hope of satisfying our Indians, the longboat returned to the ship with the sailing master, José Cañizares. Day and night he had gone exploring what parts of the harbor he could. . . . This would have been about a quarter past six o'clock in the evening, and the captain, as a mark of kindness, asked if I should like to take a walk along the shore. The surgeon and I accepted the favor, and setting out in the longboat, we went ashore without delay. We were mindful that the Indians might have gone away offended; so, like the hunter fearless of dangers, who leaps over the rough places and forces his way through obstacles until he meets his quarry, we went up the slopes, taking chances, hunting for our Indians until we should find them. In pursuing this venture we did not share our intentions with the captain because, if we had, from that moment he would have had nothing to do with it in view of the risks involved in our desire to visit the rancheria at so unseasonable a time and in so remote a place.

Notwithstanding all this, and even though we had no notion of how soon we might reach the Indians, we were nevertheless making our way by their very path. As night was now approaching, we were considering a return to the ship, and were of two minds about it, when we caught sight of the Indians. At the same time seeing us, they began inviting us with repeated gestures and loud cries to their rancheria, which was at the shore of a rather large, round cove. [Probably Belvedere Cove]

Although we might on that occasion have succumbed to dread, we summoned our courage because we had to, lest fear make cowards of us. We thought that if we turned back and for a second time did not heed the call of the Indians, this might confirm them in their resentment or make them believe that we were very timid—not an agreeable idea, for many reasons. As none of those who came along declined to follow me, ignoring our weariness we went on toward the rancheria. As soon as the Indians saw that we were near their huts, all the men stood forward as if in defense of their women and children, whom undoubtedly they regard as their treasure and their heart's core. They may have thought, though not expressing this openly to us, that we might do their dear ones harm; if so, their action was most praiseworthy.

We were now almost at the rancheria. As we were going to be there a while, an Indian hustled up some clean herbage for us to sit on, made with it a modest carpet, and had us sit on it. The Indians sat on the bare ground, thus giving us to understand in some degree how guests should be received. They then made quite clear to us how astonished they had been that we had not joined them at the shore, but we succeeded in giving them some reassurances. When I saw there was so large a gathering I began to speak to them for a short time, though I knew they could not understand me unless God should work a miracle. All the time that I was speaking, these Indians, silent and attentive, were as if actually comprehending, showing by their faces much satisfaction and joy. When I had finished speaking, I said to those who had come with me that we should sing the Alabado. When we had got as far as the words 'Pura Concepción, - there was a great hubbub among the Indians, for some of them had come with two kinds of hot atole and some pinoles, and they gave all their attention to urging our participation in the feast. So our chorus stopped singing, and we gave the Indians the pleasure they wished, which was that we should eat. After the sailors had finished with the supper that our hosts had brought, I called to the Indian who seemed to me the head man of the rancheria and, taking his hand, began to move it in the sign of the cross, and he, without resisting, began repeating my words with so great clearness that I stood amazed and so did those who were with me.

One of the sailors had brought a piece of chocolate. He gave some of it to an Indian who, finding it sweet, made signs that he would go get something of similar flavor. He did so, bringing back to him a small tamale that has a fairly sweet taste and is made from a seed resembling polilla. We gave the Indians, as usual, some glass beads and received their thanks; and as they saw that the moon was rising they made signs to us to withdraw, which we then did.

◆ ◆ ◆

The behavior of these native Miwok—the thoughtfulness and respect they showed to one another and to strangers (something we would be less likely to see today)—reminds me of another Spanish friar and chronicler, writing almost two hundred and fifty years before this in Tenochtitlan, present-day Mexico City, after Cortez defeated the native Mexica (Aztecs). His men had described the city they found there as more beautiful than Seville and in many ways the people were more cultured, in spite of the rulers' grim acts of human sacrifice, a custom reputedly scorned by the 11th century king Quetzalcoatl. While Cortez was writing to Charles V of Spain, questioning whether these people had souls, Fr. Bernardino de Sahagún was interviewing Aztec princes and other native informants about their history and culture. He recorded them in several excellent volumes, which included *Huehuetlahtolli*—"The Words of the Old Ones" (Advice of the Elders).* These laid out detailed guidelines for what the young should be taught about proper comportment and respect for others. Sahagún commented that he found these people in ways more educated than their European counterparts. Even today in Mexico, the phrase *bien educado* means attentive, courteous, well brought up. The people we see in Fr. Santa Maria's account are clearly *bien educado*.

It is easy to underestimate what an axial moment this is, as one side of the earth's population is slowly coming into contact with the other during the Age of Discovery. As far as we know, through all of the millennia of human life on earth, neither had been aware of the other's existence until the voyages of explorers like Christopher Columbus, who is credited with the first Atlantic contact in 1492. (Others discount this in favor of Leif Ericsson or Amerigo Vespucci.) One can imagine that poor Capt. Ayala, laid up with his injury in the cabin of the San Carlos, was by now desperate simply to see his ship successfully complete the journey. There was so much suffering and loss in these expeditions. So much folly in their planning. And yet . . .

To illustrate what happened in a very short time, following encounters like the one we have just read, you have only to look at the two maps of California on the following pages. In the first one, you will see that this "new land," which has just been discovered by the Europeans, was heavily populated with native groups. Like Europe today, each of these had their own language, although in some cases—as in the Coast and Bodega Miwok groups, the languages were more like separate dialects. Such linguistic diversity can only develop over a long period of time, as the archaeological records testify. Miwok people had been living in the area for at least five thousand years. On the second map, you can see how thoroughly the Spanish missions and presidios penetrated into that same territory. How innocent those August days in 1775 seem when people from two different worlds—like

---

* Sahagún is a hero of mine and I highly recommend his General History of the Things of New Spain, 12 volumes translated by Arthur J. O. Anderson and Charles E. Dibble. He learned the Nahuatl language and his careful and thorough documentation of the indigenous culture and worldview has won him the titles of "the first anthropologist" and "father of American ethnography."

inhabitants of different planets—met with one another in such gentle good will.

It is estimated that at the time of these first European arrivals, the native population of California was 300,000, with some recent scholars suggesting that it was as high as 705,000 or higher. By 1845, it had fallen to 150,000. (60,000 natives deaths were recorded by the missions, during their 55 year reign over the territory.) Even with this precipitous decline, Native Americans outnumbered whites by ten to one that year. Another large group, about 25,000, perished in the wave of immigrants that arrived in the decades before 1900. In 2011, the Native American population would dwindle to 1.7% of the population of California. This figure includes natives from all of North and South America.

1781 ~ Huimen [Marin]

A BIRTH

THE RAINS HAVE ENDED. THE SKY SMILES up from the waters with a pearl and apricot light—a shy smile that will broaden into yellows and orange, throwing up gleaming laughter toward the parting clouds of spring. Moisture still lingers on the low hillsides and the bunchgrass has a silvery shine in the early morning light. Butterflies are beginning to arrive, delicate pastels luminous against the deep green of woodlands to the east and to the north —the abundant stands of redwoods and Douglas fir. The generous oak will begin to shape their acorns for the fall harvest. The elderberry trees will soon put forth their first spring shoots, which will become flutes and carry on the song of birds through the lips of humans.

Ah, the birds! They lift their bright feathers with their songs, cheerful or monotonous or ominous. Meadowlark and blackbird. Flickers, woodpecker, hawk and owl. Flocks of water birds that rise up like stars spilling their drops of water in a fine spray.

This is the creation story in living color and light. In the meadows of Marin, on the hillsides of Ring Mountain and Mt. Tamalpais, the carpets of color reveal the birth of suncups, milkmaids, footsteps-of-spring and the deep pink of shooting stars. Spreading islands of orange poppy and blue lupine, monkey flowers, Indian paintbrush and buttercups, mingled with the waves of tidytips. The land is abundant with wildlife. Teeming. The skies ring with the sounds of the returning geese and ducks and they are thick on the shores now. Elk by the thousands can be seen in the deep grass of Point Reyes and the grizzlies roam, supreme in their size and power, beside their milder cousins, the black bears.

Uncle Dunkle and Uncle Smiley and their clans may be gone, along with the wooly mammoth, the horse and the camel. But now in the last instant before midnight on our Earth calendar, some of the profusions of those early ages persist.

The area where the highway in future will debouche from the Golden Gate Bridge northward, is still covered by the waters of the bay. Marshes, lagoons and ponds cover the landscape to the northern shore of San Pablo Bay and southern Sonoma County. Wild ducks, geese and swans fly through in vast clouds.

The people are blessed by this abundance and amply provided for. Their villages

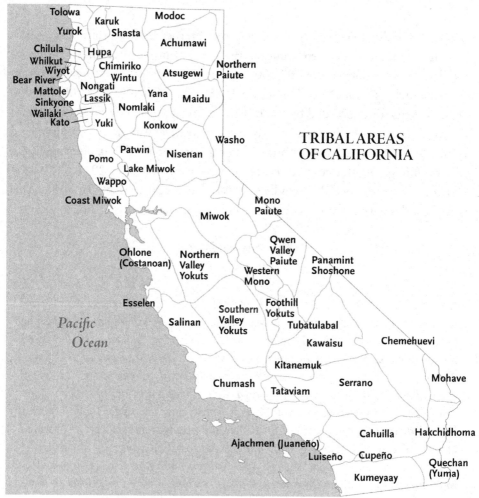

TRIBAL AREAS
OF CALIFORNIA

Pacific
Ocean

ADAPTED FROM JOSHUA PADDISON, *A WORLD TRANSFORMED*. HEYDAY BOOKS.

dot the landscape as they have for five thousand years. While they were not all occupied at the same time, 850 villages can be counted where the future will mark out Marin and southern Sonoma Counties. Wherever there is water for drinking nearby you will find them. At the edges of streams and the bays we know as San Francisco, San Pablo, Richardson, Tomales and Bodega; where there are rocks or trees large enough to provide protection from the wind. They would have fished in some version of my creek for the plentiful steelhead trout, enjoying their evening meals on Ed Grossi's vegetable farm. Do I hear them laughing softly in the nights from Mr. Fields?

Those wealthy zipcodes beyond the Golden Gate bridge—the future Sausalito, Mill Valley, Tiburon, and Belvedere—are home to the Huimen tribe of the Coast Miwoks. And there, where Mill Valley stands today and Sally and I take our walks when I am visiting, is the village of Anamas. You can see them in their tule boats, fishing near the shores. You can see the women sitting in the sun, weaving their baskets and tending their children, preparing the foods they have gathered, laughing and gossiping among themselves just as the geese do and the seabirds, just as living

CALIFORNIA
1769–1848

✝ *Missions*
▲ PRESIDIOS
◆ Pueblos & Other Settlements

◆ Sutter's Fort : 1839

◆ Fort Ross : 1812

✝ *San Francisco Solano de Sonoma* : 1823

◆ Sonoma : 1833

✝ *San Rafael Arcángel* : 1817

YERBA BUENA/ ▲ *San Francisco de Asís* . 1776
SAN FRANCISCO :
1835 ✝ *San José de Guadalupe* : 1797

✝ *San Clara de Asís* : 1776

San José : 1777

San Cruz : 1791 ✝ ◆ Branciforte : 1797

✝ *San Juan Bautista* : 1797

MONTEREY ▲

✝ *San Carlos Borromeo de Carmelo* : 1770

✝ *Nuestra Señora de la Soledad* : 1791

✝ *San Antonio de Padua* : 1771

✝ *San Miguel Arcángel* : 1797

✝ *San Luis Obispo de Tolosa* : 1772

La Purísima Conceptión : 1787
✝ ✝ *Santa Inez* : 1804
▲ ✝ *Santa Barbara* : 1782
SANTA BARBARA : 1781 ✝ *Santa Buenaventura* : 1782
✝ *San Fernando Rey de España* : 1797
✝ *San Gabriel Arcángel* : 1771

Los Angeles : 1781 ◆

✝ *San Juan Capistrano* : 1776

✝ *San Luis Rey de Francia* : 1798

✝ *San Diego de Alcala* : 1769

SAN DIEGO ▲

ADAPTED FROM JOSHUA PADDISON, *A WORLD TRANSFORMED*. HEYDAY BOOKS.

communities have done for millions of years. And just now, one mother in the village is about to give birth. A boy child. It is 1781. He will be named Huicmuse and later, he will be called Marino. No one, not a single person there with the best imagination can dream of what his future will be or how everything is about to change forever.

Who knows what the women are gossiping about? The wind shreds their voices and the words come to us only in tatters. Soon the news will reach them of Huicmuse's birth and be woven into their conversation. But there is one thing we can guess about here. They are talking about something that has never been seen in their lands before. Rarer than a meteor blazing through their nights or a comet with its wispy tail. Strange white men, across the bay in the land of the Ohlones, are building big houses, with timber stakes and roofs of tule. They are noisy and they use large objects that no one has seen or understands. On their bodies they have coverings from no animal that is known. It is said that no one has been killed. They are not dangerous. They offer gifts. There are those in the nearby village of Livaneglua who have spoken to them, although how can that be possible? But who can say. Why are they here after all? What does this mean? Have they fallen from the sky?

Huicmuse will be taught how to hunt and fish, to make hooks and arrows. He will learn the dances and the songs. The stories. So that the way of their people will live forever, as they are now as old as time.

For a while, the Golden Gate—not the bridge but the opening between the headlands to the north and the tip of the long hilly peninsula to the south—will separate two ages, two vastly different worlds. But not for long. History has a plan for all of them and is moving swiftly forward.

Anza, scouting ahead, had chosen a site near the Golden Gate. But Fr. Palou and others, on their arrival, decided to establish the presidio, where it would be more protected from the heavy winds and fog of the point. The Mission would be built about three miles away, near a stream which he called *Nuestra Señora de los Dolores*, Our Lady of Sorrows. Over time, the Mission of St. Francis of Assisi would come to be known by this name, Mission Dolores—unintentionally celebrating the sorrows that were the underside of the triumphs of the priests and soldiers.

While the people of Anamas were celebrating the new life that had come to their village, far to the south a Spanish soldier named Jose Dario Argüello was assigned by De Neve to draw up a map of a new pueblo called Our Lady Queen of the Angels of Portiuncula and on September 4 of that year, 1781, another birth took place: the pueblo that in future would simply be known as Los Angeles.

The Golden Gate that separated the two worlds on either side of the bay was momentously bridged when Juluio and Olomojoia—Huimen people from the village of Livaneglua—left their home near the willow grove of the future Sausalito and paddled their tule raft across the bay to bring their children to the Mission for baptism. Why have they gone? It seems very strange. But we cannot know the answer. Was it for the presents that the priests offered? Was it curiosity or the desire to share in some of the greater material well-being that the white people enjoyed? Was it because of conflicts or scarcities in their own village? Or was it the native spirituality of the Miwok people that opened them to the encouragements of Father Santa Maria who had visited in the *San* Carlos in 1775. It may well have been people from this village who were so hospitable to Capt. Ayala and Fr. Santa Maria six years before. Later Juluio and Olomojoia would return for further baptisms, and again in 1784, they would return in their tule boat to enter into the white man's marriage ceremony. Whatever the good fathers were doing, it was working. For some.

While tribes like the Coast Miwok and Ohlone graciously welcomed the strange newcomers, offered them assistance and received their gifts of friendship, others were openly hostile. It is impossible to characterize these encounters with a single image or description, because it often depended on the nature of the individuals involved. Juan Bautista de Anza, for example, tended to treat the native people he met with a courtesy and respect conducive to friendship. He ordered his men to do likewise. However, Ramon Laso de la Vega who later followed him north from Baja California, allowed his men to treat the local Quechans to the south more harshly with the result that they fell on a small detachment of his that had lingered behind the main body and killed them all, including Fr. Garces and his missionaries. In some cases, the livestock that had been introduced by the missionaries damaged the environment on which the local people depended for their food.

Anthropologist Florence Shipek once told me that you could look at the mortality records of the missions at any given time and have a good idea of the nature of the priests that were running them—the kind ones and the harsh ones; those who cared for, and those who mistreated the natives who came to themalthough in the end, the deaths from European diseases could not be avoided with the best of care.

SOWING SEEDS

IN THE FATEFUL SUMMER OF 1776, MANY SEEDS ARE BEING SOWN. In Ticino, of surnames and lineages that we will meet again. In Philadelphia, of a new nation and a new experiment in self-governance, which will become a model for the world. At the edge of San Francisco Bay, the bridging of two worlds: one, with a culture stretching back five thousand years into the past. The other, with a vision of the future and an energy that will transform it into a center of cutting edge research and technology to become the world's third largest economy.

The people of Ticino are unaware of the events in Philadelphia and have no knowledge of the Pacific Coast of North America. There are no newspapers in Ticino, nor in the wild and beautiful landscape by the great bay. There is no CNN with its 24/7 news updates. No internet to flash momentous happenings around the world. In Philadelphia, thanks in part to Benjamin Franklin, there are newspapers, which are reporting the disaffection with the Mother Country and the rising tide of rebellion. This gathering in Philadelphia will become the engine that drives the future in the Far West and even in the remote villages of Ticino. Thousands of miles separate the people of these three places. Events on that July 4 afternoon in 1776 are about to bring them together. Our friends in Philadelphia—Thomas Jefferson, Benjamin Franklin and John Adams—will be key players in this drama.

✳ ✳ ✳ ✳

July 2002 ~ Grossi Farms

LAZARO'S NEW CAR

FIVE O'CLOCK IN THE AFTERNOON. IT IS A BEASTLY HOT DAY. The mercury is pushing toward 100 and the heat hasn't abated in the late afternoon, when a breeze usually comes in from the west. As much as I like the walk home, only a few blocks away, I'm not looking forward to it today. This is before Mr. Fields and I had moved from our location at Laurie-Ann's. I look down the long dirt road, dry as dust, and notice that the nursery and farm workers are heading to their cars. If I can get a lift to the end of the driveway, I will be able to walk in the shade of the eucalyptus trees that line Petaluma Hill Road. I see Alfonso strolling toward the parking lot. "*Es muy caliente, verdad?* Hot, isn't it? Can you give me a lift up to the highway?" He nods toward the parking lot with a mischievous smile. "Lazaro can take you. He's got a new car." He points to a shiny red SUV that is just starting up. These guys may live in meager conditions but the one sign of making it, the consolation for the hard work and long separation from family, is a new car. That is, of course, after the major chunk of the pay check has been sent home to Mexico.

I hurry to catch Lazaro before he takes off. "*Puede darme un ride hasta la carretera?*"

"Si Señora!" he grins and opens the door for me to climb in. We start off in a slow, stately fashion. He has little things hanging from the mirror and on the dashboard that are the proprietary signs one sees in all Mexican vehicles from tractors to long-distance buses.

"This a beautiful car, Lazaro!" He leans back proudly and we proceed at a snail's pace down the dirt road. He wants to be sure that I have time to appreciate his new child. There are food wrappers on the floor and a discarded soda can. "Lazaro, how can you have trash in such a lovely new car?" For a young man living like a bachelor, it is not really surprising to me but I can't resist teasing him about it. He says nothing. In moments, we have reached Petaluma Hill Road.

"Congratulations, Lazaro. This is really a beautiful car," I say, getting out.

"Any time, Señora. Any time you need a ride, just let me know."

A while later, we were visited by another scorcher. As I neared the parking lot, I thought of Lazaro and his new car. He was standing by it, smiling at me. He nodded, in one of those expressive gestures the Mexicans have for nearly every occasion. It let me know he was ready, if I wanted a lift to *la carretera*. He once again opened the door for me and I stepped in. This time he might have just picked it up from the assembly line in Detroit. It was impeccably clean. It shone brilliantly from every available surface and the leather had the odor of fresh polish. Once again he looked straight ahead and we set forth at our majestic pace. "Your car looks really wonderful, Lazaro." He smiled proudly, without turning his head. I had difficulty recognizing this young man on wheels as the one I usually saw afoot. I suppose a car will do that.

"Any time you need a ride, Señora, just let me know," he said.

PART II

EARLY MIGRATIONS

The dust of many crumbled cities
settles over us like a forgetful doze,
but we are older than those cities. . . .
Humankind is being led along an evolving course,
through this migration of intelligences,
and though we seem to be sleeping,
*   there is an inner wakefulness that directs the dream.*

— Jalāl ad-Dīn Muhammad Rūmī
13th century Persian poet
(translated by Coleman Barks)

"I have something more to say before I leave you,"
Sótuknang told the people as they stood at their Place
of Emergence on the shore of the present Fourth World.
*   "The name of this Fourth World is Túwaqachi, World*
Complete. . . . It has height and depth, heat and cold, beauty
and barrenness; . . . Now you will separate and go different ways
to claim all the earth for the Creator. Each group of you will
follow your own star until it stops. There you will settle."

— Frank Waters
The Book of the Hopi

THE EARTH CALENDAR

THE MOON IS A BONE-WHITE DISK THAT FILLS THE SKY. So close you could almost touch it, but there are no fingers for touching. Spring brings heavy winds and high tides, drawn toward the great white moon. The planet is fire and ice, burning and freezing, melting and congealing. But Spring brings new life. First life. Microscopically small. Neither sunlight nor moonlight can find it. February's tiny oval masses of organic carbon have become bacteria by March. A living thing, like the first new buds on a tree. In the churning seas, jellyfish are taking form and early shelled organisms. Sea anemone and coral.

Throughout March, Earth slowly brings forth new living organisms. Blue-green algae have begun to harvest sunlight to store energy, producing oxygen in the process. Oxygen levels are rising in the atmosphere. As an infant at birth leaves behind a fluid realm to breathe air for the first time, earth life too makes an extraordinary shift. By April, living things will take their first breath of oxygen, breathing out carbon dioxide. In June, the very air will become toxic to all living things not dependent upon oxygen. Carbon dioxide levels will rise, causing acidification of the oceans. This will prove fatal for marine life requiring stable carbon dioxide levels to form their shells. Insects will die out in massive numbers. Sea anemones and coral beds will all but disappear. It is the earth's first great extinction, two and a half billion years ago. But that great extinction gives way to new and richer forms—July's children, dedicated to sustained life. Membranes form around the new cells and a nucleus at their center can hold genetic material: biological software that not only sustains the patterns of an individual organism and holds an outline of its future, but contributes the means to replicate itself. This is a turning point. From now on, things will move quickly.

By September, many-celled organisms have clustered into cell colonies. At the end of the month, another milestone is reached, turning the page on a new chapter: sexual reproduction. Life is stabilizing and cohering. Individual forms create and diversify. Become more resilient. Find new strategies. As the earth is striped with nights and days, turning in the sunlight, settling into seasons, rhythms develop, felt by the early bacteria; by the blue-green algae, making energy from the sun; vulnerable DNA replicating in the safety of darkness. Patterns lay down that take hold. Rhythms that endure, become intricate, will make birdsong, drum sounds, early music and late Beethoven quartets; that will become the tapping of feet upon the Earth. Dancing.

By November, life fully emerges from the nourishing placenta of the oceans onto land as mountains begin to rise and the first trees take root. Moonlight dapples the primordial forest floor, paler than the moon of early spring. More distant. Life will grow in the seas and late in the month, the waters too will be teeming with new creatures. Jellyfish and the ancestors of the steelhead which one day will glide through the waters of Copeland Creek.

At the end of November, the first footprints that we know of will appear on the Earth, like Buzz Aldrin's and Neil Armstrong's footprints on the surface of the Moon. Early four-footed animals step out of a shallow lagoon in southeastern Poland onto dry land, three-hundred ninety-five million years ago on November 30th of our Earth calendar. Animals are on the move. Exploring. Seeking nourishment. Shelter.

On December 26th of our Earth calendar, a massive meteor strikes the Earth in the Yucatan region of Mexico. The six mile wide (10km) meteor creates a crater over a hundred and ten miles wide (180km) and twelve miles deep (20km), causing the fifth great extinction of planetary life, including those terrestrial giants, the dinosaurs.

The game speeds up by the last day of the year as lumbering dinosaurs are replaced by "the fleet of foot"—like lions, zebras, horses and two-legged creatures, not as swift as the horse but agile and clever. On December 30th, the Earth's surface on the east side of Africa begins thinning and softening, following the cracking of its outer shell. The cracking has caused a great rift, where Olduvai Gorge and the Great Rift Valley will later appear. Throughout the day, over millions of years, the hot interior beneath begins to bubble up through those cracks, forming lava beds and then volcanoes. The largest of these is at least as large as the present Mt. Kilamanjaro and will be known as Ngorongoro, two and a half million years later. The lava will form a lid on Ngorongoro.

About eight a.m. on the last day (3.6 million years ago), two early humans* are walking through the wet volcanic ash. Whether they speak together on their ancient stroll we will never know, but they speak to anthropologist Mary Leakey when she comes upon their footprints over three million years later. "Yes, we have been here in Africa a long long time."

Just after dinner time on New Year's Eve, a huge volcanic eruption blows through the lid of Ngorongoro and leaves behind it a crater fifteen miles (24km) wide, sloping upwards for two thousand feet along its rim. When the rains come, their water flows down the slopes of the crater. Lush grass will grow in its moisture, fertilized by the residue of volcanic ash. The spread of that volcanic ash will blanket an area of over two thousand square miles (5,000km) that will be called the Serengeti by the Maasai people—"endless plains."** To the east lies Mt. Kilimanjaro and the western wall of the Great Rift Valley.

The wide and fertile Ngorongoro Crater and the endless plains of the Serengeti will become a wildlife Eden in the heart of Africa. And here in the noonday sun of New Year's Eve, following an ice age, the first great migrations begin. Wildebeest will travel by the millions across the endless plains in search of greener pastures, in the

---

* australopithecus
** The entire Serengeti eco-system today covers 12,000 square miles (30,000 square kilometers)

company of zebras and gazelles, and the predators who follow them—lions, hyenas, jackals and others—on their own quest for food. Three of our current months later they will return, in a seasonal pattern of going and coming. It is the tracks of these migrations that have preserved the vast savannah across millions of years.

Elspeth Huxley, writing in her diary two million years later in 1933, can still evoke for us the wonder of those primordial sights that have been sustained over so much time. She lived with her family in Kenya from 1912 to 1923. Here she is returning to Africa through the same area where the early couple walked, leaving us their footprints.

> It was one of the great sights of the world. Even without the animals it would have been spectacular, with the thin pure light of sunrise, the colour of a fine Moselle, flooding over this enormous savannah and picking out every tree, every fold in the surface of the plain; far beyond, the white dome of Kilimanjaro seemed to hover in the western sky. But it was the animals that brought life and wonder to the scene. Thousands, tens of thousands of them could be seen from the carriage window, from pygmy mongooses peering out of their burrows to—if you were lucky—mighty elephants in family parties, from dappled, mild-eyed giraffes like tall-masted ships of the veld to graceful little shiny 'tommies' or zebras shimmering in the sunlight: lumbering kongonis, heavy-dewlapped elands, a rhino perhaps, standing fore-square with horn uplifted, silver-backed jackals trotting home to their dens after a night's foraging.

Twelve months for life to solidify, take root, stand still, rise up in place like the mountains and trees. And then life begins to move. To spread out. Not as colonies of cells but colonies of birds and fish and monkeys and bison and creatures too numerous to count. It is in this last month of December, after almost an entire year of preparation, that everything that we think of as life, as Earth, as meaningful, as important, will finally come into being. On Christmas day of the Earth Calendar, fifty million years ago, an event will take place that plays a major role in our story.

The Earth Calendar ~Christmas Day

PANGAEA

AFRICA IS ON THE MOVE. IT IS HEADED TOWARD EURASIA—a huge, stolid landmass. In fact, according to this story, the continents are all cozily together at first in one great blob of land called Pangaea that pushes and pulls and separates and fractures in the vast waters that swathe the planet. You could canoe from Georgia to Scotland, if you were sturdy and the weather was right. It isn't, of course.

By Christmas Day of the Earth Calendar year, Pangaea has split apart into separate continents. Not very long ago, only about three of our calendar days—(a few million years before)—India, with Australia attached and scrambling along at about 6 inches or 15 centimeters a year (which it still is) ran smack into another part of Eurasia in a huge fender-bender. The Himalayan Mountains were the wrinkle of that crunch. Now here comes Africa, sailing across the basin of the Tethys Sea which lies between them. Or did. It grinds across the sediments of that basin like a great monstrous bully so that the basin-which-is-no-longer-a-basin buckles up into huge folds which it pushes relentlessly ahead of it. The edges of the plates break up and in places slide over one another. The African plate pushes so hard against the Eurasian landmass that its edge is forced down at a dramatic angle. So steep, in fact, that it bends it clear down into the hot mantle of the earth. Just like a plastic plate that slides into the heat of a gas burner, the edge of the land softens up so that Africa rides over Eurasia for more than six hundred miles—a thousand kilometers. The Tethys Sea slowly disappears under this rude intrusion, leaving behind it the beginnings of the young ocean that will carry us westward: the Atlantic.

As you can imagine, it was a mess. Debris on a colossal scale, like New Orleans after hurricane Katrina in 2005, multiplied a million-fold. We have to remember time and duration. The layered rhythms of the planet, from the breathing in and out of waters and the growth of mountains over millions of years to the mayfly that lives for a day. Hurricane Katrina was in and out in a couple of days, not millions of years. But those upthrust houses and deep crevices where once there had been living rooms . . . It's the same principle in miniature.

If you are a skier, the good news is this: One of those upthrust folds is now Mont Blanc, the Matterhorn and the high peaks in the Pennine Alps. Steep valleys are being carved that will be called home by Celt and Lombard farmers. High meadows are being prepared for the grazing of cows and goats. Dominic Grossi is up there waiting for Time to catch up with him, as my steelhead trout waits patiently for California, and for Copeland Creek.

But not so fast. We need a finishing carpenter here to hone and plane and carve. Sad to say that he can't arrive until New Year's Eve, just before the celebration. He is part of the same guild that will be busy on the other side of the world, where the independent and headstrong North American plate ran away from home and headed West. They are all busy carving out a landscape for us on both sides of the new Atlantic. They are moving the scenery into place for the rest of our stories. They are the wonder workers of the Ice Age: glaciers.

In the long perspective of Earth time, we are like the small creatures who came to take up residence in the ruins of those New Orleans houses and buildings that were devastated by hurricane Katrina. For their entire lives, the ceiling that slid down into the kitchen and the car that got slammed through the wall of the garage and now looks like a gigantic accordion, is the nature of the universe. My world and welcome to it!

You may give a thought to the lizards, spiders, woodchucks, mice, birds and the rest of the transients that homestead there, as we later meet the people who will take up residence in the slates and faults and upthrust slabs that Africa has made in its collision with Eurasia. A process that still goes on, inch by inch, centimeter by centimeter, season by season—even as we ski by day and drink hot toddies by night before a roaring fire in the shadow of a glacier.

◆ ◆ ◆

I suppose I was fortunate: For the first two decades of my life, the earth stayed put. It wasn't until the upheavals of the 1960s, under a Pluto-Uranus conjunction in the heavens, that things started to move. The continents I mean. There is nothing as eternal or irrevocable as the pictures in a child's geography book. From that I learned that there were seven continents, each one a different color, and seven oceans all bright blue. Over the centuries, many a clever and observant person—Benjamin Franklin was one of them—had observed the odd fact that South America and Africa could almost fit together like the pieces of a puzzle. But there was no logical reason for the vast separation they now enjoyed. That is until the 1960s when the earth seemed to shift under a good many established foundations to rapidly remake the map of the social and physical landscape. Plate tectonics were discovered and now no continent was safe from revision over time. We know for an empirical fact that they are all on the move, in slow migration—or at least the plates that make them up and shift them about.

Supporting discoveries cascaded into the next decades from geologists, paleontologists and archaeologists. And even from amateurs like the fossil hunter in 1972 who dug into a hillside in the Piedmont region of northern Italy and discovered a specimen of an ancient eel, far from either the Adriatic or Mediterranean Seas. The detailed outlines of its body were perfectly preserved in the thin lamina of anhydrite rock, which he had just split apart with his small hammer. He sent his find to the Institute of Geology at the University of Turin, where the hunt was taken up by paleontologist Carlo Sturani. Sturani visited the cliff site and began a detailed investigation of his own, which yielded an abundance of fossil treasures. There in the middle of the country, to the northeast of Rome, he found coral, conch, herring, small flounder, dragon flies, turtles, fresh water reeds and the roots of trees still in place. The three-hundred foot cliff read like a book, telling the story of an ancient, moderately deep sea that had dried out to become a tidal flat with algae and mud cracks. Over time it became a shallow lagoon, which then turned into a brackish lake, sometimes filled with fresh water. Then the lake withered again into a peat bog as the region changed from marshland to a sequoia forest.

In the last chapter of the cliff's story, written in a tenth of an inch of rock, it was once again an open sea. The transformation from sea to land and back to sea again had taken less than half a million years. About 45 minutes in our calendar of the earth's history. If the Lombards had come along a bit earlier, they could have cast about them and had fish with their polenta. No need for the long hike to Milano to sell chestnuts in the streets.

Sturano's lake may have come and gone and come and gone again after the

PANGAEA

From the Ancient Greek pan ("entire") and Gaia ("Mother Earth")

Africa-Eurasia rendezvous and it is true that the landscape was torn up pretty badly. Yet one *could* say that this migration of Africa into Eurasia was a purposive act of stone and earth, of water and fire to shape the just-so place for the elegant little ladybells, softly tolling their fragrance in Ticino's Monte Giorgio or the rare wild gladiolas—*gladiolus imbricatum*—which grace the same landscape with dense purple blossoms through the spring and early summer. Or perhaps it was just for *me* (as we self-involved humans are inclined to believe), sitting here typing away to tell you its story!

In fact, the most lasting result that we know of has a very marked effect upon our human species, still waiting in the wings: the Mediterranean Sea. This is what remained of that ancient ocean, the Tethys Sea, which became closed off with the arrival of Africa and separated from the westward-moving Atlantic so that it became a landlocked ocean "in the midst of the earth"—which is what Mediterranean means. It is not the blue and tranquil poster child that beckons from travel agency walls and brochures. How could it be, when two continents meet beneath it in such geologic tension?

DECEMBER DAYS ~ THE EARTH CALENDAR

225 million years ago

December 13th

(in-breath)

Land masses coalesce into Pangaea

150 million years ago

December 19th

(out-breath)

Pangaea land mass separates
(Tethys Sea is open east to west)

100 million years ago

December 23rd

Separation into Continents

Earth today

December 31st

(In-breath)

Africa's collision with Asia on Dec. 25th
has created the Mediterranean Sea
(Merry Christmas!)

DECEMBER 31ST ~ NEW YEAR'S EVE

The Last 15 seconds of the Earth Year.
Global consciousness develops within the human species. (That's us!)

- 3rd Century BC – Greek astronomy recognizes the earth as a sphere, producing an early globe. The oldest surviving globe is from 1492 (without the New World). Nevertheless, the common view of Earth is flat, until the voyages of Columbus & others.

- 1519 AD – Magellan circumnavigates the globe providing proof that the Earth is round.

- 1520 – The Mayflower voyage carries the first settlers across the Atlantic. A year before, Cortez arrived in Vera Cruz, Mexico. Continents drifting together in the human mind.

- December 7, 1972 – The first view of the "Blue Planet" taken from space by Apollo 17.

- 1972 – Scientist James Lovelock, in collaboration with microbiologist Lynn Margulis, introduces the Gaia Hypothesis, which depicts the Earth, "Gaia," as a single living organism. His book *Gaia: A new look at life on Earth* brings this view of Earth into the mainstream.

It is at least not impossible to regard the earth's parts—soil, mountains, rivers, atmosphere etc,—as organs or parts of organs of a coordinated whole, each part with its definite function. And if we could see this whole, as a whole, through a great period of time, we might perceive not only organs with coordinated functions, but possibly also that process of consumption as replacement which in biology we call metabolism, or growth. In such case we would have all the visible attributes of a living thing, which we do not realize to be such because it is too big, and its life processes too slow.

— STEPHEN HARDING, 2007
Animate Earth

I have fancifully depicted Earth as breathing in and out to accentuate its living rhythms and long time periods. The inner body of the earth is as hidden from us as the interior of our own bodies. The tectonic plates, which shift about during these long periods of the Earth Year, are no more than its skin, its crust, its carapace. And of that, 70% is water and only 29% is land. Some three thousand miles down is its inner core. When I was a child digging in the back yard, my mother would say "That's it. Just keep digging and you'll reach China." I did keep digging in other ways and I did reach China, via my graduate studies in Chinese philosophy much later in life. But the truth is that the opposite point of the earth is about six thousand miles as the crow flies, assuming the crow can fly through layers of heat and rock. What Buckminster Fuller called "Spaceship Earth" is perfectly designed to carry us flying through space at 67,000 miles per hour around the sun, as we whirl like a top about our axis at a thousand miles per hour at the equator. Even while we are sitting still, reading a book or watching TV. Now is that any stranger than the fact that the chair I sit on is made up of dancing molecules, which are made up of atoms, which are mostly empty space?

It is only in the last century that we humans have conceived and experienced our planetary home in its global richness and carried a picture of it in the mind's eye, beamed home from astronauts in space: Mother Earth, seen in her entirety. Pan-Gaia.

This is the long look at Earth, with the chronoscope extended to the limit of its seeing. But we will slowly be zooming in through time and space, until Dominic Grossi comes fully into view. Stories nested within stories, macrocosm to microcosm. As this process of moving plates is slowly reshaping continents over eons, the migrations of people have a mini-tectonic affect of their own, all in that last fifteen seconds of December.

◆ ◆ ◆

The first room in our gallery of stories presents portraits from this ancient region—the Mediterranean Sea. It is a place of many origins as the geographical backbone of Western history. Covering nearly a million square miles, it touches the locales of almost every early civilization that shaped our history, from Egypt and

Phoenicia to the lands of the Old and New Testament; the Greeks, the Romans and all of the European kingdoms which rose after them, with the exception of the most northerly ones. But there was a constant migration southward from those areas as well, seeking its more hospitable climates and food sources. From their base in Italy, the Romans extended their empire to the far north, opening up the flow of people and trade to Great Britain and Germany and Scandinavia. It was not far at all from the eastern Mediterranean coast to the cradle of civilization that developed between the Tigris and Euphrates. The Adriatic, the Aegean, and the Ionian seas are all part of the Mediterranean. At its furthest edge, to the northeast, the Sea of Marmara connects it to the Black Sea. To the west, the Strait of Gibraltar, the ancient Pillars of Hercules, open out onto the Atlantic.

THE MEDITERRANEAN SEA
SEA STORIES
BLACK STONES

A MAN AND BOY ARE STANDING ON A BEACH.

The boy is about seven years old, slight with dark hair and eyes as clear black as the pebbles on the beach. His father is not tall but he is a sturdy man with muscled legs and strong shoulders. A well-traveled man. Far-ranging and far-seeing. A long arm sweeps across the horizon and limns a scene for the boy, who watches rapt as the imaginary landscape unfolds. He nods. His lips move. He is repeating what his father says. The man reaches down, pauses thoughtfully, and then selects a stone which he places in the boy's hand. The boy looks up into the man's eyes and finds there the father's intent and the stone's message.

The years pass.

The island beach sees many storms. Black pebbles wash out to sea and the sea brings them back. Makes faithful deliveries on the incoming tide with a steady rhythm.

The man never again returns.

But the boy grows into a man and as a man, returns. Each time, he stands looking out to sea, his lips move, his arm sweeps the horizon, and at the end he bends to the ground, pauses reflectively, and selects a black stone. He closes it in his hand and behind his own eyes, he sees with the eyes of his father. Each stone is a story. Before his own hearth in Vrontados, a cairn has grown, honoring the gods and the heroes whose stories they represent. Honoring Hermes, the messenger god who brings them.

Above all, he listens. The sea is singing and its song has a rhythm. An ebb and flow. A cadence. He stands and once again his lips are moving. Now he is singing with the sea. His are the words. The stories they tell are his father's. And his father's before him. And before that, a long lineage of bards. Of singers whose words go back, far back, even before the disaster that brought the black stones to this shore. Before the Great Darkness that swallowed one of the world's finest cities, far down into the deep sea. A monstrous earthquake and a fiery eruption that hid the sun and was felt in far-off Egypt and beyond. Poseidon, Earth-shaker, had wiped those once-proud people from the face of the Earth. All that was left were the black stones.

But there was Memory. There were the Muses. Like a salve over a wound, singing of the story knit the world back together. Nothing was forgotten. Fathers told sons, bards carried the songs abroad as far as ships could reach. On the mainland, five miles across the water, and on the islands of the south—Crete, Delos—Theseus still danced with Ariadne and their friends, only now it was young men and maidens re-enacting their joy, threading new labyrinthine paths with their feet to the rhythm of singing. And the great genius behind them both, brilliant artificer and designer of the labyrinth of Knossos who could create wings to fly upward toward the sun . . . Daedalus. Mysterious Daedalus. Neither warrior nor king, yet his deeds might outlast them all.

Now the boy is an old man. His father had not lived to be so old. He has returned to the beach, with the aid of a staff and of a boy. Not his son. But still his heir. In spite of his blindness, with his free hand he gestures with the accuracy of an inner eye, eastward toward the near shores of Asia Minor, southward toward Naxos and Crete, and toward the Greek shore which lies invisibly behind them. His staff rises and falls rhythmically as his lips move and the boy's lips move in synchrony, feeling the tempo of the staff and seeing with his master's hand the great armies of Greek ships—a thousand of them, plowing the waves of the wine-dark sea. They will pass to the left of them and far up the coast to the East, another great city would soon fall. A new curtain of darkness was about to fall on the age old lands. Not Knossos but Troy. Not Theseus and Ariadne, but Achilles and Hector, the great combatants, the noble heroes. More stories to be sung, carried as far as ships may go.

The old man's name is Homer.

The beach of black stones still exists, nearly three thousand years later. The island is Chios. By one account, Homer was born on this island in a village called Vrontados on the Eastern shore, fives miles across the Chios Strait from Turkey. Scholars today have differing theories of where he was born. Some say it was in Smyrna, in modern day Turkey. Most scholars favor Chios. Some say he didn't exist at all and the story of the Trojan war was one passed down through many voices and perhaps written down by someone like Homer. Certainly no one doubts the length and power of the oral tradition that reached the historical Greece we know from the sixth and fifth centuries BC especially. For my story, I choose Chios and turn first to the ancient stories that came down through Homer from those days of King Minos, which is as far back as memory can so far reach toward the peoples that rose up from that treacherous sea to build great cities at the end of their migrations.

Some seven or eight hundred years before Homer's stories were written down, one of the worst natural disasters in human history took place as the deep frictions of the movements of the African plate against the Eurasian plate caused heated water to rise along their separation and burst through the surface in a volcanic eruption.

The convergence of these plates probably began about 180 million years ago when the North Atlantic is born, about mid-December on our calendar, but only became visible in the Upper Jurassic, 150 million years ago. It was a very long, slow business and one might ask, like Kant, if one tectonic plate collides with another in the sea and there are no eyes to see it, is there an event? Humans are a long way off. Of course there are many eyes, not human, that are watching.

It is with the eruption of Thera that this collision of the plates bursts into human history and becomes an "event." The world changes dramatically overnight, physically and culturally.

We owe a great debt to Mnemosyne, Greek goddess of Memory and to the Muses for keeping those ancient stories alive, and to our particular human chronoscope, Homer.

I lay this story down like a carpet on the ground or like the simple foundation of a house, upon which all other stories will be built, right into our present lives.

THE SEA PEOPLE

THEY CAME FROM THE EAST. FROM ANATOLIA, or perhaps from Iran—the Persia of ancient times. They settled on the island of Crete and there they built beautiful cities, on Crete and on neighboring islands. The cities grew into metropolises; centers of a large trading empire. The royal and religious center was at Knossos, on Crete. At its height, in the 17th century BC, it was a thriving city of one hundred thousand people. The royal palace at Knossos, set atop Kephala hill, covered six acres and parts of it reached five stories high. Its tall brick-colored columns made of cypress, with their round black capitals, could be seen from a great distance. The royal complex contained grain mills, oil presses and wine presses. There were countless rooms filled with large clay vases to store oil, grains, olives, dried fish and beans as well as valuable gold objects.

Fresh water was brought to the palace by aqueducts from springs some five or six miles away. One branch of it brought water to the town while another passed through the palace, driven by gravity through terra cotta pipes to fountains and to spigots. A separate sanitation system drained into a sewer away from the hill. In the Queen's chamber, within the royal apartments next to the Hall of the Double Axe, was a seat above a drain that flushed by pouring water from a jug—one of the first water flushing toilet systems. The queen also had her own bathroom with a bathtub.

The centerpiece of the palace was a royal chamber with an alabaster throne built into the north wall. Gypsum benches lined the other walls and opposite the throne, a lustral basin for purification. The throne was flanked by the Griffin Fresco, with two griffins couchant (laying down) facing the throne, one on either side. Double doors opened onto an anteroom with four broad steps and four doors that opened to a central court from its west side.

They were sea people and their ships went everywhere.

In the ancient world that we know of, there was no one like them. Their free and graceful artistic style captures the natural and human landscape in a life-like way. It lacks the rigid severity conveyed in Egyptian art, which was the other advanced Mediterranean culture of the time. Even the dolphins on the walls of the queen's chamber appear to be dancing. Light and color were everywhere. Unusual for the time, many of the homes in the towns had windows and the light that poured in illuminated the brilliant frescoes.

GOLDEN BEES

THE GOLDSMITH SITS BACK WITH A SIGH AND WORKS his shoulders to ease the tension in his back that comes from the prolonged period of concentration. The sigh has nothing to do with his aching back. It is one of contentment in the moment of the day when the sun slants over the land at such an angle that the gold of its westering light pours through his door and window and seems to touch the heads of leaping dolphins on the rear wall as if caressing them. He has always thought of this light as the purest essence of the gold he fashions. Its source. The finger that reaches out for the dolphins is surely Poseidon's own, though this is the god who rules the sea, not the sun, and moves the land when it pleases him to. The honeyed light of Crete. Divine elixir of the bees, sacred to the Mistress of the Labyrinth. His work is to capture that. Make it tangible and everlasting. Nothing but gold could last so long.

The object on his work-table is nearly complete. Two life-like golden bees form a circle—their heads and the tips of their bodies touching. Each, with two slender feelers, holds between them the golden heart of a flower with its tight cluster of pollen-laden seeds from which the bees draw their nectar and magically transform it into honey. To the left and to the right of the bees extends a wing of delicate filigreed gold, from which hang two golden disks, along with a third disk suspended from the center of the piece where the two bodies meet. Above the heads of the bees is a drop of honey and a container of thin wires that adorns the piece like a crown. The most difficult work was the fine granulation for the stripes on their bodies, their round eyes and the central cluster with its concentric circles of grains. The filigree work, the granulation and even the work of soldering the gold parts requires extreme delicacy and skill. He doubts that there was another goldsmith in all of the kingdom who could have accomplished it.

It is his finest piece, commissioned by the Master Craftsman who serves the princess-priestess of Knossos, Ariadne. He of the Labyrinth, said to be the most wise and crafty of artificers—Daedalus. Designer of that riddle in stone that torments and then ends men's lives. He had watched the youth of Athens arrive across the bay at Heraklion, when he and his wife lived in their lovely home above Akrotiri, facing south to Crete and to Knossos. It is said that the king harbors a monster at the heart of the serpentine path of the Labyrinth—part man, part bull—who waits to devour its lost victims. King Minos ordered Daedalus to construct a place for this dark thing and hence, the Labyrinth.

The goldsmith's wife, Phythia, was asked to become part of the princess Ariadne's retinue. Word of her beauty, clear voice and the lithe grace of her dancing—much sought after for festivals—had reached Knossos. His own work was already known there, so the move to the palace seemed natural. Although not a priestess herself, Phythia serves in the ritual events, some of which are in secret and some of which mark the feast days of Knossos along with the thrilling event of the Bull Dancers who honor the gods, willingly or unwillingly, by their daring acrobatics as they grasp the bulls' horns and somersault over their backs. The young men and maidens from Athens, sent every seven years as tribute to King Minos in recompense for the loss there of his son Androgeus at the hands of the Athenians, were required to participate in these festivities. If they didn't meet their end in the bull dance, they were sent into the labyrinth. Some said that after wandering the long winding path with no exit, they were devoured by the minotaur. This seemed a poor end to those youth who showed the most valor and agility before the spectators. Surely they, at least, deserved a better end.

The goldsmith dismisses those thoughts. Master Daedalus once suggested to him that the brightness and grandeur of Knossos and its dominions were ensured by confining its darkness in one hidden place that freed the rest to pursue their excellence. An excellence admired throughout the empire governed at Knossos, which is spread far and wide around the Mediterranean. But the goldsmith secretly misses his fine and spacious home on the hillside of Thera, overlooking the town of Akrotiri and the sea—far from the dark and convoluted conspiracies of the palace. Life was freer and more jovial among the wealthy merchants who made their homes there. Akrotiri is the trade and financial center of the kingdom, graced with lovely homes like his own, decorated with frescoes and floor paintings, with large windows that let in the sea air.

Here at Knossos his wife is sworn to secrecy in her service of the Priestess, so that too had come between them. He no longer asks. And about the Labyrinth, he does not wish to know. That entire section of the vast palace is off limits. He and the other craftsmen occupy choice studios—a vast area in the upper stories of the enormous palace compound—with good light for work, all of the materials they could want, and vistas to inspire. Their talents are highly valued and well paid. The royal quarters are ornamented by their exquisite work—beautiful vases painted with scenes of the bull dance; frescoed walls with scenes of the city, a huge bull's head carved in black serpentine with gold horns, doorways decorated in relief, and tiny miniature stone carvings and seal-engravings. Still other pieces have found their way to the palaces and homes of rulers and wealthy merchants around the Mediterranean, from Egypt to the Black Sea. But this, he thinks, as he picks up the gold pendant that is nearly complete, this is for the princess Ariadne—a gift for a revered and beautiful priestess, designed by Daedalus and crafted by himself. One of a kind. All that remains is to polish it to a high luster.

When he has finished this task, the royal goldsmith rewards himself with a favorite walk, which leads him through palisades filled with flowers and sculpture, *walls adorned with frescoes, the light of Crete pouring amply through spacious arches and doorways to a staircase that winds upward to a small pavilion. This is the highest point in Knossos, with its vista over the nearby villages to the sea. From here, he can see the path of gold that the sun casts on the waters at day's end. Just as he is settling into that relaxed and satisfying reverie, a shadow appears on the sea, approaching the port. A familiar silhouette and one he dreads to see. The ship has arrived from Athens, carrying the king's tribute.*

THESEUS AND ARIADNE

'There, then, I saw Minos, glorious son of Zeus, wielding a golden sceptre, giving sentence from his throne to the dead, while they sat and stood around the prince, asking his dooms through the wide-gated house of Hades. . . . And Ariadne, the daughter of Wizard Minos, whom Theseus on a time was bearing from Crete to the hill of sacred Athens.

— HOMER
Odyssey. XI

ONE OF THE OLDEST STORIES WE HAVE OF THE MEDITERRANEAN begins here on Crete. We think of Western civilization as beginning with Athens, but Athens is still a relatively unimportant place when the Minoan culture is at its height in the late third millennium BC. The ruling god of the Greek pantheon, Zeus, was said to have been born in a cave on this island and nurtured by bees, those sacred intimates of Minoan priestesses. While I have imagined the goldsmith, I have not imagined the exquisite pendant that he fashioned, which was discovered millennia later in the ruins of Mallia on Crete. And as for the Minoan culture itself, it was never considered a historical reality in modern times until Knossos was unearthed by Sir Arthur Evans in the first years of the twentieth century. It was Evans who gave a name to the people after the mythical King Minos, who was appearing less and less mythical as the excavations continued.

According to that myth, most durable of chronoscopes, an ancient King, Minos, reigned over a vast empire from his palace of Knossos on Crete. The god who ruled the Minoans was Poseidon—Earthshaker and god of the sea. Poseidon had given to King Minos the gift of a beautiful white bull, which was to be sacrificed to the god in return. But Minos so loved the white bull that he kept it in his herd and sacrificed another in its place. Angered by this, Poseidon caused the wife of Minos, Pasiphaë, to fall in love with the bull. From this unnatural passion was born the Minotaur, half man, half bull. Minos directed Daedalus, the ingenious craftsman, to create the labyrinth to house this monster at its center.

When Minos's son Androgeus was killed in Athens, Minos sought retribution through the demand of a tribute of seven maids and seven youths to be sent, according to some versions, every seven years. They were expected to participate in the daring and dangerous bull dances, a ritual sport celebrated uniquely on Crete. The bull was sacred to the Minoans and is seen throughout their iconography. Those Athenians who survived were fed to the Minotaur.

The famous myth has as its hero, Theseus, son of the Athenian King Aegeus and also—it was said—of Poseidon. Theseus, determined to put an end to this evil practice, joins the youths sent in tribute and vows to kill the Minotaur. On arrival, he meets the beautiful Princess Ariadne and they fall in love. Ariadne provides Theseus with a ball of thread that he uses to find his way out of the labyrinth after slaying the Minotaur. Theseus emerges triumphant and departs Crete with Ariadne. Soon after, the palace is destroyed by earthquake.

The Labyrinth itself is probably the greatest remaining mystery surrounding both the legend and the place. No labyrinth was found in the palace, unless it is the hundreds of labyrinthine rooms and corridors which make up the vast compound, as some believe. It survived on later coins, which depicted both a circular maze and a rectangular one; not a true maze because it was represented as being unicursal—a single, though most circuitous and puzzling path. In ancient writings, it has also been called the *choros*, or dancing-place of Ariadne, which does not suggest a stone structure, but possibly a floor design. Hold that thought! We shall return to it in the far-off future.

A BLACK SUN

But at a later time there occurred portentous earthquakes and floods, and one grievous day and night befell them, when the whole body of your warriors was swallowed up by the earth, and the island of Atlantis in like manner was swallowed up by the sea and vanished; wherefore also the ocean at that spot has now become impassable and unsearchable, being blocked up by the shoal mud which the island created as it settled down.

— PLATO
Timaeus 25c–d (Bury translation)

IT HAPPENED BOTH QUICKLY AND SLOWLY—overnight and over years. It is one of the greatest disasters in human history. The island of Thera, site of the beautiful Minoan city of Akrotiri, lay seventy miles from the island of Crete, site of the royal Minoan palace at Knossos a few miles inland. It began with a violent earthquake in a region known for its seismic activity. The two continental plates lay beneath like two gods simmering in their anger. Or just the one, Poseidon, whom the people knew as Earth-shaker, god of the Sea. Anticipating aftershocks, the people grabbed their most valuable possessions and put them in protected places. Some, even then, would have rushed to the boats to evacuate. But this was only the beginning. Deep under the sea where the continents fought their slow but inexorable battle, the quake broke open the crust of an old magma chamber that lay like a sleeping demon which awoke every seventeen thousand years to wreak its destructive havoc. The moment of awakening had come as two kinds of magna interacted and brought 150 *billion* tons of magma to the surface with a roar that was heard as far away as Egypt and beyond.

The eruption rose twenty-five miles into the air and its black cloud hid the sun for days. The ash alone was deadly. Once inhaled and mixed with body fluids it became like cement. Water flowed back into the chamber from the sea, meeting the magma with a huge explosion which ripped rocks from deep within the crater and sent them flying into the sky as magma bombs weighing up to eight tons with a roar that reached 300 decibels. The only way to imagine this is to compare it with the greatest cataclysm in modern history, the 1883 eruption of Krakatoa in Indonesia. It was said those explosions were so violent that they were heard 2,200 miles (3,500 km) away in Perth, Western Australia and 3,000 miles (4,800 km) away on the island of Rodrigues near Mauritius, off the southeast coast of Africa. The sound of Krakatoa's destruction is the loudest sound in recorded history, reaching levels of 180 decibels, one hundred miles (160 km) away. Recordings show that the shockwave from its final explosion reverberated around the globe seven times. The ash cloud was reported to have reached twenty seven miles. By comparison, the roar of Thera's eruption, at 300 decibals, must have been colossal. Hard as it is to believe, the most deadly events were still to come.

As the initial pressure of the Thera eruption decreased, the huge column collapsed into a downward pyroclastic flow, moving at 180 miles per hour with a temperature of 700 degrees Celsius or about 1300 degrees Fahrenheit. This caused the sea water to boil and moved it along on superheated beds of steam at about 200 miles per hour. Along the coast of Crete, the catastrophe generated tsunami waves as large as 60 feet high and 30 miles wide, which continued for hours, at roughly half hour intervals, possibly for days. Ash from the eruption has been found 500 miles away in the Black Sea. In the aftermath, the growth of plants was stunted as far away as the British Isles. The ash deposits, according to archaeologist Stuart Dunn, were ten times greater than Krakatoa. The explosion itself, probably three times as great. The tsunami created by the Krakatoa eruption was felt by sailors far off in South Africa. Such an event occurring at the nerve center of the Mediterranean super power of its time would be comparable to a catastrophe of that magnitude occurring in one of the major centers like London, Paris, Rome or New York; a ripple of destruction extending for hundreds of miles.

This is a story that has been unknown in its full magnitude until our most recent story-tellers—the geologists, archaeologists, soil scientists and volcanologists—could reconstruct the event from the physical landscape: a story written in layers of rock and ash.*

* In the vanguard of this work were archaeologist Sandy McGillivray, geologist Floyd McCoy, tsunami scientist, Kostos Synolaskas and Israeli soil scientist Hendrik Bruins, among many others.

Most scientists date the eruption of Thera (now called Santorini) at 1628 BC, although the traditional date for the destruction of Knossos was closer to 1500 BC. While Knossos itself was not destroyed in the Theran eruption, lying inland beyond the reach of the waves, some scientists have calculated that a wall of water as high as 140 feet rolled across Minoan Crete, destroying the coastal cities. Remnants of Minoan people and culture remained. This we know from artifacts. But what we can't imagine or reconstruct is what such an event did to the psyche and spirit, not only of the surviving Minoans, but to all in the ancient world who heard it or heard of it in reports that reached them. The explosion is described as having been 10,000 to 40,000 times greater than Hiroshima. Who can possibly imagine this? What was Earth-shaker telling them?

James Cameron, well-known from his 3-D blockbuster film *Avatar*, produced a Hollywood documentary (i.e. complete with high-tech special effects) called *Exodus Decoded* in which Canadian-Israeli film-maker and Emmy-award winner Simcha Jacobovici introduces people, places and historical data to support his proposal that the Biblical Exodus actually occurred around 1500 BC and the events described in the Old Testament, including the Ten Plagues and the crossing of the Red Sea, can be explained by the impact of the Santorini earthquakes, eruption and the following tsunami.* This is a story that continues to change as scientists make radical new discoveries at an accelerating rate.

By the time of Homer, the event seems all but forgotten. (How many people remember the Krakatoa eruption of just a little more than a century ago?) Of course Homer writes some eight hundred years later and has an epic disaster to report in more recent times—the Trojan War, with all its man-made misery and reshaping of the Mediterranean cultural landscape. Yet Homer has not forgotten the early people of Crete and they have lived on in legend in surprising ways. The world of the great King Minos lives on into our present day in a single image: the labyrinth created by Daedalus. It appears in a most unusual way in the *Iliad*.

---

* These correlations were made before the earlier 1628 BC date was proposed. This would place the event before the time of Moses, whom Jewish tradition gives a lifespan that corresponds to 1391–1271 BC. Jerome gives 1592 BC as his birthdate. But there is still research to be done on the event.

THE LABYRINTH

HOMER DESCRIBES A DANCING FLOOR that Daedalus constructed for Ariadne next to the labyrinth. Craig Wright has a wonderful description of this in his book *The Maze and the Warrior*: "It was here that Ariadne taught Theseus the dance of life and death that signified the maze. Homer envisages this floor emblazoned upon the great shield of the warrior Achilles, hero of the siege of Troy. Depicted around the shield are Ariadne and other youths, with men and women alternating in a row. They have formed a chain and joining hands as they dance in a circular motion they produce a labyrinthine pattern that initiates Theseus to the twists and turns of the maze. The leader moves forward along one path until he reaches the center and then turns back in the opposite direction. At that moment the dancers toward the front of the line are moving backward while those farther back are still moving forward. In this way the dance begins to outline a labyrinthine pattern of parallel tracks."

Other early sources, like Plutarch (46–120 AD), describe this dance as being performed by Theseus and the Athenians on Delos, as a victory dance, after they had sacrificed to the god of the island. It is still preserved among the inhabitants of that island as the Crane Dance. It also consisted of measured turnings and returnings imitative of the labyrinth. A beautiful vase called the Francois vase, cast by the Ergotimos and painted and signed by the Athenian artist Kleitas in 570 BC, depicts Theseus leading the Athenian youths in the dance with Ariadne standing nearby. The vase was found in an Etruscan tomb.

Centuries later, Virgil will reconstruct this dance as the Trojan ride in his *Aeneid*. It appears to be a version of the original dance, preserved in a new form. This one is done on horseback, if you can imagine it. It is an intricate set of movements executed by young warriors led by Aeneas in honor of a fallen Trojan comrade. Wright sees the dance as both a victory dance, in the manner of Theseus's Crane Dance on Delos, and an initiatory ritual for the young warriors. It must have taken careful training and intricate precision to perform. I would love to have seen it.

Another Etruscan vase, dated at 625 BC and found at Trigliatella in Italy, testifies to the existence of such a horse-dance performed at funeral games in imitation of the Cretan labyrinth. It depicts young warriors on horse-back with their shields and to their right, a drawing of the Cretan labyrinth to show the pattern of their ride. The vase is labeled, in Etruscan, "Troy" in the outermost path of the labyrinth. Craig Wright suggests that the import of the word "Truia" or Troy "is that the descendants of Troy were recreating Troy itself, the model of the intricate, yet impregnable city of the ancient world."

Amazingly, traces of this tradition lasted into modern times in England and Wales. A children's game was played by Welsh shepherds called "Caerdroia" or "Troy Town" after an ancient labyrinth about Troy itself and Welsh herdsmen still cut maze-like symbols into the turf which they call "The Walls of Troy." Turf mazes in England were often called "Troy town" (a name connected as well with Scandinavian mazes) or "Julian's Bower" after the Trojan hero Aeneas's son, Ascanius, who becomes Julius on arrival in Roman lands. Wright tells us that the impregnable city of Troy becomes replaced by the Old Testament Jericho and later by Jerusalem. "All of these later resonances spring from the Greek myth of Daedalus and the epic story of Troy."

Two stories, some seven hundred years apart, will echo down millennia.

> And, as the Cretan labyrinth of old,
> With wand'ring ways and many a winding fold,
> Involv'd the weary feet, without redress,
> In a round error, which denied recess;
> So fought the Trojan boys in warlike play,
> Turn'd and return'd, and still a diff'rent way.
> Thus dolphins in the deep each other chase
> In circles, when they swim around the wat'ry race.
> This game, these carousels, Ascanius taught;
> And, building Alba, to the Latins brought;
> Shew'd what he learn'd: the Latin sires impart
> To their succeeding sons the graceful art;
> From these imperial Rome receiv'd the game,
> Which Troy, the youths the Trojan troop, they name.
> Thus far the sacred sports they celebrate:
>
> —Virgil
> *Aeneid* Book V
> (Dryden trans internet classics)

SEAFARERS

THE MEDITERRANEAN SEA IS BORN ON CHRISTMAS DAY on our Earth calendar, in the late Cretaceous Period. To my mind, she is better understood as the daughter of the Tethys Sea—Tethys being the daughter of Gaia and Uranus in Greek mythology, the twin archetypes of Earth and Upheavals. Here lie the mountains of the gods, Mt. Olympus and Mt. Ida. Also Vesuvius and Etna.

For a more accurate picture of the Mediterranean, turn once again to Homer and to Virgil, who knew this sea so well. Not the azure but the wine-dark sea, the hoar sea, the sounding sea, the place of Scylla and Charybdis, of clashing rocks and whirlpools. Of enchanted islands where men could be turned into pigs or be devoured by one-eyed giants. In *The Odyssey*, Homer tells us that the ships of the Greek (Achaean) king, Menelaus, returning home from victory in the Trojan War, were tossed off course by Mediterranean storms and lay stranded off the Isle of Pharos, until Proteus—"the immortal old man of the sea who never lies, who sounds the deep in all its depths, Poseidon's servant"—tells them what is needed to be on their way.*

In a sense, a main character of Homer's *Odyssey* and of Virgil's *Aeneid* is the sea. They are both about two warriors from the Trojan War, one from each of the two great armies that fought there—the Greeks and the Trojans—making a treacherous sea journey after the decade-long battle had ended in victory for the Achaeans and the destruction of Troy. The City of Troy, long thought to be only a city of legend like Knossos, lay in the far eastern corner of the Mediterranean in present day Turkey near the Sea of Marmara, which connects the Aegean Sea with the Black Sea and separates Europe and Asia. Odysseus was trying to return home to Ithaca, a place in Greece where his wife Penelope and his son Telemachus awaited him. Aeneas and the Trojans were fleeing the dying city and headed toward their own "new world." A place where the refugees could find a home; where they could found a new city.

As the *Aeneid* begins, Aeneas and his men are sailing just off Sicily. They are men of Troy, survivors of their city's defeat. We are seeing the scene, in part, through the eyes of the goddess Juno (GR: Hera), still stung by having her beauty snubbed by Paris and the events of the Trojan War.** And Juno, we are told, "cared more for Carthage than for any walled city of the earth . . ." Carthage was far from Troy, on the coast of North Africa, but bound to the events of Troy by the Mediterranean. It is *not* far from Sicily, where Aeneas has arrived in this opening scene. The obstacle for the success of Juno's plan is an ancient prophecy that generations of Trojan blood would one day "overthrow her Tyrian walls"—the walls of Carthage. "And from that blood a race would come, with ample kingdoms, arrogant in war." Rome!

Juno is a goddess spawned by the cultures of that great Sea in the Middle of the Earth, first as Hera, wife of Zeus in Greece, then as Juno, wife of Jove to the Romans: the divine pair, as reckless and unpredictable as the sea's weather. When Virgil speaks of Tyrian walls, he is describing Carthage as the outpost of Tyre, which is how it began. Tyre is in present-day Lebanon and was the ancient home of the Phoenicians, (the Biblical Canaanites) who were the greatest traders of the ancient world, after the Minoans. Between 1500 BC and 300 BC, they spread their influence throughout the Mediterranean as far as the "tin isles" of Britain. By establishing a center in North Africa on the Mediterranean, they advanced and secured their commercial shipping interests. Tyre was much more important then than Beirut, which lay to the north. We will hear again of Carthage as our stories continue.

Those Mediterranean goddesses were clever schemers and very determined

---

* Robert Fagles' translation)

** According to the story, a quarrel broke out among the Greek goddesses over a golden apple that was to be awarded to "the fairest" of them. Zeus appointed Paris of Troy as their judge. Paris chose Aphrodite to receive the golden apple. In return, she made Helen, "the most beautiful of women," fall in love with Paris and they ran away together. Unfortunately, Helen also happened to be the wife of Menelaus, king of the Achaeans, who led the Greeks to war against the Trojans in revenge. Hence the immortal description of Helen as "the face that launched a thousand ships."

to have their way, prophecies notwithstanding. Juno instructs Aeolus, god of the winds, to send a hurricane against them. "The race I hate is crossing the Tuscan Sea, transporting Ilium (Troy) with their household gods—beaten as they are—to Italy. Put new fury into your winds and make their long ships founder." Desperate housewives of TV fame pale beside these early goddesses. Aeolus complies.

> *Spearhead reversed,*
> *He gave the hollow mountainside a stroke,*
> *And where a portal opened, winds in ranks,*
> *As though drawn up for battle, hurtled through*
> *To blow across the earth in hurricane.*
> *Over the sea, tossed up from the sea-floor,*
> *Eastwind and Southwind, then the wild Southwest*
> *With squall on squall came scudding down,*
> *Rolling high combers shoreward.*

We have watched events like this in Indonesia and Florida and Louisiana from our living room chairs. You have to recognize the power of this reporting, made memorable by a poet. Consider that these lines were recited generation after generation through the Western world, right up into the present. Here the vantage point shifts to the eyes of the sailors as the storm bears down upon them.

> *Now one heard*
> *The cries of men and screech of ropes in the rigging,*
> *Suddenly as the storm cloud whipped away*
> *Clear sky and daylight from the Teucrians eyes,*
> *And gloom of night leaned on the open sea.*
> *It thundered from all quarters as it lightened*
> *Flash on flash through heaven. Every sign*
> *Portended a quick death for the mariners.*
>
> *Aeneas on the instant felt his knees*
> *Go numb and slack, and stretched both hands to heaven,*
> *Groaning out:*
> > *"Triply lucky all you men*
> *To whom death came before your father's eyes*
> *Below the wall of Troy . . .*
> > *As he flung out these words, a howling gust*
> *From due north took the sail aback and lifted*
> *Wavetops to heaven; oars were snapped in two;*
> *The prow sheered round and left them broadside on*
> *To breaking seas; over her flank and deck*
> *A mountain of grey water crashed in tons.*
> *Men hung on crests; to some a yawning trough*
> *Uncovered bottom, boiling waves of sand.*

The Southwind caught three ships and whirled them down
On reefs hidden midsea, called by the Italians
"The Altars"—razorbacks just under water.
The Eastwind drove three others from deep water
Into great shoals and banks, embedding them
And ringing them with sand, a desperate sight.

Before Aeneas's eyes a toppling billow
Struck the Lycian's ship, Orontës ship.
Across the stern, pitching the steersman down
And overboard. Three times the eddying sea
Carried the ship around in the same place
Until the rapid whirlpool dragged it down.

A few men swimming surfaced in the welter.
So did shields, planks, precious things of Troy.
Iloneus' good ship, brave Achatës' ship,
The ship that carried Abas, and the one
Aletës sailed in, hale in his great age,
Were all undone by the wild gale: their seams
Parted and let the enemy pour in. (6–8)

Aeneas is saying that after ten years of battle and the terrible scenes of destruction in Troy, it would nevertheless have been better to die beneath those walls than to face this enemy, the sea. I have heard such tales of men returning from the world wars, the Viet Nam War and no doubt the Iraq War as well, in which men fought side by side through terrible battles which they survived, only to die back home or on the way back, in a plane crash. For their surviving comrades, it is a bitter tragedy like the one that Aeneas is recounting here.

Odysseus, on his return from the war, was equally beset by treacherous seas. Here, as in many places, through Homer we meet Scylla and Charybdis, which lie on a passage between two headlands, "one a sharp mountain, with storm cloud round the peak" that never dissolves and sheer cliffs of polished stone." Midway up the mountain lies a "cavern full of mist" which is the den of Scylla, a great twelve-legged monster with six long necks and heads. Opposite this is a tongue of land, below which lies the whirlpool "which swallows down the dark sea tide," Charybdis. "Three times from dawn to dusk she spews it up and sucks it down again three times, a whirling maelstrom."

In later times, all these descriptions were thought to be purely imaginary. But there are at least two such places that fit the general description, even if embellished here with multiple heads and arms: the strait of the Bosphorus where the Mediterranean opens into the Black Sea, not far from where the Greek ships landed for their war with Troy, and the Strait of Messina off Sicily along that treacherous seam where two continents meet. If you regard these as descriptions of actual locations, then you appreciate all the more the power of the early storytellers to convey the "monstrosity" of these places where multiple arms of the sea reach out to grab you and multiple heads are waiting to spew and devour. Indeed the clashing plates we know now are captured with a mythological power.

A timeless mythology allows us to view these epics together, as the stories themselves take place close in time. But Odysseus's story is being composed almost five hundred years *after* the event, in Greece. We now have evidence from the last century that Troy did exist and that the Trojan War was likely an actual event. Its memory was preserved in story throughout that area of the Mediterranean. Now add to that the fact that the story of Aeneas and his return from the same war was composed, as the *Aeneid*, some seven hundred years after that in the north of Italy, almost a millennium after the event. This would be like reading about an American hero of the Viet Nam War in 2300 AD and then another account written about a Vietnamese hero of the war in the year 3000. When you consider that floppy disks have become obsolete after less than 50 years, what is the likelihood that our storage devices and the zillions of gigabytes they contain will be accessible a thousand years hence? Much of the knowledge of the ancient world was destroyed by fire in the great library at Alexandria, as most of the books of the Mayans were destroyed by the conquering Spanish. Increasingly, our own records are virtual and ephemeral. It is hard to imagine them enduring for a thousand years. Looked at from this perspective, the human oral tradition seems the most resilient form of storage.

So let us return to Virgil, who was born in Northern Italy near the foothills of the Alps in what we will meet later on as Lombardy. He did not write the *Aeneid* because he wanted to preserve the story for its hero, but for much more political reasons. The Roman Emperor Octavian (later called Augustus), wanted him to write a work that would in some way praise his regime. For better or for worse, much great art has emerged from the vanity of rulers. Velasquez's portraits for Charles I, Michelangelo's work for the Medici's, Handel's music composed for the coronation of King George II, and Mozart's compositions for the emperor Joseph II. Virgil spends the last ten years of his life on this work, which will lay in retrospect the cornerstone of Roman history.

These origins in no way diminished the quality or impact of these works. Virgil gathered both story and fact into a masterpiece. That Scylla and Charybdis move to a different, yet no less dangerous location in the Mediterranean, does not substantially change the story. Here is his account of their destructive force from the pen of Virgil:

> Now then, at sea again as the wind takes you
> Toward the Sicilian shore, and headlands northward
> Dwindle up the narrows of Pelorus.
> Steer for the coast to port, the seas to port,
> A long sail round, away from shores to starboard.

These land masses in the past, they say,
Though one unbroken mainland long ago,
In cataclysm leaped apart: a change
That the long ages of the past could bring—
The sea rushed in between, to cut away
Hesperia's flank from Sicily and washed
With narrowed tide the sundered shores and towns.

Now Scylla haunts the starboard side, Charybdis,
Never appeased, the side to port—and deep
In her whirlpool gulps down the great sea waves
Three times a day and spews them up again,
Sending up the whiplash of her spray to heaven.
Scylla lies immured in a rocky cave
In clefts of inky darkness, darting out
Her faces, pulling ships upon the reef.

This is surely an early statement of a geological fact. It is a local story embedded in an earth story, which is something we can only begin now to understand with the aid of our scientific discoveries. Scylla and Charybdis have survived into our present lexicon as a poetic description of being "between a rock and a hard place." Put another way, this Christmas Day of Earth's history continues to leave its imprint upon our everyday lives: The Scylla and Charybdis we have just met lie on either side of the edge of collision between the African and Eurasian plates. They still haunt. They are still unappeased. They still move.

This collision also caused a counter-clockwise rotation of the Apennines region which can be seen in the shapes of Sicily, Italy and Greece. On the northeastern tip of Sicily, near the Messina Strait, lies Mt. Etna—the most active volcano in Europe and the oldest in recorded history. The earliest documented mention of its eruption goes back to about 2000 BC, and it has erupted 192 times since, most recently in 2002-2003.*

A scene that lingers with me from the *Aeneid* occurs near the beginning when the terrible Mediterranean storm sends the Trojans to seek refuge on the nearest shore—the site of Carthage in present day Tunisia. The gods have sent him to Queen Dido's realm, which she is founding on the African coast, leaving behind her native home, the Phoenician capital at Tyre on the present Lebanese coast. Aeneas's mother, the goddess Venus, has covered him in an invisible cloak as he climbs a ridge and has his first view of the city and its towers lying below him:

. . . There the Teucrians
Were hard at work: laying courses for walls,
Rolling up stones to build a citadel,

---

* There is dramatic photograph of this from space at http://boris.vulcanoetna.com/
ETNA_2002.html .)

> *While others picked out building sites and plowed*
> *A boundary furrow. Laws were being enacted,*
> *Magistrates and a sacred senate chosen.*
> *Here men were dredging harbors, there they laid*
> *The deep foundation of a theatre,*
> *And quarried massive pillars to enhance*
> *The future stage . . .*

We are seeing an ancient city go up before our eyes. I have seen the ruins of so many ancient cities, but it is something else to see one freshly being built in Virgil's vivid poetry. My favorite part is yet to come, as Aeneas continues his exploration of the city. In a grove in the middle of the town, a great temple is being built, planned by Dido to honor Juno, who had shown them where to build their city.

> *. . .It was while he walked*
> *From one to another wall of the great temple*
> *And waited for the queen, staring amazed*
> *At Carthaginian promise, at the handiwork*
> *Of artificers and the toil they spent on it:*
> *He found before his eyes the Trojan battles*
> *In the old war, now known throughout the world—*
> *The great Atridae, Priam and Achilles,*
> *Fierce in his rage at both sides. Here Aeneas*
> *Halted, and tears came.*
>
>   *"What spot on earth,"*
> *He said, "What region of the earth, Achatës,*
> *Is not full of the story of our sorrow?*
> *Look, here is Priam. Even so far away*
> *Great valor has due honor; they weep here*
> *For how the world goes, and our life that passes*
> *Touches their hearts. Throw off your fear. This fame*
> *Insures some kind of refuge."*

This is such a beautiful scene, and it speaks again of time. Our chronoscope here, which brings a distant time into view, is art: what the artists have wrought on the walls of Dido's temple here in Carthage, perhaps as early as 1200 BC, recounted by Virgil so freshly in 20 BC, translated by Robert Fitzgerald in 1981, re-read by me in 2006, and now by you . . . when?

Two gifted story-tellers of antiquity, Homer and Virgil, keep an ancient memory freshly alive through their epic poems. According to one Onesicritus, the helmsman of Alexander the Great's royal ship, Alexander went to Troy and slept with a copy of the *Iliad* under his pillow. This would have been before he died in 323 BC, almost five hundred years after Homer wrote it.

I have experienced a series of synchronistic events around the writing of this—little nudges from the chronoscope. The following minor headlines have appeared under the heading "What's New?" on the Compuserve Homepage where I receive my email:

- "The Legend of Odysseus Comes Alive"
- "Extraordinary Find in Ancient Greek Palace"
- "Guess What Was Found Inside An Egyptian Tomb?" (Answer: A play by Aeschylus)
- Ancient Greek Rest Stop: Heliki—Island of Poseidon

I read inside the little pane on my screen the discovery of Ajax's palace as little green animated dollar bills float wavily across it like leaves to announce great savings on mortgage rates. The world is a wonder.

These appeared alongside items like—

- "How to deal with a smelly coworker"
- "Jessica Simpson's New Life"

And next to that, under "Need to Know"—

- "This Male Body-type is a real turn-off"
- "50% of Men on First Date say No to this"
- "Want to be Successful? Do just one thing!"

I suppose this is democracy in action. The inalienable right to be inane. But I am encouraged that Odysseus and Ajax and Achilles can still hold their own with Jessica Simpson and Brad Pitt. In fact it's downright remarkable.

> *. . . Our life that passes touches their hearts*
> *Throw off your fear. This fame insures*
> *Some kind of refuge.*

PAUL

IN THE SAME TREACHEROUS AREA OF THE SEA where the Trojan ships foundered, another violent Mediterranean storm lays down its marker on the landscape of history. Malta lies off Sicily, between Sicily and Carthage. It is here that the apostle Paul, traveling as a prisoner under a Roman guard, washes up on the shore after the ship had run aground. Today there is actually a Church of St. Paul's Shipwreck in Valetta. In fact, unlikely as it sounds, his shipwreck is popularly considered the greatest event in Malta history and there is a feast day for the event (February 10th) in the Catholic calendar.

Such a celebration is in sharp contrast to the original event. Paul had been arrested in Jerusalem, accused of bringing Gentiles into the temple there, in an act of what we might call today a sectarian conflict; divisions among the Christian Jews. After two years of imprisonment, Paul was invoking his rights as a Roman citizen to be tried in Rome, which was the destination of the ship.

Paul was traveling with several other prisoners in the custody of a centurion named Julius, who seems to have treated Paul with some care. After a short trip down the coast of Turkey, Julius finds them an Alexandrian ship leaving from the port of Edrimet on the southern coast. The ship struggled against the wind, as Aeneas and his shipmates had before him, making slow headway and continually being blown off course. Here is the account of it in Acts:

> As they sailed along the shore of Crete, a wind of hurricane force, called the "northeaster," swept down from the island. The ship was caught by the storm and could not head into the wind; so we gave way to it and were driven along.
>
> We took such a violent battering from the storm that the next day they began to throw the cargo overboard. When neither sun nor stars appeared for many days and the storm continued raging, we finally gave up all hope of being saved.
>
> When daylight came, the ship struck a sandbar and ran aground. The bow stuck fast and would not move, and the stern was broken to pieces by the pounding of the surf. The soldiers planned to kill the prisoners to prevent any of them from swimming away and escaping. But the centurion wanted to spare Paul's life and kept them from carrying out their plan. He ordered those who could swim to jump overboard first and get to land. The rest were to get there on planks or on pieces of the ship. In this way everyone reached land in safety.

They are able to winter there on the island of Malta and the account in Acts tells us that when Paul healed the father of the town's chief of an ailment, others who were ill or injured were brought to him and were healed by him during his stay there. At the end of three months, Paul will continue on to Rome, leaving behind him a staunch population of Christians who will remain devoted for centuries to come.

Paul was born only fourteen years after the death of Virgil around 5 BC. Although later dates have also been suggested, if this is true his parents would have been contemporaries of Virgil. And like Virgil, he is an important link in our future stories. Both Virgil and Paul were Romans, although they were born in different parts of the empire and would receive very different treatment at its hands. One is the peak and the poetic summary of the old world that extended back over a thousand years and the other is the foundation of a new one, which reaches into the present. I am always amazed at the consequences that can flow from a single human life, and these two men, like others in our stories, bear that out.

We tend to view history as if it were a thin bright tapestry depicting scenes from a great saga. Even when we make careful distinctions between myth and history, fiction and nonfiction, they all remain tapestry-like or, more accurately, like the pages of a book, as in reality they are usually related to us. Neither myth nor history seems to bear any relation to the hard-edged realities of mundane life.

As an example, I'm thinking of Paul in around 50 AD, ten years before the Mediterranean shipwreck, traveling with Barnabas along the ancient road between Antioch in Syria and Jerusalem. They might have been two members of any group—company employees, political party members, businessmen—discussing as they go how to handle the approaching meeting; a business trip back to headquarters. Their company is a small group in the large flow of things and the greater world of the empire has no idea of the concerns that trouble them. Yet that conversation, and more so the encounter that lies before them, will cleave the world in a way that will alter history. It is true that this is a company of men and women who carry a radical vision of change into their daily lives, but even Paul could never have envisioned, say, the multitude of people who would turn out onto the streets of Mexico twenty centuries later in a then undiscovered continent to greet a Christian Pope, then flashing mirrors toward his departing plane in a conflagration of joy and faith. Paul and Barnabas—whose mission was to spread the new religion of Christianity among the gentiles or non-Jewish people (from *gentilia*, people)—knew that they would not win converts if the strict Jewish rituals around eating and circumcision were imposed on them. And this could only obstruct the dissemination of the larger Christian message.

When they arrived in Jerusalem, they were warmly received by their fellow Jewish Christians but not on the subject they had come to discuss. For the Jew, circumcision was a holy symbol of the people's ancient covenant with God. Most of the Christian Jews were still faithful worshippers at the beautiful temple in Jerusalem built by Solomon. The apostle James was reluctant to take such an extreme step. Peter took their side. Paul offered the conciliatory gesture of providing financial support for the struggling Jerusalem community from funds taken in by the wealthier Antioch church, which he had founded in that city. It was finally agreed that pagan proselytes would only be required to abstain from immorality and the eating of strangled or sacrificed animals. Later another group of orthodox Jewish Christians came to Antioch from Jerusalem and found Peter sharing a meal with the gentiles. Jewish law prohibited eating with uncircumcised proselytes, so he

MAJOR CHARACTERS & PLACES — EASTERN MEDITERRANEAN

was persuaded to remove himself from the table of the gentiles and eat among his own. These disagreements would eventually lead to Paul's arrest.

Those who go and those who stay. Both have their place in the scheme of things. But the die was cast and the split could ultimately never be bridged. The tree of Abraham had branched into two directions which would always be allied at their root.

Paul traveled north again to Phrygia and Troas, where he met Luke, an uncircumcised proselyte to Judaism to whom tradition would later attribute the authorship of the third Gospel and Acts.

This momentous meeting of Paul and Luke takes place in modern day Turkey, in a region known as the Troad. This region had been largely Greek since Alexander had swept through here on an expedition that started in 335 BC. Neither Paul nor Luke would have been thinking of two events that had transpired on the same ground, though far distant in time from them: One, over a thousand years in the past, the Trojan War, and the other over eighteen hundred years in the future.

In 1872, Henry and Sophia Schliemann would stand on a plateau of the same Troad, looking down at the mouth of the Scamander River, within sight of Mt. Ida, as Henry unfolded his vision of excavating what he believed to be the ruins of Troy. It was his own madman's scheme. No one of his time had ever believed that the Trojan War was anything more than a fanciful legend or that such a city as Troy had ever existed. Achilles, Odysseus, Hector, Priam . . . These were the names of great fictitious heroes out of the first works of Western literature, the *Iliad* and the *Odyssey*. The *Aeneid* refers to the Trojans often as the Teucrians, after the Greek legend of their founder—Teucer, son of the Cretan prince Scamander and the nymph Idaea. Virgil tells us that Teucer left Crete with a third of his people to escape a famine there and became the founder of the new city of Troy. (Might that have been following the natural disaster that devastated much of the island?) Here below Henry and Sophia gleamed the Scamander River, and Henry's dreams of the greatest find in Western archaeology.

His dream came true and shocked the academic world of his time as the Cyclopean Walls of the city and the fabled treasure of Priam were unearthed. Although later archaeologists would deplore Schliemann's methods and debate the actual location of walls and treasures, Troy was no longer dismissed as a city of fable. Troy was real as were Priam, Hector, Achilles and Odysseus. Though the tale was undoubtedly embroidered by art and by the reigning worldview of the time, the *Iliad* was history and not myth. For Paul and for Luke, it mattered little whether the Trojan events were real or imaginary because the whole pantheon of the pagan world was about to be displaced in a conquest as complete as the Greek conquest of Troy.

Paul travels on with Timothy to Macedonia, homeland of Alexander the Great. They are now on European soil. Paul's travels carry him as far west as Sicily, according to St. Chrysostom (and by a few disputed accounts, to Spain). There he crosses the path of another Semitic people who came west from Paul's own region of Asia Minor over a millennium before him: the Carthaginians. Paul was from Tarsus in southern Turkey, less than one hundred fifty miles from the town where Virgil's Aeneas was born. Remember that the Carthaginians were originally Phoenicians who traveled out from their center in Tyre (Lebanon) and established colonies in North Africa, Sicily, and Spain. Dido's Carthage became Rome's nemesis, as it had been to the Greek residents of Sicily. Paul is following in the steps of Odysseus and Aeneas. Does he hear the wind roar out of the cave of Aeolus? Likely not. What he hears in Sicily's ancient streets is the wind of spirit. "Listen to the wind, Nicodemus." He has come to do battle with ancient gods in their own citadel. Sicily is a little island for such big footprints: Odysseus, Aeneas, Hannibal and Paul. Aeneas, as one of the few Trojan survivors, had left the Troad on a mission to bring his household gods to Italy. To Latium. And Odysseus? He just wanted to go home. But like many others, it is the journey, not the arrival, that he is remembered for.

386 AD ~ The Mediterranean, off Sicily

IT IS EARLY MORNING BUT THERE IS LITTLE TO DISTINGUISH IT *from the turbid night or the blackness that had come on with the late afternoon of the previous day. The oldest of the sailors had given their ominous warnings when the sun was high in the sky; the air as clear as glass and the sea was preternaturally still. A quiet had come over the boat then—a small merchant ship bound for Sardinia and from there, to the Italian port of Ostia. The storm has hurled itself over the sea from the southwest like an avenging monster exploding out of the depths or hidden in the sky. The waters are churned up into huge vertical cliffs and canyons, tossing the vessel like a brittle leaf, spinning and sliding down through steep troughs.*

The hours pass but the storm is unrelenting. Finally even the most seasoned sailors are abandoning hope. They have left their oars and the rigging to huddle among the terrified passengers, clinging to whatever solid object they can find; crying out for their lost lives, about to disappear into their watery graves. As the first faint streaks of silver appear out of the angry darkness of the sky to sketch a new dawn, the storm shows no sign of abating but a figure can be seen moving haltingly among them, grabbing at handholds wherever they can be found on the battered deck, to reach those crew members who have abandoned hope of surviving the merciless gale. The figure is a woman and to their amazement, she is urging them to return to their posts to save the ship. "A vision," she keeps repeating, in her strong, reassuring voice. She has had a vision and God has promised her that they will all reach the shore safely. It is enough. She has breathed a new spirit of hope into them. They struggle to their feet. Return to their positions to renew their battle with the demons of the sea.

This is Monica.

✳ ✳ ✳ ✳

Grossi Farms ~ The Present

UNDER THE PLUM TREE

Today is an important day. Chuck, a completely unknown person, comes to try to release Mr. Fields from the two-year-long grip of mud that has held it fast and listing to starboard. Me with it. Laurie-Ann has arranged this with him. Chuck has come to paint her house but has shown unusual interest in my truck. "I can fix that," he told her, while I was at work in the stand. The motor starts, but nothing will coax it forward or back. The wheels are stuck in the adobe mud into which it was driven in a torrential downpour two years ago. We are hoping that this is the only problem with the poor old dear. In a way, it coincides with my dissertation project, in which I too have been mired up to my neck. Yesterday, after innumerable and exasperating printing problems, Kinkos spit out a copy for me and the end is in sight.

And now there is Chuck. I think of Chuck as one of Mr. Fields' friends rather than mine, though I'm happy to count him among my friends too. The fact is that a 315 page dissertation or a book to be published in the spring is not nearly as inspiring to him as a view of Mr. Fields' interiors. When he lifted up the hood, he purred. He moved his hand tenderly across all of those cold, greasy metal objects, touching each one with admiration and approval. Even finding a new one in his obviously well-populated world of automotive objects. He tracked down a tube that led from it and surmised that whatever this was, it would even produce air for my tires. I had no idea what he was talking about but didn't want to interrupt the litany; the quiet songs of praise. This was a great moment for the long-neglected Mr. Fields and therefore for me too. Never mind that it was in a foreign language. So was the Mass, for centuries. He found things to marvel at even on the underside of Mr. Fields' rear end. "He's got five something-or-others," he crooned. "What do the five-something-or others do" I asked. It seems they assure that the wheels move in synchrony with one another. Why ever wouldn't they, I wondered.

I forgot to mention that all of this was done with a flashlight in the pitch dark. I had waited all morning for the arrival of Chuck for our 9:30 a.m. meeting but he never showed. At noon, discouraged now about Mr. Field's prospects, I trudged off to work. As I was striding down the long dirt road to the farm stand, a truck pulled up next to me and there was Chuck, sincerely apologetic. He didn't look like his voice on the phone. I expected someone tall and lanky, chain-smoking Marlboros. Chuck is small, compact, energetic, with hazel eyes that have a softness, almost an appeal in them. An appeal to the world for something only he knows. He wanted to lever Mr. Fields up and dig and seemed confident of our success. This is the man's world I have been introduced to this summer through Farmer Ed. The question is never Can it be done but only How. There are no Impossibles. We agreed that he would start on this project and communicate with me in an hour to tell me how it was working. Later he called to tell me that he needed a something-or-other and would return the next morning promptly at 9:30. I knew it would probably be later. I was not prepared for earlier.

That same evening, I was in bed reading when, as the poem goes, "I heard such a clatter, I sprang from my bed to see what was the matter." There was a rap on the door. "Who is it," I grumbled. I discourage night visitors. "It's Chuck. Have everything I need to do it."

"Now?"

"Sure. I even brought the gasoline."

"But I go to bed early and it's getting late and who knows how long this will take and it's completely dark . . ." I spluttered. Then I realized that I was probably looking a gift horse in the mouth and Chuck clearly operated on a schedule from another world.

"Don't worry. You can just go right ahead with what you're doing. This won't bother you at all. Shouldn't take too long."

"If it does, can I . . . well . . . just go to bed?"

"Sure. No problem."

Like a magician, he produced a stand of lights that made the back yard look like Yankee Stadium for a night game of the World Series. I retreated to the back of Mr. Fields. Suddenly I was levered up at the other end and a vigorous thumping rose up under the camper. There was no way I was going to read or sleep through this. Chuck was in the middle of a heroic task. Would I sleep while Hercules was cleaning out the Augean stables? (Well on second thought . . .) I opened up the back door of the camper into the airy dark, punctured by the glow of his stadium lights, to ask him if he needed any help. I descended carefully from this aerial perch to observe the goings-on.

I have never seen such energy in my life. He stabbed and pried and dug furiously with a long metal pole. Clouds of broken adobe mud and rock were flying everywhere. Sheets of sweat were pouring off the man. It was amazing, "Day or night it's the same," he said. "What is the same?" I asked. "Day or night, when I work I sweat." I hadn't thought about that. It wasn't a warm night and the sun was far off, heading for Shanghai. After a little over an hour of this frenzied labor, Chuck spun the wheels proudly under the airborne back end. Free! They really did look like such happy things. I was proud as a parent watching her kid walk or ride a bicycle for the first time. Chuck produced the gasoline can, pouring some into the tank and some into the carburetor and started it up. For a moment, it seemed to go nowhere and my heart sank at the thought of a serious transmission problem. Chuck rocked it back and forth and it suddenly roared forward onto even ground. The stadium lights glowed and I cheered as if we had just won the World Series. Mr. Fields is no longer a statue embedded in a cement plinth. He is a vehicle again and Sheri and Mr. Fields are cleared for take-off.

◆ ◆ ◆

The last day under the plum tree. Well no longer under the plum tree because Mr. Fields and I have been moved to higher ground under an open expanse of sky. It's a whole different experience to be level. I've been living at a 30 or 40 degree angle for over a year and being even feels odd.

All of the time I was in Mr. Fields under the plum tree, I enjoyed a privileged perspective. I remember a bower of blossoms high up in a hidden crotch of the tree. Had it not been for the rainstorm that marooned Mr. Fields, just so, at his odd angle, I would never have caught sight of it from my open hatch as I lay looking upward through the branches, listening to the Sacred Music Concert on a Sunday morning. I marveled at such profuse and delicate beauty, much of it never to be seen by a human eye. How much of the planet is filled with such unseen wonders?

Yet perhaps *not* unseen. For many of those millions of years through the months of the Earth calendar, nature was proliferating in its myriad forms and along the way there *were* eyes to see it. Just not ours. And not until mid-November, during the Cambrian explosion, when I imagine Beethoven's *Ode to Joy* breaking forth on the planet as so many new creatures burst onto the earth and the first eyes began to see. That was the work of November. Eyes to see. Through the first weeks of December would come the ears to hear.

Looking up into the plum tree, I counted for myself how much seeing is going on there right now, from the eye of the bird to the eye of the ant, the fly, the beetle, the bee and who knows what other tiny thing. All of those seeings are different. And none of those eyes see the range of color and form that my own eyes can see. But perhaps there is a community of seeing, by all of our eyes, that creates the manifold presence of the tree.

The plum tree was my own private bird feeder when summer came and the plums ripened and the branches filled with orioles and grosbeaks and other beautiful birds. I remember the delicate sounds of birds' feet landing on Mr.

Fields' roof, moving from one side of Mr. Fields to the other as the birds supped on the fallen fruit. The occasional peering eye of a sparrow or a robin as they paused next to my skylight's edge to watch me as I worked. Light dawning on the gracious eucalyptus trunk and dying with a golden flare in its highest branches at day's end. All this because of a rain storm. All this because Mr. Fields got stuck and sank deeper and deeper into the mud. There, exactly there, under the plum tree.

◆ ◆ ◆

Today is moving day, which has been the whole point of this effort to release Mr. Fields. Laurie-Ann has sold her house and is moving into Cotati Co-Housing. Ed and Susie have kindly offered their farm as Mr. Fields' new home. "Where shall I park it when I bring it?" I asked Ed. "Under the eucs," he said.

"The eucs?"

"The eucalyptus trees."

I hadn't ever been that far back on the farm and had to go see for myself where the eucs were. Nice, I thought. Perfect.

I asked Chuck to drive with me the half-mile from Curtis Drive to the farm, just in case something crucial had deteriorated in the two years it was a fixed sculpture. I felt like a royal monarch driving down the street in Mr. Fields. I don't think it had ever occurred to anyone that it moved, or that I could drive. I had only ever been seen on foot in the neighborhood.

Mr. Fields proceeded without a hitch at his stately pace. As we processed down the dirt road of the farm, the fellows stopped in the fields to watch, and I waved from my great height in the truck's cab. Oh it felt grand.

Sheri and Mr. Fields were now officially in residence Under the Eucs.

✳ ✳ ✳ ✳

NORTH AFRICA TO LOMBARDY
~ LAND STORIES

Tagaste, North Africa ~ 4th Century AD

MONICA

THE SAHARA DESERT SPREADS ACROSS THREE THOUSAND MILES of North Africa from the Atlantic to the Red Sea. Along its northern rim, the Atlas Mountains extend from Morocco on the Western edge, northeast through Algeria into modern Tunisia, where the port of Carthage once lay. This is the bumper of Africa, which takes the brunt of the collision with Europe, pushing up the Atlas Mountains to the south as the Alps rise to the north. With peaks as high as 13,000 feet, the Atlas Mountains cradle the coastal lands in a moist, temperate Mediterranean climate with cooling streams and green vegetation, though not immune to the searing winds that blow off the desert known as the Sirocco.

Monica is from the town of Tagaste* in Numidia—today's Algeria, near the border of Tunisia. In Monica's time it is a town two hundred miles inland from the Mediterranean, governed by nearby Carthage. At an elevation of 2000 feet, it is dotted with forests of pines and yews, with open spaces where cork trees grow, home to pheasants, quail and wild boar; in the remoter areas, jackals and Barbary sheep.

Monica is 18 when she marries Patricius who is 41, a Berber like herself. The Berbers are the native people of that region. They have been described as the first Caucasoid people in Africa where they had lived long before the arrival of the Phoenicians who founded Carthage and established their rich and powerful Punic culture in places like Sicily and Spain as well as North Africa.

Monica was born into a Christian family. Patricius is a pagan. He is a small, dark swarthy man with quick, black eyes. Hot-tempered, though generally kind and well-regarded in his community, where he is a member of the municipal council. He is sometimes unfaithful to Monica, but she forgives his infidelity and prays ardently for his conversion to her own faith.

Patricius owns a small estate of land which he supervises. Farming is all-important in this region. A few wealthy *patroni* own huge estates with splendid villas, cypress groves, orchards, extensive vineyards, fields of grain and well-stocked fishponds. Patricius is not so wealthy, but he does well enough with his livestock and vineyards. His olive trees.

When the African Septimius Severus, of Berber and Roman ancestry, became emperor of Rome, he conferred citizenship on freemen born within the municipalities of the African territories. These new citizens, like Patricius, proudly took on Latin names and used the Latin language. This is the heritage they passed

---

* Present day Souk Ahras, Algeria

on to their children, in most cases adopting as well the worship of the Roman gods. Most of them—and likely Patricius and Monica—still often use the Punic language among themselves; the language brought by the Phoenicians a thousand years ago to their new outpost at Carthage. Some of the servants and laborers who have come into town from the mountains still speak Berber. Monica's name is Berber.

Patricius is 46 when their first child is born—Augustinus Aurelius, recalling two great Roman Emperors—on Sunday, November 13, 354. He is followed by a second son, Navigius and a daughter, Perpetua. Perpetua was likely named for the Carthaginian noblewoman Perpetua, who lived in the time of Septimius Severus. Monica's life would have been much influenced by one significant incident in the life of Dido's city, Carthage, which—in spite of the determined efforts of Juno—fulfilled the ancient prophecy and fell to Aeneas's progeny, the Romans, who "overthrew its Tyrian walls" in 146 BC. The lives of gods and goddesses in those times were certainly filled with frustration.

To fully understand the character of Monica, we will twist our chronoscope back a bit to look briefly at that event.

Carthage ~ ca. 200 AD

PERPETUA AND FELICITY

TOGETHER THEIR NAMES MEANT ETERNAL HAPPINESS. *They grew up together in Carthage and there, together they died, around 203* AD.

"When my father in his affection for me was trying to turn me from my purpose by arguments and thus weaken my faith," Perpetua wrote from her prison cell, "I said to him, 'Do you see this vessel—this water pot? Can it be called by any other name than what it is?' 'No,' he replied. 'So also I cannot call myself by any other name than what I am—a Christian.'"

She is a young, beautiful, well-educated noblewoman of Carthage, the mother of an infant son and the wife of a man of good position. Her mother is a Christian along with two brothers, one of the early generations of followers in North Africa. Her father, a pagan, continually pleads with her to renounce her faith and save her life, but at age 22 she is imprisoned. She is joined in prison by the slavewoman Felicity, her companion, the slave Revocatus, and two free men, Secundulus and Saturninus—who also refused to denounce their Christian faith. They are soon joined by Saturus, who appears to have been their instructor in the faith and now chooses to share their punishment. This is her account, which has survived.

"A few days later we were lodged in the prison, and I was much frightened, because I had never known such darkness. What a day of horror! Terrible heat, owing to the crowds! Rough treatment by the soldiers! To crown all I was tormented with anxiety for my baby. But those blessed deacons who ministered to us, paid for us to be moved for a few hours to a better part of the prison and we obtained some relief. All went out of the prison and we were left to ourselves. My baby was brought and I nursed him, for already he was faint for want of food. I spoke anxiously to my mother on his behalf and encouraged my brother and commended my son to their care.

"My brother then said to me: 'Lady sister, you are now greatly honored, so greatly that you may well pray for a vision to show you whether suffering or release is in store for you.' And I, knowing myself to have speech of the Lord for whose sake I was suffering, promised him confidently, 'Tomorrow I will bring you word.' And I prayed and this was shown me.

I saw a golden ladder of wonderful length reaching up to heaven, but so narrow that only one at a time could ascend; and to the sides of the ladder were fastened all kinds of iron weapons . . . And at the foot of the ladder was a huge dragon which lay in wait for those going up and sought to frighten them from the ascent. The first to go up was Saturus, who of his own accord had given himself up for our sakes, because our faith was of his building . . . He reached the top of the ladder and, turning, said to me: 'Perpetua, I wait for you, but take care that the dragon does not bite you.' And I said: 'In the name of Jesus Christ, he will not hurt me.' And the dragon put out his head gently, as if afraid of me, just at the foot of the ladder; and as though I were treading on the first step, I trod on his head.

And I went up and saw a vast garden, and sitting in the midst a tall man with white hair in the dress of a shepherd, milking sheep; and round about were many thousands clad in white. He raised his head and looked at me and said: 'Thou art well come, my child.' And he called me and gave me some curds of the milk he was milking, and I received them in my joined hands and ate, and all that were round about said 'Amen.' At the sound of the word I awoke, still tasting something sweet. I at once told my brother and we understood that we must suffer, and henceforth began to have no hope in this world.

What follows is in another hand:

On the day of their martyrdom they set forth from the prison. Behind the men walked the young noblewoman Perpetua, "abashing the gaze of all with the high spirit in her eyes," and beside her the slave Felicitas. . . . Perpetua was singing. The mob cried out that they should be scourged for their boldness. Accordingly, as the martyrs passed in front of the "venatores," or hunters, each received a lash.

To each one God granted the form of martyrdom he desired. Perpetua and Felicitas were exposed to a mad heifer. Perpetua was tossed first and fell on her back, but raised herself and gathered her torn tunic modestly about her; then, after fastening up her hair, lest she look as if she were in mourning, she rose and went to help Felicitas, who had been badly hurt by the animal. Side by side they stood, expecting another assault, but the sated audience cried out that it was enough. They were therefore led to the gate Sanevivaria, where victims who had not been killed in the arena were dispatched by gladiators. Here Perpetua seemed to arouse herself from an ecstasy and could not believe that she had already been exposed to a mad heifer until she saw the marks of her injuries. She then called out to her brother and to the catechumen: "Stand fast in the faith, and love one another. Do not let our sufferings be a stumbling block to you." After giving each other the kiss of peace, they were killed by the gladiators. Perpetua had to guide the sword of the nervous executioner to her throat.

No saints were more universally honored in all the early Church calendars. In the fourth century, in the time of Monica and her family, their "Acts" were publicly read in the churches of Africa. The tale of Felicitas and Perpetua would have been fresh in that area, as it remained fresh for centuries after that, even as the great cities of the region—Carthage and Leptis Major—were declining. It seems significant that Perpetua's mother was a Christian and her father a pagan, as Monica too was a Christian and her husband a Pagan. This is part of another collision that is going on, which in its way will prove as cataclysmic as the shift of the earth's plates.

Few people today could imagine that the most vibrant early Christian Church in the Roman Empire was in Africa from a very early date. Some say it was introduced into Egypt by the apostle Mark. Certainly St. Paul was active throughout the Mediterranean area and may have converted people in Sicily, for example, who carried their beliefs into North Africa. The oldest known manuscript of a Christian hymn (the Oxyrhynchus hymn discovered in 1918) was found in Egypt, composed there in the third century, before the established church under Constantine. I find the words very simple and touching:

> . . . Let it be silent
> Let the Luminous stars not shine,
> Let the winds (?) and all the noisy rivers die down;
> And as we hymn the Father, the Son and the Holy Spirit,
> Let all the powers add "Amen Amen"
> Empire, praise always, and glory to God,
> The sole giver of good things, Amen Amen.
>
> [M.L. West translation]

Monica was surely inspired by Perpetua's story and, simple Tagastian housewife that she was, she nevertheless plays an ample part in this larger tectonic shift that will move empires, as the African plate moved mountains.

AUGUSTINUS AURELIUS

IT IS SOMETIMES SAID THAT THE FIRST-BORN CHILD carries the hopes and expectations of the parents in the purest concentration. That may have been the case with Monica and Patricius. Or Augustinus Aurelius may just have been an exceptional, and at times exceptionally *difficult* child. When he was a young adolescent, accompanying his father to the public baths, Patricius saw with pride the clear signs of his son's virility and looked to his future with great expectations of his success. Monica was unimpressed by this and nourished different hopes, not for his body and mind, but for a safe haven for his soul in the kingdom of heaven as a Christian. Patricius forbade this, but her real opponent, as the years went on, was Augustinus Aurelius himself. He was a passionate and brilliant young man, but his passions were unbridled and he ran wherever they carried him. In early adolescence, this amounted to little more than youthful pranks like stealing pears from a neighbor's orchard. Patricius recognized his obvious talents and laid plans for his education. He made financial sacrifices to see that his son received a classical Latin curriculum at the local school. When he was 12 years old, Patricius sent him with a tutor to a school in Madaura, twenty miles south of Tagaste. Augustinus Aurelius ducked classes and was violently resistant to his violent teacher of Greek, who never spared the rod. Homer would suffer from this opposition. Latin, on the other hand, he loved.

Patricius intended to send him to Carthage for the next stage of his education and we can be sure that Monica looked on this plan (correctly as it turns out) with some alarm. Carthage was in ways a decadent city now, full of temptations for the unsuspecting youth who were cast into it, like a teenager from a small Midwestern town suddenly let loose in New York City or LA. But Patricius understood that this was necessary to an entrée into the larger world, where he knew that Augustinus Aurelius would become a success and make him proud.

Unfortunately, Patricius had not saved up enough money to afford to send him to Carthage yet, so his son returned home for a year to wait for the economic upturn. As it turned out, the upturn would come from a wealthy patron, Romanius, who also saw the clear prospects for so bright a young man.

It was not a good year to be idle in Tagaste, as any mother of a sixteen year old might guess. As one writer put it, "a year of idleness led the adolescent student into acts of dissipation and sexual adventure,"* summarizing Augustinus's own admissions of later years. But it is also during this year that Patricius died, converting to Christianity on his deathbed, so one can imagine the tumult in that young sensitive soul.

Augustinus Aurelius went off to Carthage the following year to study a course in rhetoric, which would lead him to a career as a lawyer. There he took up with a group of coarse friends, whom he later called "the wreckers," and frequented the theater. He would describe the city as "a cauldron of illicit loves." But here also he entered into a long-term relationship with a woman whom he would continue to love dearly for the rest of his life. She would bear him a son, Adeodatus, whose name meant God-given in Berber. Some have calculated that he actually met this woman and conceived the child by her in that year in Tagaste, and given the circumstances of that year, it seems possible.

While studying in Carthage, he encountered the teachings of a relatively new sect (later denounced as heretical) called Manichaeism, which contained elements of Babylonian, Judaic and Christian sources. It was founded by Mani—son of a Parthian (Persian) nobleman born in present day Iraq and a member of a Jewish Christian sect. Mani's visions led him to leave his father's sect to teach his own version of Christianity. It was a complicated, gnostic religious system but it was based on a fundamental concept of the duality of light and darkness. Goodness was thought to be manifested in what belongs to the realm of light: knowledge, spirit,

* Gary Wills, *St. Augustine.*

and soul. Evil, or darkness, was viewed as connected to ignorance, matter, and the body. Augustinus Aurelius was beginning his lifelong quest to understand the dual forces of light and darkness which were in enduring combat within the human soul. He was seeking to reconcile the two parts of himself, endowed by nature and accentuated by his parentage: a lusty sensuousness and a higher spiritual call toward a purer, still unidentified Truth.

It was the reading of Cicero's *Hortensis*—a work now lost—that awakened in Aurelius the longing to find a true wisdom, which Cicero insisted would demand thoughtful, philosophical contemplation and study.* So strong was this impulse in the young African that he abandoned his career as a lawyer in the imperial civil service, which was the career planned for him by his father and Romanius, and returned home to Tagaste. His mother was appalled by his relationship with the heretical sect, the Manichees, and she refused at first to allow him to enter her house. Nothing is said in his later account about her response to his relationship with his concubine or his child. That was apparently minor compared to this threat that the Manichees posed to his soul. Her prayers for his conversion redoubled. A year later he opened up a school of rhetoric in Carthage where he taught for eight years. He found the students rowdy and nerve-wracking but he persisted in the position until a friend from Tagaste, Alypius, wrote him from Rome urging him to join him there, where he would find more serious students and better pay.

The relationship between mother and son was a close one and even as he went his own ways, he continued to be influenced by her and at times may have felt suffocated by her single-minded Christian determination, rooted in the blood of those African women who went before her, and a strong fiber of Berber heritage as well. She fought against his decision to leave for Rome, beyond the reach of family. She insisted that if he went, she would go too. She actually followed him to the ship as he was departing, beseeching him to stay or to take her with him. But he is determined now to make a new life in a new place so he deceives her by telling her that the ship is not leaving until the following day and slips off without her.

NAVIGIUS

NAVIGIUS LOOKED UPON MONICA'S TRIALS with her oldest son with surprise and admiration. He had always admired his older brother but never understood why he found it so difficult to follow Monica's wishes. Perhaps he had an advantage as the younger son, but he also found it easier to quietly obey her desire that he follow her Christian ways, without making it too obvious to his father. Patricius was also so focused on Augustinus Aurelius that he paid little attention to what Navigius did. He was considered an "easy child." There was also the good fortune that Navigius knew from an early age what he wanted to do and both parents were

---

* Cicero was a contemporary of Virgil, born some thirty years before him in 103 BC and one of the leading thinkers and statesmen of ancient Rome..

equally pleased with his choice. As a boy, he had followed the local mosaic workers about and spent hours watching them lay the tesserae into beautiful designs in the floors of public buildings. He was not allowed to follow them into the private houses where they were employed, but he saw enough to convince him that he wanted to do that same work. He was deft with his fingers and made small designs with pebbles in the family yard as a child. Patricius and Monica were in agreement about sending him to apprentice with the local Master Pictor when he reached the age of 14. Some of the finest mosaics in Roman Africa were produced by the mosaic workers of Tagaste, and it was said that the most beautiful mosaic pavements in the whole of the Roman empire were to be found in the African provinces, so Navigius grew to be a respected young artisan.

With the departure of his brother for Rome, Monica focused more attention on her younger son and he had reason to be grateful for her intrusion into his affairs. Monica's parents had connections with several Christian communities across Numidia. Through this grapevine, Monica had heard of a Christian church in the west of the province that required extensive restoration and some addition to its elaborate floor pavement. That Navigius would participate in such a work to the glory of God (and be paid for it) was a splendid prospect and soon it was arranged that the team of workers from his master's studio would do the work.

Navigius and his team arrived in the Chlef Valley just after sunset on their fourth day of travel west across Numidia. They were being put up in the homes of church members to save them the cost of an inn. Navigius would be rooming with a Berber family of six, including three children under the age of seven. They all chattered away at supper and had a barrage of questions about life in Eastern Numidia and the cities he had visited there. Tired from his travel, he did his best to make conversation and then fell gratefully into bed soon after. He was up early the next morning and set out for the church by first light.

Castellum Tingitanum was a garrison town built by the Romans in the first century, following their conquest of Africa. It lay on the left bank of the Chlef River, in the middle of a vast plain, thirty miles (fifty km) from the sea. According to his hosts, the town had been nearly destroyed by a violent earthquake but the people had just rebuilt on the same spot. "It happens," they said, in a matter of fact way. Nearby was the basilica. It was much larger than he imagined.

The basilica had been constructed with a semi-circular apse at the east and west end. It was about eighty feet long (25m) by fifty feet (15m). He entered it through the west portal and walked slowly around the west apse to the north aisle. The entire floor was worked with the most complex mosaic designs in circles, squares, interlocking rope-like designs, entwined laurel leaves. Laid out on the floor immediately before him was a square maze, about eight feet on each side. He studied it carefully, trying to make sense of the pathways. What at first looked like a hopeless confusion of paths that led to dead ends, he began to see as a single path that led through four quadrants, back and forth, leading one way and then reversing but always leading finally into the next quadrant. At the completion of the fourth quadrant, the path led into the center. The central square was filled with letters, and these also appeared to him first as a meaningless jumble. But then he began to see it: Another maze had been formed, which instead of pathways used words. At the very center, in the shape of a cross, was the letter "S" that began the word "SANCTA" in four directions—rightward and leftward as well as up and down. After each word, moving upward was the word ECCLESIA. "Holy Church." Looking carefully, he could see that those two words threaded their way through the random letters that surrounded them. He thought of a verse from the Gospel of Matthew, often repeated by his mother: "For strait is the gate and narrow is the way that leads to life and those that find it are few." Was this something of what the original designer had intended?

Navigius had worked on magnificent mosaics in wealthy homes and buildings in places like Thuburba Majus* but he had never before seen, let alone worked on, a Christian church such as this one. Their most recent commission had been a mosaic in a house in Dougga. All of the figures they recreated in tile were of pagan gods and heroes; motifs common to all of the places that he had worked. This was altogether new, and it filled him with a sense of reverence and purpose. But also puzzlement.

A few minutes later, the Master Pictor had arrived and stood next to Navigius, studying the mosaic. "Have you ever seen anything like this before?" Navigius asked him. The Master nodded. "Yes," he said. "One is in a very beautiful home near the market in Thuburbo Majus. In the frigidarium of the private baths, we did a large labyrinth that had Theseus in the center, chopping off the head of the Minotaur. The area around them is filled with left-over parts from the Minotaur's victims. Not exactly what I would want to look at while cooling off in the frigidarium, but it did turn out beautifully. They were very pleased with it. I did another one for a Roman tomb at Soussa, near Carthage. The design of the paths was just like this one, but at the center of it was the dying minotaur. No Theseus this time. Just the dying minotaur at the center. Of course Theseus and the minotaur is an old story but this . . . This is new. I have never seen one in a church."

"I think I would rather meet 'Sancta Ecclesia' in the center than the Minotaur," Navigius quipped. The Master nodded and led him to the area of the church where they would be working.

It pleased Navigius to think that this work would be something that his mother would appreciate. She had never quite approved of his labors on pagan subjects, however beautiful, and she had little interest in his last project on a Bacchus mosaic. She would approve of this new twist in an old design.

* In Tunisia.

SAINT REPARATUS

One of the most remarkable facts connected with the early Christian religion is that neither its founder nor any of its immediate successors left any specific directions either as to the liturgical forms of worship to be observed by his followers nor laid down any rules to be observed in the government of the newly established church. . . . It appears to be in Africa . . .that fixed liturgies and rites first became an integral part of the Christian religion.

—James Fergusson
A History of Architecture in All Countries

IN THE FIRST ERA OF THE ROMAN EMPIRE, TEMPLE ARCHITECTURE was largely focused on its external perspective, featuring a common design of columns, without the addition of arches or vaults. This design wasn't suitable to the interior and more private acts of Christian worship. But as the Roman temples evolved into a more internal architecture that relied on arches and vaults rather than columns, it lent itself more readily to Christian needs and could accommodate a congregation. Of course there were no "congregations" until Constantine's Edict of Milan allowed Christians to openly practice their religion. The Basilica that evolved after Constantine, designed originally for use as a public building, became the perfect physical setting for a congregation of worshippers and that form for Christian churches has endured with little change to this day. Early Christians, as James Fergusson noted above, were basically a democratic group without governing bodies or a separation of laity and clergy. Before Constantine made Christianity the state religion, Christian communities were safer if they remained inconspicuous. As a distinction between laity and clergy began to develop, the physical structure was designed to reinforce it, separating the lay congregation from the sanctified clergy who would officiate for them as divine mediators. Quite literally, the Christian church was becoming a concrete thing. We know that at a Council convened in Carthage in 256, over 80 African bishops attended. By the time of Constantine's edict, church building began in earnest.

The Basilica of St. Reparatus was one of the first of its design, built on the right bank of the Chlef River in Algeria near the Roman garrison of Castellum Tingitanum in the fourth century AD. The basilica was completed around 328. It is the first Christian church known to have employed the figure of the labyrinth. Versions of the Cretan labyrinth, often with the minotaur at the center or Theseus in the act of slaying the minotaur, endured into Roman times, just as the story had continued to live on. As we have seen, it had morphed from the ingenious maze-like invention of Daedalus for the Minoan King, into the image of Troy and a ritual dance of victory and later in honor of fallen heroes. Here near the southern Mediterranean shore, it is as if the collective unconscious of humans was busy under the waters of convention reshaping the landscape of the human soul and its mythos. On the next page, the two Roman labyrinths mysteriously image the pivot from the pagan to the Christian world that was seeded in the time of Paul and is beginning to blossom during Monica's time; yet also how a two thousand year old legacy from Knossos survived its destruction and was steadily transformed within the human imagination.

I have imagined Navigius as a mosaic worker because in his era, this art had been raised to such a high level, especially in Tunisia and Algeria where literally thousands of mosaics were being created for townhouses, country estates and baths. Many of the finest workers came from his hometown of Tagaste. This was an art form born out of the Mediterranean region, which reached its height in the North African colonies of Rome. Over two dozen significant archaeological and historical sites can still be found in Tunisia alone. Carthage, Thuburbo Majus, Doura, Capsa, Dugga and Bulla Regia are only a few of the cities that were richly ornamented with this art. In El Jem, on the Eastern coast of Tunisia, the Solertiana House had its entire 12,000 square feet covered in exquisite mosaics. One of my favorite mosaics from this time, also in El Jem, is the figure of Oceanus whose full lips and large eyes gaze out of its small stones with an astonishly alive and intimate expression. Such mosaic work was so commonplace at the time that it was not thought of as an art form, but simply an architectural phase of the building process. Works were unsigned and the humble artists were unknown, yet many were capable of rendering in colored tesserae scenes that could have rivaled fine paintings of the Renaissance, a millennium later.

Aïcha Ben Abed, director of Monuments and Sites for the Institut National de Patromoine in Tunisia, participated in the early 1990s in the Getty Conservation Institute course on conservation and management of archaeological sites in Cyprus. Armed with this background, and in collaboration with the Getty Conservation Institute, she became the driving force of an effort in Tunisia to preserve mosaic sites in situ wherever possible through the training of technicians and the development of a program for the long-term care of the Tunisian sites. The Bardo National Museum in Tunis houses one of the finest collections in the world of Roman and Byzantine Mosaics. I especially recommend the book *Tunisian Mosaics: Treasures of Roman Africa* by Aïcha Ben Abed, which is filled with rich illustrations of these ancient works.

In the two labyrinths on the following page the path that lies between the lines is unicursal and leads, through many twists and turns, to the center. There are no dead ends, as there are in mazes.

FROM THE MINOTAUR TO SANTA ECLESIA:
OLD WORLD TO NEW IN MONICA'S TIME

3RD CENTURY AD ROMAN LABYRINTH ~ CONIMBRIGA, PORTUGAL

4TH CENTURY AD ROMAN LABYRINTH IN ST. REPARATUS CHURCH (ALGERIA)

Something important is happening there on the banks of the Chlef River, regularly shaken by the African-Eurasian continental rendezvous. In recent times, four major earthquakes occurred there within fifty years. The last one in 1980 destroyed a major part of the city and caused 2600 deaths. Yet here also the labyrinthine symbol which had endured for two thousand years as emblematic of the fight between hero and monster, was being transformed into something new. Who the designer was and what was in his mind, we will never know.

Ostia ~ 385 AD

MONICA IN OSTIA

MORNING. A ROSE MIST TO THE WEST where "home" had been. A gleaming river. Part of the city still in shadow. Sea birds fly up out of the dark spaces, flashing suddenly into light and color. The gulls' shrieks are one more voice in the Babel of languages that blankets the city with a thick, indecipherable tapestry of sound. A flotilla is heading languidly upriver to feed that voracious beast of empire: Rome. Vessels loaded, driven, ridden by Romans, Greeks, Nubians, Gauls, Arabs, Jews, Numidians, slaves and freemen. The new day is in full cry in Ostia as the sun climbs over the Eastern wall; Rome shedding its regal beneficence from the distant heights of the Aventine, the Palatine, the Capitoline hills.

Ostia is a city in its own right with its streets of shops, elegant public buildings, spacious homes with atriums and patios, its sixteen public baths. At its height, it was a city of fifty thousand people but it has declined with the movement of the empire's center to the north and to the east—Milan and Constantinople. But it is still the hand of Rome, sending and receiving goods and people from around the empire. The River Tiber is its arm, thrust southwestward from the heart of the city.

At the river's edge, dockworkers are carrying their heavy burdens of merchandise. The harbor is filled with ships from the coast of Asia Minor, Cyprus, Syria, Crete and Egypt. Grain to feed the Romans has arrived from North Africa in great quantities. There are ships bringing tin from Great Britain, silks from China and the Far East, cotton and spices from India, ivory and wild animals from Africa, fossilized amber gems from Germany. Greece and northern Italy provide the marble for the grand buildings. Gold and silver arrive here from Spain to mint the coins and fashion jewelry.

Small crafts are towing ships to their anchorages or out to sea to catch the wind for their westward sail. The city is alive with the industry of carpenters, sail-makers, rope-makers and the makers of pumps and sailing instruments. Official mensores are busy measuring the loads of grain, and beside them their clerk accountants enter the figures in their carefully kept records. In the harbor master's office, the tax officials collect the taxes for the city, the port fees and the custom fees. And then, of course, there are the sailors. Oarsmen and the nautae who man the anchors and sails. The officers and the general staff.

A panel of light moving along the wall and across the bed wakens Monica. She rises and dresses quickly, still feeling the fatigue of their desperate sea journey. She is a small woman in a big city, thinking about the son toward whom she is slowly making her way. She is a widow who has settled the affairs of her husband's estate in Tagaste and has set out with her son Navigius and her two nephews, Lastinus and Rusticanus. Augustinus's good friend Nebridius has also joined their party. Patricius in his last days fulfilled Monica's greatest wish for him by converting to Christianity on his deathbed, thereby joining her forever in an eternal life of the spirit. Years have passed. She feels oddly free now. A tourist in a new town.

She dresses quickly and joins the others for a quick breakfast of salted bread with cheese and some dried fruit and then they are out on the street, weaving themselves *into that tapestry of life and sound that is Ostia. They make their way through the noisy throng that surges in every direction. A short, angled alleyway takes them to the Forum of Corporations, which lies between the large theater and the warehouses lining the river. Here the offices of the empire's trading centers do business under shaded colonnades. Each office is identified by a black and white mosaic with the symbols and names of the place they represent. Libya, an elephant. Marseilles, a bridge. Sicily, a wild boar. Navigius points with pride to the logo from Carthage—a dolphin. It was work done by his own team of mosaic workers in Tagaste. While the others inquire about transportation into Rome, Monica slips into a small Christian church on the other side of the theater to give thanks for their safe arrival.*

It is late morning by the time the group makes its way through this human wall of industry to take in the sites on the main street of the city. The Decumanus Maximus runs along the south side of the amphitheater. Prosperous shops on the lower level face the well-paved street. Above them are balconies for each apartment, most adorned with flowers. There are public toilets, theatres, baths and four public libraries. A preview in miniature of what they will see in Rome.

At the west end of town, they arrive at the marina and just north of that, a wide beach which fronts on a neighborhood of garden apartments owned by the well-to-do citizens of the town. The sea that had so savagely attacked them only a day ago now wears its most benign and peaceful mien. They walk among mulberry, palm and umbrella trees. In the apartment gardens, the wisteria is in bloom and myrtle; violets and roses grow in profusion. Like vacationers on holiday, they stroll past cherry orchards and pear orchards. In places the air is sweet with the scent of lemon blossoms. Yesterday might well have been a dream.

After a light meal, Monica and her party head back up the Decumanus Maximus to join the stream of people passing through the giant stone arch that marks the entrance to the Via Ostia, which leads to Rome. Here they hire a carriage for the next leg of their journey. It is a pleasant afternoon ride past meadows and pastures. They make one stop at the site of a small church that was built by the Emperor Constantine over the grave of St. Paul. For a devout Christian like Monica, this is one of the holiest places in the world. It has just been rebuilt on a grander scale by the Emperor Theodosius and lies just over a mile outside of the city.

When Monica and her shipmates arrived safely in Ostia in 385, it was a thriving place which had been founded some seven hundred years before to protect Rome from attack by sea. Over time, it developed into Rome's major port, since that city lay several miles inland and was conveniently connected to Ostia by the Tiber River. In the early days of Rome, small vessels could come up the river and deliver their loads of grain and other commodities to the heart of the city at the foot of the Aventine. As the city grew, this was no longer possible. Both Caesar and Augustus laid plans for a man-made port at the mouth of the Tiber. The port of Ostia was finally opened under Nero. The colossal statue which was erected on a man-made island at the entrance of the harbor can still be seen on Nero's coins, commemorating the event. We are told by early writers that the island was built on the stone-filled skeleton of the gigantic ship that was used by the emperor Caligula to bring the Vatican Hill obelisk from Egypt. The existence of this ship was confirmed in the 1950s, when its remains were discovered during the building of the Rome airport. It was an enormous vessel, over three hundred feet (95 m) long and over sixty-five feet (21 m) wide, with planks four inches (10cm) thick, making it extremely heavy. Unlike the other grain carriers which traveled from Egypt and carried a thousand tons, it is estimated that this one could have carried sixteen hundred. The obelisk still stands in St. Peter's square. The port was moved slightly inland, farther up the river, after two hundred ships, lying exposed in the harbor, were destroyed by a single storm in 67 AD. By some accounts, this was the same year and roughly the same place where St. Paul met his death at the hands of the mad Roman emperor Nero.

Three centuries after Caligula, Monica and her family probably traveled in a much smaller, fifty to sixty-five foot ship (15 to 20 m) from Carthage. It was likely a ship propelled by oar and sail, with a gracefully curved stern post, higher in the water than the prow. We can still see such a ship depicted in a beautiful mosaic from the 3rd century in Althiburus, near Carthage.

Ostia must have been a welcome sight for the storm-tossed travelers. I have to think that her heart was high after those first days and that she headed into Rome filled with hope and expectation.

ROME
~NOW AND THEN

Rome ~ 2003

OLD FRIENDS IN NEW PLACES

THERE IS AN UPSIDE TO TURNING 60 THAT IS LITTLE NOTED. Actually there are two. The first is that something happens when one's horizon condenses into a clear terminus that slowly approaches. It is a cheerful deception of youth that life just goes on and on, vital, problematic, challenging and unmeasured. This contraction of the landscape after middle age can lead to an attentiveness to so many details of the journey, and an expansion of our dear old time-space experience. In our Earth Calendar, we contracted time along the earth's chronological axis. In human time, we can do the reverse: elongate moments through recognition of each of them in a new way. I remember an old man of ninety (I myself was quite young), moving his fingers tenderly across the fur of his old brown dog, Happy. "Look at the color of that!" he said. "And it's so soft. It's like gold." The poor old dog was blind by then and I looked hard with my young eyes to see what the old man was seeing, but I couldn't. Later on, I saw a dog of the same color that had just died and I understood. Where, between one moment and the next, had the golden color and the softness of that fur gone?

I began to realize that I was a guest on quite an unusual planet in the solar system. I would stay a bit and then yield my room to someone else. As an American, I was enjoying luxury accommodations, with everyone catering to my every whim and free to indulge in the best luxuries money can buy: freedom, time to contemplate and dream, access to all the places on the earth and to every story that goes went with them. Luxury accommodations, even as a poor writer living in an old camper. That is why I listen very carefully in the morning when I awaken to the song of a new bird. I grab a piece of paper and sketch out the melodic line and put it in my journal. Who else in the galaxy has this experience! I need to listen. I need to hear it. We are too busy and energetic in youth and even middle age to attend to these things. But someone should do it. In the quietude of age while the ears still work.

The second thing is that friendships aged by time have a priceless sweetness, beyond any description. Shared memory and experience that need no words, even after long periods of separation. I was having such an experience with my friend of forty years, Virginia Igonda, who had given me a graduation present of a trip to Italy to visit her in Orvieto. I was 59 and just graduated from the California Institute of Integral Studies with my Ph.D. I was happy as a kid, getting on the plane in San Francisco for the first leg of a trip I hadn't taken in 35 years.

Virginia is a decade older than I am but has twice the energy and bravado and twice the beauty. She should have been born in another century as a queen or at least a duchess. (Our friend Gene Eagles, with a flare for the dramatic, always addressed her as "Your Grace.") Her Grace had borrowed a car to meet me at the Leonardo da Vinci airport in Fiumicino, which is not far from the remains of that ancient city, Ostia. Only crazy people drive in Rome, I said. But there she was, looking elegant and unfazed. "I have the car right outside. I'll come round to pick you up."

We entered a maelstrom of traffic going in every direction, swarming around the perimeter of the city, which struck me as a hopeless tangle of highways and byways and low-ways. But we were full of stories and questions and gossip and the joy of reunion. The day was beautiful and Italy was about to open up before us. "My friend Kirk says we should take the Via Cassia. It's much more scenic." And we are scenic sorts of people, so we did. Or we tried to. It can be very elusive in that fine mesh of streets around the center of Rome, but finally we left the urban sprawl behind and the highway narrowed into a more peaceful road that ran first through level countryside and then began to curve into the forested hills.

We were in animated conversation, like any two old friends meeting. So much to tell. So much to hear. A road is a road is a road. I'd driven on 80 and 90 and 10 across the U.S. and you couldn't tell one state from another if one of the ubiquitous green signs didn't flash you a welcome or farewell as you sped by at 70 mph. This was no different, except that the signs were in Italian and the cars were smaller. Had I been reading a guidebook at that moment or looked across the highway to our left, I would have understood better what ancient path we were following. Off in the distance was Trigliatella, where those Trojan warriors performed an intricate horse dance on an ancient urn. Here and there, as we drove though the Valle de Baccano, I could have seen stretches of the pavement laid down by Hadrian in 127 BC. As modern Italians had laid down new pavement on an ancient path, Hadrian was essentially doing the same thing: modernizing the old Etruscan road.

We had to take breaks in conversation several times to sort ourselves out in the tangle and follow the right signs in the right direction as routes crossed one another. As it was, we must have gone round the city three or four times before we had a solid hold on the Via Cassia. Friendship is never the shortest distance between two points.

Just before Sutri, we stopped to eat at a lovely hotel-restaurant. After a leisurely Italian meal, we walked around the grounds and visited a small chapel on the property. The entrance to the hotel was a long straight cobblestone road, lined with deep green cypresses that seemed to hold the soul of Italy in their serene and graceful boughs. I took a picture of Virginia standing down by the entrance of the road. Centered at that perspective point between the row of cypresses, my friend became a painting, my lens a brush, the afternoon a canvas, and the moment eternal. A mist was falling, swelling up through the valley. When I look at that picture now, it is like all of the pictures, ancient and more recent, of the old Roman roads—the Via Appia, the Via Flaminia, the Via Aurelia, the Via Cassia. Underneath the jungle of signs and automobiles, the same roads lead outward from the old heart of empire, starting somewhere near the Milvian bridge where Constantine fought his decisive battle. You can call the Via Cassia S22 and the Via Flaminia, S2 but as Lao Tzu said "The way that can be named is not the eternal way." Via means way as, I reflected, does Tao.

When I saw the signs for the Sutri baths and Etruscan tombs, I became silent with wonder. *Etruscans!* We were in Etruria and we were following along the paths of a people who lived here some three thousand years ago. The Etruscans had done some modernizing of their own along this route around 600 BC, when they introduced the war chariot into Italy and needed to make sturdier roads for them to travel over. If they had known what they were starting, if they had seen the souped up horsepower chariots flying across the autostrada, they might have thought twice.

As we continued north, it began to rain. Harder and harder. Pretty soon the windshield wipers were not keeping up and I was seeing Umbria as if from the bottom of a river, in waves and splashes. I was trying to follow the map as Virginia said, "We should be getting on the autostrada around here." "Right," I said. "I'm watching." We were in one of those chaotic traffic patterns again and the Niagara Falls on our windshield wasn't helping. I gathered that the drivers here followed the same rule of the road I had observed in Mexico City drivers: he who hesitates is lost. When in doubt, *go faster.* Virginia, perhaps helped along by her Argentine roots, stayed with the program, but we were utterly stumped by the signage at the critical moment of entrance to the autostrada. A gigantic sign with gigantic arrows rippled through the wave of water directly ahead and above us. The letters in the middle said ORTA and I remember also TERNI and NARNI, but the arrows pointed straight up and straight down. What kind of a choice is that? Were we suddenly entering a new dimension? Neither one of us had a clue what it meant and by now we had missed the autostrada.

I said before that the signs were the same and only the language changed, but I was wrong. These signs were made by people with a different world view, and it wasn't because they rolled their "R"s. Virginia used her naturally good sense of direction and I, the map-reading skills I had developed to make up for my lack of that sense, but the signage continued to be elusive and distorted by waves of water. To this day, I can't figure out where we went, except that we kept seeing the signs for Terni and Narni and, worse still, no matter what alternatives we tried, we kept ending up at that same Dantesque sign with the up and down arrows and whatever we chose, it seemed to take us downward into a deeper circle of hell. But Virginia sped right along and we didn't hesitate in our making of wrong decisions, so we at least avoided going Up to heaven the fast way.

Darkness fell on our already darkened confusion and the only certain thing was the rain. We stopped when we reached a town to ask for directions in a gas station. Of course the first question was "Where are we?" and the answer was "Todi." Virginia looked alarmed. "How do we get to Orvieto?" "You have to take the autostrada." "How do we get to the autostrada?" "You have to go to Orta." "But we just *came* from Orta" (several times). "You have to go back."

At one point, when we were actually on the autostrada for a spell, we saw a white serpentine glow in the opposite lanes as far as the eye could see. Traffic was at a dead standstill over there. "Well at least we miss *that*," I declared. I tried to reassure us with the thought that it could be worse. It worked. Until we reached Orta for the umpteenth time and finally got the autostrada going in the right direction. Except that it wasn't *going* at all and the white serpent had just turned into a red one. We hadn't missed anything.

Friendship may not be the shortest distance between two points but it eases the passage between *any* points. Near or far. Or in this case, stock still between heaven and earth at Orta, slowly inching north. We just sat back, gazed at the watery line of brake lights and resumed our conversation. We had done something like this before, returning to San Diego from Tijuana with a hand-painted harp, which Virginia had commissioned from the Rosenthal's *Taller de Muebles Finos Artesanales* in Erongaricuaro, a village on Lake Patzcuaro in central Mexico. Receiving word that delivery had been made to Tijuana as agreed, Virginia and I had made a pleasant day out of crossing the border for lunch and shopping. When we returned to the border crossing, we found ourselves in a long line of cars, like this one, going nowhere.

Vendors of the most unlikely items strolled among the captive vehicles. Gaudy polyester blankets on a sweltering day. Tiny violins that played at a thin screech as the vendors nodded in at the windows. It was too hot to keep them closed. *No gracias. No gracias. No gracias.* "Who on earth would buy this stuff?" we asked each other. The hours droned on. Bad day at the border. "You know," Virginia said, "my mother could really use a new blanket." In came the blanket. I can't, for the life of me, remember who needed a screechy little violin, but in came the violin. By the time we reached the border, the back seat was full of useless goods. I think it was a conspiracy.

To Virginia's relief, the rain had stopped as we approached her hill town over a nearby ridge and she paused with pure Etruscan pride to point out her home. Against the clear, dark night the lights shone on the ancient town and even from here the clear line of the *duomo* was illuminated. Orvieto.

ARMS AND MEN

Arms, and the man I sing, who, forc'd by fate,
And haughty Juno's unrelenting hate,
Expell'd and exil'd, left the Trojan shore.
Long labors, both by sea and land, he bore,
And in the doubtful war, before he won
The Latian realm, and built the destin'd town;
His banish'd gods restor'd to rites divine,
And settled sure succession in his line,
From whence the race of Alban fathers come,
And the long glories of majestic Rome.

THIS IS HOW AENEAS'S STORY BEGINS. This is how a story lives. How it shapes the character of a city, a people, a civilization to come, for thousands of years. When you see a plant that has died away of a winter come poking back through the concrete in the spring, or the nubs of buds pressing through snow-laden branches of trees, you realize the stubborn, sturdy strength of life to persist. And so it is with a story told down through generations of a single family or an entire people. Especially if you have a story-teller with the gift of a Homer, a Virgil. These opening lines of the Aeneid summarize the fate of Aeneas that the rest of the work will unfold in lyric detail.

I remember reading this work in Latin 3, in high school. Latin was a real chore and I took it only to please my father. "If you know Latin, you can figure out the meaning of any word. Understand scientific terms. I took two years of Latin and then I stabbed Virgil." A terrible phrase, that. It was an academic expression for skipping ahead or something. Something he was proud of and gave him a soft spot for the old poet, as can happen through the tricks of adolescence and a good teacher. I also had a good teacher, Mrs. Spicer, and I think I may have stabbed Virgil too (it's a wonder how he lived on through all this) because I was able to skip Cicero (Latin 3) and go on to Virgil (Latin 4). A matter of scheduling not aptitude. I had struggled on through Latin 1 for his sake and then felt that I had done my filial duty. But in his gentle way, he was insistent. "If you've got a start on Latin 1, you really have to go on to Latin 2 or it's wasted." Latin 2 was more miserable than Latin 1, in spite of the wonderful Mrs. Spicer. It seemed to me that I was only developing the ability to read tombstones. "Ah," said my father at the end of that struggle, "now you can read Virgil. You mustn't miss Virgil if you've done all that work." So I did. With a sigh and a heavy heart.

Arma virumque cano, Troiae qui primus ab oris.
Italiam, fato profugus, Laviniaque venit . . .

Mrs. Spicer made us memorize this. I'm glad she did. Glad I still have it almost fifty years later on a cold winter morning. I understood then that it was singing. A grave, martial waltz in ¾ time. The sound that makes stories last and keeps them intact the way the national anthem, or Yankee Doodle, or Rockabye Baby—or so many beautiful hymns—persist like the life force in the tree. I was still trudging forward with My Latin Homework—all it was to me then—and I can't recall at what point things changed and Aeneas suddenly appeared to me through all those conjugations and declensions; the *Aeneid* alive in its beauty, having traveled westward through time and space with the slow preciseness of the continental drift.

Aeneas leaves behind a once-great city and the comforts and treasures of a civilized life. His father was a cousin to the Trojan king Priam, and Aeneas himself was Hector's principal lieutenant. Troy was a wealthy city that had gathered riches from trade with the east and the west. It was known especially for its massive city walls, behind which its citizens had once felt safe. We have already seen an allusion to these walls when a shepherd, two millennia later, carves a labyrinthine shape in Welsh turf and calls it Caerdroia or "Troy Town."

Priam's people spent ten years under siege behind those walls, until the crafty Odysseus (Ulysses) conceived of the gift of a massive horse to be rolled in through the gates, secretly carrying the army of Achaians who would destroy the city, desecrate the temples, and bring an end to the Trojan civilization forever.

This departure of Aeneas, with his father Anchises and his son Ascanius, is not something he would ever have chosen to do: Setting sail on dangerous seas in uncharted territory. Yet we see it every night on the news. Refugees leaving their homes behind because of the Iraq war, the Sudanese fleeing Darfur, Indonesians fleeing the destruction of tidal waves, Lebanese fleeing internal wars, the thousands who fled New Orleans after the hurricane. The people who leave, not because they want to, but because they must.

The story of Schliemann's discovery of ancient Troy, described earlier, will also be subject to revision over time. It was actually his assistant William Dörpfeld who uncovered the walls. A 1999 book by Susan Heuck Allen, *Finding the Walls of Troy: Frank Calvert and Heinrich Schliemann at Hisarlik*, asserts that the original idea of Troy's location (in present-day Hisarlik) actually came from a man named Frank Calvert, who was once an American consul. Calvert owned the property and in this account persuaded Schliemann to carry on a dig there. If nothing else, Schliemann's persistence and very public persona brought Troy back to life in the modern imagination. He and his beautiful wife Sophia (beautiful wives are always a plus) became the subjects of Irving Stone's bestselling book *The Greek Treasure*.

No new discovery wipes out the past or eternally fixes the present. Our modern certainties will themselves grow old and likely be looked on in later centuries with wry tolerance or outright scorn. "Poor benighted sods, if they only *knew* . . ." And who knows, in a few millennia, if we can keep ourselves going that long, America might be looked upon as a distant, mythical Camelot and George Washington, no more than a legendary hero invented by a storyteller.

For now, we know that there was a Troy, as we have also found Abraham's Ur and the Minoan's Knossos. Scientists are piecing together fascinating evidence of a great flood which lifted the level of the Mediterranean and sent it rushing through the Dardanelles into the Black Sea, dramatically rearranging the landscape and flinging the people along its shores into new homelands to start new lines, new histories, long before Aeneas and Odysseus set sail from that same region.*

Alas, epics are not composed and sung about peaceful times when everyone is well-fed, satisfied, following their bliss or watching the Super Bowl. They arise out of the terrible moments of tumult and destruction when the world, as it is known, is breaking apart and the people are on the edge of extinction. They are written in the winters of our discontent. *The Iliad*, the *Aeneid*, the *Mahabharata* and within that, the *Bhagavad-Gita*, where two great families, cousins to one another, face each other across "the Kuru field of justice" before an great battle.

The *Aeneid* takes place between the departure of the last surviving Trojans from their homeland near the Dardenelles and the Black Sea, to their arrival—after many adventures—in Italy to begin their new line. Aeneas is received there by Latinus, King of Latium, who is told in a prophecy that his daughter Lavinia would be betrothed to one from another land. Although she had been betrothed to Turnus, King of the Rutulians, Latinus decides to heed the prophecy and wed her to Aeneas. This was still a wild country, inhabited by different tribes and the great city we know as Rome was far off. But if any of the story is to be believed, Latinus made a clever choice, although it led to war with the Rutuli and the defeat of the spurned Turnus.

Aeneas founds a city that he names after his wife: Lavinium, now Lavinio, near Anzio. It is strange to think of the blood shed here as recently as World War II, when 110,000 Allied troops stormed the beachhead in an attempt to break through the enemy line and march on Rome. So much time, so little change. The exact site of Lavinium is said to be Practica di Mare.

The second President Bush, seeking to reinvigorate the NATO-Russia relationship, sent Secretary of State Colin Powell to a meeting in Practica di Mare to support the creation of a NATO-Russia Council in Practica Di Mare, Italy, in 2002.

This is from Colin Powell's speech there, published by the center for arms control and nonproliferation:

May 28, 2002

SECRETARY POWELL: Well, good afternoon, ladies and gentlemen. President Bush is this afternoon finishing up what we believe has been a most successful and historic trip to Europe. In Berlin and Moscow and Paris, and now here in Rome, we have made common cause against the grave threats to our liberty, to the safety of our people, and to civilization itself.

In his meetings, the President consulted with Chancellor Schroeder, Presidents Putin and Chirac and Prime Minister Berlusconi on our mutual security agenda.

. . .

---

* An excellent book on this subject is *Noah's Flood: New Scientific Discoveries About the Event That Changed History* by William Ryan and Walter Pitman.

> We agreed that . . . we must continue to expand and deepen security relationships among the members of the community of free nations. . . .
>
> In Moscow, Presidents Bush and Putin signed the most dramatic nuclear arms reduction agreement in decades.

Intentional or not, on the very place where Aeneas sets up his household gods in Latium, leaders of the modern world are convening to discuss the age-old issue of arms and men, of peace and war.

Following the lead of his father Aeneas, Ascanius, now called Julius, founds another city in the Alban Hills called Alba Longa (southeast of Rome today). From Alba Longa's royal line come the orphaned twins raised by a she-wolf, Romulus and Remus. The historian Livy (a contemporary of Virgil) gives us a list of kings from Aeneas to Romulus, and here we see names that will later be engraved on the Roman geographic and political landscape: Aventius (the Aventine hill), Tiberias, Agrippa. If the first to bear these names were mythical, the latter were very real indeed; emperors of the superpower that Rome would become.

The legend of Rome's founding begins with the twins' grandfather Numitor, king of the ancient Italian city of Alba Longa, who was deposed by his brother Amulius. Numitor's daughter, Rhea Silvia, was made a Vestal Virgin by Amulius. This means that she was made a priestess of Vesta, the goddess of the hearth, and forbidden to marry. Nevertheless, Mars, god of war, fell in love with her and she gave birth to twin sons. There is an archetypal theme to this story that we find across many cultures*: Amulius, fearing that the boys would grow up to overthrow him, had them placed in a trough and thrown into the River Tiber. At that time the river was in flood, and when the waters fell, the trough with the two boys was washed ashore, where their basket was caught on a fig tree in a marsh that was later known as the Velabrum. They were found by a she-wolf who, instead of killing them, looked after them and fed them with her milk. A woodpecker also brought them food, for the woodpecker, like the wolf, was sacred to Mars.

Later, the story goes, the twins were discovered by one of the king's shepherds. He took them home to his wife and the two adopted them, calling them Romulus and Remus. They grew up as bold and strong young men, leading a warlike band of shepherds. One day Remus was captured and brought before Numitor for punishment. Numitor, noticing how unlike a shepherd's son he was, questioned him and before long realized who he was. Romulus and Remus then rose against Amulius, killed him and restored the kingdom to their grandfather.

Romulus and Remus chose the place where the she-wolf had nursed them to found their own town. Romulus began to build walls on the Palatine Hill, but Remus scoffed at them for being so low. He leaped over them to demonstrate this, and Romulus in his anger killed him.

Romulus is not a very likeable fellow and like the first family in the Garden of Eden, his race is founded on a fratricide and ignominy. The killing of his brother

* Note, for example, the similarities to Moses and King Arthur.

is followed by his continued building of the new city, naming it Roma after his own name. Its first citizens were outlaws and fugitives, to whom Romulus gave the settlement on the Capitoline Hill. Unfortunately, there were not enough wives for all these men, so Romulus decided to steal women from the Sabines, an Italian tribe. To this end, he proclaimed a festival and invited many Sabines to it. While the attention of the men was elsewhere, Romulus's men rushed in and carried off the women. This was the famous "Rape (carrying off) of the Sabine women," which later became a favored subject for painters from Renaissance artists to Pablo Picasso.

The Sabine men where furious and led by their king, made war on Romulus. When the fighting had reached its peak, the Sabine women, who had grown fond of their Roman husbands, rushed between the ranks and begged both sides to make peace. So the battle was stopped. Romulus and the Sabine king, Titus Tatius, ruled together over the two peoples until Tatius was killed in battle.

For the rest of his life, Romulus ruled alone, proving himself a great leader in peace and war. He did not die but disappeared one day in a violent storm. The Romans, believing he had been taken up to heaven, worshipped him under the name of Quirinus.

NUMA

It is impossible to determine what elements of the legend of Rome's founding, if any, are true. It may be a copy of a Greek tale, invented to explain the name of Rome and certain customs. For instance, Roman brides were taken from their families on their wedding days with pretence of force, a custom which may originate with the story of the Sabine women.

We do know that the ancient Sabines were in Latium before Rome was founded, concentrated in a territory northeast of the city. Latium spread across present-day Lazio, Umbria and Abruzzo. Fact or fiction, the bloodlines of the Romans and the Sabines were joined in those early days. Livy tells us that the second king of Rome was a Sabine, Numa Pompilius. There are many things I like about Numa, probably in direct proportion to the things I dislike about the brutal and unscrupulous Romulus. Numa is said to have been born on the day Rome was founded—the youngest of the four sons of Pompilius. He lived a severe life of ascetic discipline, shunning all luxury. The story of the Sabine women, in Livy's account, would have taken place in his father's time: a fresh and terrible memory that an ascetic life might seek to atone for. Tatius, a colleague of Romulus, married his only daughter to Numa. She died after 13 years and Numa retired to a country life. There, the story goes, he met the nymph Egeria by a spring in her sacred grove. It is she, we are told, who taught him to be a wise legislator.

Numa was around forty when he was offered the kingship. He was residing at a famous city of the Sabines called Cures and he refused the offer. His father, however, persuaded him to accept.

Over time, Numa was celebrated for his wisdom and piety. The story recounts that the god Jupiter had favored Numa by causing a shield to fall from the sky onto the Palatine Hill with letters of prophecy written on it about the destiny of Rome. Numa had eleven matching shields made, the *ancilia*, the sacred shields of Jupiter, which were carried each year in a procession by the priests of Mars.

Numa is traditionally credited with a calendar reform that adjusted the solar and lunar years. He established the traditional occupational guilds of Rome. In the historian Plutarch's words—

> "So, distinguishing the whole people by the several arts and trades, he formed the companies of musicians, goldsmiths, carpenters, dyers, shoemakers, skinners, braziers, and potters; and all other handicraftsmen he composed and reduced into a single company, appointing every one their proper courts, councils, and religious observances."

Plutarch is our major source of information for this early period. He was a Greek historian and biographer born in 46 AD who later became a Roman citizen. He saw in Numa the influence of the Lacedaemonians, which was the ancient Greek name applied by Homer and others to Sparta. Plutarch noted that "Numa was descended of the Sabines, who declare themselves to be a colony of the Lacedaemonians." You may recall Menelaus from the *Odyssey*—the Greek king whose ship is stranded off Alexandria until they receive aid from Proteus. Menelaus was King of Sparta and the husband of Helen; she "whose face launched a thousand ships" and ignited the Trojan War.

Plutarch offers another interesting and surprising detail about Numa. He says that the early religion of the Romans was "imageless and spiritual." Their religious lawgiver, Numa, he says, "forbade the Romans to represent the deity in the form either of man or of beast. Nor was there among them formerly any image or statue of the Divine Being; during the first one hundred and seventy years they built temples, indeed, and other sacred domes, but placed in them no figure of any kind; persuaded that it is impious to represent things Divine by what is perishable, and that we can have no conception of God but by the understanding." This is certainly in sharp contrast to the monumental temples and statuary built to the gods by later Romans. It is Numa, according to legend, who established the sisterhood of the Vestal Virgins and built the most sacred temple in Rome, the round temple of Vesta, which protected the sacred fire—the "hearth fire"—of the city. Numa's prohibition against images notwithstanding, this temple would hold the wooden statue of Pallas Athena, said to have been brought from Troy to Italy by Aeneas. The temple became known as the Palladium.

Numa Pompilius died a natural death (fairly uncommon for the later Roman rulers) in 673 BC when he was over eighty.

While Numa and Aeneas are still considered figures of legend, and the founding of Rome occurred some six hundred years after the purported dates of the Trojan War, what becomes significant is the way in which later people take in the stories for their own (which was certainly the deliberate intention of Augustus when he commissioned Virgil's work) and shape a distinct culture out of them. In this respect, they become powerfully "true" in a manner beyond their historical legitimacy. The work of historians may be to prove whether Moses existed or the events of Mohammad's life are factual, but nothing can erase the profound and enduring impact they have on millions of people as the bedrock of their lives.

Rome ~ 385 AD

ARRIVAL IN ROME

MONICA AND HER COMPANIONS ARRIVE IN ROME at the foot of the Aventine Hill and proceed from there, through the busy cattle market, to the home of friends in the African neighborhood in the Velabrum. The swampy area where the she-wolf's twins had washed ashore has been filled in after the great fire in the time of Nero that destroyed most of the city. Her son, Augustinus Aurelius, had also stayed in the Velabrum, but with Manichaean friends whom Monica would at all costs avoid. The Velabrum is home to immigrants from Africa and the Levant. The apartment building where they are staying is filled with people from Carthage, Leptis Major and Alexandria, as well as from the smaller towns, like her own Tagaste. Their apartment currently houses three families of immigrants from that town. Conditions are crowded but no one seems to mind. Like Monica, the women especially are happiest when surrounded by friends and family and lively activity. In the larger houses live merchants who have thrived on the trade between Carthage and Rome. They meet a family of Berbers from the Aures Mountains who run caravans to the south, across the desert to Bilma. She listens eagerly to their stories, learning of distant places she has never seen which lie beyond the mountains.

The following morning, joined by Augustinus's good friend and countryman Alypius, they set off with their friends Lucius and Tita, Tita's brother Marcus, and his wife Flavia to explore the city. The young men have more enthusiasm for this than she has. The city oppresses her with its monstrously large buildings, many of which rise so high that they shut out the light. Several are temples to pagan gods and many to the vanity of emperors. They walk east along the Via Nova and then turn left, passing through the Arch of Titus to the Via Sacra. Beyond that stands the huge Basilica of Constantine, which houses the Hall of Justice with a council chamber and meeting hall.

Lucius works for the water authority and provides a running commentary on the city's water system. Marcus works for one of the city's main architects and her son Navigius, whose life is also closely involved with building projects, plies him with questions. The women carry on a conversation of their own on their favorite shops and markets. Monica is not much interested in either conversation, so keeps half an ear on both. They walk first along side the Cloaca Maxima, one of the principal water channels in the city's system of aqueducts. She is impressed when Lucius says that the amount of water distributed through the city each day is nearly a million cubic meters. Arches up to a hundred feet high direct the water through aqueducts, in some places siphoning it directly into the city's palaces. There are fountains on almost every corner. Some of them are very elaborate. Lucius guides them next into the massive coliseum built by Vespasian. Land that had formerly been for the exclusive use of the mad and decadent emperor Nero is now a huge amphitheater, one hundred and sixty feet tall, created for the use of the people. Lucius considers this a highly commendable gesture on the emperor's part.

"Consider where the funds for this came from," Marcus argues. "This was built from relics of the Jewish temple after Vespasian had sacked Jerusalem. Twelve thousand Jewish captives were brought back to build this." Lucius ignores him, to point out what he considers to be the greatest wonders of all. Reserved seating, tickets with numbers. A retractable roof. An awning of colored canvases that can be unfurled to shade spectators on hot days. Five thousand animals were slaughtered in a single day during its opening ceremonies. Men were killed by animals. Prisoners were executed and gladiatorial events offered up their victors and victims.

"I wish I had been here when we had live naval events in the arena. Battleships on water. Can you imagine it? Just look at this! This is one of our main projects. You can see some of the channels here for water, which was diverted from one of the aqueducts to flood the arena. They used water channels below that were left from Nero's artificial lake. Then there are drain pipes to drain the arena into the sewers that empty into the Tiber River."

"Why did they stop?" Nebridius asks.

"They came up with a new form of theater. They constructed the hypogeum under the amphitheater where the water system had been. The water channels were replaced by a system of elevators and trap doors that let gladiators and wild animals pop up into the arena to kill their victims. They constructed lion runs and cages for the criminals." Monica felt sick. She stepped away from them, pretending to look at some rare flowers growing at the base of a small fountain. No doubt she was thinking of Perpetua and Felicity and other fellow Christians who had fallen victim to this practice to provide "theater" to the spectators.

Lucius leads the way through the Forum of Trajan to the Trajan Market. This vast shopping complex was built into the side of the Quirinale hills, with steep staircases rising up six levels. Hundreds of people are moving through the system of corridors on the first and second levels. The three upper levels contain the Great Hall, a large, central empty space covered with large cross-vaults and windows to let in the light. They walk along the Via Biberatica among the various market areas that form the modern urban area of Rome. The ground floor is paved in geometric black and white mosaic and the walls are adorned with frescos.

Lucius is a great admirer of Trajan and insists that thanks to him, a city that was crumbling after the destructions of Nero and general neglect, has been repaired and brought back to its former glory by Trajan. Marcus concedes only that Trajan built Trajan's forum.

"But think again of how Trajan found the money for this! He launched a military campaign to conquer Dacia, then plundered hundreds of tons of gold and silver from his new province." Yet even Marcus has to admit that the overcrowded downtown district of the forum was relieved by his building of a new forum. The city's population was one million and growing. Trajan had used the talents of Rome's architects and builders, especially the Greek architect from Damascus, Apollidoris. The only way to expand was to carve out a flat space, using tens of thousands of slaves to level the stone hillside for the creation of new prime real estate. The forum here is a magnificent marble complex that includes Greek and Latin libraries, colossal statues and a large plaza, along with a two-story basilica where laws are made and cases tried; the largest type ever built in Rome. In the center of it is the monumental statue of Trajan. It is a carved column one hundred twenty-five feet tall whose façade depicts the victories of Trajan in his war with Dacia. The forum is a six hundred thousand square foot city of marble appended to the ancient city of Rome. Lucius explains to Navigius that Trajan's market was built to shore up the face of the hill that had been cut away, hence its concave shape.

They enter the vast Roman shopping mall as Lucius continues to reel off numbers to impress them. "There are over one hundred fifty store fronts selling goods that range from footwear to fine art. You can buy things from all over the world here. This is a main street for the masses!" Monica had to admit that these masses looked well-heeled and happy.

And then, of course, there were the baths. "Oh you MUST see the Caracalla Baths," Tita trills in her high voice, her Latin still strongly laced with the African accent. Lucius agrees, promising Navigius that he will appreciate the engineering feats and sheer size of the building complex. Monica is growing tired of engineering feats and sheer size but the young men are as eager as any tourists to take it all in. "The main bath house is seven hundred fifty-feet in height with an equal length." From his head full of facts (a storehouse of useless information Monica is thinking), Lucius tells them that the whole complex covers thirty-three acres and can accommodate sixteen hundred bathers. "This is a leisure center available for free to all of the city's citizens! The busiest time is around 3 in the afternoon when people get out of work and head to the baths to unwind and relax. We can be out by then."

Monica shudders at the thought of more monstrous piles of stone but she remains silent and outnumbered. The baths are open to women in the morning hours and to men in the afternoon so they arrive in the late morning. Alypius is eager to spend time in the library. There are two libraries, located in the East and West sides of the bath complex. Each is divided into two rooms. One houses texts in Greek and the other contains the Latin works. The other young men follow Lucius through the two palaestra where wrestling and sparring matches have drawn a large crowd and young athletes are working out. Once again they are surrounded by portico shops selling everything under the sun as well as sheltered gardens and promenades, gymnasiums, rooms for massage, galleries and museums. Works of fine art and sculpture are everywhere.

The women go directly to the changing rooms near the center of the bath area and then to the tepidarium, a huge vaulted and mildly heated hall. From here they move on to the steaming hot pools, for as long as they can tolerate the heat and then they cool off in the refreshing cold pools of the frigidarium. Tita insists that they also have a massage so they pass into the room of the masseuses. Fully relaxed by their massages, they continue on to the north end of the complex to a huge pool beneath an open sky with large bronze mirrors which are mounted on the walls and positioned to direct sunlight toward the pool.

As noon approaches, the women return to the changing rooms and the men take their turn at the baths. Monica, Tita and Flavia walk through the gardens and visit the portico shops, with their displays of exotic foods, medicines for every possible ailment, and elegant clothing with prices to match. Throughout the plaza, Monica observes groups of men who are in animated conversations. Some conversations she overhears are on writers and philosophers or politicians. Others are on business and trade. Was her son Augustinus once among these men, participating in their discussions? She was sure he would have been.

As always, it is the sheltered gardens that please her more than the elaborate baths, colossal structures or even the shops. When the men return, the group dines in a restaurant nearby, following the custom of the Romans. Then sated and relaxed, they stroll slowly back with the tide of people returning to their homes on the Aventine or Capitoline or, like themselves, in the Velabrum. Lucius declares that they have saved the best for last: the oldest and most famous part of the Imperial City, the Forum. The court and offices in the basilica of Constantine are emptying out and their officials and office workers join the throngs of Romans seeking their pleasures or their homes. To the left, they pass the Temple of the Vestal Virgins and Monica finds herself wondering about the lives of the women who live there. Without conscious intention, the group pauses by the small round Temple of Vesta and for once even Lucius falls silent. It is the smallest structure in the forum and Lucius has no great pronouncements to make on its architecture. If they know that they are standing beside the original hearth and heart of Rome, no one speaks of it. They move on then into the spacious plaza flanked by the imposing facades of the Basilica Emilia and the Basilica Julia. Domitian rides atop his tall horse in bronze splendor. It is easy to forget in the midst of such impressive architecture that the forum had originally been created as a gathering place for public assemblies, orations, political and judicial activities, and games. The buildings were only meant to shelter these activities in hot or rainy weather and represented the democratic impulse of the original republic. Now they are the seats of imperial power and a magnet for tourists.

When the group reaches the massive marble arch of Septimius Severus, which is in fact three arches, Nebridius, Navigius and his cousins leap up the staircase, nimble as goats, to see the statue of the emperor and his two sons—Caracalla and Geta—and to take in the view. To many people in this city and to visitors from distant parts of the empire like Navigius and her nephews, it is a most admirable mass of marble with an excellent view. But to a devout Numidian Christian like Monica, the memories of the living emperor are still a fresh wound. He was one of their own, with Berber blood as well as Punic, from the city of Leptis Major on the African coast. Yet he had persecuted the Christians in their region like Perpetua and Felicity. The bright day in Rome has suddenly grown dim and she begins to wonder what this city might have done to her son. The sight casts a pall over Monica. She *wanders away toward the far side of the rostra, seeking a quieter corner. They have already lost Alypius to another library. This one is in front of the Temple of Concord, just at the entrance of the forum.*

Monica suddenly finds herself alone for a moment. While the others join the sight-seers for the view from the top of the Arch of Severus, she finds a little bench to sit on near the small grove in front of the House of the Vestal Virgins. This is a large compound, hidden from the view of the public. Its six priestesses live there in seclusion. Monica feels curious about them. She knows that the young women are chosen from the best families by the Pontifex Maximus before they reach puberty, to live in celibacy here for thirty years: Ten as students, ten in service and ten as teachers. After this they can marry and have a family, but few—she has been told— choose to leave their luxurious surroundings to submit themselves to be ruled by men under the strict restrictions against women by Roman law. If they do, however, they are highly honored.

Before her once again is the Temple of Vesta—such a small, round modest building in comparison to the others in and around the forum. Here in the heart of the ancient city its eternal flame is still being kept alive. Here the Pontifex Maximus, the high priest, has had his office since the time of Numa Pompilius, the first Pontifex Maximus who had officially established the Vestal Virgins as the guardian of its flame. Within resides the wooden statue of Pallas, the Palladium that Aeneas was believed to have brought with him from Troy. Monica cannot know that the eternal flame that has burned here for a millennium will soon be extinguished forever.*

As she looks back toward the Arch of Severus, she can see that the sun is falling quickly over the rim of the Capitoline Hill, shedding its last light on the tall columns of the Basilica Julia and the Curia. The bronze horseman is lit up in its flare. Domitian about to arrive or leave, who can tell? It is said that he rode a white horse with the Flavian family for the triumphal procession of his brother Titus, arriving from Judea after his destruction of Jerusalem. He might have been any horseman from any of the triumphal processions from any part of the ever-expanding empire. They always ended here, at the foot of the Capitol, with offerings to Juno and the masses of Romans gathered to cheer them on. They have been coming and going and coming for four hundred years, from ever farther and farther away. As she watches, the sun slips down behind the hill and the darkness slowly swallows up first horse and horseman and then begins to climb the great marble pillars and columns of the city.

Monica rises and moves to stand near the Arch of Augustus, watching for the others to come across the plaza. She has already seen Alypius descending the steps of the library and he is coming toward her from the other direction. For a moment, she pauses in the gateway between the old city and the new and is seized by an acute feeling that this is a portal in her own life between her past and her future. Behind her is the hearth she had cared for for a lifetime, like the young women in the building beside her. And ahead? The unknown. And her son.

---

* It was extinguished in 394, less than ten years later, by the Emperor Theodosius.

WOMEN AT THE TURNING POINT

THE 300S—BC OR AD—MEAN VERY LITTLE TO US as we rush about the Real, stopping at the 7-11 to fill the tank and buy milk. The Real, of course, is Us and only Us. Now. Stabbing little tattoos on a cell phone to check up on myriad things that were never checked up on in the nineteen hundreds let alone the three hundreds. The fourth century is a diarama of frozen figures, a chapter in a book, ashes of the past. It is we who stand alive at the cutting edge. History has risen to consummate itself in our loins and realize itself in our thoughts. The old questions are settled by our new discoveries. How on earth did the Earth get along before us?

But there it is! Just squint a bit and you can see it. Stand still a few moments and listen. They are as alive as you and they believe, even more than you do, that they've conquered the world and brought humankind to an apogee.

Listen! Can you hear the rush of water beneath the city? Can you feel the pulse of industry as stone columns are lifted into place? Arches, majestic stonework, all underground and constructed with the sole purpose of guiding waters from the Nile into the desert to fill a network of hundreds, perhaps thousands, of underground chambers. You can stand in one of those cisterns today, cleared by archaeologists, and believe you were standing in the King's chamber. On the street above you rise the drab dilapidated neighborhoods of crumbling brick houses of a poor, underdeveloped twentieth century Alexandria. The economy only began to revive in the nineteen nineties when new office and apartment buildings went up. But none will match the engineering feats of the original construction and reconstruction of the city.

Give the chronoscope a slight twist and squint a bit harder. Do you see a slim young man pacing out the hot empty desert pavement on an April day? You can see his broad gestures sketching out a city in the dry air. His generals nod. His engineers take note. Ten miles of walls will be needed to frame a grid of streets, the main avenues as wide as a hundred feet. "We will dig a canal to the Nile to bring in fresh water. Boats with grain, fruit, stone and skilled stoneworkers. Temples, baths, libraries." The young man pauses, gazing at the desert mirage of the city that will be his monument in this desert place he's found in North Africa on the way to visit an oracle. It is April, 331 BC. Eight years later Alexander, still a young man of 33, will die in the ever fateful city of Babylon, in the land where civilization is to said to have been born and where hundreds now die from roadside bombs and other forms of destruction that we humans have perfected.

Alexander's immense empire, from Greece to the Indus valley, is divided among his three generals. The canny Ptolemy, granted Egypt, schemes to steal Alexander's body and remove it to Alexandria, where he will build a lavish tomb that will draw tourists from far and wide to his new metropolis. It is under Ptolemy, as the next pharaoh, that the city reaches its splendor and the great engineering feats are first performed. A forty story lighthouse, the Pharos, will rise in the harbor and stand as one of the seven wonders of the world for seventeen centuries. Imagine!

Ptolemy is a clever fellow. No doubt about it. He fulfills Alexander's dream of wedding the civilization of Greece with that of Egypt, an ancient culture long respected by the likes of Plato and Socrates, not to mention his own mentor Aristotle. The seeds of their thought will blossom in those empty desert sands, once Ptolemy has set about his work. Now you're watching the city rise as Aeneas watched the building of Dido's Carthage. Ptolemy carries from Greece a love of learning and intellectual thought, grafted onto the vibrant life and artistry of the pharaohs. As hordes of Egyptian slaves had built the pyramids, they now raise temples, colonnades, public baths and a massive gymnasium. Theaters, villas and warehouses. The difference may be that some of these are now available for their own use, unlike the pyramids and palaces reserved solely for the royal family.

Ptolemy founds the Mouseion, a research institute with lecture halls, laboratories, an astronomical center and quarters for visiting scholars, mathematicians, philosophers, poets and musicians. Archimedes and Euclid will lecture, study and write here. Underneath its roof, Eratosthenes—a mathematician, poet, geographer, musician and first head librarian of the Mouseion—will argue that the Earth is a sphere and measure its circumference with near perfect accuracy, seventeen hundred years before Columbus makes his famous voyage. As Euclid created the field of geometry here, Hipparchus will found the study of Trigonometry and Herophilus is credited with propounding the scientific method and founding the Academy of Medicine with his fellow physician, Erasistratus. There will be a room devoted to the study of anatomy, and equipment for astronomical observations.

Ptolemy's son will add to this the greatest library of the ancient world, thanks to his requirement that all foreign ships hand over their scrolls for copying. Resident scholars—there were usually about a thousand at any one time—will collate, correct and translate these texts from Assyrian, Persian, Jewish, Indian and other languages. The great Greek classics from Homer and Hesiod to Plato will be collated, edited and preserved here.

Twenty-first century children, sitting in school rooms in Paris, London, Berlin, Oslo, Duluth, Istanbul, Buenos Aires, and Sydney will learn at some time basic principles laid down by Archimedes and Euclid, right there in Ptolemy's desert city. Ptolemy grants to the Jews their own quarter near the royal quarters. The Jewish philopher Philo, the great Platonist philosopher Plotinus and the Christian theologian, Origen will study together under the same Alexandrian teacher, Ammonius Sacchus. Plotinus, after spending time in Persia, will bring to Plato's teaching an intellectual flavor of the East, like the cross-pollination of the spices from the rich multiethnic cooking that fills the streets. Ships arrive from the east by way of the Red Sea to the Mediterranean. Greeks, Jews, Phoenicians, Nabataeans and Arabs live side by side in this cosmopolitan city. All of this is happening in the third century BC.

The reign of the Ptolemys ends in 30 BC with the death of its last and most vivid ruler, Cleopatra, who could be said to have accomplished through passion what

Alexander did through might and imagination. In her love for Julius Caesar and Mark Anthony, not to mention her political wiles and ambitions as ruler of Egypt, she weds the great civilization of a waning Hellenistic Egypt, with the waxing star of Julius Caesar's Rome. But that is another story.

For now, twist the chronoscope back to its position in the late 300s AD, some six hundred years later. As Monica stands waiting at the Gate of Augustus in that late afternoon in 385, a remarkable young woman is coming of age in Alexander's North African city, a city still revered as a center of learning in the world. Her name is Hypatia, and on this afternoon, she is nearing her sixteenth birthday. She is sitting in one of the library's reading rooms, studying works of Plato, Aristotle and the mathematicians who followed in the wake of Euclid and Archimedes. She takes a break from her studies to step into the fresh air. Spring in Alexandria brings the gardens alive in vivid color and the students of her father, Theon, are walking among them, deep in conversation.

Theon will be the last fellow of the Mouseion.* Hypatia will become a mathematician and philosopher. The Christian historiographer, Socrates Scholasticus—a contemporary Greek Christian living in Constantinople—will write this about her:

> There was a woman of Alexandria named Hypatia, daughter of the philosopher Theon, who made such attainments in literature and science, as to far surpass the philosophers of her own time. Having succeeded to the school of Plato and Plotinus, she explained the principles of philosophy to her auditors, many of whom came from a distance to receive her instruction. On account of the self-possession and ease of manner, which she had acquired in consequence of the cultivation of her mind, she not infrequently appeared in public in the presence of the magistrates. Neither did she feel abashed in going to an assembly of men. For all men, on account of her extraordinary dignity and virtue admired her the more.

Two North African women, about to engrave themselves on the long collective memory, pass one another at not so great a distance along the Mediterranean coast, where deep below them the heat of slowly colliding plates stills burns and occasionally thunders up out of Etna's mouth. Hypatia will surface in our own time as an emblem for the banner of the women's movement, proof that women left their mark on history, now also her-story; capable of meeting and even surpassing the intellectual achievements of their male contemporaries.

Where the road from Ostia ends at the foot of the Aventine, Monica passes close to a third woman, a Roman, who is also about a task that will engrave itself on memory. On the heights of the Aventine, the wealthy of the city have their palaces. In one of these, an aristocratic woman named Marcella has gathered a group of women who are studying and working with an Illyrian Christian priest, ascetic and scholar named Jerome. Jerome is working on a new translation of the Latin Bible based on the Greek New Testament. He has traveled widely and lived for a

---

* The original library complex and collection created by the Ptolemys suffered successive destructions. It is not clear in what form the institution survived in the time of Theon.

time as a hermit in the Syrian desert. He studied Hebrew under the guidance of a converted Jew and was in correspondence with Christian Jews in Antioch, where Paul had once had his church. Later he was ordained a Christian priest and came to Rome with Pope Damasus I as a leader of the Roman Christians. Marcella was the first woman of her class to live a life in the world by Gospel precepts, recommended to her by priests from Alexandria and inspired by the Egyptian anchoresses. This included fasting, strict abstinence, prayer and care for the poor as well as austere clothing without ornament.

Marcella's group has recently been joined by a woman from one of the richest senatorial families; a family that even claimed descent from Agamemnon—one of our heroes of the Trojan War. True or not, Paula has been inspired by her friend Marcella and is enthused by plans to form a semi-monastic community in the East, though she comes from a distinguished family, is highly honored in the city, and moves about it dressed in silks and carried by her eunuch slaves. She joins the group with her daughter Paulina and later in the year, her son, Toxotius will be baptized as a Christian and join them. Paula and her family will leave their posh lives in the city behind to visit the Holy Land and take up ascetic lives in the town of Bethlehem, where she will build and direct a hospice, a monastery, and a convent. Marcella will remain behind in her home on the Aventine, offering aid to the poor and pilgrims, living ascetically and overseeing her "house of virgins."

◆ ◆ ◆

Things are about to change dramatically in the city of Rome. In 394, just nine years later, the Emperor Theodosius will order the closure of the Temple of Vesta and the Vestals will be banished from the Atrium. It is said in later years that with sorrowful tears the priestesses watched the flames flicker and die, then destroyed the inmost shrine. No one knows what became of the sacred emblems that they guarded, including the Palladium carried by Aeneas out of Troy.

In 410, the Goths will invade the city of Rome and its long decline will begin. Marcella will witness this invasion of the Goths under Alaric from her high vantage point on the Aventine. The Goths will soon storm that peak and they will beat her with whips to make her reveal where her riches are hidden. Eventually she will convince them that she has given her riches to the poor and has nothing to hide. They will take her, with her spiritual daughter Principia, to the Church of St. Paul where Monica had stopped on her way from Ostia to Rome. Alaric has designated it as a place of asylum. She will die a few days later.

In Alexandria, during the same time in March that Monica was traveling in 385, Hypatia will fall victim to a dispute between the Imperial Prefect Orestes and the Bishop Cyril of Alexandria. Her chariot will be waylaid on her route home by a Christian mob, possibly Nitrian monks led by a man identified only as Peter, who is thought to be Peter the Reader, Cyril's assistant. She was stripped naked and dragged through the streets to the newly Christianized Caesareum church, where she is brutally killed. Some say she was flayed with pot shards and set ablaze while still alive, though others will say those actions happened after her death. It is again the Christian historian from Constantinople who gives us a written account, full of the respect and admiration that he felt she deserved.

Although Hypatia was a pagan, she was respected by a number of Christians and there were thought to be both Christians and pagans among her students. She was later held up by Christian authors as a symbol of virtue. But even in death, she was an instrument of the political intrigues between Christians and pagans in the city. She would enter the modern centuries, both admired and reviled. A seventh century Christian writer would accuse her of being "devoted at all times to magic, astrolabes and instruments of music" through which "she beguiled many people through Satanic wiles."

Several works on mathematics and astronomy are attributed to her, possibly in collaboration with her father.

History, it seems, is impartial and persecution is an equal opportunity employer.

Three women. Marcella, with her friend Paula, was simply seeking to live more deeply a Christian life. Hypatia wanted to use the resources of Alexandria and her own mind to probe the principles of number and nature.

Monica just wanted to reach her son.

* * * *

Grossi Farms ~ The Present, October 10

UNDER THE EUCS

I am settling in happily here at Grossi Farms and I love my location under the eucalyptus trees near the back of the farm. Darkness is falling so much more quickly. One feels the planet's turning to the bone when living without electricity. The diurnal-nocturnal patterning of light and dark, heat and cold, moist and dry is laid delicately, but with the sureness of endless repetition, just below memory and thought; down there in the ancient brain that keeps us alive and sensate and in tune with the fabric of nature and the universe.

I lay awake last night reading Jack London's *Martin Eden* by flashlight. The lid was open above me and I had watched the faint flush of coral light to the east, over Sonoma Mountain, and through the eucalyptus branches the first bright stars winked through the clear, purple-black sky.

Martin Eden's literary success was beginning to descend upon him, after two years of wracking poverty and unanimous rejection of his writings. The avalanche of success would crush him with the impervious fickleness of nature. But at the moment, the first checks, the first acceptances were bringing a momentary and inexpressible joy which I followed through the flickering yellow circle from my flashlight.

Then I heard it: Pouring imperiously down from the eucalyptus tree came a call I had only heard once, when Mr. Fields was parked two blocks away at Laurie-Ann's house. It had awakened me on a bright moonlit night and I had risen up through the hatch above my bed to catch a glimpse of it. The call was loud and more like a fowl than a bird. But it came from high up in a tree at the end of the yard and split wide the quiet of the night. In the brightness of the moon, I could make out its shape on the naked limb. Was that also autumn when I heard it and the leaves were gone? Was this a creature heading south on its annual flyway? Or was this just its autumn song, harsh for the dying away of things.

The brazen bird above me screeched on, but it was not a screech like the call of the barn owl. It was a different, wilder call. Unfamiliar. The bird was big. Once more I lifted myself out of the hatch and craned upward to see it. But the bird was kept invisible as a woman in purdah by the eucalyptus leaves. I aimed my flashlight toward its call and it remained unperturbed. Likewise its responder. That's the other strange thing. A conversation was going on. But the response came in an entirely different voice. It couldn't possibly have been the same kind of bird. Do different species talk to one another?

I call the first bird the Joey bird to remember its sound: Jo-EEE! Rising up the scale to a piercing –EEE. The second bird replied at first in a low, brief murmur like a disinterested spouse who doesn't feel like talking. Not to be put off, the Joey bird repeated Jo-EEE again. He had certainly caught my attention. There was something bloodcurdling in that sound. And each time, the responder, just above me, perhaps in the same tree, grew slowly more articulate. First a low, hoarse sort of call. The husband lost in the reading of the paper has begun to realize that his wife is telling him something important. Even urgent. Yet the simile isn't a good one because I was convinced these birds were of a different species and the mating season had long past.

Now I was much more intrigued by the responder, who also remained unperturbed by my probing flashlight, safe behind the curtain of leaves. And here is the honest truth: I was afraid. "If one of those birds should suddenly appear," I thought, "such big birds—I'll faint with terror." Silly as women jumping onto chairs when a tiny mouse appears or a grown man running from a garter snake. The primordial fear is for nature herself and the uninvited, untamed creatures we fear are emblems of a vast inscrutable power as old as time that could rise up against us in any moment and shake us like toys. Snuff us out like a small candle.

But ah the mystery! The invocative darkness pierced by blazing unknown worlds. Billions of them. And none know my name. Or care. I love that. I love being laid out anonymously against such immensity. I am part of that! I am painted here in the same scene with the Milky Way and the Moon; Venus, Arcturus, vineyards on the hillside, pumpkins in the field, the twinkling lights of Santa Rosa, and something wild and deep that rises in the throat of a bird to give voice to it all.

The great horned owl who lives in the next tree has entered the conversation and the second bird's voice has risen to a distinct, slightly husky, croaking call no less disconcerting and provocative than the first. What are they talking about? Why are they filling the fields with their voices?

Deprived of any possibility of seeing them, I return to Martin Eden at the threshold of his success, aiming my flashlight back on the immediate and scrutable page. The avalanche is slipping toward him. The social acceptance that appears with his success; praise for the very same works from the very same people who once scorned him, makes him bitter. The light slowly goes out of his soul. What he has learned, the philosophy he has honed, the beauty he has captured in his net of words does not save him. The triviality and venality of the world overtake him. Squeeze the joy out of him. The death of Love, not the rejection of the loved one, extinguished the bright flame which once drove his youth and creativity. It is the avalanche.

I pause for a moment to think on this. What of the beauty that was the core of his love and creativity? That had not gone. There was still the endlessly profound stirring of the planet around him through light and dark, heat and cold . . . Brissendon was right; that brilliant, cynical consumptive friend who had died by his own hand: He should have left it all, returned to his beloved South Seas before it was too late. But now it is too late, he realizes. For too long he mistook the Editors, the Successful, for the mountaintop, when all along his bold bright instinct told him otherwise. And now what was once the snowy Himalayan mountaintop of the throbbing human world was falling upon him. It was not a real mountaintop of course. Nothing of the hoary duration, power, elevation of the real Himalayas. It was all in his mind. Yet it killed him nevertheless as the Himalayan peaks had killed so many human climbers in its real avalanches. A shrug, a twitch of a massive snowy shoulder, and like stick-figures, they fall.

I don't like the ending of this book, although it is the ending to Jack London's own life. An overdose at 40, similarly embittered by success. It happened just over there. Beyond Sonoma Mountain. In the Valley of the Moon. It seems as if Martin Eden's philosophy was inadequate. His Spencer, his biology, his Darwin not enough. Nor his Nietzsche. Nietzsche, another great voice for beauty, died a madman. Torn apart by it perhaps. Dismembered, like Dionysus, for his ecstasy.

Perhaps his philosophy was too much. It cracked against the dark. Or against the light, too thin a shield. Something goes wrong. What is it?

I look up through the darkened screen toward Sonoma Mountain, which I can't see; towards Glen Ellen, with a slight shift of my head to the left, toward the ranch that London bought with his success to restore the soul that had been injured by it. It is now Jack London Park. What would Martin Eden say to that? What would Jack London say?

And then it comes to me: the silence. The birds have gone. While I was tracking words across the page—dead words of a dead man—they lifted their huge wings and with a smooth pressure on the dark air, moved effortlessly upward and away. If I had only listened, I might have heard. If I had only watched, I might have seen.

The urgent birds of presence have gone. Sonoma Mountain has dissolved into darkness as the slender young moon swims westward through the sky.

Mr. Fields and I are content.

We sleep.

✳ ✳ ✳ ✳

MILAN

ROME TO MILAN

MONICA AND HER COMPANIONS BEGIN THEIR JOURNEY NORTH *standing before the Golden Milestone near the Temple of Saturn. Caesar Augustus had erected it as the starting point of all roads leading out from Rome and distances were measured from this point. Constantine referred to this gilded bronze marker as the umbilicus of Rome. It seems especially appropriate that the god of time, order, measure and structure should preside over the point of origin. Of departure and arrival. It is a milestone for Monica as well. A departure from her African past toward an unknown future. Her spirit had already made that turn as she knelt in the church of St. Peter* over the holy place where St. Peter was buried, just as she had visited St. Paul's church outside the city. These were the true highlights of her time in Rome. She had offered up to St. Peter her prayers for the journey and, as always, that the soul of her son Augustinus would open to her own Master. Augustinus is now a professor in Milan and it is to Milan that they are now headed.*

The high winds and rain of the previous day had washed the city clean and the morning landscape sparkles as their carriage moves across the Via Flaminia and heads toward Narni. Outside of the city the green countryside opens up before them. They pass more large farms, as they had outside of Ostia. She recalls that Augustinus had departed by a different route and made the journey to Milan in great style and speed. Symmachus sent him with the Royal Mail. The empire's postal service could carry a letter as far and as fast as five-hundred miles in twenty-four hours.

There is a festive atmosphere as the small party sets out in their carriage. They have bought meat pies from a seller at the Constantine gate, which are much favored by Romans, and other delicacies for lunch on the journey. The wide road of hexagonal paving stones is lined with cypress trees like guardians of a royal way. Her young companions are debating over their favorite places and most admired monuments in the imperial city. Alypius, who is joining them for the trip to Milan, gazes thoughtfully over the countryside and says little. Monica feels a lifting of the heavy oppression she felt in the city. The others cannot decide whether the Caracalla Baths or Trajan's mall is the greater wonder. Nebridius speaks up for the quality of art in the museums. They recount their favorite meals and Monica expresses distaste at the idea of dining on such beautiful creatures as flamingoes—a specialty of a restaurant where they had dined. No one had chosen it from the elaborate and exotic menu. Her son Navigius had taken in all of the mosaic pavements and declares that there are none as fine as those in North Africa. But he has high praise for the architectural and engineering marvels of the city. After treating them to his discourse on buildings, bridges and aqueducts, he moves on to a detailed description of how the splendid road they are traveling was built. More detail from the encyclopedic Lucius.

It goes on like that during the first hours of the trip, but then a comfortable silence settles over the carriage. The passengers are lulled by the steady rhythms of horse and

---

* The original St. Peter's Basilica was built by Constantine over what was belieived to be his burial site about fifty years before Monica's visit. It lasted until the 15th century when a new basilica was reconstructed on the same site, where it is today.

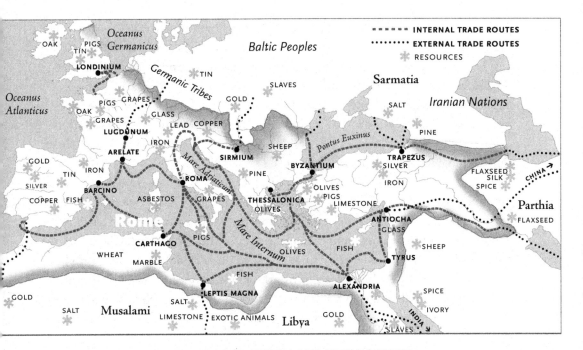

ROMAN ROAD SYSTEM AND TRADE ROUTES

carriage into a trance-like state or into sleep. Heads nod. Monica is able to let the pleasures of the journey and the prospect of their arrival fill her mind.

Throughout their days of travel, they see merchants pass, rich and poor travelers, in small groups or large caravans. They speak to some of them at the inns that have been built at stopping points along the way. They meet people traveling for their health, to visit the sanctuaries of the god Asclepius in Greece, especially Epidaurus, and at places along the Mediterranean Coast. Some are traveling on their vacations down to the Bay of Naples from the north or to the Egyptian Nile.

The Roman road system extended into Turkey, Syria, to Antioch, Palmyra and Petra. Trajan reached the "land between the rivers"—Mesopotamia—and conquered it by building a pontoon bridge across the Tigris and Euphrates. His Via Traiana ran the whole length of the desert land from Damascus to Aqaba. To the north of that it ran parallel to the River Jordan and the Red Sea. Guard stations and signal towers were erected along the roads so that the people of these lands experienced something they had never known before: security. At Aqaba, caravans of ships arrived from Bombay via the Arabian Sea, avoiding pirates at the narrows of the Gulf of Aden. Aqaba was also the road head for the desert caravans. By 115 AD, Trajan had brought the empire all the way to the Persian Gulf. His boldest engineering feat, all designed by his architect Apollidoris, was the building of an arched, segmented bridge across the Danube River.

This transportation system did wonders for Roman cuisine, which had previously been rather dull fare. It introduced them to pepper, for which they developed a passion. It was light and easy to transport by camel, four hundred miles over the Via Traiana, then shipped from the ports of Lebanon to Ostia, where the pepper barns beside the Tiber were always kept full. So popular did pepper become that when the Goths arrived at the gates of Rome, they demanded three thousand pounds of pepper before they would negotiate with the Romans. Cinnamon and cloves came from Ceylon. Nutmeg and its covering, mace, came from Malaya. Ginger root from from the wild parts of India. As the writer Roman writer Pliny pointed out, "They sold at Rome for a hundred times their price."

At Carmae in the north of Mesopotamia, four roads met: one from Asia Minor, one from Antioch, one from Palmyra and the one from Damascus-Aqaba. This opened the way for the carpets of Babylon; for apples, peaches, nuts, figs and lemons; almonds; currents; honey from the edge of the desert. Rice. Cocoanut oil for candies and soap. Suddenly they had access to the aromatics of Arabia—umber, aloe, musk, rose water. Incense to purify the kings. Stones of magic and beauty. Amber: traders walked from Greece to the Baltic Sea to get it. Nero sent a knight, with a large number of men, two thousand miles to the Baltic Sea to see its place of origin.

As early as 2500 BC, the Persians were building roads through their empire. By 600 BC, a road ran from their capital at Susa, nine hundred miles to present day Ankara, Turkey. Now that the Romans had opened up access to the Persian roads through their own system, the way was open to China. And from there come such diverse new things as chickens and silk. By the second century BC, China began dispatching silk caravans from within the Chinese wall to Chinese Turkestan (present-day Xinjiang, China). The loads were transferred there to middlemen who carried them across the desert and through the mountains to Persia, where Syrians and Greeks took them over the last leg of the Mediterranean.

Over the roads came ivory for the Roman artisans, pearls from the coast of India and the finest, from Ceylon. Diamonds from India's gravel beds, emeralds from India and Egypt. Cottons from the cotton trees of India and from bush cotton that grew along the Nile.

Less visibly, yet perhaps more significantly, ideas were spreading. So much of our western culture and our major religions would not have endured into the present if they had not traveled far and wide along the network of these roads. People had lived on the planet for thousands of years before this time but it is in this period, from Alexander to Trajan and his successor Hadrian, that they begin to coalesce into a world.

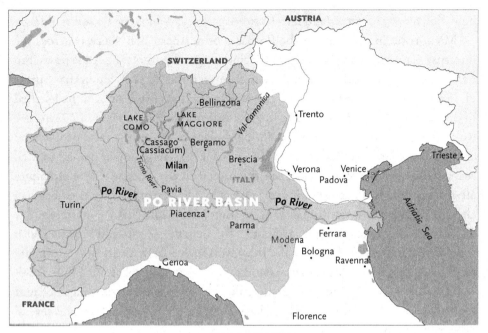

THE PO BASIN

Milan ~ 385 AD

AUGUSTINUS AURELIUS

My hope from my youth, where were you, and where had you gone? Was it not you who created me, and made me different from the beasts of the field, and made me wiser than the birds of the air? But I walked in darkness, and upon a slippery way, and I sought for you outside myself, but I did not find you, the God of my heart. I went down into the depths of the sea, and I lost confidence, and I despaired of finding the truth.

But now my mother, strong in her love, had come to me, for she had followed me over land and sea, kept safe by you through all her perils.*

—The Confessions of St. Augustine

THE CITY OF MILAN IS ONE OF THE MAIN CHARACTERS in our larger story. It qualifies as one of the degrees of separation, because many of our characters will pass through this landscape, although in different times. It lies on the Lombard plain, where the Po River flows down from the French Alps, near the border with Italy, over four hundred miles to empty into the Adriatic. It extends north to a strip of land that includes Ticino, around Bellinzona. The Lombards have not arrived and so that name is not known here yet. They are still in Germania, near the Elbe River, but they are growing restless and have started to move, probably after seasons of bad harvest. We will meet them again soon in a different story. The Ticino River

---

* From the *Confessions of Augustine*, translated by Ryan.

flows down out of Switzerland into Lago Maggiore and joins the Po south of Pavia.

Milan is set in the heart of the Po Basin of northern Italy, halfway across the immense plain spreading between the Ticino and Adda rivers. The Adda flows into Lake Como to the south. The city was over seven hundred years old in that Spring of 385. It had been founded by Celts around the fifth century BC who had settled in the Po Valley about two centuries earlier. Two hundred years later, in 222 BC, the Romans invaded the city and named it Mediolanum. It was the local people who called it Medhlan or just Milán. It didn't lack for Roman grandeur. For a hundred years, Milan—not Rome—had been the capital of the Western Roman empire after the empire had been split into two parts by Diocletian in 285 AD. Diocletian chose to rule the Eastern Roman Empire from Nicomedia (Izmit), in present day Turkey, east of Constantinople (Istanbul). By then, the empire was so vast that it was deemed impossible for one ruler to control such a large territory. A secondary ruler or "co-emperor," Maximian, was established in Mediolanum. Immediately, Maximian built several gigantic monuments, like a large circus the length of four football fields, the Thermae Erculee, a large complex of imperial palaces and several other services and buildings.

Not only was Milan the center of a network of roads through northern Italy and north into the Alps, but every kind of grain was grown there as well as vineyards for the empire's wines, sheep for its wool, and forests where its swine were bred. From the time of Augustus, Mediolanum was famous for its schools and its theater.

In the lifetime of Monica's mother, it is from this city that a life-changing event for Christians took place: the Edict of Milan. By this Edict, the Emperor Constantine proclaimed religious toleration throughout the Roman Empire. As a result of this, there were Christian communities and a number of basilicas. Saint Ambrose, who was then the Bishop of Milan, had a strong influence on the layout of the city, redesigning the center (the cathedral and baptistery built at this time are now lost) and building the great basilicas at the city gates: Sant'Ambrogio, San Nazaro in Brolos, San Simpliciano and Sant'Eustorgio. Although they required refurbishment over the centuries, they still stand among the most important churches in Milan.

We can imagine the happiness of the reunion in Milan between Augustinus, his mother, his brother and cousins and his friends, Nebridius and Alypius. Augustinus Aurelius had come up in the world since his arrival in Rome. As a teacher of rhetoric in Carthage, he had left in part because the students there were unruly. In Rome, he had taught students who were better behaved, but in the end, were not paying him regularly. His friend Symmachus, a Manichaean of some prestige there, arranged a job for him in the court of the emperor in Milan. Augustinus was a man of means now, with a large house. But none of this success had settled his restless mind and spirit. He had always been driven by two lusts—the lust of his body for its pleasures and a lust for truth—which seemed to fight in constant battle within him.

In Rome, Augustinus had moved away from Manichaeism and embraced the skepticism of the New Academy, which was something like becoming a Deconstructive Postmodernist in the twentieth century. But here in Mediolanum, he is still struggling at his soul/psyche foundations with the clashing forces of his mother's ardent Christianity, his body's lustful impulses and his mind's restless questing after truth. Upon his arrival in Milan, a new element enters the mix. He meets Ambrose.

Our images of saints, thanks to their depictions in medieval art, are usually of characters with beatific expressions and halos of gold, often bathed in the light of spiritual illumination. These two men, Augustine and Ambrose, along with Monica, will join that hallowed company in the collective imagination. But the reality in 385, in Milan, was hardly of that quality or clarity. When he encounters Ambrose, prompted by a friend to visit his church, Augustinus Aurelius—we will call him by Augustine now, as he is known to history—is obviously impressed, not so much by his sermons as by the man himself and by the particular way he lives out his ecclesiastical vocation. No one describes this better than Augustine himself in his *Confessions:*.

> Ambrose himself I believed to be a happy man, as the world judges such things, because so many powerful persons showed him honor. His celibacy alone appeared to me to be a hard thing. But what hopes he held, what struggles against temptations arising from his exalted station, what comforts amid diversities, how sweet the joys of that secret mouth within his heart as it fed upon and savored again the bread You gave him—such things I could not guess at, nor had I any experience of them.
>
> He did not know the passions that seethed within me, nor my pit of danger. Yet I was unable to ask him what I wanted and in the way I wanted, for crowds of busy men, to whose troubles he was slave, shut me away from both his ear and his mouth. When he was not with them, and this was but a little while, he either refreshed his body with needed food or his mind with reading.

I find this a sad but telling passage that sums up much about Monica's son in this moment. His brilliant mind has known interplay with the minds of Manichaeans and Platonists and New Academicians in Tagaste, Carthage and in Rome. He is passionate and wants to pour out his soul to Ambrose and put before him the points and counterpoints of his soul's inner dialogues. In a way, he wants a father, spiritual and corporeal, or a least a mentor. Ambrose never steps in to fill that role for him but remains this elusive model of a Christian man, busy about his pastoral life, nourishing his mind and soul in private, leading a spiritual community, and in the midst of all that—happy and holding a position of honor in a powerful city. This is different from Monica's Christianity, nurtured on the sacrifices of its early martyrs. What Augustine wanted from Ambrose, an intellectual, emotional and spiritual intimacy, was not what he got from Ambrose; it was much much more.

When Monica arrived, it was natural that she would attend Ambrose's services and she was delighted by her son's interest. Augustine tells us that Ambrose thought a great deal of his mother. "When he saw me, he would often break forth in her praise and congratulate me for having such a mother. But he did not know what sort of son she had, for I doubted all things and I thought that the way to life could not be found."

Augustine describes his misery on the very day when he is to give an address in praise of the emperor, realizing that in it he would tell many a lie and those lies would be applauded by men who knew that he was lying. "My heart pounded over such causes of care and it burned with the wasting fever of my thoughts."

This anguish seems to reach a crisis point one afternoon when he is with his friend Alypius.

> Then during that great struggle in my inner house, which I had violently raised up against my own soul in our chamber, in my heart, troubled both in mind and in countenance, I turn upon Alypius and cry out to him, 'What is the trouble with us? The unlearned rise up and take heaven by storm and we, with all our erudition but empty of heart, see how we wallow in flesh and blood! Are we ashamed to follow?

The very look of him frightens Alypius, who remains silent. Augustine rushes out into a small garden off the house. He is literally tearing his hair at this point in what is clearly a spiritual and emotional breakdown; often the prerequisite to a breakthrough. He is consumed by a turbulent anger at himself for his inability to overcome his own passions and "enter into a covenant with God" to which he has been insufficiently drawn all of his life. He sits with Alypius in the garden and continues to weep and beat his forehead in a paroxysm of inner agony. He rises, and goes to the other side of the garden where he "flings down beneath a certain fig tree to give free rein to his tears" as he tells it. There he hears a sound that stops him. A voice like that of a boy or girl chanting, over and over, "Take up and read. Take up and read." He tries to think if children made use of such a chant in any of their games, but he could not recall hearing it anywhere.

At the suggestion of a friend, he had been reading a manuscript of the writings of the apostle Paul. (Yes, our Paul of the Malta Shipwreck.) He interpreted it then as a command of God, made through the child, to counsel him in his despair to open a book and read the first words that came to his eye. So he returns to where Alypius is sitting, next to the book that had been given him of the writings of St. Paul, and he opened it to Paul's letter to the Romans, chapter 13. "Not in riots and drunken parties, not in eroticism and indecencies, not in strife and rivalry, but put on the Lord Jesus Christ and make no provision for the flesh in its lusts."

> Instantly, in truth at the end of this sentence, as if before a peaceful light streaming into my heart, all the dark shadows of doubt fled away. With a calm countenance I told it all to Alypius. Then he made known to me what had taken place in him and he pointed out what followed in the passage from Paul. 'Now him that is weak in faith take unto you,' which he applied to himself and disclosed to me. Now, although for a long time and for the better, he had greatly differed from me, he joined me without any painful hesitation. Thereupon we went into my mother. We told her the story and she rejoiced. You had converted me to yourself so that I would seek

neither wife nor ambition in this world, for I would stand on that rule of faith where, so many years before, you had showed me to her. You turned her mourning into a joy far richer than that she had desired, far dearer and purer, than that she had sought in grandchildren born of my flesh.

386 AD

CASSIACUM

The day came when I was actually set free from teaching rhetoric, although I had already been free from it in thought. Now it was done. You set free my tongue as you had already freed my heart from that profession. I blessed you, and joyfully, together with all my household, I started out for that country place. When will there be time enough for us to commemorate all the great benefits that you showed us at that time?

—The Confessions of St. Augustine

Augustine's close friend in Milan, Verecundus, has offered him the loan of his country villa in Cassiacum to recover from some health problems and to rest with his friends and family. The villa is an afternoon ride north of the city, near Como. It sits on the summit of a small hill which overlooks a valley, surrounded by mountains—the foothills of the Alps. Verecundus has built a small aqueduct which brings water from a stream that cascades through a nearby wooded ravine. This provides water for drinking and for baths.

The months spent in Cassiacum are one of those islands in time that is in fact outside of time altogether. Augustine flourishes in the country air, in the company of close family and friends. Alypius and Nebridius are his oldest friends from Tagaste. Two young, twenty-year-old scholars, former students from Milan, have joined him: Licentius is the son of his friend Romanius and Trigetius is a student who has abandoned a military career to study philosophy. Then there are his cousins, Lastidianus and Rusticus. But what brings Augustine the greatest pleasure is the presence of his son, Adeotatus. Adeotatus is fifteen and has obviously inherited some of this father's exceptional mental gifts. An old friend from Tagaste, Evodius, will soon join them. Evodius has left Africa to become an officer of the Court. Even before Augustine, he was converted and baptized, "quitting his secular warfare, he girded himself to the heavenly warfare." As one writer put it (Edward Lewes Cutts), "their happy life in this charming retirement at Cassiciacum was something like a realization of their search for truth and a happy life."

Their days together begin early and are often spent in reading. Licentius and Trigetius continue their studies in rhetoric with their former professor, reading classics under his direction. They share his chamber, so their discussions sometimes go far into the night. After a frugal mid-day meal, if weather permits, the Cassiacum companions gather under a great oak tree in a nearby meadow and spend hours together in thoughtful discussions. In poor weather, they gather in a hall of baths attached to the villa. The two students, from long habit, arrive with tablet and stylus in hand so that much of the conversation is recorded and for Augustine, they will seed several important works and form a lifelong foundation for his thought. Often the discussions go on into the evening, and a servant comes to light a torch near the tree or a lamp in the hall of baths.

Most of those present are steeped in the Greek and Latin classics. Monica has assimilated much of this through her son. Socrates' walks with his students in the groves of academe are seven centuries in the past but they are as immediate to those gathered here as they are to one another. Plato had walked with Socrates, Aristotle with Plato, and their conversations had shaped the future of Western thought for millennia. These students of philosophy must have felt themselves engaged in similar dialogues and conversations. Certainly Augustine did. From notes taken, he developed works like *On Order* and *Against the Academicians*, which preserved the dialogue form used by Socrates and Plato. Like the Greek masters before them, their discussions were on life and the soul. On truth and happiness.

The Academicians are philosophers of the time who maintain that man is not able to discover truth, but that happiness consists in the search for it. Lively debate follows around the subject. Licentius is in agreement with this idea, while Trigetius argues that happiness could only be found in a life of virtue and wisdom, but the mere search for these would be sufficient for happiness. Augustine summarizes their debate by defining happiness as a life in which human instincts, desires and wants are in conformity with human reason and that no happiness is possible if reason, hungering after truth, were incapable of satisfying its desire. This is the critical point that he has reached in his lifelong effort to reconcile the two parts of his own nature in a higher level of understanding. "To declare that it is not possible for us to discover truth," he says, "is to declare the uselessness of the faculties which distinguish us from the beasts. It is to annihilate the highest and noblest part of our being. One only arrives at truth after long and painful research, but this research is not without its charm to the intelligence. Wisdom is a star which does not come to shine in our souls as easily as the light of the sun enlightens our eyes.*

At the end of the discussion, Augustine concludes that "in whatever manner wisdom is to be attained, I see that I do not yet know it. Nevertheless, being only in my thirty-second year, I ought not to despair of acquiring it some day: since I am resolved to apply myself to the search, despising all those things which men regard as desirable. I confess that the reasons of the Academicians give me much fear in this enterprise; but I think I am sufficiently armed against them by this discussion."

Augustine now finds the authority for his life in the teachings and inner presence of Christ, to which he has committed himself. "As for things which one is able to examine by force of reason (for my character is such that I desire with impatience not only to believe the truth, but also to be able to perceive it by the intellect), I

* Paraphrased by Edward Cutts in *Saint Augustine*

hope to find among the Platonicians a doctrine which shall not be opposed to our sacred mysteries." Plato had written in a letter (over eight hundred years before) that "Reason is the soul's pilot," and Augustine too is trying to knit together a spiritual and intellectual vision. He is seeking to wed the worldview of the ancient Greeks, particularly Plato and his later followers, to an emerging worldview rooted in Christian ideals.* Augustine would later write that a people is a "multitude of reasonable beings united by their agreement in the things that they respect" (*City of God*, XIX, 24). Such an idea foreshadows the July Fourth moment when the Founding Fathers, almost fourteen hundred years in the future, will enshrine similar ideas in their Declaration of Independence and the Constitution that follows.

On the last day of this discussion, night arrives before its conclusion, and a servant brings a torch to light the scene. It is the turn of Alypius to reply, but instead, he declares his pleasure in what he has heard. "I cannot sufficiently admire," he says, "how Augustine has treated so pleasantly a subject so thorny, with what force he has triumphed over despair, with what moderation he has put forth his own views, and with what clearness he has solved such obscure problems. Oh, my friends, you wait for my reply. Listen rather to the master. We have a chief who can lead us into the secrets of truth, under the inspiration of God himself."

By night, Augustine retreats to his chamber, spending the last hours of the day in prayer to God and in deep meditations. Often during this time, he edits and revises notes from conversations during the day, shaping them into his books.

Both his mother and his son Adeotatus find their way into these books, as Augustine was slowly weaving the diverse and tangled strands of his early life into a strong, whole and meaningful fabric. One can only imagine Monica's feelings as she listens to her son, day after day, and finds her own spirit expanding into a new life following the death of her husband and her departure from the only home she had ever known.

In one of the writings from this period, Augustine introduces his mother into the discussion and the literary Monica is taken back by this. "What are you doing? In what books have you ever seen women allowed to enter into such discussions?" Augustine replies that if ever anyone should read his words with genuine interest, "they will not be offended to see me talk philosophy with you. Among the ancients there were women who gave themselves to the study of philosophy, and your philosophy pleases me much. What they call in Greek, philosophy, is called in Latin, the love of wisdom. . . . I would not have included you in these memoirs if you had not loved wisdom; still less, if you had loved it as well as me. But I know that you love it still more than you love me, and I know how much you love me!

"You are so advanced in the divine science, that you are terrified neither by the fear of any misfortune, nor by the dread of death; and this equanimity proclaims the attainment of the very kernel of philosophy. How could I hesitate after that to become myself your disciple?" He is speaking to the woman who had given terrified sailors the courage to guide their vessel safely through a mighty Mediterranean storm.

---

* Thomas Cahill, in his work *How the Irish Saved Civilization*, has described Augustine as the first medieval man and the last classical man.

On November 13th, 386, friends and family, with the exception of Alypius who had gone to Milan, gather at dinner to celebrate Augustine's 32nd birthday. After dinner, the conversation once again returns to the nature of true happiness and Monica offers an opinion of her own—that only those people are happy who attain what they desire, provided that what they desire is good. Augustine approves of this definition, adding that the good must be a permanent good, and that only God can be this permanent good. From this emerges a final conclusion on the subject of their discussion: Happiness consists in the knowledge and possession of God, and that this ought to be the end and aim of all human endeavor.

While Monica is clearly a participant in the intellectual discussions at Cassiacum, she still has much time on her own, which she will likely be spending in the company of her son Navigius, the cousins and others friends, including the caretakers and neighbors who are surely eager to show her their favorite places. Fifty miles to the north of Cassiacum lies Bellitio, a Roman fort town near a large and beautiful lake with lovely valleys that rise up from it. This is the town that will become Bellinzona and the lake is Maggiore, with the river Ticino to the north. The Lombards have not yet arrived, but there are small, isolated hamlets occupied by Celts.

To the east, lies Val Camonica—land of the Camuni, an ancient people who had lived in that valley since the Iron Age. I like to imagine the Cassiacum companions making an excursion to Val Camonica on hearing of the thousands of paintings and petroglyphs from an ancient time. It would have given Navigius pause to see a primitive stone carving that could be identified as a labyrinth, although this one follows the pattern known from Cretan coins.*

Through the winter months, even the lower slopes of the mountains are clad in their white capes. Nights grow colder and occasionally drop below freezing. Some days were too foggy and chilly to gather in the meadow. But the house is spacious and warm and the bath hall remains a favorite gathering place.

For the Cassiacum companions, the world outside does not exist. Not Trajan's mall or the forum or the great cities throughout the empire. It is an intimate group of friends enjoying peace, reflection, the treasures of friendship and the higher contemplations of mind and spirit. But this country retreat on the Lombard plain is like a hermetic vessel in which gold is being distilled from the mundane "prima materia" of the world. When the vessel is opened up and the contents poured out, it will have a world-changing effect that lasts into this day. After all, two future saints are being born underneath that fog and chilly rain and the oak tree in the meadow.

Just before Easter week 387, they return to Milan. Augustine, with his son

---

* There is today an active Camonica Club of North America, with a large membership of Swiss-Italians. "Our focus is on, first Camunian heritage; and second on Brescian, East Lombardian, Lombardian/Ticinese, original Austrian (the Langobard province of the Lombardy/Tri-Veneto/Trento region), Padanian, Alpine, and European heritage. This should also include our spiritual heritage: from the ancient Cernic [pre-Christian] tradition to the Ambrosian Rite," which includes, among other elements, the musical additions to the liturgy under Ambrose.

Adeodatus and his friend Alypius are baptized by Ambrose on Easter morning. According to the tradition, when the baptism was ended, Ambrose sang the first verse of "Te Deum Laudamus," Augustine the second, and so in alternate verses the noblest of the Church's Canticles was born.

Augustine, after considering where he can best serve God, resolves to return to his native country; his son, his mother, his brother, and Alypius accompany him, with the addition of Evodius, his Tagaste friend who has also resolved to dedicate himself to the service of God as a follower of Augustine. They travel to Rome and thence to Ostia, the port of Rome at the mouth of the Tiber where Monica's Italian journey began, ready to embark for Africa.

Ostia ~ 386 AD

MONICA'S LAST DAYS
From Augustine's *Confessions*

SHE WAS STANDING BY THE WINDOW.

The window looked out on the garden of a friend's house where we were staying in Ostia. It was in a quiet part of town, south of the Decudamus Maximus on the road to Laurentum. She said she had stayed before on the riverside, to the north of town. A very busy area and noisy. But this was removed from the din of the city, and of Rome and of Milan . . . So much had happened in that year since her arrival. We were tired from our long journeys and here we hoped to gather our energies for the voyage home, back to Africa.

I came and stood beside her, sharing the quiet of the evening and the last colors fading from the garden. We talked together, tenderly, forgetting all those things that were behind us and stretching forth into those things which are before us, beyond us. We were pondering, in the presence of that Truth—which you are, oh God—what the eternal life of saints would be like. That life which the eye has not seen, nor the ear heard, which has not entered into the heart of man. When our discourse had reached that point that is the highest delight, to the sweetness of that life that is the very edge of earthly senses, we reached toward that which is utterly incomparable and beyond expression. And still we rose together with an even greater, glowing affection toward this Inexpressible.

We proceeded step by step together through all bodily things up to that heaven where shine the sun and the moon and the stars down upon the earth. Yet higher we ascended, by means of inward thought and discourse and admiration of your works until we reached the very edge of our own minds. Transcending them, we attained to the region of abundance that never fails, in which you feed us forever upon the food of truth and where life is that Wisdom by which all these things are made, both those which have been and are to be. The Wisdom itself is not made but is as it was and will be forever. To have been in the past and to be in the future do not belong to it, but only to be—which is eternal. And however much we may speak of it, and long for it, we attain it in only a slight degree by an effort of our whole heart.

We sighed together, lingering in that space beyond words that is the first fruit of the spirit. Then we returned to that space of speech where a word both begins and ends. But what is there like your Word, oh Lord, remaining in Yourself without growing old and yet renewing all things.

Together we agreed that if, for any person, the tumult of the flesh falls silent—silent the images of earth and of the waters and of the air; silent the heavens; silent the very soul of the person itself—then should that person pass beyond himself by not thinking upon himself. Silent his dreams and all imagined appearances and every tongue and every sign, and all things that come to be through change would become wholly silent to him. Into this silence, God alone speaks.

And then we stood quietly, as if joined at the very edge of such a silence. How long that was I cannot now remember, but finally she spoke. "My son, for my own part, I find no delight in anything in this life. What I can still do here and why I am here I do not know. All of my hopes in this world have been accomplished. There was only one thing for which I desired to linger a little while in this life, and that was that I might yet see you a Christian before I died. God has granted this to me in more than abundance, for I see in you his servant, beyond all need for earthly happiness. What then am I doing here?"

I do not recall how I answered her in this, but scarcely five days later she fell sick with a fever and for a while lost consciousness, withdrawn from all present things.

Then she regained her senses and looked at me and my brother as we stood there. I stopped my weeping but could not speak. But my brother spoke and said, encouragingly, that she should die in her own country. We would take her home right away. She looked at us reproachfully. "Put this body away anywhere," she said. "Don't let care about it disturb you. I ask only that you remember me at the altar of the Lord, wherever you may be." When she had expressed this last wish, the sickness overtook her.

On the ninth day of her sickness, and the fifty-sixth year of her age, and the three-and-thirtieth of mine, was that religious and holy soul freed from the body." *

* Adapted by the author from several translations of the *Confessions* of St. Augustine

California coast ~ 430 AD

THE SEED

"... I have found it! Lo! here is a scion of the Eldest of Trees! But how comes it here?"
... And Gandalf coming looked at it, and said: "Verily this is a sapling of the line of
Nimloth the fair; and that was a seedling of Galathilion, and that a fruit of Telperion
of many names, Eldest of Trees. Who shall say how it comes here in the appointed
hour?"

—R.R. TOLKIEN
The Return of the King

IT IS HAPPENING SO SOUNDLESSLY. INVISIBLY. Beneath the rounded surface
of the world in the soil of northern California, while on the far side of this curving
shell of earth and stone and water are sounds of turmoil. Of armies marching.
Of cities falling. Of people fleeing. Vandals are on the move in North Africa and
Augustinus and his priests are praying for relief. For a peace that will never come.
The light of the Roman Empire is fading quickly and its days are numbered. But here
in the forest of the West is silence. And for the seed, darkness. All living things begin
so in a dark and silent place.

On its own scale and in its own time, the seed too faces struggles. Of all the seeds
beneath the surface of this forest, less than one percent will survive. It is another
just-so story. The amount of sunlight, moisture and soil temperature must be just
right. Not too many days of sun nor too few. Neither too dry nor too wet. Access to
surface minerals.

But the just-so moment is here for this seed. It swells and breaks open, unseen
in the silent dark. A slender root reaches out, and then downward into the soil as a
bright green stem presses upward, bent double as the hump of its fragile back leads
the way upward. To become a strong young seedling it must first have a strong root.
Tiny, thread-like tendrils will spread out from the first larger roots. None will reach
more than four or five feet below the soil. A remarkably delicate base for a tree that
may grow to the height of a twenty five story building—two hundred fifty to three
hundred feet. The seed has met its appointment with an existence that will outlive
the Vandals and the Romans and events far off in its long long life. Descendant of
the Eldest Redwood Tree. One hundred forty-four million years before, in the third
week of December.

❋ ❋ ❋ ❋

Grossi Farms ~ The Present

FROM THE LOFT LIBRARY

The wind is roaring through and hurling things right and left. Through the open hatch above the bed where I am working, I see a rain of leaves and twigs and seed pods blown aslant from the tops of the eucalyptus trees. I'm glad they rain away and not down or Mr. Fields would be pummeled by them. Glad to see those pods, like huge hailstones, being distributed by the wind's force across the field. Nature is sowing with her breath as she does with her water and her fire, as energetically committed to the spring tasks as every bird, beast and farmer, which are her sometimes unwitting instruments. I wish the job could just be done in this one great blow, stripping the trees of those lethal ballistics which fall from the great height of trees and land on Mr. Fields with the impact of boulders. They wake me in the night with their sudden, loud percussion as they strike the roof.

How are the owls faring in their daylight sleep, heaving on the rolling waves of air beneath their branches like sailors in a gale at sea? But Mr. Fields stands firm as I work, partly from the sheer weight of books that serves as ballast, and partly because its wheels are clutched in the firm grasp of adobe soil.

My little loft-library is filled with books. Books of my own. Books from Sonoma State Library. Books from the Rohnert Park Library. Notebooks. I have converted a spacious double-bed into a single-bed by filling its perimeter with my eclectic collection of thrillers, Chinese sages, reference books, ephemerides and whatever volumes I can find to answer my current questions about mostly everything.

Thinking about Augustine in his garden in Milan, I reach behind me to a small wooden bookcase that contains my personal treasures: the American Heritage paperback dictionary, which has now divided itself into two volumes, each held together with doses of masking tape. A through ME and MI through Z. Two versions of the I Ching and two Chinese-English dictionaries. Richard Tarnas's *Passion of the Western Mind*. The Dover Chinese-English edition of the Confucian Classics—*Analects, Great Learning* and *The Doctrine of the Mean*. Rob Hand's *Planets in Transit. The New English Bible*. It is no wonder I feel some sympathy for the multiple worlds of Paul and Augustine! My little library is a checkerboard of many traditions; a microcosm of our own diverse culture in the 21st century. From this I extract *The New English Bible*.

Is it synchronicity that I open it exactly to the page that Augustine did? I start reading before I recognize the chapter:

"Not in riots and drunken parties, not in eroticism and indecencies, not in strife and rivalry, but put on the Lord Jesus Christ and make no provision for the flesh in its lusts."

On the page, there are sentences underlined in green ink with a straight-edge by Mother, after her scholarly father. In the margin next to these, my father has placed an M in a circle—for Muriel—to confirm that they are her annotations. Then there are sentences underlined with a black ballpoint: my father's. So revealing! Their respective signs never made sense to me. Mother, the Capricorn.

Dad, the Pisces. I always saw Dad as the grounded person. The Rock of Gibraltar holding strong against mother's emotional tsunamis. But here his lines billow like soft waves beneath the words and hers are straight and clear, rectilinear. Capricornian in their orderliness. Tsunamis notwithstanding, Mother's mind was the foundation of our family thought and culture. It was she who set our course and made the rules.

I see what I have not seen before on this page. The legacy is deliberate. Not only Paul's letter to the Romans but Dad's letter to us, written after my mother's death. Mother was always the articulator. Often with more words than you ever wanted to hear, coming at you like the arrows of her lines. Dad would start to tell a story but then quickly fall back on my mother's gifted tongue: "You tell it Miff. You tell it better than I do."

But nothing about my mother and father has ever communicated so eloquently as what I now read literally between the lines of this book. Dad is saying, *This is who we are. This is what we were really about.*

Green underline—Mother:

"There is no authority but by act of God, and the existing authorities are instituted by him; consequently anyone who rebels against authority is resisting a divine institution." The last three words were doubly underlined. And this, from my rebel mother! She had rebelled against her father, the Christian minister (a rebel in his own way) and resisted being bridled by authority of any kind. Yet there was an Augustinian quest in her too. In her, Odysseus's desperate and circuitous journey home.

Black underline—Dad:

"He who loves his neighbor has satisfied every claim of the law." My gentle, generous father, untroubled by anything but his wife (whom he adored) and his bills.

Green underline: Mother.

The next green line cuts straight beneath the exact phrase that seared Augustine's soul in Milan. " . . . No reveling in drunkenness, no debauchery or vice, no quarrels or jealousies." If this was a supreme challenge to the lusty Berber, it was no less so to my passionate Welsh mother, both open like Lear to the wild storms of their own natures.

Black underline—Dad

"Love cannot wrong a neighbor; therefore the whole law is summed up in love."

My mother has been gone for almost thirty years. I am older now than she was when she died. My father has been gone for ten. But today I meet them freshly and see them more clearly than I ever did before. I turn to the first blank page of the book and see my mother's name carefully inscribed by her across the top. *Muriel Ritchlin.* And in his wave-tossed letters the inscription of my father—

"To open a door,
Lots of love,
Rich"

Two blank pages later, mother has made two notations:

"Life after death, p.317"
"End of the world, p.136"

Two themes that stalked and puzzled her later years. My mother loved the occult. She wanted always to see beyond the edges of things. Edgar Cayce, Gina Cerminara's *Many Mansions*, Jane Robert's *Seth Speaks*. Books on flying saucers. She was a feminist and an astronaut before feminism and space travel. (Of the Tide commercial where two women compare sheets across a backyard fence: "Can you imagine having nothing more important to do in life than *compare sheets?*")

The day after she died, when my brother and sister and I had flown back from our various distant locations, we were all sitting in the living room when the doorbell rang. It was the UPS man delivering a package for Muriel Ritchlin. Speechlessly, I received it and bore it delicately like a relic to the others. We just stood there for a few moments, not sure what to do with it. No one really wanted to open it, but we all wanted to know what it contained. What message it carried from beyond. Mother had died suddenly, in her sleep, from a heart attack. Maybe there were answers to fill that abrupt vacancy for us.

"You do it," Dad said. Perhaps because I was the eldest.

It was a book.

The title was *Life After Life*.

I could see my mother winking at us, repeating her favorite line from Shakespeare: "There are more things in heaven and earth, Horatio, than are dreamt of in your philosophy."

She was home.

As my Mother's spirit was setting out on its mysterious journey in that August of 1977, another Voyager was taking off from Cape Canaveral. The two events are linked together in my memory and imagination. Quietly, swiftly, this Voyager moves on through the limitless dark, carrying within it a message from Gaia, literally on a Golden Record. Soundlessly past Mars and Venus, Jupiter and Saturn. On past Uranus, Neptune and Pluto, sending back our first close-up photographs of these distant relatives. In 2012, it passes the ultimate frontier in the furthest migration humans have ever known: It crosses the heliopause, an invisible boundary where the Sun's grasp—the impact of its solar winds—gives way to interstellar space. Now for the first time in this galactic immensity, Gaia sings out, proclaiming its 4.4 billion year history. Birds are singing, whales humming, splashing. The wind sighs and thunder roars. Earth sounds. Along with Bach's *Brandenburg Concerto*, Beethoven's *Fifth Symphony*, the "Queen of the Night" aria from Mozart's *Magic Flute*, the *Navajo Night Chant*, aboriginal songs from Australia, bagpipes from Azerbaijan and pan pipes from Peru. Blind Willie Johnson sings "Dark of the Night" and Louis Armstrong performs "Melancholy Blues." And there we all are—those last minute creations on New Year's Eve. . . . A mother feeds her baby, a man is crossing the African desert, children in schoolrooms, scientists in labs . . .

This ultimate migration carries the sum of all our migrations and the frontiers crossed in human understanding, including the fundamental equations discovered by our mathematicians and the structure of the DNA molecule.

The Golden Record also carries these words, written by U.S. President Jimmy Carter:

> We cast this message into the cosmos. . . . Of the 200 billion stars in the Milky Way galaxy, some—perhaps many—may have inhabited planets and space faring civilizations. If one such civilization intercepts Voyager and can understand these recorded contents, here is our message: This is a present from a small distant world, a token of our sounds, our science, our images, our music, our thoughts, and our feelings. We are attempting to survive our time so we may live into yours. We hope some day, having solved the problems we face, to join a community of galactic civilizations. This record represents our hope and our determination and our goodwill in a vast and awesome universe.

Through the miracle of technology and telemetry, we are those who go.

* * * *

Grossi Farms ~ The Present

FARMER ED IN THE DOG HOUSE

Yesterday I was trapped in my camper by another torrential downfall of rain. I was still working on the IONS* job. Still stuffing plastic bags in various corners of the lid cover over my head which continued to leak. It was so dark in the camper that I had resorted to using the precious battery time of my lamp.

When the storm finally died out in the late afternoon, I picked my way through the adobe mud, skirting small lakes and cutting over to the edge of the vineyard where I could walk on grass, away from the big equipment routes with their deep oozing ruts. I needed to borrow the Grossi's old pick-up if possible. It was late Saturday afternoon and the rains meant that a vital pumpkin selling day had been lost and the stand was closed.

When I rang the doorbell, Ed came to the door smiling, but a little cowed too. The high note of his usual humor seemed to have dropped an octave. I attributed it to the rain and immediately offered my condolences for the weather.

"Bad day at the stand I guess."

"Not too bad. We stayed open till about 2 or so. About fifteen people actually slogged through the mud to get pumpkins. People are crazy."

"I just wanted to ask if I could borrow the pick-up. And I wanted to ask Susie if we're still on for lunch tomorrow. Is she here?"

"Yeah, she's ironing." A voice rose from around the corner where stood, I knew, the trusty ironing board in front of the TV in the kitchen.

"Hi honey." Her voice wafted toward me with the steam.

"We still on for lunch tomorrow?"

---

* At that time I was a proof reader for the *Institute of Noetic Sciences Review* (later *Shift*).

"You bet."

"Can I steal her away for lunch, Eddie?"

"You can have her the whole day," he said, then quickly amended it. "Just kidding honey," he called back through the steam. He looked at me sheepishly. "I'm in deep doo-doo," he said. Uh-oh.

"What did you do, Eddie?"

"Well you know that old Mexican guy that comes around asking for our old corn?" It goes without saying that Ed always gives him whatever he wants.

"Sure I do."

"Well he came by today and said he wanted some chickens . . ."

"*For soup!*" Susie interjected from around the corner. (I was confining my muddy shoes to the Welcome mat.)

"And you know what this idiot did?" Susie's voice was rising up to the octave Ed's had left.

"He *gave* them to him." Eddie gave a futile, penitent shrug. "But here's the kicker," the steamy voice went on. "*He gave him five HENS!* Can you believe it? We've had nothing but roosters around this place making all sorts of racket so you'd *pay* someone to take them and Eddie gives away the *hens*. Farmer Ed. How many years farming? An agricultural degree from CalPoly? And he can't tell the difference between a hen and a rooster?"

"They didn't have that course in the curriculum," Ed protested meekly. The disembodied voice continued.

"I went out this morning and saw that he'd caught these chickens and I figured somebody wanted to start a flock. I put them in the barn so they wouldn't get cold. But *soup?* Wait till Jessie hears about this. Some of those are her favorites that she personally feeds. You think *I'm* mad. Wait till Jessie finds out." Jessie works in the nursery and takes charge of TLC for the chickens.

"Like I say," Ed said encouragingly. "She's free all day tomorrow."

Next day, I head toward Susie's house to meet her for lunch. I stop in front when I hear the tractor. Ed is giving a hayride, twisted around and talking to the kids as he goes, telling them about the farm. When he sees me, he calls out above the noise. "Sheri, tell Susie there's a baby Norfolk terrier down at the stand."

Susie has just come out, looking like a million. A magazine cover. "I will NOT have a dog," she says. "Never. What on earth is he thinking of? He's crazy."

Of course she said the same thing about her two beloved cats.

THE LOMBARDS

往 *(wang) This character for wang, "to go," depicts vegetation which springs up from the earth, rambling in tufts, here and there*

— G.D. WILDER AND J.H. INGRAM
Analysis of Chinese Characters

775 AD ~ *Monte Cassino, Italy*

PAUL THE DEACON

THERE ARE CERTAIN OBSCURE PEOPLE IN HISTORY, mostly immortalized in footnotes, who catch my fancy and become very much alive for me. Paul is one of those. He is remembered as Paul the Deacon, though I am not sure why. He led an active and significant life, earning the respect of no less a personage than Charlemagne and he was well-traveled for a person of his time. But I have him in my mind in a still cameo from his most inactive years—from 774-783. These may be the years that earned him the title of Deacon for they were spent in exile in the monastery of Monte Cassino.

Monte Cassino lies twenty-five miles northwest of Naples and was the first of its kind, founded by St. Benedict around 529, on the site of an ancient Temple of Apollo that had crowned the hill. We do not know for sure if Paul entered the monastery willingly or unwillingly. Paul was a Lombard, and his exile in Monte Cassino coincides with the fall of the Lombard kingdom in 774. There, in his seclusion, he has time to reflect on the fortunes and misfortunes of his people. It is a quiet interlude in an active life. The time spent in Monte Cassino brings to mind a similar period in the life of Martin Luther spent in hiding in the Wartburg castle, where he wrote his translation of the New Testament.

Paul would not actually begin his *History of the Lombards* until his return to Monte Cassino at the end of his life. In 782, Paul wrote to Charlemagne requesting release from the cloister. His wish granted, he leaves Monte Cassino and travels north to plead the case for his brother, who had led an unsuccessful revolt against Charlemagne with other Lombard nobles and was now in prison.

Paul was born around 720 to two wonderfully named parents—Warnefridus and Theudelinda. Having myself grown up among Toms, Joes, Jims and Bills, Warnefridus and Theudelinda are endowed for me with an operatic grandeur. They must have had some prominence among the Lombards because they were able to have their son educated by a well-known grammarian named Flavianus, possibly at the Lombard court at Pavia. Paul receives a classical education in the best tradition of the ancient Greek *paideia*. Dates in the 700s seem remote to us in the 21st century. 1300 years in the past. A dark age growing darker with the passage of time. Yet nearly that amount of time had passed since the emergence of the Greek *paideia* in Athens to the year of Paul's education.

The proper molding of a man's character for successful participation in polis life required a sound education in the various arts and sciences, and thus was established the *paideia*—the classical Greek system of education and training, which came to include gymnastics, grammar, rhetoric, poetry, music, mathematics, geography, natural history, astronomy and the physical sciences; history of society and ethics, and philosophy—the complete pedagogical course of study necessary to produce a well-rounded, fully educated citizen.

—RICHARD TARNAS
The Passion of the Western Mind

This cultural legacy from antiquity, which had guided Augustine's education in Roman Africa, still formed the basis of intellectual training in eighth century Italy and moved young Paul into the highest circles. King Liutprand (another great name), one of the most powerful of the Lombard kings, patronized religious figures, scholars and teachers so Paul came of age in an environment receptive to his gifts. His life continues among the operatically named. He becomes a tutor of Adelperga, the daughter of King Desiderius and wife of the Duke of Benevento. His knowledge of Latin and Greek no doubt leaves him much in demand for official needs.

Paul shows his literary flair early by writing verses to Adelperga and the Duke of Benevento. His literary skills and experience in the Lombard courts do not go unnoticed by the great Frankish King. Charlemagne is surrounding himself with learned scholars from far and wide. Paul will tutor Charlemagne's daughter Rotrude in elementary Greek and compose *The History of the Bishops of Metz* at the request of the court's archchaplain.

Following the period of his services in court, Paul joins the convent of St. Peter near Civate on Lake Como. This is important to the topography of our stories and provides a significant degree of connection to all of them: Civitate is about eight miles from Cassiacum, that "island in time" where Monica and Augustine spent such an important time together with their companions; a time that was to lay the foundation of what Augustine was to become on his return to Africa. Civate is also roughly fifty miles from Monte Carasso and many Ticinesi will pass through this neighborhood in their winters.

It is Paul's last work that interests me and impresses that single image of him in my mind. Not his illustrious activities in the great courts of Europe. Not his toiling across those high passages in the Alps to reach the court of the king to save his brother, but those quiet hours in the warm south in Mediterranean solitude at Monte Cassino when he sets pen to paper to tell the story of his people in *A History of the Lombards*. As you will see, this also forms an essential link to Dominic Grossi and the people of Ticino.

According to Paul, the Lombards—or Langobards—came from "the island which is called Scandinavia" and were known as the Winnili. "The region of the north," he writes, "in proportion as it is removed from the heat of the sun and is chilled with snow and frost, is so much more the healthful to the bodies of men and fitted for the propagation of nations, just as, on the other hand, every southern region, the nearer it is to the heat of the sun, the more it abounds in diseases and is less fitted to the bringing up of the human race." (Spoken like a true Yankee.) These sentiments notwithstanding, Paul's story is filled with the southward movement of peoples changing the face of Europe. Not a word is said about them passing a stampede of people northward, heading for that salubrious chill. It is to Naples that Paul will head to end his days, like Yankees impelled toward Floridian retirement.

Paul explains that the reason for this migration is that the healthful northern region "brings forth so many human beings that it can scarcely nourish them." Hence the emigration of many peoples who, in his words, "become the scourge of portions of Asia and parts of Europe."

He has a point. He is summarizing with marvelous economy the history of Europe during the Dark and Middle Ages. "Everywhere ruined cities throughout all Illyria and Gaul testify to this, but most of all unhappy Italy which has felt the cruel rage of nearly all the nations." He cites the Vandals, the Rugii, the Heroli and the Turcilingi among "other fierce and barbarous nations to have come from Germany." In like manner also the Winnili, that is Langobards (that is Lombards) which afterwards ruled prosperously in Italy.

For over-population or whatever reason, the Winnili set themselves on the move in large numbers under their two leaders Ibor and Aio, "brothers in the bloom of youthful vigor." In Paul's account, they abandon their native soil in search of foreign fields. They bid farewell to their own people and country and "set upon their way to seek for lands where they might dwell and establish their abodes."

Abandonment of their native soil in search of foreign fields may be more than metaphor. Over-population, climate change, any number of factors may have reduced the capacity of the land to feed its people. It is often a simple arithmetic progression which in good times leads to expansion of population that in turn brings on bad times when the land cannot support the increase. Land remains finite. Climate changes. We know that.

The name Winnili doesn't seem nearly so elegant as "Lombard" for a distinguished people but it sticks in my mind as an important key to the future of those northern people. According to one authority it means "eager for battle" and to another, it is derived from the Gothic word for "pasture." The foreign fields of the Winnili will partake of both meanings; at some times, bloody fields of battle and at others, the search for a peaceful and fertile place as far from embattled Europe as possible. For some of them it will be pastures reached by that hardy, independent people in remote valleys of the Alps.

Through Paul's eyes at Monte Cassino, the Europe-on-$5-a-Day I saw in my twenties takes on a new texture and context. Peoples on the move, just as they would later be on our own continent. Paul tells us that the brothers, Ibor and Aio will lead their people into a region called Scoringa, which was probably in the Elbe Valley of present day Germany, starting out near the mouth of the Elbe. Here, in

Paul's narrative, the pasture-seeking Winnili become the "eager for battle" Winnili when called upon by the Vandals in the region to join them in war or pay tribute. They decide that "it is better to maintain liberty by arms than stain it by the payment of tribute." They send word to the Vandals that they will fight rather than be slaves.

"The Winnili were then all in the flower of their youth, but were very few in number since they had been only the third part of one island of no great size." This is confirmed by the great Roman historian Tacitus who speaks also of the small number of Langobards, as they will be called, and describes them as being renowned as a small band surrounded by many powerful nations, yet determined to protect themselves through battle rather than through submission.

Legend tells us (through the voice of Paul's narrative) that it is in battle with the Vandals that the Winnili will receive their new name. Frea, wife of the god Wotan, beseeches her husband to bring victory to the Winnili and counsels the women of the Winnili to take down their hair and arrange it upon their faces like a beard. (The likely object of this was to make the number of warriors appear double in size.) Wotan has promised to give victory to those whom he sees first at sunrise on the day of battle. Frea secretly turns the bed around to favor the Winnili in the east, and her husband's first comment is "Who are those long-beards?"

So the Winnili, aka Langobards (long-beards), engage in a fierce battle with the Vandals, winning the victory. But victory does not guarantee them good pasture or the sustenance of the land. In time, they suffer great privation and hunger and are forced on the move again in search of a more hospitable environment.

I can understand now why historians fell back on labels like the Dark Ages and the Barbarian Invasions to avoid the hopeless task of sorting out a froth of small groups whose names seemed constantly to be changing and so defy the possibility of a tidy taxonomy or timeline. The Dark Ages were not so much dark as inscrutable. Paul had no such qualms and was blithely unaware that he was living through the Middle Ages on the way to a High Renaissance.

The Winnili-Langobards prepare to pass over into Mauringa (possibly east of the Elbe), but the Assipitti people block their way. The Assipitti people also have a large fighting force compared to the small army of the Langobards, so once again, the Langobards resort to trickery. They spread the word that they have among them Cynocephali—"men with dogs' heads who wage war obstinately and drink human blood." Then they set up their tents out over a wide area and kindle many fires in their camps to give the impression of a great army. The Assipitti are duly frightened and decide not to attempt a battle. They choose instead another course of action: They have a very powerful man whom they trust to vanquish anyone put up against him in combat. They challenge the Langobards to send one of their warriors to fight this man, on the condition that if their own warrior wins, the Langobards will "depart the way they had come." If the Langobards win, the Assipitti will not challenge their passage through their territories.

The Langobards are in a quandary about whom they should choose to go against this formidable adversary until a certain man "of servile rank" offers himself on a condition of his own: If he wins, the stain of slavery will be removed from him and his offsping. This agreed to, he fights and conquers his Assipitti rival, winning for the Langobards the means of passage and for himself and his descendants, the rights of liberty.

This is a telling story, confirmed in its essence by later historians. A precedent is established among the Langobards: "In order that they might increase the number of their warriors, that they confer liberty upon many whom they deliver from the yoke of bondage, and that the freedom of these may be regarded as established, they confirm it in their accustomed way by an arrow, uttering certain words of their country in confirmation of the fact." This custom of incorporating those peoples whom they subjugated in their wanderings into the body of warriors and freemen seems only to have been granted among the Franks and Langobards. It made of the Langobards, in Paul's words, a composite race. Their languages and institutions, as well as their ultimate success as a people, were no doubt affected by this. This system of emancipation will have an important effect upon furthering the union of the Langobards and Romans after the Italian conquest. But that is getting ahead of Paul's story.

In time, the Langobards see a need to ordain a king for themselves, rather than remaining under the rule of chiefs or dukes. These fiercely independent people had always ruled themselves by a general assembly which selected their leaders. The long history of wars during their wanderings convinced them that they needed a single commander-in-chief—a king—who could represent their developing nation in foreign affairs and the negotiation of treaties.

In Paul's account, Agelmund, son of Aio is chosen. This is likely a collapsing of time for the sake of story, since a longer period is inferred by the events and the first King would have been generations after Aio and Ibor. But it is the story, the rough sketch of a people we are after, and this expansion and then consolidation of the Winnili as they travel south shows them maturing into the formidable Langobards who will find themselves in the midst of the greater machinations of European power politics, playing major and decisive roles.

CONSTANTINE

MONICA IS BORN IN THE TIME OF CONSTANTINE THE GREAT. History is literally pivoting on its axis with Constantine, as we have seen. He is born in a town in present day Serbia while the Langobards are pasturing in the Elbe Valley. His father, an army officer, is raised to the rank of Caesar as co-emperor and he is sent to serve in the court of Maximian in the Empire of the West. Constantine, however, was brought up in the court of the "senior emperor" Diocletian. (Remember, it was Diocletian who decided to divide the empire in this way in 295, placing Maximian in the West at Mediolanum-Milan.) After the usual series of political intrigues, murders and conquests, Constantine defeats Maxentius, the son of Maximian, at the battle of Milvian Bridge to become emperor of the West. Legend has it that on the night before the battle, Constantine has a dream in which he is instructed to paint the Christian monogram ☧ (the *chi rho*) on the shields of his men. Constantine attributes his victory to the Christian God, whom he worships thereafter.

This is a man who has been raised in the court of Diocletian, in a period in which some of the worst persecutions of Christians had taken place. As we saw in Monica's story, his conversion to Christianity results in the Edict of Milan,* and paves the way for a major shift in European Christianity. From now on, Christianity would be transformed from the religion of the lamb to the religion of the lion, becoming a potent player in the political dynamics of Europe. In 325, Constantine convenes the Council of Nicaea, inviting 1800 Christian bishops from throughout the empire, with the exception of Britain. It is at this council that the date of Easter is officially set and the Nicene Creed is created, which is still recited in Christian churches today.

Constantine becomes ruler of both East and West after defeating the Emperor of the East in 324, and the Empire is reunited. In his search for the most effective geographical center for the administration of his empire, he tries several places, including Milan and Ticinum (Pavia), and finally settles on the old Greek city of Byzantium, which he will rebuild and name New Rome, although it will later be called Constantinople (Istanbul). Here he will raise one of the greatest churches of Christendom, the Hagia Sophia, "Divine Wisdom." For a thousand years the church and the city will remain cultural icons. Wave after wave of crusaders, the noble and the brutal, the devout and the mercenary, will flow over the city until it falls finally at the hands of the Mongols in 1453.

The movement of the capital of the empire from Rome to a location almost a thousand miles east to Byzantium-Constantinople in 330, will have profound political and religious effects on the empire in the short term. As we have begun to see in Monica's time, the Western sector of the Roman Empire increasingly weakens

---

* While the Edict of Milan concerned more than the rights of Christians, its granting of religious liberty to Christians and the restoration of their properties and meetings places is what it is most remembered for.

as control of the empire moves east. This will be important to the Langobards in the future as they begin to move out of the Elbe Valley. Having intensified their reputation as "eager for war" during their engagements with various tribes, the Langobards are on an inevitable path toward engagement with one Roman Emperor or another. The 6 degrees of separation surely applies to rulers great and small of a small continent like Europe. The Langobards, the Vandals, the Assipitti, Gepidae, Hermanuli, Heroli and a host of groups are seeking a foothold just beyond the reach of the Roman Empire.

According to Paul's account, it is the emperor Justinian who takes notice of the Langobards' prowess in war and enlists them as allies and confederates of his empire. It may also be Justinian who fomented a war between the Langobards and the Gepidae in an effort to break up a friendship between two peoples who could threaten his empire. In the end, he decided to back the Langobards and sent an army of ten thousand Roman cavalry and three thousand Heroli against the Gepidae, with the result that the Gepidae made peace with the Langobards, although the conflict continued intermittently.

ENTER THE LOMBARDS

Now it is official: The Langobards—we may now call them the Lombards, as history does—have appeared on the horizon, descending from the heights of the Alps where they have crossed over from Pannonia—the ancient Roman province of central Europe including present-day western Hungary and the northwest Balkan Peninsula. In 568, pressed by groups on the north and east of them, 130,000 Lombards—men, women, children and baggage—make the slow and difficult crossing of the northeastern Alps into the rich plains of the Po Valley. Within five years, they will hold Verona, Milan, Florence and Pavia, which they make their capital. In 643, their king Rothari publishes a code of laws that proposes to protect the poor against the rich and provides for freedom of worship. By 744, under their most powerful king, Liutprand, their kingdom will extend through northern and central Italy.

The Lombards develop a progressive civilization in which the king is elected and advised by a council of notables. His legislation is usually submitted to a popular assembly of all free males of military age. In 774, the Frankish king Charlemagne, whom we meet in Paul's story, sweeps down into Pavia and has himself crowned there as "King of the Lombards."

King Desiderius, Paul's royal patron, is banished to a monastery and Paul himself takes up residence at Monte Cassino, likely under duress, and writes his history.

Pavia, Italy ~ 720

AUGUSTINE AND LIUTPRAND

AUGUSTINUS AURELIUS IS TRAVELING BY BOAT from Sardinia to Genoa. He sails by night in a small ship, leaving from the port of Cagliari. They are following a route that the vessel plies regularly, carrying trade goods to the Genoese republic on the mainland. It is April and the sea is still unpredictable, still threatened by sudden storms. It would have been better to wait until the drier summer months when the sea lay calm between island and coast. Augustinus Aurelius had never liked journeys by sea. But a sense of urgency lay over the mission.

In Genoa, rain falls heavily on the cobbled streets and rooftops and the clattering hooves of horses drawing the royal coach through the city go mostly unnoticed. The coach carries no emblem to identify it, although its interior is of a quality to guarantee the comfort of its passengers—a king and a bishop. The errand is a secret one but of highest importance. In a hidden container of the coach, the king carries with him twenty thousand gold pieces. They are on their way to receive Augustinus Aurelius, who will travel with them back to Pavia. The king is Liutprand. Augustinus is about to become a Lombard. Posthumously.

The year is 718, two years before the birth of Paul the Deacon to Warnefridus and Theudalinda.

It is such a small, rather secretive event and doesn't appear in the major history books. But it is a key event in our particular story of things. Africa has made another significant incursion into Eurasia, albeit a much more quiet and gentle one in its way. North Africa meets Lombardy. The Berber saint will be laid to rest just sixty miles from that place of his youth, Cassiacum.

Seven years earlier, an army of seven thousand Berber infantry and three hundred Arab cavalry under the brilliant Berber leader Tariq ibn Ziyad had crossed the narrow strait between the Atlantic and Mediterranean known in ancient times as the Pillars of Hercules. He lands at Gibraltar, which will hereafter bear his name— Jabal al Tariq in Arabic, Gibraltar in the Anglicized version. It means the Rock of Tariq. Through this incursion of the North African army into Europe—specifically into Spain—Tariq's army successfully deposes the Visigoth king, Rodrigo. Since that time, Arab conquerors and pirates have been harassing the coastal cities of Sardinia. The leaders of the Church of San Saturnius in Caligari have grown fearful that their greatest treasure might be plundered. One could say that Augustinus Aurelius is up for sale and has gone to the highest bidder. Of course we don't know any of these details for certain as the story is hidden in layers of legend.

Augustine had returned to Africa after his mother's death in 386. He sold his patrimony and gave the money to the poor, keeping only his house. This he converted into a monastic center for himself and his friends, continuing in a more formal way what had begun there on the Lombard plain in Cassiacum. In 391, he was ordained as a priest in Hippo Regius (now Annaba, Algeria) and later became the Bishop of Hippo. The Vandals invaded North Africa and laid siege to Hippo Regius in 430. Augustine was already ill when this occurred and he died in August of that year. Although the Vandals burned the town, Augustine's cathedral and his library were preserved.

Decades later, the Vandal King Huneric expelled the Catholic Bishops, and it was at this time, according to the early historian Bede, that Augustine's remains were removed to Cagliari in Sardinia, where they lay in peace until another invasion occurred—this time from the south, as Tariq ibn Ziyad led the Moorish invasion into Spain. Once again there was upheaval along the fault line of two continents, and Augustine's eternal rest, at least of his earthly remains, was threatened. Thus it is that in the spring of 718, nearly three centuries after Augustine's death, the Lombard king Liutprand embarks upon his secret mission.

For some strange reason, it will not be until October that the saint is finally laid to rest in a church in Lombardy and even then, a controversy will arise centuries later as to his exact location within the church. Augustine in death seems to drift farther and farther from Augustine in life. It makes one seriously question the advantages of immortality.

One final note, here in our Mediterranean landscape on the isle of Sardinia,

which lies almost due north of Tagaste and Carthage. While Augustine's remains are enjoying a venerable if temporary rest on the southeast of the island near Cagliari, there lies on the northwest coast the less venerated remains of an anonymous person who is now into his or her second millennium of undisturbed rest. The twentieth century gives this individual some passing recognition for an image on a wall nearby. The figure of a labyrinth, very reminiscent of the Cretan labyrinth we have met on coins and in other places. It has been recorded as the oldest labyrinth on record, dated at 2000 to 2500 BC, although some have suggested that it was inscribed at a later date. What might interest us even more is that several ancient writers have placed Daedalus here at the end of his life. David McCullough, who brought our John Adams so richly alive in his biography of him, recently turned his pen to a work on labyrinths and mazes in *The Unending Mystery*. "Daedalus went on to die a peaceful death of old age in Sardinia where, coincidentally, one of the oldest known rock carvings of a labyrinth—dating probably from 1500 BC—was found on the wall of a tomb near Luzzanas."

2500, 2000, 1500 BC.... What matters to us now is the repetition, the rhythmic iteration, of an image that flares out into story; into meaning. Gaia comes together first, according to our larger story, as Pangaea. Pangaea breaks apart into new continents. Africa then moves back toward Eurasia in the "Christmas Day" collision. The globe takes shape within another rhythm paced by the human mind: A flat earth. A round earth. A globe. The human psychic creation of the Earth within its imagination continues to evolve and be refined. The labyrinth—born of primordial spirals found on rocks and cave walls throughout the world—serves as a potent degree of connection and fulfills the mind's reach toward apprehension of that whole in which we find our ourselves, savoring the last sip of champagne on New Year's Eve.

TARIQ

Ceuta, North Africa, 711

Assalamu alaikum wa rahmatullah
Peace be upon you and God's blessings
Assalamu alaikum wa rahmatullah
Peace be upon you and God's blessings

TARIQ IBN ZIYAD ROSE FROM HIS PRAYERS *and stepped out of his tent into the deepening night. He gazed up at his counselors and friends, Deneb, Rigel, Aldebaran and the three stars of the belt—Mintaka, Alnilam and Alnitak. The sight of the brilliant stars which had watched over him through his childhood took him back to those early years in the Wadi Tafna, sitting on the banks of the river, dreaming his simple child's dreams. His life had been anything but simple, and all of it, beyond those dreams. The memory that always returned to him as the touchstone and talisman of his life was the journey he had taken with his father and uncle. It had been his father's idea to give him what he described as the essential education and initiation into manhood, a trip south with the great salt caravan. His father had planned from beginning to end how he would teach his son about his ancestry and the ways of the land that his people, the Berbers, had occupied since the beginning of time.*

They had left from the city of Tlemcen, after his father had shown him how the Tafna River disappears under the mountain to create a series of deep caverns. There they joined a donkey train which would carry salt, cloth, beads, and metal south to the edge of the Sahara, where the caravans began. Goods would then be transferred to camels and they would set out across the desert. At the southern rim of the Sahara, the cargo would be exchanged for gold, ivory, and other goods. The caravans would then return, carrying the new cargo north, while donkeys and porters took the original cargo to places farther south.

When he was five, Tariq and his family fled into the mountains to escape the Arab army of Hassan ibn Naaman, which was advancing out of Egypt. Arab armies had been continually seeking to conquer their lands, but the Berbers put up a fierce resistance and succeeded in driving them back. Queen Kahine of the Zenata tribe— the tribe of his mother's family—had called them all into the mountains. Many of the Zenata people were converts to Judaism, as some of his father's people had been converts to Christianity in the time of their Berber ancestor who became the Bishop of Hippo. True to her name, the Prophetess, Queen Kahina had foreseen the serious danger from Hassan ibn Naaman's army. She called all of her relations into her protection. As they were about to depart, word came that the Arab army had reached Carthage and razed it to the ground.

Yet nothing in Tariq's childhood could prepare him for the terror, thrill and awe of that journey south. He had never ridden a camel before or seen for himself that the desert is an endless sea of waves and the waves are of sand.

◆ ◆ ◆

From Tlemcen, they cross the high plateau, rimmed with mountains, ascending along their eastern edge through forests of cedar, oak and pine, catching glimpses of wild bear, sheep and gazelle. When they reach Ain Sefra, known as the gateway to the Sahara, they can see to the south the rugged beauty of the Atlas mountains. The land drops steeply to the east for about three thousand feet to red dunes that seem to roll in across the vast distance to lap against the mountain's base. There they begin the descent toward the desert and the trek to the gathering place of the caravan at the Tuat oases.

After the emptiness of the erg, the desert of dunes that they had crossed to reach the oasis, Tuat is a lively and welcome center of life, teeming with groups arriving from the north, some as merchant traders but many others as refugees, fleeing the Arab armies which are once again advancing out of Egypt after their earlier defeat by the Kahina's armies.

The Tuat region is not a single oasis but a string of fertile oases and small hamlets that stretch in a line south for many miles. There has been a large population of Jews there since the second century, but they are now about to be overwhelmed by the numbers of Zenata people arriving. The Kahina herself is a converted Jew, like many of the Zenata, so this is a natural place for them take refuge. As they leave the oasis headed south, the sight of thousands of camels moving in endless lines that reach as far as the eye can see will remain imprinted on Tariq's mind for the rest of his life.

They reach Timimoun in the mid-morning. Its distinctive red mud buildings are vibrant in the morning sunshine. The town is built at the edge of an escarpment that overlooks an ancient salt lake toward a vista of sand dunes stretching far into the distance. The narrow streets are thronged with donkeys laden with merchandise to be transported south and with the household goods of the refugees who will take up new lives among the people here.

From Timimoun, they continue on to In Salah. It is at In Salah, at the eastern edge of the oasis, that Tariq first meets Juba. Juba has been his uncle's guide and protector since he began leading caravans south as a young man. Juba is one of the "blue men" who ride alongside the caravan for protection on light, swift camels, or ride on ahead to scout the waterholes. They are Tauregs, nomads of the desert, and another branch of the Berber tribes. They hold power over the major caravan routes and wells and many have grown prosperous from the fees they charge for protecting large caravans. Juba's weathered face shows the years he has spent in the harsh Sahara landscape, but it is home to him and he knows it like the face of a friend. Walking beside him at the head of the caravan, Tariq learns to see the desert with new eyes. His first glimpse of the red dunes from Ain Sefra is a bewitching sight. Awesome and beautiful with their subtle curves and soft billows and in places, sharp knife-life crests that reach as high as a thousand feet. But the charm of that first sight wears off as they walk through them hour after hour in temperatures that reach over 110 degrees. In order to cross the desert as quickly as possible, they rise in the middle of the night, traveling for seventeen hours on end with only brief rests and a meager meal of millet, dates and water. Riding a camel part of the time—perched atop the camel's load—only offers an alternative torture since he has difficulty at first finding a comfortable position. In some places, the nights are frigid cold, the temperatures *dropping dramatically from the searing heat of the day.*

After a while, however, he falls into the mesmerizing rhythm of the patient, enduring camels and the vast empty landscape. His conversations with Juba help to pass the time. It is Juba who teaches him about the stars and how to use them as navigation aids. At every moment, Juba seems to know exactly where he is and what lies ahead, although the landscape of dunes is to Tariq's eyes an endless and shifting surface with nothing distinctive on the horizon to tell one place from another. He asks Juba about this. The deeply rutted face of the old man creases into a smile that reveals the gaps in his teeth but is full of patient humor.

"When you look out there," he says, "you see sand, do you not?"

"Of course. What else it there to see? What do you see?"

"I see wind. Everywhere."

"What wind? It is still as glass out there."

"The erg is filled with the footsteps of the wind. It is made of wind, cutting its patterns into crests and gullies and ripples. Wind is the great enemy out here and the sands move to its command. When I look, I can see that the blast of the sirocco has been through here and very likely we will meet up with it in the next day or two. It is wind that makes the dunes sing."

In two days, the bright blue sky suddenly darkens into a yellow fog and a collective cry of alarm ripples through the long line of camels and men. Tariq is walking beside his father and uncle, stumbling in a haze of heat and exhaustion, when they suddenly couch their camels and instruct him to cover his face completely and huddle into the leeward side of the animals. His heart nearly leaps out of his chest as a great roar is heard and the powdery sand rolls over them like a tsunami. It goes on like this for what seems like hours, though it may have been less. When it finally passes, the sand has penetrated into every crevice and invaded all of their supplies. There is never a meal, never a drink that is not heavily laced with it.

From the great sand seas of the erg, they pass into landscapes known as regs—vast flat plains covered with stones. There are stretches where they travel four hundred miles between watering places, arriving parched and on the edge of desperation. The bones of camels and men litter these places, reminders that the desert is fickle and the long-sought wells are sometimes dry. One of these stretches lies between the salt flats of Taodenni, where the caravan has taken on large blocks of salt for sale in the south, and the well at Arawan.

◆ ◆ ◆

Timbuktu.

They arrive just after dawn.

Tariq's first feeling is one of triumph and relief that they have survived the difficult journey but that quickly gives way to disappointment. What had he expected? Not this meager collection of small sandstone dwellings that is barely noticeable against the landscape. The camels respond eagerly to the sparse layer of grass. Not luxuriant palms but tough little thorn trees dot the landscape.

As the sun lifts over the rim of the desert and news of the caravan's arrival spreads, the small town comes to life and Tariq is busied with the chores of watering the camels and setting up camp beyond the town. In the next two days, merchants from the caravan and merchants in Timbuktu will enter the lengthy process of negotiating the sale of their goods. Tariq asks his uncle what the few merchants in a sparsely populated place like Timbuktu would want with their luxury items brought from the port of Algeria. In response his uncle extends his arms toward the east and toward the west. "There is a very old route that passes through here from the distant lands of Arabia and Egypt in the east, to the gold fields in the west. Some of these goods will be sold at a good price on the caravan's return. Timbuktu may not look like much to you as a town, but its value lies in its location on both the north-south and east-west caravan routes. At the other end of the village is a large warehouse maintained and protected by Tuaregs where the goods are stored between the arrival of the caravans."

Tariq has known from the beginning that his father will leave him here in Timbuktu while the caravan continues south to Kano, its final destination. There in the grasslands of the Sahel, the camels will be put out to pasture for a season to prepare them for the next trip north. But his father has been mysterious about the reason for this separation and the prospect of staying on in the desolate little town by himself is not an appealing one. What could his father possibly have in mind for him?

Once the buying and selling of goods among the merchants is completed, his father tells him to load up his camel and prepare for a short journey. This surprises him.

"But you said I would be staying on in Timbuktu."

"Not in Timbuktu, but near it." Looking around him he can see nothing beyond the little cluster of sandstone houses but he knows better than to press his father on the subject. He will know the answers soon enough.

They have ridden for only an hour or so when a large goatskin tent comes into view. As they get closer, several smaller ones can be seen nearby.

"Are they Taureg nomads?" he asks.

"Nomads, yes. Tauregs no, although they are related. These are Sanhaja Berbers of my own family."

Tariq is surprised that his prosperous merchant father would have such poor relatives in so remote a region. His heart sinks further as he begins to suspect that his future for the next three months lies in this desolate place.

He is in for a great surprise.

Tariq has never seen such a luxurious interior in any of the houses he has been in on the coast. The tent is much bigger than it appears from the outside. It is open across the long front and on the other walls hang rich tapestries, which Tariq recognizes as among the best of Berber designs and materials. Draped across the ceiling are swathes of colorful silk that must have come from the East, like the carved ivory tables and ornate bronze lamps. The floor too is strewn with richly colored rugs and plush embroidered pillows, some inset with small mirrors. There are low divans and ornaments of fine-worked gold. A silver tea pot, tray and cups sit on a low, elegantly carved table of a wood unfamiliar to him.

It isn't until his eyes have adjusted from the outdoor glare that he can see an elderly man, attired in a brown burnous and turquoise turban, sitting in the rear of the tent and beckoning them forward.

The first thing he notices are the startling blue eyes that watch him intently as he approaches. A neatly trimmed mustache covers his upper lip and his jaw is clean-shaven. Although he is clearly very old, there is something about him that seems quite young, fresh. Perhaps it is his alertness.

"Tariq, this is Ameqran, the man I call my Father, but he is the brother of my grandfather. He is also my teacher and in these months, out of the generosity of his heart, he will be your teacher. During this time you may call him Father as well and you should honor and obey him as you have honored and obeyed your own parents. It is a great privilege to study with him and what you learn here will remain with you your whole life, as it has with me."

With those words, and a touch of his hand, his father turned and vanished from his life, though only until the caravan moved north again in three months. Now as he turns back to Ameqran, the man he would call Father, he sees in the shadows a young man sitting very still, with his head bent.

"Asmun, come and meet your new brother," the old man says to him. Tariq is surprised at the size of Asmun when he stands up. He is unusually tall, with broad shoulders and dark wavy hair. As he steps forward, his keen brown eyes raise to Tariq's with a light and warmth that brings him the first sense of comfort he has experienced since arriving in Timbuktu.

"You will be studying together, Tariq. Asmun has been brought here like you by his father, who is my own son. You are both most welcome in my household and I hope you will be blessed by your time here."

From then on, Tariq and Asmun are inseparable, sitting most days at the side of their old Father; every day more impressed by the scope of his knowledge. He has close by him a large carven ivory chest inside of which he keeps precious rolls of writings that have been brought to him over the years from Egypt, India, Greece, Rome and, more recently, from Arabia. These are his richest treasures from the caravans that have passed through here over many decades. Each of these becomes a source of study, through the old man's translations. His knowledge of languages seems endless—Greek, Latin, Copt, Hebrew, Arabic . . . As a young man, he had traveled in all of these places and often lingered to study with a teacher and learn a new language. From Greece have come treatises on astronomy filled with detailed diagrams of the movements of stars and planets, as well as writings in history and philosophy. From Egypt have come manuscripts on medicine and magic and writings on the soul's journey after death. There are Hebrew writings from Talmudic scholars as well as Egyptian Coptic writings from the Christian gospels. And now, he shows them, new works are being circulated from Arabia. He has managed to get hold of one of the early copies of the Koran, as dictated by the prophet Mohammad. His father, who had also been a merchant-scholar like himself, had met the prophet in Mecca, where there is a great marketplace around the Ka'aba—a center of pilgrimage even before the arrival of Islam. At Muhammad's request, his father had led a group of his followers into Abyssinia to escape persecution from Meccan tribes.

"I do not expect that you will become astronomers or physicians or prophets, although you may become teachers in ways you little expect. But to have this understanding of the richness of this world and of its knowledge is to nourish wisdom and guide you in whatever path you may choose."

More valuable than his rare and extensive library, in which he has invested the greater part of his wealth, are the stories and insights of Ameqran himself. Through his eyes, they see places in the world that are far beyond the borders of their lives. He also seems to be able to see into the future and to predict, like the Kahina, events that lay ahead on their path.

After the first week, they are joined by another boy named Izri, who is a year younger than Tariq yet filled with the energy of two people. He is small and lively in contrast to Asmun, but he falls naturally into their fellowship and quickly absorbs the teachings of Ameqran.

Their days are not all spent in passive study. Ameqran has assigned the captain of his guards to their training in horsemanship and the use of weapons. They learn to ride the lighter Taureg camels bred for racing and enter into competition with the best of the young Taureg riders.

The three months speed by and come, for them, too soon to an end. On the last day, they sit in the tent with their spiritual Father as he gives them final instructions.

"You have learned a good deal now of distant lands and I have shared with you learning from their wisest men. This is a treasure you can never lose, however poor you may be in other ways. I have one last treasure to share with you, which is the gift of ancient people of your own land." They waited for him to produce a scroll from the carven chest, but he made no move toward it. His keen blue eyes settled on each of them with a glint of amusement as he saw their curiosity turn to puzzlement. Finally he told them that this work is not in his possession and they would have to journey to find it.

"You will take your leave of me tomorrow and go with my blessing. Bilal will lead you to the location of my last gift, which you must hold as a secret among you for the rest of your lives. You will see your own land in a new way, and understand that it is very old and everlasting. Bilal will take you then to the place where you can rendezvous with the caravan heading north."

They travel northeast, through the Air Massif and into the mountains of the Hoggar until they arrive at the beautiful oasis of Djanet at the foot of the Tassili plateau, whose cliffs rise from fifteen hundred to twenty-three hundred feet before them. The first three days of travel from there is on easy ground and their light camels make good time. But once they reach the foot of the Asakao pass, the climbing becomes treacherous and difficult. They emerge into an open landscape rimmed with picturesque hills but the wind blows hard and bitterly cold across the open landscape. From here the path narrows into a steep ascent and the loose scree proves treacherous for the camels. They strain and balk at obstacles, sometimes cutting their feet on the sharp edges of the rocks. But Bilal caresses and cajoles them until they press forward. At the top of the pass, a magnificent panorama opens up in all directions revealing the contrasting landscapes of mountain and desert that make up the Sahara. Soon after, they reach a wadi where the camels are able to graze and take their rest. There have been recent rains and the camels drink their fill of the fresh water. Wildflowers bloom in small patches among the sparse vegetation of the wadi. They trek on then into the darkness to a place Bilal has chosen for their camp.

At dawn, a mist has risen and dew has frozen on their blankets and supplies. They trudge on against an icy wind across a bare plateau until they reach huge rock barriers. Here the monotonous landscape suddenly breaks into gigantic, otherworldly shapes of sandstone pinnacles, columns and valleys. They are surrounded on every side by monumental pillars unlike anything they have ever seen. They walk on through what might have been the ruins of ancient cities with spires and plazas and avenues, but which are only the wildly diverse shapes that have been carved out of the sandstone.

By water.

It is Izri who first figures it out. He says so to Bilal, who only smiles and keeps walking. "How could this be possible?" says Asmun. "The Sahara is the driest place in the world. Look how desiccated this landscape is. Even flash floods from the wadis couldn't produce something like this. These pillars look to be shaped by giant rivers where there ARE no rivers."

"Tassili n'Ajjer," Tariq says suddenly. "That means 'the place of the rivers'."

"Fine," said Asmun. "But where are they?"

After walking for three days through this landscape, they arrive just before nightfall at a large natural amphitheatre about a thousand yards across and surrounded by tall cliffs, eroded at their bases, forming caverns. These caverns provide a welcome shelter for the travelers and Bilal indicates that they will set up a base there. The next morning, Bilal beckons them to follow him and they begin to explore this curious new setting. Once again they have the feeling of being in an ancient city, with a plaza at its center and avenues snaking out in all directions toward recesses in the cliffs that are as commodious as houses. As they explore these recesses at Bilal's direction, they make the most extraordinary discoveries. Ameqran's last treasure soon becomes clear to them.

The walls of the shelters are filled with hundreds of paintings of human figures and of animals—many of which they have never seen. There are warriors mounted on steeds, racing, with javelins raised; horses drawing chariots, cattle with their cattle-herders, mouflon sheep pursued by dogs, giraffes, antelope. They are shocked at the sight of such large herds of cattle where not even one could survive today. Discussing it among themselves, they realize that they are looking at groups of people who have survived in quite different ways in the same region. There are hunters in some scenes, herders in others, and in more recent paintings, warriors and chariots, where no chariots could possibly pass.

As evening falls, they sit before their fire and talk long into the night about what they are seeing. Bilal is not especially talkative, but he answers their questions when he can.

"Have you been here often?" they ask him on the first night.

"Many times, with my master. When he was younger, he brought students here himself, but I was always with him."

"How does he explain these strange creatures we are seeing and this strange landscape?" Izri asked.

"He studied all of this for many years and talked to as many of the older local people as he could find. Also, he has traveled in places where there are elephants, lions, river horses that you may know as hippopotamus, and other such creatures as can be found in places like the Sahel, green and full of water. In his own life time he has seen the desert grow drier and the rainfall decrease. It is clear to him that this was once a place where large rivers ran and cattle were raised. They depict different periods of history but even the most recent of the paintings—those with horses and chariots—are quite old, he says. The chariots likely belonged to Carthaginians. At a certain point the cattle disappear in the paintings and he believes that is because the rivers dried up and could no longer support them."

They found Tuareg women and children in some of the shelters whose husbands were away on caravans. They had built small corrals of stones to shelter their goats.

Continuing on from their first camp, they arrive at a rocky citadel that hangs over a steep gorge. This too has been cut through with winding passages like an ancient labyrinth. Once again the walls are filled with paintings. Life-size figures are painted in red ochre. Enormous cats, war chariots, more scenes of cattle.

Their next camp is at Jabbaran, a small sandstone massif that rises from the Tassili plateau. The shelters scooped out of the rocks by erosion are deeper than those they have encountered elsewhere. After crossing a barren plateau, they arrive at a group of sandstone domes at the bottom of a depression. As they proceed, the rock forms become more numerous and more majestic. Once again a virtual city in stone opens up to them and the walls are covered with hundreds of paintings. The word Jabbaran means "giant" in the Taureg language and they are indeed that. In a deep shelter with a concave ceiling they find a figure that measures some eighteen feet high. It can only be recognized as such when standing away at a distance, and even then, it is barely recognizable. It has a huge round white head with a double oval in the middle of the face. Asmun comments that as many as twelve different cultures are represented in this group of paintings. Oxen of all sizes, painted in a variety of styles. Lines of exquisite delicacy. Giraffe, elephant, antelope, wild ass, goat and domesticated sheep. A hunting scene is comprised of no less than one hundred thirty-five figures, all vividly realistic—hunters with bows, a wounded rhinoceros shedding blood, on the point of charging. They calculate that the painting occupies over sixty square feet. The top figures are more than twelve feet from the ground. There are thousands of bits of pottery, hundreds of grinding stones, bone fossils, arrow points, stone axes.

In another area of the cave paintings there appears the large figure of a kneeling woman, nearly six feet in height, her head leaning against her arm. Her face has a purity of line and elongated eyes that give the effect of a classical Mediterranean beauty. On her head is a diadem, indicating her high position. Queen Dido perhaps or a goddess. Bilal observes that her hand is draped with a knotted veil, like those worn by Taureg women when they sing as a choir at wedding festivals.

The following day, they climb the Aouanrhet cliffs that rise high above Jabaran like an eagle's eerie, six-thousand feet up slippery scree that challenges their camels.

Izri, light as a mountain goat, prefers to scamper ahead on foot, finding shortcuts among the rocks. They are rewarded for their efforts when they reach the rock shelter where they find more paintings that identify it as an ancient, sacred place, further attested to by its remoteness. There are two figures of women around five feet tall. One figure is fading and has been overpainted with the figure of a man in red ochre with a striped body and wearing a mask of an antelope's head with horns. Under that is a large, bonnet-like covering, and there are two ears, barred with two parallel lines. The legs are straddled, like those of a man on horseback. Blossoming flowers, like tulips, spring from his arms and thighs, like a god of vegetation.

Nearby in an isolated rock shelter is another remarkable figure: The graceful shape of a woman, running, finely painted in yellow ochre and outlined in white. One of her legs just touches the ground, while the other is raised high in the air, mid-stride. From her outstretched arms and from her knees and belt fall delicate fringes waving lightly in the wind. Two horns extend on either side of the head and around and above them, a mass of dots that resembles a cloud of grain falling from a wheat field. The body is covered from the shoulders to the belly, at the base of the back and on the breast, with curious decorative designs. Parallel rows of white spots with red lines likely representing scarification, as could be seen in many places in Africa. The rounded curves of the figure suggest the robust and graceful bodies of negro women to the south. It is the most finished and elegantly painted work they have yet seen.

On the same rock face there is a kneeling woman, a man blowing a trumpet, and most surprising of all, a huge, decorated fish. Also a floating woman, and what appears to them as a man emerging from an egg.

The very inaccessibility of this suggests that it is a rare and ritual sight. A sanctuary. A high place for religious initiation, hidden from the rest of the world.

Continuing on they reach the Sefar massif, where once again Bilal leads them through remarkable ancient galleries. The main access is through a deep canyon, with tributary canyons cut through the rock as in previous places. The massif is made of many different levels, some like cities suspended in the air filled with gigantic rock formations, which dwarf the small party climbing among them. Strange figures from another world continue to appear in the rock art. Domesticated dogs and women doing field work suggest a time of agriculture. Some places are so inaccessible that they have great difficulty reaching them. In one such area, there is a large antelope in red ochre and a pregnant woman, lying on her back as if she were about to give birth, suggesting a maternity or fertility cult. Praying women often appear, as well as the presence of large animals; in one site, a lion more than twelve feet long. Elephants, giraffes, mouflons, warthogs, antelopes . . . An entire world teeming with life on silent rock.

Given the unusual setting, the perspectives on the figures is often startling. The boys are taken back by an eight foot tall figure with a large white head and women of smaller size, raising their arms toward the giant as if in supplication. A sensation of the power and mystery, the sacredness of the place, fills each of them.

At their final campfire on the Tassili plateau, they explore together with Bilal the meaning of Ameqran's final gift to them. "If the master were here, he would tell you that this is the oldest book in the world. He calculates that most of the paintings are thousands of years old and provide a long history, not only of the people, but of the land itself. Of change. Constant change, just as he says you are about to see in your own lives."

Ameqran had told them this. Events are shaping up, he said, that would change the face of Africa once again and each of them would have a part to play. With this last gift, they decide, he is offering also his last lesson: even those changes would change and become just one more scene in this long long history of the land.

✦ ✦ ✦

Tariq's reveries are broken by the sound of soft footfalls behind him. Asmun appears on his right, and just as he had done, stands looking at the stars, without a word. Moments later, he hears firm, quick footsteps to his left and Izri appears. "Everything is ready," he says. Tariq nods. It is clear now what Ameqran had been preparing them for those many years ago. The time has come.

At dawn of that day in 711, Tariq ibn Ziyad led a force of 7,000 men, mostly Berbers from all of the tribes, across the eight mile strait which separates Africa from Spain. Once they are all across, he establishes his base atop a gigantic rock and from there, he speaks to his troops, prior to sending them into battle against the Visigoths who are the rulers of Spain.

Oh my warriors, whither would you flee? Behind you is the sea, before you, the enemy. You have left now only the hope of your courage and your constancy. Put far from you the disgrace from which you flee in dreams, and attack this monarch who has left his strongly fortified city to meet you.

Remember that if you suffer a few moments in patience, you will afterward enjoy supreme delight. Do not imagine that your fate can be separated from mine, and rest assured that if you fall, I shall perish with you, or avenge you. The one fruit which he desires to obtain from your bravery is that the word of God shall be exalted in this country, and that the true religion shall be established here. The spoils will belong to yourselves.

*Remember that I place myself in the front of this glorious charge which I exhort you to make. At the moment when the two armies meet hand to hand, you will see me, never doubt it, seeking out this Roderick, tyrant of his people, challenging him to combat, if God is willing.**

The truth is that Tariq ibn Ziyad, an Algerian Berber** like Monica and Augustine, does not step upon the world stage until this momentous crossing. Like Augustine, he will become a pillar of his tradition: Muslim and Monk from identical backgrounds, each causing major shifts along that fault line between Africa and Europe. The rock on which he makes his camp will ever after be known as *Jabal al Tariq* or *Gibr Tariq*, which means "Tariq's Rock"; Gibraltar, in English. Many romances have grown up around him in Islamic tradition and I have simply added a layer of fiction to give a feel for the time, the place and the people. The *azalei* or salt caravans continue to this day, although in diminished numbers. Sometime before this historic event, the stories suggest that Tariq is taken as a slave into the household of the Muslim general Musa bin Nusayr, no doubt following Musa's successful conquests of North Africa. Slaves are required to convert to Islam, but this is not such a big step for them. The nomad Berbers and the Arab Bedouins had much in common, and Musa is recorded as saying that of all non-Arabs, the Berbers are most like them, although they had proved the hardest to conquer. In another prescient moment, Queen Kahina, the Prophetess, foresaw her own death in battle and in advance of that, sent her two sons to Musa to serve him and to convert to Islam. Tariq ibn Ziyad would have been his Muslim name.

Tariq's crossing of what is now known as the Strait of Gibraltar qualifies as a cultural tectonic event that will help to shape the future of European civilization. Like the geological event, it will be wrought through violence and upheaval. Tariq's army defeats the Visigoth forces of Rodrigo, many of whose subjects are happy to see the tyrant deposed. This victory is quickly followed up by the invasion of Musa's forces and Islamic civilization spreads to Europe.

Asmun and Izri are based on actual historical figures. They are friends of Tariq who made the crossing with him. Izri will become a scholar of note and a leading figure among the Berbers, along with the son of Tariq's sister. Asmun's grandson will become the Shaykh of Cordoba and introduce an important legal text into

* This speech comes down through tradition as preserved by the Moorish historian Al Maggari, who wrote in Africa long after the last of the Moors had been driven out of Spain but it has become part of Tariq's legend. It appeared in English translation in 1917.

** Although some historians have suggested that he was Arabic or even Persian, this was the commonly held belief about him. Present-day Algeria was part of Numidia in those early times.

North Africa. Tariq will continue on to conquer Toledo, a city believed by some to have been established by second century Jews fleeing the Roman destruction of Jerusalem. He will serve as governor for a while.

The city of Cordoba, following the Moorish (Arab-Berber) conquest, will soon rival Baghdad as the most sophisticated metropolis in Europe. The rest of Europe had fallen into its Dark Ages with the fall of the Roman Empire in 476 to the Visigoths. Cities are sacked, libraries destroyed, and treasures of the Western classical world are in ruin or lost altogether.

By comparison, Cordoba became a city of light. It literally had street lights, large, airy houses and buildings, paved roads, hospitals and libraries. The arches of its great mosque would influence later Christian churches.

This Golden Age of Islamic culture made important contributions to the later European world at a time when the earlier accomplishments of the centers of Graeco-Roman learning—like Athens, Alexandria and Rome—were being lost. Islamic scientists developed algebra, trigonometry, astronomy and sophisticated studies of anatomy, as the scholars of the Mouseion had in their Golden Age. Islamic scholars proposed the theory that disease is disseminated through small airborne organisms, which led to the isolation of people with disease in wards, thus hospitals. Intrigued by light, lenses and the human eye, their discoveries led to the invention of the modern camera. A thousand years before the West, they are removing cataracts from the eye.

One of the most important contributions of Islamic culture occurred around 750 when they encountered paper in Central Asia and adopted it for use in the bureaucratic administration of their vast empire. Scribes were employed, including women, and the acquisition and copying of books became a widespread industry. At a time when monasteries might possess only four or five books, streets of booksellers with as many as a hundred shops appeared in Islamic cities. There is now a single intellectual community that covers five continents, with the House of Wisdom in Baghdad as a magnet for scholars and intellectuals who came to use the libraries associated with the palace. This included people from radically different cultural traditions. In a reverse movement, scholars are being dispatched throughout the empire in search of ancient texts. As a result, the knowledge of the ancients is being gathered, discussed and transformed into a new body of knowledge. This means that the classical thinkers like Plato and Aristotle are being recovered and preserved from the ruins of the Roman Empire at a time when they are being dismissed by the Christian church as the work of pagans. It is one of the great historical paradoxes that the Arabs are sometimes said to have saved Western civilization. Several works of Plato and Aristotle, for example, only became known to us in later centuries through translations of Arabic texts which had preserved them.

Although Muslim rule in Spain would later become more despotic, for a while it would be home to Jews, Christians and Muslims, flourishing together and sharing their culture and beliefs without hostility.

Once Islam is firmly established in North Africa and Muslims are regularly making their pilgrimage to Mecca for the Haj, the caravans swell in size to as many as ten thousand camels, making that difficult trek across the Sahara. Timbuktu is not founded as a city until the tenth century, but I have suggested in this story the seeds of what it is to become.

TIMBUKTU

MEDIEVAL STORIES OF A DESERT EL DORADO LADEN WITH GOLD sparked interest in the collective imagination. But it is not until the 19th century that Europeans set out to find and map it. Unfortunately, it proved too difficult to reach, which is what gave rise to its connotation as a remote, inaccessible and mysterious place in expressions like "There is nothing like it from here to Timbuktu," which I heard often in my childhood. My father would tease me when I went out to play—"Are you off to Timbuktu?" It connotes a nowheresville. A place to disappear. And many Europeans did, claimed by thirst in the desert or hostile tribesmen.

Timbuktu's legend tells of a woman who grazed her goats near a well. Tuareg nomads set up base camp near the well, a few miles inland from the mosquito infested Niger. When they went off to graze their livestock in the desert, they left their belongings with the trustworthy woman until they returned. Her named was Bukhtu, and Timbukhtu meant "Bukhtu's well."

Timbuktu would have become a critical trade juncture in part because of its location near the Niger River. It is "where camel meets canoe." The river brought gold from the south and could take salt and other things in return. Camel trains from the north brought dates, European fabrics, glass, jewelry, tobacco and salt across the Sahara. The boats from the south brought grain cereals, honey, gold, and slaves. Gold and slaves made Timbuktu what it was in the Middle Ages. Two thirds of the world's gold came from Mali in the 14th century, passing through Timbuktu, as well as the white gold from the Sahara, salt. Before refrigeration, salt was the only means of preserving meat and other foods, which made it a precious commodity.

Following the Arab conquest in the time of Tariq, Arabic provided a common language that could be used for contracts. This also put calligraphers much in demand. Wealthy merchants began to trade in books, which now became a measure of their wealth. Profits from manuscripts began to rival profits from gold, salt and slaves. It kindled the interest in scholarship.

By the end of the 13th century, inhabitants of Timbuktu are boasting of their libraries. Paper is imported from Europe and China and calligraphers start copying Islamic texts from abroad as well as the work of the town's own scholars. They are richly rewarded in gold and camels and even houses for this work. (Now there is only one calligrapher still practicing the craft.)

In a BBC program, "The Lost Libraries of Timbuktu," host Aminatta Forna takes us to this remote place to tell the story of manuscripts only recently brought out of hiding there that will rewrite Africa's histories. They have been hidden away for hundreds of years to protect them from invaders and curious, greedy foreigners.

In the 13th century, the Ghanian empire, which had ruled over Timbuktu, was displaced by the Malian empire and was visited by its pious king, Kankamusa, who passed through Timbuktu on his pilgrimage to the Haj. Kankamusa is considered the greatest emperor of West Africa—very wealthy and also very religious. He was traveling with a huge retinue of men and women and fifteen tons of gold, which he distributed so lavishly in Egypt and in Mecca that the price of gold collapsed. The stories of the lavish wealth of Africa, which became associated with Timbuktu, began to spread throughout the Mediterranean and a new El Dorado was born. Kankamesa also brought Arabic professors back from Mecca to enrich the scholarship of Timbuktu, although it is said that they could not measure up to the scholars of that city. He commissioned a great palace and other edifices, designed by an Andalusian architect he also brought back from Mecca, as well as a magnificent mosque. Only the mosque has survived.

Knowledge was highly respected in the Islamic world of the time so the prolific scholars and professors of Timbuktu became prosperous and well-known. It became the most important center of learning in the region, known for the "piety, tolerance, wisdom and justice of its inhabitants" (Ibn Batutta). A contemporary scholar there, Ismael Diadié Haidara, curator of the Fondo Kati Library of ancient manuscripts, insists that because of the quantity and thoroughness of the Islamic scholars in Timbuktu, a great and deep understanding of Islam developed there. "They are able to give it a real meaning and because of their great mastery of Islam, it has always strived toward an Islam of great tolerance." He believes that the tolerance is also due to the fact that there was already a culture present in Timbuktu when Islam arrived, so it is filtered through this culture and influenced by it. One foot in Islam and one foot in an occult world of African roots.

The city had three mosques in the fourteenth century, the largest having been built by a wealthy Taureg woman. The three together formed a large scholastic community, Sankoura University (not on the European model), which gave rise to yet more scholarship and books and Timbuktu's golden age.

Timbuktu's books are now owned by families who began collecting books over eight centuries ago, much as the fictional character Ameqran had done. Astronomy, medicine, theology—including sayings of the prophets—and even recipes for things like toothpaste can be found in them. One local public collection has over forty thousand manuscripts. According to the head librarian interviewed by Fornatta, "Every week we get about seven hundred manuscripts." Most are written in Arabic, but there are many written in African languages using written Arabic characters. Languages like Tamashek [Berber] that recount the history of Africa are considered especially valuable.

In 2001, South Africa's president Tabu Mbeki visited and recognized the manuscripts as one of the continent's greatest cultural treasures. He offered funding for their preservation and sent a trained conservateur from South Africa to work on the manuscripts and to train locals to do it. It is a great treasure on a continent that had long been believed to have no written documentary heritage. At least 300,000 manuscripts are known to exist in the region, but as of 2009, only a thousand or so have been read and studied. Work could take decades. And many may still be buried in the desert sands. The French too took away manuscripts during their reign, which is one of the things that sent them underground. The people are slowly bringing them out, but many are still suspicious and protective.

Not far away, significant archaeological discoveries are being made near the Niger River, which has always been important as a long-distance trade route. It rises in the hills near the African west coast and flows almost three thousand miles—north then east then south. We now know that as early as 500 BC, this area was one of the most densely populated areas in the world, even rivaling early civilizations such as Mesopotamia. Archaeologist Doug Park and his team from Yale have excavated a large city site ten miles south of Timbuktu. It appears that there was an urban landscape all along the borders of the Niger River. The city that Park is studying covers 70 to 100 hectares, which may have been larger than the ancient Mesopotamian cities like Ur. In medieval times, Timbuktu, according to Park, would have been twice the size of London, and the nearby city that he is excavating would have been twice the size of Timbuktu at its height. These findings underline Tassili n'Ajjer's mute testimony to epochs of a fertile richness and large population in the now dessicated regions of the Sahara.

The local people of the middle Niger did not want Europeans to know about their cities or their treasures so the Tauregs especially were hostile to the early explorers and several were killed. French rule was brief (1893 to 1960), but it introduced into Timbuktu a system of compulsory education in French spreading literacy for the first time across all of the classes of people in Timbuktu in a way that the Arabic and Koranic schools had not. The common people had remained illiterate but now they could read—French. The result was that knowledge of Arabic was lost, and with that, the ability to read the treasured manuscripts, which are now accessible to only a small minority. In 1960, Timbuktu became part of the new Republic of Mali, no longer under French rule.

Aminatta Forna believes that the manuscripts now being brought to light after so many centuries could cause a renaissance in this town. "Timbuktu could become a lighthouse for people."

THE TREASURES OF TASSILI N'AJJER

Prehistoric paintings exist everywhere in the Sahara, from Mauritania in the west to Egypt in the east. Many are old, very old, reliably dated to thirteen millennia ago, and astonishing in all particulars, fluid, expressive, impressionistic, interpretive.

— MARQ DE VILLIERS
Sahara

AND WHAT OF THAT GALLERY OF MASTERPIECES ON STONE, Tassili n'Ajjer? It remained a well-kept secret from the outside world until the 1930s when a Frenchman entered the area as part of a police operation and shared his discoveries with one of the earliest archaeological scholars, Abbé Breuil. Under Abbé Breuil's tutelage, another Frenchman—Henri Lhote—set out with a team to chronicle the works in a series of skillful reproductions by the finest artists he could find for the task. His record of the journey in word and picture, *The Search for the Tassili Frescoes: Rock Painting in the Sahara,* makes great reading and I highly recommend it.

In 2004, Dutch and German tourists were kidnapped in the area. Some of the tourists were held for several months before German and Dutch troops were sent in to free the hostages from their rebel captors. The kidnappings have since stopped most, if not all, tourists from travelling towards the magical rock paintings of the Tassili, as insurance brokers are unwilling to provide coverage. The prospect of kidnapping provides wonderful security services. Ultimately it is the treacherous landscape itself, now life-threatening where it once teemed with life, that preserves its treasure.

There are more than fifteen thousand paintings and engravings in Tassili n'Ajjer, the oldest now recognized as being at least seven thousand years old and possibly as old as nine or ten thousand years. They are "books" of a different kind—at least as valuable as those in Timbuktu—which tell a much longer story of the evolution of the landscape, the people, the animals, and changes in the land itself since around 6000 BC.

In the rock art prior to 5000 BC are found the large figures with unusually large round heads, identified by Lhote as the "round head" period. He facetiously dubbed these "Martian" figures but there have been many over the years who took this seriously and have seen the figures as extra-terrestrial in the van Daniken mode. Terence McKenna thought they represented shamanic experiences and noted the presence of mushrooms in some of the paintings. This is not such a far-fetched idea when we consider the art of the present-day Huicholes in Mexico and our current knowledge of the widespread use of hallucinogenics in native religious cults.

These figures disappeared around 5000 BC and were followed by the very beautiful naturalistic representations of hunting scenes and scenes of daily life, alive with vibrant figures of a variety of animals and dancing humans. The landscape then would have been a moist savannah, like the Serengeti, fed by the rivers that originally gave the Tassili N'Ajjer its name. People, animals and land are flourishing in the moist climate as they did in the Ngorongoro Crater far to the southeast in ancient times and still today. These scenes date roughly from about 6000 to 1500 BC, including the period of the cattle-herders. The people had domesticated oxen and perhaps even giraffes for riding (one of the latter is depicted with what appears to be a bridle). Horses are seen in art between 1500 BC to the first century AD.

After 1500 BC, it appears that a major climatic change takes place, thought by some to be associated with a shift in the earth's axis.* The cattle disappear. And then the horses. They are no longer seen after 500 BC, no doubt due to increased aridity. In the latter days of that period, there are scenes of upheaval; horse-drawn chariots, probably of Garamantes conquerors, attack fleeing herdsmen. The Garamantes were a Saharan Berber people who lived in southwest Libya from about 1000 BC. They founded prosperous Berber kingdoms between 500 BC and 700 AD. Herodotus describes the Garamantes as "a very great nation" who herded cattle, farmed dates and hunted, making use of four-horse chariots. Their kingdom in central Libya went into decline with the loss of good agricultural land as the climate changed.

In the first century, the first camels appear in the art, coinciding with the introduction of the camel into the Sahara. That may come as a surprise to people who have come to think of the camel as virtually inseparable from the African sands, as if it had originated there. If not there, where DID the camel originate? It originated right here in North America, as the La Brea tar pits will testify. At least that is the story so far.

Around 500 BC, writing appeared for the first time in the rock art. The writing is in the Tifinagh script still used by Taureg nomads but the language itself is unknown and remains untranslated. The origin of this language is known as "Proto-Tifinagh," or as Libyco-Berber script. It was in use between about the 3rd century BC and the 3rd century AD. One of its variants was used in the area where Monica lived and also in Tunisia. Numidian bilingual inscriptions in Libyan and Punic appeared at Dougga, site of such beautiful mosaics in Roman times.

This is an intriguing detail for linguistic scholars because Proto-Tifinagh script is also found in Val Camonica—the valley that Monica could have visited from Cassiacum, located to the east of Milan. Canadian-American archaeologist and epigrapher, David H. Kelley, considers that Proto-Tifinagh script is in fact identifiable at ancient sites in Peterborough, Ontario (Canada), Scandinavia and Valcamonica.

---

* Such shifts have occurred throughout Earth's history. "Since observations began in 1899, the North Pole has been drifting southwards 10 centimetres per year along longitude 70° west . . . This drift is due to the changes in the distribution of Earth's mass as the crust slowly rebounds after the end of the last ice age. . . . In 2005, this southward drift changed abruptly. The pole began moving eastwards and continues to do so, a shift that has amounted to about 1.2 metres since 2005" (from the British Journal *New Scientist*, December 2013).

I have found that the late Bronze Age of Scandinavia, corresponding to the early Iron Age of Italy and North Africa, shows a lengthy series of innovations in all areas of iconography, including apparent Proto-Tifinagh inscriptions in both Scandinavia and Italy.... The date is about 800 BC....

It looks to me as if a single trade route united an area from the gold-mining zone along the Niger [River] to Scandinavia, and I think that oceanic voyagers from Scandinavia, linked into that route, reached Ontario.

I came across this quotation in an *Atlantic* article by Mark Stengal, "The Diffusionists Have Landed," in the January 2000 issue. Stengal cites Kelley as an influential archaeologist and epigrapher who contributes regularly to the *Journal of Archaeology* (i.e. not a crackpot). Nevertheless, I found this difficult to take in until I read a result of genographic studies of DNA that showed a Berber presence in Scandinavia. Not only Berbers but possibly Minoans, in the land of origin of the Winnili/Langobards/Lombards: There is speculation that an inscription from the late Bronze Age in Kongsberg, Norway, from about 1700 BC, has been identified as Minoan Linear A, suggesting that their trade routes carried them far north. In 2005 two professors of archaeology, Kristian Kristiansen, University of Gothenburg, and Thomas B. Larsson, University of Umeå in Sweden, published a book entitled *The Rise of Bronze Age Society* (Cambridge University Press) in which they argue, based on a large body of evidence, that the richness of the Early Bronze Age culture of Denmark and Scandinavia can only be explained in terms of a contact between the Minoan-Mycenaean civilization and Scandinavia.

The story keeps changing. That is the most important point here. Nothing is much as we thought it was in the nineteenth century when my grandparents were born. It is not only the technical changes which have been dramatic since that time. It is the *story* that changes, enlarges, enriches. Humans have been hard-wired from the beginning to tell stories, to arrange their lives in narrative experiences. Science is just the latest form of that magnificent obsession, and science's story changes faster than any of the ancient myths and tales, yet in an interesting way, it knits them all together.

EARLY MIGRATIONS

往 *wang depicts luxuriant vegetation that springs up from
the earth in tufts, here and there; roaming, wandering*

CONTINENTAL PLATES, CREATURES OF WATER, BIRDS OF THE AIR, humans and animals of the land . . . All are on the move, though at different rates and rhythms. The movements develop patterns, intimately tied to the days and the seasons of the sun and the moon, guided by the regular movement of stars across the skies. One thinks of wandering and roaming as an empty, mindless activity but that does not seem to be the case. It is my own sense that these millions of years of life on the planet were developing an intimacy in which every living thing and all that surrounded it were affecting one another, collectively acting and being acted upon, honing and shaping and tending one another. Without this intimacy such migrations would not have been possible or successful.

I remember sitting on a hillside in Baja California looking out over the sea. A large flock of egrets landed, some very near me and others a distance away. I watched them for a while and then, quite suddenly—as if someone had blown a whistle to announce their departure—they lifted up as one and flew off. The amazing thing was that the egrets near me were facing the opposite direction from the egrets much farther away yet their lift-off was perfectly synchronized. The aerial ballet of starlings and other birds show this same graceful synchrony. It suggests that before humans, all of nature functioned like a single wave of consciousness. As the 18th century philosopher Bishop Berkeley might have put it, all held in the Mind of God.

While land and creatures are on the move through millions of years, some things are solidifying. Cells grow into organisms, organisms into colonies; families grow into clans, clans into communities, cities, civilizations. Thought, too, is coalescing among larger and larger groups of people. Augustine's Christianity, seeded in North Africa, matures in Roman Italy, returns to Africa and becomes a pillar of Western thought for centuries to come. Tariq ibn Ziyad will lead a stream of Islam out of Africa into Spain, where it will have a lasting impact on European culture. The Winnili, like the wildebeests, are looking for greener pastures.

But bear this in mind: All of written history, as far back as our human stories reach, comes into being only in the very last minute of our Earth year. Less than sixty seconds.

It gives one pause. What might the New Year bring?

PART III

PUSHING UPWARD

Within the earth, wood grows:
The image of Pushing Upward.

— *I Ching,* Hexagram 46

 chu

go, go out, to spring from, to issue, to beget

The character depicts a small plant that has grown another pair of leaves.

THE TREES

*One felt as if there was an enormous well behind them, filled up with ages
of memory and long, slow, steady thinking; but their surfaces were sparkling
with the present; like sun shimmering on the outer leaves of a vast tree, or
on the ripples of a very deep lake.*

—R.R. TOLKIEN
Pippin on the Ents, *Two Towers*

IT IS JUST PAST MID-MONTH—DECEMBER ON THE EARTH CALENDAR. There
is a cold snap and then a warming that gives life to new growing things. The seas are
running high. Over the next week the bees arrive. Now the earth can flower. These
small fuzzy creatures carry an electrostatic charge and are perfectly designed—just-
so—to collect pollen. They will forage among the blossoms, pausing from time to
time to groom themselves like tiny fastidious cats. They are packing the pollen neatly
away in specially designed pollen baskets on their legs or abdomen. The massive
tyrannosaurus and mastodons will come and go but the honeybees will survive—
small, industrious creatures working miracles in the forty-some solar days of their
lives. And with them, the flowers. Of course this is an orchestral work and every living
thing participates in the performance. I call this long movement *andante con moto*,
flowing in an animated motion. Trees begin to leaf out into magnolias, figs and plane
trees. The conifers and monkey puzzle trees are thriving. The giant tyrannosaurus
rex still plods across the landscape and huge ungainly raptors lift themselves into the
air.

These are not the only giants on the earth. By the end of the week, towering
redwood forests have migrated from northern China, across Beringia and down
the Pacific Coast of America: one vast forest stretching across continents. The huge,
majestic trees populate the regions of present-day France, Switzerland, Austria,
Bohemia, Germany, England and the Norwegian island of Spitzbergen. During
the glacial periods on the last day of the Earth year, they will migrate south—just as
humans will—toward the Mediterranean. There, over time, they will slowly perish.

California ~ ca. 1000 AD

*I am not going to tell you my name. . . .It would take a long while: my name
is growing all the time, and I've lived a very long, long time; so my name is
like a story . . . We do not say anything in it, unless it is worth taking a long
time to say, and to listen to.*

— TREEBEARD
in R.R. TOLKIEN's *Two Towers*

Time. We have seen that the earth has layered rhythms, from the mayflies that live for a day to the Sequoia Sempervirens which can live for centuries, millennia: A family of trees that go back over 144 million years. Trees that lived with dinosaurs in the time of giants. Trees that will lift their lofty boughs above nineteenth century immigrants to Humboldt county. Spalettas and Buzzinis and many others, full of hopes as large as trees.

The redwood forests will drift across the American continent, their cathedral canopies towering over parts of Canada, Pennsylvania, west through Texas, Colorado, Wyoming, Oregon, Washington and California. In most of those places they will lose a competition with migrants of another sort, slow and deadly. The migration of glaciers and a changing climate will slowly kill them off, leaving only the coastal belt on the Pacific Coast of America.

As usual, Tolkien caught it just right. Of all the varying rhythms of the earth, we can imagine the redwood tree's as being very very slow, as a single tree may live for a thousand to two thousand years. To the north of the great bay beyond the Golden Gate, the small shoot that had appeared in the time of Augustine has grown tall in the great forest of redwoods. It is still almost a thousand years into the future before it will receive its name—*Laurelin*—but it is already being venerated by the people of this place.

In music, there is something called a *drone* that is a single note, usually a low one, that is played continuously throughout a piece as melodies are played or sung in all their varieties above it. The ancient trees provide that role for our stories, as does the earth beneath each of their landscapes. Layers of time and life that blend together in the great Gaian symphony.

THOSE WHO STAY

From now on, through hundreds of millions more years, [organic life] will become increasingly centered, focused, self-organizing, localized like the small plant that issues from its center, begets. Instead of floating and rambling, they dig in deep and begin to ascend upward, in search of sunlight. They begin on land as the soft mosses and ferns, growing higher and higher until they form trees and forests.

I REINTRODUCE THIS COMMENT FROM THE BEGINNING of the book about the shift that occurs over time from algae and other early organisms rambling in a fluid environment to plants centering, rooting themselves and rising up as trees, because it is an apt analogy for the stage that follows the long migration in which the "pastures" are finally reached and the wanderers, whether Odysseus, Aeneas or the Winnili, put down their roots and claim a home. The movement is an upward one of building on solid ground, "begetting," raising families for the future and, on a large scale, building towns and cities.

There is also a parallel ascent within the individual human being, which we will meet in Petrarch's ascent of Mt. Ventoux. There are still more migrations ahead, but in this period there is a significant amount of building going on. The great cathedrals of Europe are about to go up and the first universities there will soon be established. What we think of as the Ancient World, which had already passed through such a cycle of building and expanding from at least the time of the Egyptians, Minoans, and the lost civilizations of Africa, has now faded away and in its place, new civilizations and new forms of culture are taking hold. We are entering a period when we can actually look back and find some of our own roots.

Ticino ~ 11th Century

After the year 1000, the Lombards began intensive settlement of the Ticino area, homesteading the area with stone houses in the security of the high Alpine valleys above the Ticino River.

—T. ANTHONY QUINN
On Wings of Gold

THE LOMBARDS HAD BEEN A POWERFUL PRESENCE IN THE REGION of present-day Italy for centuries, since crossing the Alps into Italy from Slovenia in the Spring of 568. By the seventh century, they ruled over 36 duchies in Italy, leaving only a small corridor around Rome and the toe and heel of the boot still under the control of the Byzantine Empire. The last Lombard to rule as king was Desiderius, duke of Tuscany, whom we met with Paul the Deacon. He was defeated by the Franks in 774 and Charlemagne had himself crowned King of the Lombards in Pavia (where Augustine had become a recent resident). The Lombards to the south, however, remained independent and by the end of 977, they had formed a united Lombard principality, in alliance with the Holy Roman Empire. In less than a century, the principalities to the south fell to the Norman conqueror Robert Guiscard, not long after the Norman invasion of England. But the northern region of Lombardy, which originally extended north to encompass parts of the canton of Ticino, remains under that name to this day as the northernmost province of Italy and one of our major characters as a common landscape to many of our stories.

Before they arrived in Italy, the Lombards came under the influence of Christianity. Alboin converted to Arianism—a Christian sect later declared heretical—when he allied with the Ostrogoths for the invasion of Italy. Once in Italy, there were more pressures to convert to Catholicism, particularly when a Lombard king married a Bavarian queen, the catholic Theudalinda. At first, the conversion mostly affected the aristocracy while the common people still held to their pagan beliefs and practices. Nevertheless, there is evidence that Lombards built some of the earliest Christian churches in Italy. The church of St. Peter of the Golden Sky in Pavia was restored by King Liutprand between 720 and 725. No doubt he wished to consecrate his church with the saintly bones of Augustine and there he found his own eternal rest.

At the turn of the millennium, the increasing population of the northern cities, along with the constant political and military conflicts, has led many of its people to move northward, following the Ticino River into the Magadino Plain that now forms the southernmost region of the canton of Ticino. Ticino's three rivers provide essential water, although during the hot summers they become stagnant in the flatland areas and malaria is a constant problem. Bandits often roam the valleys and armies from the Italian duchies to the south send their agents to impress men into their service or to collect taxes by seizing the peasants' cows or goats. To avoid this, they climb into the high valley hillsides and plateaus. There they create their own isolated settlements where they can go about their lives in peace, even if the resources are meager and the life poor. In T. Anthony Quinn's description, "Most often, they just wanted to be left alone, away from wars, plagues and politics. Across the Valle Verzasca, little more than a rocky gorge, the peasants built a wall with a locked gate to keep the outside world at bay. Favored settlements were up boxed valleys with no outlet."

MAGISTER COMACINI

THEY HAD ALL HEARD IT, STOKING THEIR FIRES AND PREPARING the breakfast polenta for their families. The sweet trill of the passero solitario, the Blue Rock Thrush whose song broke so tenderly into the harsh winter silence. It was the sound they waited for every year to give them hope that the bitter season was coming to an end. Soon the yellow mountain cowslip would appear and the fragrant narcissus. The children trotted nimbly to their favorite lookout spots and the women, too, turned their eyes south whenever their outdoor chores permitted. There was a certain status to be acquired for the first person to catch a glimpse of their men returning from the plains of Lombardy, like the wives of sailors home from the sea.

Of course they didn't all arrive at one time. They arrived in small groups, according to where they had been working through the winter. The first to arrive was usually the largest group. These were the men who had been working in Milan, Como and the smaller areas around those cities. Small groups arrived from Pavia or Ravenna, or even farther to the south from Florence. These were their most skilled workers—expert stone cutters with good jobs working to the south or as far away as Russia. There was a great stir when the group with Giovanni the Red arrived from Pavia with the Magister Comacini. This had been arranged a year before—that he would come in the Spring to launch their project. The women and older children had been talking about it all winter. This was the year in which the building of their church would begin.

✦ ✦ ✦

The men start out at first light and climb upward through the forest in silence, a small vapor of breath preceding each one in the chill air. They move with utter sureness, as if climbing a stairway to their bed at night. This forest is more an intimate home to them than the small stone houses in which they only eat and sleep and sometimes make love. They are men of stone and trees. One particular tree, the chestnut. For them it is the abro, the bread tree, a tree of life. It is abundant in its kinds—over fifty have been counted —some early fruiting, some late-fruiting, guaranteeing them a long harvest and a variety of fruit. The medium-sized Torcione, the small, sweet, thin-skinned Luina; the smallish Pinca, the sturdy Magenta, which gives a good wood for carving and the hearty Buné negro, which weathers the rains without rotting. They know them all like members of their own family. Those that are good for flour and for bread. Those that are best eaten fresh, and those that are good for drying. Those that are best given to the animals for their feed.

They move through their still-dormant vineyards and begin the climb upward through the graceful, uplifted arms of the chestnut forest, showing in the early light only the first dainty display of green, the unfurling of their slender leaves. But that faint green nimbus that shines, ethereal, through the dawn mist is the promise of good things to come. In June, the small flowers will open into the long catkins, heavy with their perfumed pollen to soften spirits frozen by winter. Then will come the fruits, concealed in their sharp, spiny burrs, as protective as a mother fox. But they will open in time to skillful prying hands, revealing the tender, creamy-white flesh of the sweet chestnut.

The harvest will end on St. Martin's Day, a day associated with the chestnut throughout Europe from ancient times. St. Martin—the kindly saint of Tours, who gave half his cloak to a poor beggar and ever after became associated with that act of charity. Giving sustenance to the poor. But there is no one poorer than the peasants of Ticino. To whom will they give? Ah, to the animals. Every year on that day, the pigs and goats are set free to graze under the chestnut trees, the harvest officially being over. They root about to find whatever treats have been left behind. It is the day, too, of the last harvest meal before the season of fasting begins in earnest.

A European day of Thanksgiving that will evolve over time into the Advent season.

> *É dia de São Martinho;*
> *comem-se castanhas,*
> *prova-se o vinho,*

people chant in Portugal. "It is St. Martin's Day, we'll eat chestnuts, we'll taste the wine."

In Malta, the children recite an old nursery rhyme,

> *Ġewż, Lewż, Qastan,*
> *Tin Kemm inħobbu*
> *lil San Martin.*

"Walnuts, Almonds, Chestnuts, Figs. I very much love Saint Martin."

In Poland, they are saying "St. Martin is coming on a white horse," meaning that the first snows are due. And centuries off into the future, in America, these will all blend together into another December song, "Chestnuts roasting by an open fire, Jack Frost nipping at your nose," although the American sweet chestnut trees will by then be long gone.

St. Martin's Day will mark the turning point from the season of warmth and plenty to the season of cold and want and fasting. It is not ceremony that makes it so, but nature. The ceremony is the people's way of celebrating nature's turnings, and carefully turning with her. For the next six months, they will be fed only by what the chestnut trees have given them: flour and dried fruit to store up for the winter. The men set out to the south to find work in the Italian provinces, leaving the little food to be divided among the women, the children and the animals. They carry their loads of chestnuts to be sold on the street corners in Milan and Pavia and other cities. Chestnuts will be turned into money to buy needed goods.

If the forest is their Mother, what waits at the top of the steep ascent through the sharp spring morning is their Father. They go to build His house. The place has been carefully chosen now for months and all the plans are made. It will be hard work for them, quarrying and hewing the stone. But this is what they do. Stone, like chestnuts, is the thing they know. They are climbing up Monte Bernardo to a rocky plateau which looks out over the Magadino Plain and Bellinzona. They had climbed up here with all of their families in the early autumn, once the place had been chosen. They had picnicked together under the chestnut trees, by the light of the last warm days and talked of the time to come when their children would be baptized here, their couples wed, their old people eulogized before their final resting.

Bringing up the rear, is the Magister Comacini and his two sons, walking solemnly, already conscious that they are entering into some private, holy space in which a finished church would one day take shape. The three seem very different from the animated, laughing newcomers who had been sitting around their fires for the last week, telling stories of their travels and the details of buildings they had worked on. The nave of San Antonio in Piacenza, a bell-turret for a baptistery in Settimo Vittone, a campanile in Pavia. It was wondrous work and it took a wondrously long time! The Magister Comacini had spent twelve years in Como working on the nave of San Carpoforo. His sons had spent part of their apprenticeship in Milan, working on the Church of the Holy Sepulcher there. It was important, he explained, for them to work under different masters with different specialties.

The oldest of his sons, Luigi, has been working in Pavia at the new church of San Michele Maggiore. He explained that it was built on the model of San Pietro del Cielo d'Oro, King Liutprand's church, which was familiar to many of them. "But there is one very strange difference," he said. "On the floor of the church choir is what they call their Labyrinth. It is a large round mosaic, a kind of maze that leads inward to the center, where Theseus and the Minotaur—do you know that story? (a few nodded)—are fighting each other in the middle. To me, that was strange enough to find in a Christian Church. But then there are these creatures on the four sides. They looked like a flying horse, a dragon, a goat and a goose." The Magister Comacini, who was a very learned man, spoke up and said "Three of them sound like constellations. Capricorn, Draco, Pegasus . . . But I don't know about the goose. Anyway, continue."

"But there is also a scene of David and Goliath. On Goliath's shield there are words, something like "I am wild and strong and desire to inflict mortal wounds." On David's shield are Biblical words I recognized. "The mighty shall be brought down and the humble exalted."

"Well that makes sense to me," Giovanni the Red commented. "I've been in that church many times and looked at that mosaic. Both stories mean the same thing. Just what the Bible said. Good always conquers evil, whether it's a monster or a giant." There was a thoughtful silence after Luigi's story. The people loved to hear of such exotic things as this from faraway places.

Then the Magister Comacini went on with his story. In France, after his apprenticeship, he said, a craftsman is expected to journey throughout the country—into the principal villages, towns and cities, stopping wherever he could find employment. In each of these places, there was a house to receive them and "la Mère" as she was affectionately called. "The Mother." The house too was called "la Mère." In this way, they not only gained a variety of experiences in their craft, they provided a service which was highly valuable to the people.

"Isn't it dangerous to be on the road in all of these strange places, so far from home?" someone had asked. The Magister Comacini had laughed and said "Our home IS the road. But building craftsmen have become very organized. The French have their Compagnons de Devoir—Companions of the Work—and they take care of one another and insist upon certain codes among their workers and also among their employers. We in Lombardy have been very well looked after by the laws passed under Rothair some three hundred years ago. And it is of great value to us to be freemen."

The people listened and felt elevated by the presence of the Magister Comacini in their midst. It would not have happened had he not been a cousin of Giovanni the Red. The Magister's parents had stayed behind in Pavia when Giovanni's father had moved his family to the Ticino. The Magister, like his stonemason father and grandfather, loved his freedom to work and to travel. Giovanni's father, and Giovanni himself, had loved their tranquility.

The men, as they climb through the early morning, carry their tools on their backs—stonecutting tools for now. Hammers, chisels . . . The sounds of metal on stone are about to ring out throughout Europe and Great Britain as small churches and great cathedrals rise up against the horizons of villages, towns and cities. This is the century's own internet—a network that binds together even remote villages like this one with a common thread, a common work, a common purpose. Thanks to the Romans, those legendary descendants of Aeneas, also a common language: the Latin spoken in their churches, even though the spoken dialects vary from place to place.

As the work on the church proceeds over the years, the people scattered in small hamlets along the mountainside will begin to move closer and form a parish. Monte Carasso will be born.

When the city of Rome fell in 476, as the Goths stormed the walls of the Imperial City, it is often thought that Europe entered a Dark Age in which the arts of classical Greece and Rome went into total eclipse. Many suggest that the fall of Rome began, in fact, when Constantine moved the capital of the empire from west to east, from Rome to Constantinople, the site of present-day Istanbul. The rise of beautiful and elaborate churches in the 11th and 12th centuries is evidence that the building arts had not disappeared at all, but moved their ground.

It was common, even during the height of Roman life, to take refuge from the crowded streets and summer heat of Rome on the shores of Lake Como, in the region where Verecundus had his country place in Cassiacum. As the city of Rome was increasingly menaced by foreign invasion, many Romans took permanent refuge in that area, including the master architects—the Roman College of Artificers. According to some accounts, by the time of the Lombard invasions, they had concentrated themselves on the Isola Comacini, a small island in Lake Como from whence may have come the title "Magister Comacini." There is no doubt that during Lombard rule of the region, architecture enjoyed a rich revival under the patronage of the rulers, planting the seeds that would later flourish in the Italian renaissance.

Along the shores of Lakes Como, Lugano and Maggiore were stone, marble and timber yards, as well as nearby forests, which could provide the building materials essential to the trades of master builders. They were traveling masons and artisans who went where there was work, often employed for years on a major project. They had been organized into schools or guilds in Rome and they preserved their brotherhood for protection on the road and in the foreign communities where they worked. These were the first guilds in Europe and are cited by some as the origins of freemasonry, which developed in the 17th century.

In 643, the Lombard king Rothair made into law detailed protections for the builders, as well as for their customers. They were referred to as the Magister Comacini, a phrase that denoted Master Mason. Concrete evidence of the skill of these artisans can be seen throughout northern Italy in the 11th and 12th centuries.

There is an invisible thread that runs through the building trades into this period, which seems to connect with that elusive and inventive hero, Daedalus—creator of the Cretan labyrinth in the Minoan palace of Knossos. One writer of a history of cathedral-building during this period comments that "Daedalus was called by the ancients the Father of architecture and statuary. He was also the inventor of many mechanical appliances. In short, a good prototype of a Comacine Magister."*

When work begins on San Bernardo Church, Europe is coming alive again, as if awakening out of a long winter's sleep. The decline and fall of the Roman Empire was as far-reaching and devastating in its effects as its rise had been glorious and spread like a river at flood-tide. Its monuments had fallen to ruin and its populace into depraved and abject poverty. The Roman politican and historian Procopius lays much of the blame for the final and complete destruction on the sixth century emperor Justinian, with whom he had close contact as the aide of the emperor's leading general, Bellasarius. By then the seat of power of the empire had moved to Constantinople—the former Byzantium and future Istanbul. Justinian, ruling from that capital, was determined to reclaim the lands to the west and restore the empire to its former extent and glory. Procopius, writing *The Secret History* at the end of his life, doesn't mince any words in reciting the emperor's deeds.

> He brought on the Romans' disasters which surely surpassed both in gravity and in number all that had ever been heard of in any period of history. For without the slightest hesitation he used to embark on the inexcusable murdering of his fellow men and the plundering of other people's property; and it did not matter to him how many thousands lost their lives, although they had given them no provocation whatsoever.

Procopius estimated that "a million million" lost their lives during this period and cites Libya as an example of the magnitude of destruction. Procopius had visited Libya when its cities were thriving and its farms and fishing industry productive. According to his figures, 80,000 Vandals perished in an armed revolt there, adding that the number of their women, children and slaves can hardly be guessed. This number is small, he suggests, in comparison to the Moorish inhabitants "who perished to a man along with their lives and little ones. . . . Libya, in spite of its enormous size, has been so utterly laid to waste that however far one went it would be a difficult and remarkable achievement to find one person there." He estimates that at least 5 million died. This may account for the disappearance of the once great Berber people of Libya known as the Garamantes, whose chariots appeared on the walls of Tassili N'Ajjer.

In Italy, which he describes as three times the size of Libya, (presumably referring to continental Roman territory), the lands were even more completely depopulated as the Gothic Empire, which had stretched from Gaul to the cities of Sirmium and Venetia, was devastated by the ravages of war and disease.

While most historians dispute the lavish numbers of Procopius, none doubt that Europe became a wasteland during this period, largely denuded of its former

* *Cathedral Builders: The Story of a Great Masonic Guild* by Leader Scott

population. Even without the destructions wrought by constant war, the pandemic plague that broke over Europe and Asia struck a major blow to their populace. It likely began in Egypt or Ethiopia, spread north through Europe and east through Asia, reaching Constantinople. Even the emperor was afflicted and between five and ten thousand people were said to have died per day in that city. Between 541 and 700 it killed 40 to 50% of the population and a quarter of the population of the eastern Mediterranean. It is estimated that a hundred million people died worldwide. It was probably the bubonic plague, which ebbed and flowed through several generations and returned in full force in the 14th century, as we will see, as the Black Death.

As the new millennium dawns, Europe is slowly reassembling itself around a new center—the Christian Church—and will begin the ascent toward new cultural heights in the Italian Renaissance. Just as with the rise of Rome and the rule of its emperors, it would have its share of atrocities and oppression, along with an unprecedented collective benevolence and its soaring cultural and individual inspiration.

Like the first bird of spring, lifting its songs in Ticino, the first new songs are being heard from the troubadours in southern France, whose tradition will spread throughout Europe. We hear the first telling of the Grail Legend, in varied forms, which seems to express something higher in the soul than the brutalities of Roman and Barbarian wars and the lust for power of their leaders. One can see in the narratives a compressed account of the turning of European peoples and their civilization from the dark night of death and destruction which had laid waste to their lands, toward a renewal and a resurrection. The Arthurian legends seem to have braided together a cycle of stories drawn from various traditions. The setting of Arthur's court, Camelot, is by one tradition in Wales, not far from the Roman center of Caerleon, where I once lived in the Wye Valley. A magical place where one might indeed encounter a Merlin. An early account came from the pen of Geoffrey of Monmouth, just across the river from my cottage.

In the story of the Welsh knight Perceval, we meet the Fisher King or Grail king who has been severely wounded in battle; wounded in the groin, as if to emphasize the barrenness into which his kingdom has fallen, like so much of Europe and Asia Minor. A wounding of the psyche of the entire European and Near Eastern world, which had been born out of Greek, Roman and Judaic culture. The tale takes its first poetic and enduring shape in *Le Conte de Graal* by Chrétien de Troyes, written at the end of the 12th century in France. The setting of his works extends over a geography that reaches from Constantinople and North Africa through France, Spain and Great Britain, testifying to the positive role of the Roman Empire, following on the spread of Greek culture to the Indus by Alexander the Great, in uniting previously diverse peoples and regions.

The legends begin with battles and conquests but shift away from that to more archetypally feminine themes of love, chivalry and virtue. Women figure significantly in the stories, often as vessels of a transcendent grace and beauty; like the young woman Percival sees in the castle of the Fisher King, giving him his first glimpse of the Grail, which she is bearing in a vision. The Holy Grail is a sacred object—in varying stories a dish, plate, or cup—used by Jesus at the Last Supper and said to possess miraculous powers. The maiden chides Perceval for not asking the important question, "Whom does the grail serve" and it is this failure which hides the grail again for many years to come and prevents the healing of the king and his kingdom.

In one account, Joseph of Arimathia—who received the body of Jesus after the crucifixion—used the Grail to catch Christ's blood before interring him. Joseph was a wealthy merchant whose dealings in tin took him to the British Isles where, according to the account, he hid the grail in a well in Glastonbury. The quest for the Holy Grail is undertaken by King Arthur of Camelot and the knights of the Round Table. This story, including the tale of Percival just cited, first appears in the works of Chrétien de Troyes. The legend appears to combine Christian lore with a Celtic myth of a cauldron, similarly endowed with special powers.

Joseph Goering has recently written a book in which he adds yet another thread to the origin of the grail story, this one coming out of the Pyrenees mountains between Spain and France. In *The Virgin and the Grail: Origins of a Legend,* he suggests that the grail story was inspired by images in the churches there of the Virgin Mary with a simple but radiant bowl, called a "grail" in local dialect. These images appeared in churches in the Spanish Pyrenees fifty years before Chrétien de Troyes wrote his great work on the theme. Goering looks back to the Pyrenean religious paintings and argues that they were the original inspiration for the grail legend. He explains how storytellers in northern France could have learned of these paintings and how the enigmatic "grail" in the hands of the Virgin came to form the centerpiece of a story about a knight in King Arthur's court. In Goering's theory, neither Chrétien nor his audience knew exactly what it represented or why it was so important. And out of the attempts to answer those questions the literature of the Holy Grail was born.

I have recounted this because these villages have much in common with the Alpine villages of Ticino and our Magister Comacini, not the least of which was their remoteness. This protected them from the Arab invasion and occupation of the rest of the Iberian peninsula. Nevertheless, at the beginning of the second millennium, merchants and itinerant monks arrived there along with Christian pilgrims traveling to Jerusalem and Santiago de Compostela. Catalonia, as the region was and is now called, was more open to outside influences than the more protected and inward turned realms of Leone and Navarre. The local counts and lords of the Catalan region paid little heed to their Frankish overlords and went their own way. Ramon Borrell II, count of Barcelona, established a dynasty at the beginning of the new millennium, which would endure into the fifteenth century. New cultural styles were brought to Catalonia, particularly from Lombardy. This can be recognized in the churches built in the high rural villages of the Vall de Boi, a landscape similar to the Ticinesi villages in the valleys of Versazca and Maggia. Evidence of the influence of the craftsmen and artists from the Lombard region can be seen in the fact that the word *lombard*, in Catalonia, became synonymous with "stonemason" or "supervisor." The magister comacinii left their mark. It is from here that Romanesque architectural and artistic influences made their way throughout the Iberian peninsula in the next four centuries. And perhaps from here too, that seeds of the Grail legend were sown and the role of Mary in the story first left its mark.

I have seen pictures of those churches in the high Alta Ribagorça region of the Pyrenees, surrounded by their steep mountains. Each village in the valley contains its Romanesque church, surrounded by enclosed fields. There are still extensively used grazing lands on the higher slopes, as there are in Ticino today. And the churches ... Well they look for all the world like San Bernardo, above Monte Carasso.

July 4, 1054 ~ Chaco Canyon, New Mexico

A NEW LIGHT

When we began our migrations, we came up to this world from the world below, the Creator telling the people that there are certain places that you are to live and giving them signs of recognition as to where these sites are to be found. The migrations probably began over a period of centuries, always looking for that place that was to be the center of our world.

—PAUL PINO, Laguna Pueblo

PERFORATED OBSIDIAN, THE SKY. *Light pouring through it as through a sieve. The silence before dawn is like a weight of stars. The spare, flat landscape beneath it, a density of darkness. Creatures lay still, gone to ground. Birds drowse beneath folded wings on ledges and branches. People, held in the small death of the night's sleep. Life suspended. Waiting. The wheel of the hours turns silently. The deep silence is more fearful than sound. Or the sound itself of darkness and starlight.*

To be awake in these hours, it is a wonder. Or the most lonely feeling in the world. Yet these are the hours of instruction, when the heavens speak in the arcane language of an order, slowly impressed on memory, and certain men listen. And watch. How to pick out regularity in the swarm of stars. How to read the hieroglyphs of their patterns. How to see in the wanderings of planets, the sureness of cycles. The repetitions. The very lives of the people depend on the few who can read that book and tell its story. It is a story in stone, published in their buildings for eons to read. Several are awake now, taking their sightings, their measurements. They cannot imagine the new page that will be written by them this night.

It comes near dawn. If it were 722 years later, it might have been dismissed as an early Independence Day celebration. Except that it doesn't burst down on them as a shower of sparks but remains as a great and terrifying light. Three times the size of Venus and close to the crescent moon. A star where no star had been before. This they confirm with one another in awed, excited voices. Others begin to awaken until slowly, the whole community stirs and all heads are pointed upward like a collective arrow toward the new light.

When the sun is fully up and the people are about their daily activities, the star can still be seen, a persistent glimmer in the bright sky, even at noon. There is the ever-present sound of stone ringing upon stone as the builders continue their endless work and another edifice rises slowly above the desert floor. And all the while the star looks down upon them day and night. It is an ominous presence. What is it saying? What is its message to them?

After purifying himself in ritual prayer, one of their writers on stone who translates the ciphers of the sky takes up his pouch of paint, his yucca fiber brush, and begins the delicate work of telling its story. The story is also a map. The sandstone shelf on which he paints is on West Mesa, just outside of the great house that will be known as Peñasco Blanco. Carefully he draws a crescent moon, facing downward like an emptied gourd. Then he carefully draws rays around the large star and above that, a hand that says "from this position, following the diagram, the new star can be seen." His woman sits near him and his son. The boy's face is full of excitement as if a new plaything had been mounted in the sky just for him. The woman watches him, casting furtive glances over her shoulder, her eyes dark and enquiring. What does it mean? What will happen? He smiles and nods to reassure her and turns back to his work. There is nothing to say. Among the elders, some consider it is a good sign and others, a bad one. None can remember it happening before. He is thinking of the friends who have moved away near the new great houses that have been built at some distance. They too are watching and thinking. There will be a gathering at the Great Kiva. A ceremony is being planned and the dancers will be called.

At the center of Chaco Canyon stands Fajada Butte, rising over four hundred feet (135 meters) above the canyon floor. Behind a configuration of three large slabs are spiral petroglyphs, which mark the cycles of the sun and moon. The large standing slabs have been perfectly angled so that a vertical dagger of light will pass through the center of the spiral at the summer solstice. At the winter solstice, two noonday daggers frame the large spiral. At the equinoxes, the smaller spiral is bisected at midday by a fainter dagger of light. During the minor northern standstill of the moon, a moon shadow bisects the spiral at moonrise and during the major northern standstill, just touches the spiral's left edge. A straight groove has been pecked next to each spot

With these markings the people orient themselves in time and space, and tune their lives to the cycles of the heavens and of the seasons. Without these they would be adrift. Hunger and disaster would come upon them. The city they are building is a replica of the heavens and assures their safe passage through this life and beyond.

In the lifetime of this stone-writer, the sky will speak with a dazzling voice. In twelve years, a great comet will sweep across the sky, bringing more fear and confusion to the people. A sight that will be seen in Europe on the eve of the Battle of Hastings and strike fear as well into their hearts. A decade later will come a solar eclipse, visible to the south of Chaco Canyon. And one year later, in 1077, sunspots *large enough to be seen by the naked eye will appear, reported in China, Korea and Russia. They will remain visible for two years. There will also be the great tongue of fire, pouring out of the earth like an angry god and raining flaming stones for days upon the land around it. Although this eruption occurs almost two hundred miles to the west, word will spread quickly and refugees arrive at Chaco to take shelter. The sun will hide its face by day behind a cloud of ash.*

Taiowa is displeased. Sotuknang will send Spider Woman to them once more.

We can only imagine what the appearance of a supernova in the sky above a sacred city, built as an earthly reflection of the heavens, would be like. Consider the vastness of a flat landscape that stretches for miles around them. A high desert plateau, six thousand feet. No ambient light. No trees to blot out the view. Just an immense bowl of glittering sky, intimately known by their wise men and astronomers and gravid with meanings and portents, markers of plantings and of ceremonies. All of the trillions of bits of information stored in our libraries and computers are overhead for them. Not held in private places but arrayed across the firmament for all to see, no matter how far separated in space. In 1976, I was in the high desert of Baja California visiting Kumeyaay indian friends when Comet West streaked across a brilliant sky. "This means 50 years of bad times," they said. This is still a wide-spread belief among indigenous people of North America. Imagine what Chacoans and others must have thought of a series of such events in those times!

A world away from the cities of Lombardy, unknown to any Europeans, similar sounds are echoing off canyon walls, floating across the vast, empty spaces of the Southwest. The Pueblo people of Chaco Canyon are about a much larger building project. They are quarrying sandstone blocks and hauling timber across great distances to build what will be the largest buildings in North America until the 19th century. Other building materials are being brought on foot from the dense forests of oak, ponderosa pine, juniper and piñon in mountains up to 70 miles (110 km) away. The work has already required generations of skilled builders, working closely with skilled astronomers to orient the buildings in a way that aligns with the movements of celestial bodies in the heavens. Like the ancient Chinese, the people of Chaco Canyon and sites across the Americas saw their human task as putting themselves in harmony with the heavens by creating their cities as mirror images.

The ceremonial centers and living quarters of Pueblo Bonito will cover two acres—eight thousand square meters—when it is completed; over 650 rooms in structures that in some places are four to five stories high. The massive masonry walls are as much as three feet thick. It will be the size of Rome's coliseum. The entire Chaco complex will be the size of Ireland.

On the other side of the world, in China, astronomers are also taking in the sight of the supernova. It is recorded in their historical records as a "guest star" and it is from them that we know if it. Curiously, there is no record of it in Europe so the people in the Ticinesi villages may not have seen it. There are various theories about this. One is that it wasn't seen in Europe because no one looked for it. The prevailing view of the learned was that the universe and its phenomena were fixed, including the planets in their cycles. There would be no sudden anomalies. It is hard to believe that this would blind the people to such a great light in places still free of the distractions of electricity. The fact that it wasn't recorded doesn't mean that it wasn't seen, but the climate and topography of Europe may have played a role in hiding it under clouds and behind trees and mountains. Some scholars have calculated that the event actually took place in April or May, when weather conditions may have been more inclement for viewing.

The great mystery of Chaco Canyon is why the site was chosen in the first place. It is a very forbidding landscape where summer temperatures can reach 110 degrees and winter temperatures drop below freezing. There were no rivers, no lakes, no major water sources. The people did not arrive here in search of green pastures, access to water and food, as most of the migrating European peoples did. What signs pointed them to this place we may never know. But in spite of the arid conditions, which could support only small settlements, twelve generations of people devoted themselves to the building of these structures. They built communities and 95,000 miles of roads through the Southwest.

Then, suddenly it seems, they left. They sealed up doorways and vanished from that site. That is the second great mystery? Why did they leave?

The Chacoans left behind no written record to answer this question. But once again we may fall back on a rich oral tradition and consider their stories. They might not answer the questions to a scientific satisfaction but they give hints. Stories should never be overlooked as evidence of a people. Virgil and Homer have taught us that. Here is a story still told in many versions by the Hopi clans of New Mexico who consider themselves, like all the Pueblo people of the Southwest, descendants of the Chacoans.

EMERGENCE: THE FOUR WORLDS OF THE HOPI

AS TOLD TO FRANK WATERS BY WHITE BEAR FREDRICKS
(EXCERPTED FROM *THE BOOK OF THE HOPI*)

THE FIRST WORLD WAS TOKPELA (ENDLESS SPACE).

Before that, there was only the Creator, Taiowa. All else was endless space. There was no beginning or end, no time, no shape, no life. There was only an immeasurable void that had its beginning and end, its time, its shape, and its life in the mind of Taiowa.

Then the infinite Taiowa conceived the finite.

First, He created Sótuknang to make it manifest.

Taiowa said to him, "I have created the first power and instrument as a person to carry out my plan for life in endless space. I am your Uncle. You are my Nephew. Go now and lay out these universes in proper order so they may work together in harmony according to my plan."

Sótuknang follows Taiowa's instructions and creates Spider Woman to remain on the Earth as his helper.

"Look around you," said Sótuknang to Spider Woman. "Here is the earth that we have created. It has shape and substance, direction and time, a beginning and an end. But there is no life upon it. We see no joyful movement. We hear no joyful sound. What is life without sound and movement? So you have been given the power to help us create this life. You have been given the knowledge, the wisdom, and the love to bless all the beings you create. That is why you are here."

So Spider Woman molded some earth into two beings, the twins Pöqánghoya and Palöngawhoya. She covered them with a cape made of a white substance, which was the creative wisdom itself, and she sang the creation song over them.

Pöqánghoya, traveling throughout the earth, solidified the higher reaches into great mountains. The lower reaches he made firm, but still pliable enough to be used by those beings to be placed upon it and who would call it their mother.

Palöngawhoya, traveling throughout all of the earth, sounded out his call as he was told to do. All of the vibration centers along the earth's axis from pole to pole resounded his call; the whole earth trembled, and the universe quivered in tune. Thus he made the whole world an instrument of sound, and sound an instrument for carrying messages, resounding praise to the Creator of all.

"This is your voice, Uncle," Sótuknang said to Taiowa. "Everything is tuned to your sound."

"It is very good," said Taiowa.

When they had accomplished their duties, Pöqánghoya was sent to the north pole of the world's axis, and Palöngawhoya to the south pole, where they were jointly commanded to keep the world properly rotating. Pöqánghoya was also given the power to keep the earth in a stable form of solidness. Palöngawhoya was given the power to keep the air in gentle ordered movement, and told to send out his call for good or for warning through the vibratory centers of the earth.

"These will be your duties in time to come," said Spider Woman.

She then created from the earth the trees, bushes, flowers, and other plants. She created all kinds of seed-bearers and nut-bearers to clothe the earth, giving to each a life and a name. In the same manner, she created all kinds of birds and animals, molding them out of earth and covering each with her white-substance cape of wisdom, and singing over them. . . .

Sótuknang was happy, seeing how beautiful it all was: the land, the plants, the birds and the animals, and the power working through them all. Joyfully he said to Taiowa, "Come see what our world looks like now!"

"It is very good," said Taiowa. "It is now ready for human life, the final touch to complete my plan."

At Taiowa's direction, Spider Woman created the first beings after her own form, covering them with the white-substance cape of creative wisdom and singing the Creation Song over them. But they had no speech, so she called upon Sótuknang.

"As you commanded me, I have created these First People. They are fully and firmly formed, they are properly colored, they have life and movement. But they

cannot talk. That is the proper thing they lack. So I want you to give them speech. Also the wisdom and the power to reproduce, so that they might enjoy their life and give thanks to the Creator."

So Sótuknang gave them speech, a different language to each color, with respect for each other's difference. He also gave them the wisdom and the power to reproduce and multiply.

Then he said to them, "With all these I have given you this world to live on and to be happy. There is only one thing I ask of you: to respect the Creator at all times. Wisdom, harmony, and respect for the love of the Creator who made you: may it grow and never be forgotten among you as long as you live." . . .

With the pristine wisdom granted them, the First People understood that the earth was a living entity like themselves. She was their mother: they were made from her flesh, and they suckled at her breast. For her milk was the grass upon which all animals grazed and the corn which had been created specially to supply food for mankind. . . .

In their wisdom, the First People also knew their father in two aspects. He was the Sun, the solar god of the universe. . . . Yet his was but the face through which looked Taiowa, their Creator.

These two universal entities were their real parents, their human parents being but instruments through which their power was made manifest. In modern times their descendants remembered this.

The First People, then, understood the mystery of their parenthood. In their pristine wisdom they also understood their own structure and function: the nature of man himself. The living body of man and the living body of the earth were constructed in the same way. Through each man ran an axis, man's axis being his backbone, the vertebral column, which controlled the equilibrium of his movements and his functions. Along this axis were several vibratory centers which echoed the primordial sound of life throughout the universe or sounded a warning if anything went wrong.

The first of these in man lay at the top of the head. Here, when he was born, was the soft spot, kópavi, the "open door" through which he received his life and communicated with his Creator.

Just below it lay the second center, the organ that man learned to think with by himself, the thinking organ called the brain. Its earthy function enabled man to think about his actions and work on this earth. But the more he understood that his work and his actions should conform to the plan of the Creator, the more clearly he understood that the real function of the brain was carrying out the plan of all Creation.

The third center lay in the throat. It tied together those openings in his nose and mouth through which he received the breath of life and the vibratory organs that allowed him to give back his breath in sound. This primordial sound, as that coming from the vibratory centers of the body of earth, was attuned to the universal vibrations of all of Creation. New and diverse sounds were given forth by these vocal organs in the forms of speech and song, their secondary function for man on this earth. But, as he came to understand its primary function, he used this center to speak and sing praises to the Creator.

The fourth center was the heart. It too was a vibrating organ, pulsing with the vibration of life itself. In his heart man felt the good of life, its sincere purpose. He was of One Heart, but there were those who permitted evil feelings to enter. They were said to be of two hearts.

The last of man's important centers lay under his navel, the organ some people now call the solar plexus. As this name signifies, it was the throne in man of the Creator himself. From it he directed all the functions of man.

But gradually there were those who forgot the commands of Sótuknang and the Spider Woman to respect their Creator. More and more they used the vibratory centers solely for earthy purposes, forgetting that their primary purpose was to carry out the plan of Creation.

Then there came Lavahóya, the Talker. He came in the form of a bird called Mochni (a bird like a Mockingbird), and the more he kept talking, the more he convinced them of the differences between them: the difference between people and animals, and the differences between the people themselves by reason of the color of their skins, their speech, and their beliefs in the plan of the Creator.

Over time, the first people forgot to sing praises to their Creator and the door on top of their heads closed. "They had lost the inner vision of the kópavi on the crowns of their heads: the door was closed to them."

But among all the people of different races and languages there were a few in every group who still lived by the laws of Creation. To them came Sótuknang. He came with sound as of a mighty wind and suddenly appeared before them. He said, "I have observed this state of affairs. It is not good. It is so bad that I talked to my Uncle, Taiowa, about it. We have decided this world must be destroyed and another one created so you people can start over again. You are the ones we have chosen. . . . You will go to a certain place. Your kópavi (vibratory center on top of the head) will lead you. This inner wisdom will give you the sight to see a certain cloud, which you will follow by day, and a certain star, which you will follow by night. Take nothing with you. Your journey will not end until the cloud stops and the star stops."

The people descended among the Ant People, into an Ant Kiva, where they were protected when Taiowa destroys the world by fire. When the destruction was complete, the People emerged from their underworld Ant Kiva into the Second World.

After their emergence, the people of the Second World lived in harmony with each other for a time. They built villages and linked them with trails. They began to trade food and hand-crafted items between villages. This was when the trouble started. Everything they needed was on this Second World, but they began to want more. More and more they began to trade for things they didn't need, and the more goods they got, the more they wanted.

This was very serious, for they did not realize they were drawing away, step by step, from the good life given them. They just forgot to sing joyful praises to the Creator, and soon began to sing praises to the goods they bartered and stored. Before long . . . the people began to quarrel and fight, and then wars between the villages began.

There were still a few people in each village who sang the song of their Creation. But the wicked people laughed at them until they could only sing it in their hearts. Even so, Sótuknang heard it through their centers and the centers of the Earth. One day he suddenly appeared before them.

"Spider Woman tells me your thread is running out on this world," he said. . . . "Now my Uncle, Taiowa, and I have decided we must do something about it. We are going to destroy this Second World just as soon as we put you people who still have the song in your hearts in a safe place."

So again, as on the First World, Sótuknang called on the Ant People to open up their underground world for the chosen people. When they were safely underground, Sótuknang commanded the twins, Pöqánghoya and Palöngawhoya, to leave their posts at the north and south ends of the world's axis, where they were stationed to keep the earth properly rotating.

The Twins had hardly abandoned their stations when the world, with no one to control it, teetered off balance, spun around crazily, then rolled over twice. Mountains plunged into the sea with a great splash, seas and lakes sloshed over the land, and as the world spun through cold and lifeless space, it froze into solid ice. This was the end of Tokpu, the Second World.

For many years, all the elements that had comprised the Second World were frozen into a motionless and lifeless lump of ice. But the people were happy and warm with the Ant People in their underground world. . . . .

Eventually, Sótuknang ordered Pöqánghoya and Palöngawhoya back to their stations at the poles of the world axis. With a great shudder and a splintering of ice, the planet began rotating again. When it was rotating smoothly about its axis and moving in its universal orbit, the ice began to melt and the world began to warm to life. Sótuknang set about creating the third world: arranging lands and seas, planting mountains and plains with their proper coverings, and creating all forms of life.

When the earth was ready for occupancy, he came to the Ant Kiva with the proper approach as before and said, "Open the door, it is time for you to come out. . . . I have saved you so you can be planted again on this new Third World. But you must always remember the two things I am saying to you now. First, respect me and one another. Second, sing in harmony from the tops of the hills. When I do not hear you singing praises to your Creator, I will know you have gone back to evil again.". . . .

In the Second World, they had developed handicrafts, homes, and villages. Now, in the Third World, they created big cities and countries: a whole civilization. This made it difficult to conform to the plan of Creation and to sing praises to Taiowa and to Sótuknang. More and more of them became wholly occupied with their own earthy plans.

Some of them, of course, retained the wisdom granted them upon their emergence. With this wisdom they understood that the farther they went on the road of life and the more that they developed, the harder it was. That was why their world was destroyed every so often to give them a fresh start.

There was one woman who was becoming known throughout the land for her wickedness in corrupting so many people. She even boasted that so many men were giving her turquoise necklaces for her favors she could wind them around a ladder that reached to the end of the world's axis. So the people with wisdom sang longer and louder their praises to the Creator from the tops of the hills.

The other people hardly heard them. They began to use their creative power in another evil and destructive way. . . . Some of them made a pátuwvota [a shield made of hide] and with their creative power, made it fly through the air. On this, many people flew to a big city, attacked it, then returned so fast that no one knew where they came from. Soon the people of many cities were making pátuwvotas and flying on them to attack one another. So corruption and war came to the Third World as it had to the others.

This time Sótuknang came to Spider Woman and said, "There is no use waiting until the thread runs out this time. Something has to be done lest the people with the song in their hearts are corrupted and killed off too. It will be difficult, with all this destruction going on, for them to gather at the far end of the world where I have designated. But I will help them. Then you will save them when I destroy this world with water."

This time the people who had kept open the doors on top of their heads were sealed up by Sótuknang in the hollow of tall reeds, where they were protected as the Earth was destroyed by water.

Taiowa loosed the waters upon the earth. Waves higher than mountains rolled in upon the land. Continents broke asunder and sank beneath the seas. And still the rains fell, the waves rolled in.

So the Third World was destroyed. When the People emerged from their hollow reeds, they were surrounded on all sides by water. They made rafts and paddles and were left on their own to seek out their place of emergence into the Fourth World. They rested on small islands but could not find the place they were seeking. So they stopped paddling and opened up the doors on the top of their heads to let themselves be guided.

"See," said Sótuknang, "I have washed away even the footprints of your emergence, the stepping-stones which I left for you. Down on the bottom of the sea lie all the proud cities, the flying pátuwvotas, and the worldly treasures corrupted with evil, and those people who found no time to sing praises to the Creator from the tops of their hills. But the day will come, if you preserve the memory and meaning of your emergence, when these stepping stones will emerge again to prove the truth you speak."

"I have something more to say to you before I leave you," Sótuknang told the people as they stood at their place of emergence.

"The name of this Fourth World is Túwaqachi," he said, "the World Complete. You will find out why. It is not all beautiful and easy like the previous ones. It has height and depth, heat and cold, beauty and barrenness: it has everything for you to choose from. What you choose will determine if this time you can carry out the plan of creation on it or whether it, in time, must be destroyed too.

Now you will separate and go different ways to claim all the earth for the Creator. Each group of you will follow your own star until it stops. There you will settle. Now I must go. But you will have help from the proper deities, from your good spirits. Just keep your own doors open and always remember what I have told you."

Then he disappeared.

And here we are. In the Fourth World, the last moments of our Earth Calendar Year, discussing once again the destiny of the Earth and our own future. I recounted the Hopi story because it is yet another Calendar of sorts, filled with creations and destructions, extinctions and new species. I often wonder if the long oral traditions carry memories of real destructions like the great floods and ice ages; events of fire like the destruction of Minoan Thera.

What is so unique about this story is that it is not an ancient myth but a living history that continues to form the cultural substance and identity of the Hopi people still living in the Southwest, although the versions of the story vary. Other stories, with significant similarities, can be found among all of the Pueblo people today who trace themselves back to Chaco and other ancient sites.

"You know the thing that really gets me?" declared the late Edmund Ladd, a Zuni archaeologist who served for many years as curator of ethnology at the Museum of Indian Arts and Culture in Santa Fe. "This business that we mysteriously disappeared. What are we," he once asked, gesturing toward himself, "cottage cheese? We're here. We're Zuni, Hopi, Acoma, Santa Clara. We've been here since 5000 BC and we're still here."

In *The Mystery of Chaco Canyon* documentary, Ladd offers his own thoughts about the end of Chaco:

> "We look upon Chaco Canyon, especially Pueblo Bonito, as a place where people of great power lived at one time. Those known as the people who lived in the circular house, were people who had magical powers. Power over animals, birds and so forth. [In the end,] people began to move out. People sealed up doorways. Clans dividing and moving into different areas. Perhaps over time, the original premise on which they began to develop these places could have been corrupted."

A similar idea is expressed in the film by Paul Pino, Council Member of Laguna Pueblo:

> "In our history they talk of things that occurred a long time ago. Here at Chaco there were powerful people who had a lot of spiritual power. These people probably used their power in ways that caused things to change and that may have been one of the reasons why the migrations were set to start again. Because these people were causing changes that were never meant to occur. Certainly their leaving was not very abrupt. The migrations were very slow. Very calculated.
>
> "There are some things in our migration histories that we just don't understand. But I think some of those things were never meant to be understood. They served the purpose when they were needed and now that purpose or need is no longer there. It's no longer necessary to repeat that portion of that story."

ST. LOUIS REGION ~ CAHOKIA

At the time that the Chacoans are building Pueblo Bonito and other Chaco Canyon structures, another building project is underway across the river from present-day St. Louis at the confluence of the Mississippi and Missouri Rivers. The area has been inhabited since 600 AD, but the great building project has only recently begun at the turn of the first millennium AD. The largest building in Cahokia is a massive structure, ten stories tall with four terraces and the largest man-made earthen mound north of Mexico. It is ninety-two feet high (28m), over nine-hundred feet long (290m) and over eight-hundred feet wide (255m). My oh my! I find numbers like these difficult to visualize, so it is helpful for me to calculate that this is the equivalent in area to almost fourteen football fields (including their end zones!).* This mound, likely with a palace or temple on its top, is the largest of over a hundred mounds that have been discovered in the area.

A circle of posts used to make astronomical sightings stands to the west of what we now call Monk's Mound, carefully placed to mark the solstices and equinoxes. It has been dubbed Woodhenge after a similar construction near Stonehenge in Britain.

South of this mound spreads a forty-acre Grand Plaza that, like the plaza in the Roman Forum, would likely have been used for large ceremonies, gatherings and ritual games. This is one of four plazas that surround Monks Mound in the four cardinal directions. Before 1050, archaeologists have calculated that there were only about a thousand people on the site, but the population exploded after that date. Estimates have ranged from eight thousand to forty thousand inhabitants at its peak. The latter would make it larger than any subsequent city in the United States until Philadelphia in 1800. In 1250, its population was larger than London's. It begins to decline after 1300 and is abandoned more than a century before the arrival of Europeans. Severe drought, over-hunting and deforestation as well as periods of flooding from the Mississippi have been cited as causes for that decline. Unlike the Pueblo people of the Southwest, we do not have present-day Cahokians to turn to for their stories and their history. Neither did they simply evaporate from their great centers. Where did they go? We do have scientists with exceptional tools for unriddling the past and what we know of Cahokia comes from their research. Timothy R. Pauketat, professor of anthropology at the University of Illinois at Champaign-Urbana, has devoted decades to its study and offers this:

> Possibly, the people of Cahokia included local farmers and contingents of dignitaries and representatives from far-off peoples in the Plains, Midwest, and South. As Cahokia dissolved, the nonlocal citizens might have simply gone home. The descendants of Cahokians might include people in various tribal groups in the Plains and the South today: the Quapaw, Omaha, Pawnee, Chickasaw, Ponca, Mandan, Choctaw, and Osage, among others.

---

* Football field is in length: 360 feet or 120 yards. Width: 160 feet of 53⅓ yards, (with end zones). An acre is about the size of a football field *without* the end zones.

Pauketat notes, however, that there is no mention in the stories of these people of a great city in their past.

We know that the Chacoans also abandoned their massive ceremonial city but with more obvious intent. All of its openings were carefully closed up with stone and interior chambers set on fire. In the mid-12th century, the southwestern U.S. was in the middle of a multi-decade megadrought. Tree ring analysis has identified megadroughts in the eleventh and twelfth centuries and a period of "no" rain between 1276 and 1299 in the region. During this time there occurred the abandonment of settlements in the Southwest, including those in Chaco Canyon and Mesa Verde.

In addition to the megadroughts, sometime between 1040 and 1100, a Strombolian eruption occurred near Flagstaff, Arizona that shot a plume tens of thousands of feet into the sky with continuous lightning day and night and lava raining down like bombs. It had been preceded by rumblings of the earth, which sent nearby populations fleeing in advance of the event. It could be seen for over a hundred miles. According to some models, it could even be seen from Chaco, but certainly word of it would have quickly reached them and people from Chaco would have traveled to see it. This eruption of Sunset Crater was the first in human times. Within the same period there occurred an eruption of the Little Wells volcano just a little over a hundred miles away (200km), to the north of the Grand Canyon. Though smaller than the Sunset Crater volcano, two such events in the same century and region must have heightened the sense of living in apocalyptic times.

Viewed in the context of the Hopi story, we could imagine another chapter in which the desperate conditions in the region and the strange sights in the heavens were seen as a sign that the people had once again fallen out of favor with Sótuknang and his uncle Taiowa or that their great ceremonial complex at Chaco had fallen out of harmony with the heavens. Those whose *kopavi* remained open would see Taiowa and Sótuknang at work destroying their world once again and setting them on the way to new migrations.

Chaco's reaction, according to archaeologist Steve Lekson, was to move their capital to what is now known as Aztec Ruins to the north. Aztec Ruins (which is not Aztec at all) was another major construction project built in a decade. Lekson has an interesting theory about the migration of people from Chaco along the 108th meridian. *

The Chaco Meridian is a north-south line at approximately 108 degrees longitude that runs through or very near several extremely important sites: Chaco Canyon, Aztec Ruins (both in New Mexico), and Paquimé (just across the border in Chihuahua, Mexico). Each of these sites, in its time, was by far the biggest and almost certainly most important regional center in the Southwest. The population of each was probably between 2,000 and 3,000 people—not quite a city, but very

* This is from an article in *Archaeology Magazine* (Jan–Feb 2009) but the theory is presented in more detail in his book *The Chaco Meridian: Centers of Political Power in the Ancient Southwest.*

UNESCO INTERNATIONAL HERITAGE SITES

COURTESY OF LYNDA D'AMICO

large for the Southwest. And they followed one another as major centers in a tight sequence: Chaco from AD 850 to 1125, Aztec from 1110 to 1275, and Paquimé [more commonly known as Casas Grandes] from 1250 to 1450

So the people continued to build. Other centers were raised with impressive structures, though none so great as Chaco.

Whatever the truth may be about the disappearance of its people, for many of the Pueblo people of today, the remains of Chaco stand as a cautionary tale. What we see as a decline of power, they see as a growth in wisdom.

TOP, THE CAHOKIA MOUNDS ARE SEEN IN THEIR GEOGRAPHICAL SETTING TO THE EAST. ABOVE LEFT, THE 108TH LONGITUDE LINE PASSES THROUGH MAJOR SITES NORTH TO AZTEC RUINS AND SOUTH TO CASAS GRANDES-PAQUIMÉ FROM CHACO. I ENJOY THE FACT THAT IT ALSO PASSES THROUGH THE PLAINS OF ST.AUGUSTINE, WHERE THE VERY LARGE ARRAY OF RADIO TELESCOPES LIE AND UFOLOGISTS CITE A ROSWELL-LIKE EVENT BACK IN THE 1940S. AUGUSTINUS AURELIUS GAINS A COSMIC CONTEXT HERE.

Nothern California

A MAIDU CREATION STORY

— Maidu storyteller named HÁNC'IBYJIM.
William Shipley translation

And then, they say, Earthmaker sang.
"Where are you, my great mountain ranges?

O, mountains of my world, where are you?"
Coyote tried. He kept on singing.

> *"If, indeed, we two shall see nothing at all,*
> *traveling about the world,*
> *then, perhaps,*
> *there may be no misty mountain ranges there!"*
> *Earthmaker said:*
> *"If I could but see a little bit of land*
> *I might do something very good with it.*

Floating along, then,
they saw something like a bird's nest.

Earthmaker said:
> *"It really is small.*
> *It would be good if it were a little bigger,*
> *but it really is small.*
> *I wonder if I might stretch it apart a little.*
> *What would be good to do?*
> *In what way can I make it a little bigger?"*

> *As he talked, he transformed it.*
> *He stretched it out to where the day breaks;*
> *he stretched it out to the south;*
> *he stretched it out to the place where the sun goes down;*
> *he stretched it out to the North Country;*
> *he stretched it out to the rim of the world;*
> *he stretched it out!*

When Earthmaker had stretched it out,
> *he said, "Good!*

You who saw of old this earth, this mud,
and made this nest, sing!

Telling old tales, humans will say of you:
'In ancient times, the being who was Meadowlark,
making the land and sticking it together in just that way,
built the nest from which the world was made.'"

Then Meadowlark sang—
sang a beautiful song about Earthmaker's creation.

THERE IS NO SOUND OF METAL OR ROCK ON STONE. No huge cities rising or elaborate ceremonial complexes. There is the lapping of the sea on sandy shores, or the crashing of waves against rocky cliffs. There are the redwood forests of the northern coast, the deep forests of the Sierra foothills and the icy winds that blow along their ridges. There is the perfect silence of the eastern deserts. Yet people have lived here for thousands of years, moving through its varied landscapes to find the most abundant food according to season. There will not be such a variety of languages spoken in an area except in New Guinea. But food is ample along the coasts. There are lakes and rivers, fish, waterfowl, and animals to hunt in the forests. The climate in most parts is friendly. The people can migrate easily to the desert areas in the winter and to the mountain areas in the summer. It is a good place to live.

In the land around my creek, people have been living for thousands of years. Miwok, Pomo, Patwin and Wappo tribes may date back ten thousand years. The steelhead are rising with the swelling waters, according to their season, offering plentiful food to the native inhabitants. Sonoma Mountain has been pushing upward over the last million years, not gently growing like the redwood but thrust upward by volcanic activity. Just what the steelhead need to ride the rush of water to the sea like the surfers of the distant future.

California ~ 1975

THE PLACE OF CREATION

ONLY ONCE DID I EVER SEE MY POWERFULLY ARTICULATE MOTHER "one-upped" and left silent in a verbal exchange. It was even more amazing that this feat was accomplished by a taciturn Native American woman, not given to flights of garrulousness in the manner of a Welsh-American like my mother or Americans in general. I had invited my parents to visit me in Southern California in February 1975. For them it was a welcome contrast to Rochester, New York in February. I was driving them to Palm Springs as part of the Grand Tour. My father had never been here and my mother had visited me only once. Before that, neither had been west of Ohio.

On the way to Palm Springs, we stopped in Banning at the Morongo Indian Reservation to visit their Malki Museum. I had almost every publication of the

Malki Museum Press and had stopped there before to talk with the director, Jane Penn. My parents knew nothing of Native Americans except what they saw in diaramas in the local museum. Wigwams and canoes and women with papooses caught in a permanent stillness like a Statues game when someone yells "Freeze" and then goes off to lunch.

I introduced them to the Jane Penn, a large, striking Native American woman with a strong face and dark, penetrating eyes that watched us impassively from her desk. I think my mother was good at sizing people up quickly, but Jane Penn was something different. Not a face with mobile expressions or an eagerness to delight and have a *rapport* with you—one of my mother's favorites words. I don't recall Mother's opening lines but I'm sure she had them. In fact I am sure that she was deeply interested and impressed by what she was seeing around her and by being, for the first time in her life, in the presence of a *living* "indian." I'm sure that she was trying to make thoughtful and respectful conversation. She was good at that. But she was also aware that Jane Penn was operating on a different level, not looking at her but into her—something we Imported Americans are not particularly comfortable with.

I don't know how the conversation turned to creation stories, but I recall Jane Penn's challenge very vividly. "Do *you* know where you come from?" My mother was wary. She may have been glib at times but she was also quick-minded and insightful. She knew this was a trick question so she wasn't going to answer Florida or New York or even her father's homeland, Wales. She waited. Jane Penn pressed her. "Do you know where the Garden of Eden *is*? Can you *go* there?"

"No," my mother said quite honestly. "I can't."

"I can show you exactly where our people came from. I can show you the exact rock that it was near. We are still close to the place of our beginning. But you—you have no idea where yours is. You are just a people lost on the earth." My mother was quiet all the way to Palm Springs and only became animated again when she heard that Frank Sinatra was in town and she began watching for him.

◆ ◆ ◆

Jane Penn was a Wanikik (Pass area) Cahuilla who was born in 1910, the daughter of one of the last and greatest Cahuilla medicine men. Her grandmother, who lived to be 120 years old, and an aunt, who lived to be 96, both told her stories as a child of their Wanikik Cahuilla heritage. Many of her nephews sang birdsongs and some were Ceremonial House singers, knowing the songs that were passed on only to a special few.

Jane grew up hearing the stories and dreams of her aunt Margaret Pablo, who was herself the grand-niece of Ygindio Gabriel, a chief of the Wanikik Cahuila. When her elderly aunt died, followed by her elderly cousin Victoria Wierick, both left her precious artifacts of her people for safekeeping. Together with Cahuilla elder Katherine Saubel and UC Riverside anthropologist Lowell Bean, Jane Penn founded the Malki Museum. Their vision for the museum expanded to include all of Southern California's Native American tribes.

The exchange that took place between my mother and Jane Penn was not an unusual one. When a visitor to the Malki Museum once asked if anyone would shoot him if he dug into the Indian graveyard, she replied, "Well, if nobody else does, I will. Why don't you tell me where your relatives are buried and I'll go dig them up?" She was a powerful voice for her people.

Jane Penn's great-uncle, Ygindio Gabriel, was chief of her people when California became a state of the Union and the *Melkish* or white man was moving in huge numbers into their territory. In 1852, Chief Ygindio signed the Treaty of Temecula for his band, along with twenty other bands in Southern California. The treaty was never ratified. It was her aunt Margaret Pablo who urged her people to move beyond their bitterness over this betrayal to focus instead on communicating their culture to the newcomers. Her efforts rekindled the spark of cultural pride and identity in the hearts of her people, who had begun to leave the reservations and forget their traditions. This legacy she bequeathed to her niece, who used the Malki Museum Press and Museum to further those goals.

Native groups who did not have standard bearers like these women became lost and forgotten over time as the last traces of them disappeared on the landscape, like the people of Cahokia and Chaco Canyon, even with their great ceremonial cities.

THE 14TH CENTURY

Europe ~ ca. 1350 AD

A DEADLY MIGRATION

YERSINIA PESTIS IS ON THE MOVE, traveling more swiftly than continents, more invisibly than ships or caravans. It rises out of the steppes of Central Asia with the Mongol hordes who are among its bearers. It travels first in the lungs of the bobac marmot from places like Issyk Kul in present day Kirgystan. From there it hitches a ride on fleas that find transport on rats and finally humans. It follows the caravan routes east and west along the Silk Road making use, with the Mongol armies and traders, of the opportunities of free passage within the Mongol Empire made possible by the Pax Mongolica. Like the Roman Empire in its day, the Mongol Empire effectively connected the Eastern and Western world, following the conquests of Genghis Khan and his successors.

Yersinia Pestis finds transport on merchant ships, which carry it gratuitously and unwittingly throughout the Mediterranean. Following the caravan routes, it reaches the Crimea in Southeastern Europe in 1346, where it officially announces its presence as The Black Death, and moves on into Western Europe and North Africa during the 1340s. It is far more deadly than even the Mongol Horde and, as it did in the time of Justinian, it will decimate the population, killing an estimated 75,000,000 people. In Europe alone, the Black Death is estimated to have killed off 30% to 60% of the population, 25 to 50 million people.*

Yersinia Pestis, which is said to have visited every generation until 1700, was only one element of a Perfect Storm in the 14th century. The North Atlantic region had enjoyed a Medieval Warm Period that lasted from about AD 800–1300. It was not a global but a North Atlantic warming. (This inspired the Vikings to set forth on the ice-free seas and colonize Greenland.)

By 1300, Northern Europe was entering what is sometimes called the Little Ice Age, when warm summers could no longer be depended upon. This will last into the 19th century. In 1315, a season of unusually heavy rains led to the Great Famine of 1315-1317, with effects felt into 1322. This brought to an end that earlier period of growth and prosperity during the eleventh to thirteenth centuries when the Church of San Bernardo was built in Ticino and cathedrals and universities rose above Europe. People died of starvation on a massive scale. It affected all of Northern Europe, south to the Pyrenees and the Alps. The wheat yields—the staple of nourishment in Europe as rice is to the east—dropped severely. It is measured in the number of seeds one can eat per seed planted. In the good weather of the

---

* Some interpretations of the historical records by epidemiologists suggest a viral hemorrhagic fever was the cause, but the result is as black either way. No final and exact theory of the Plague's source can be derived from varied historical records at such a distance in time.

13th century, that could be as high as 7:1. In the bad years that followed, it fell to as low as 2:1. Our modern farms have ratios of 200:1 or more. Children were dying. Average mortality was dropping to below 30 years. (It is currently 80).

Between 1310 and 1330, northern Europe experienced the worst weather of the Middle Ages with severe winters followed by cold and rainy summers. In the spring of 1315, unusually heavy rains began to fall throughout much of Europe. It changed little through the spring and summer. The grains could not ripen. It was brought indoors in urns and pots. The straw and hay for the animals could not be cured. There was no fodder for the livestock. Salt, which was used to cure and preserve meat, could not be evaporated. Under these conditions, the prices of things soared and the peasants could no longer afford bread. People turned to eating wild roots, plants, grasses, nuts and the bark in the forests. In desperation, they slaughtered their draft animals. They ate their seed grain. Some abandoned their children to fend for themselves. People succumbed to diseases like pneumonia, bronchitis, tuberculosis. From hunger alone, before the arrival of the Black Death, the Great Famine would kill 10% to 20% of the population of cities and towns. With the arrival of the Plague, the human degeneration and desperation was so great that such unheard of things as cannibalism, child-murder and rampant crime tore at the fabric of the once vibrant European societies. Conditions undermined the authority of the Catholic Church as prayers went unanswered and some blamed the failure for corruption within the church. The chivalrous era celebrated by the bards gave way to the hard-edged warriors of the Hundred Years War.

Yersinia pestis moved swiftly through Italy, like wind through wheat, scything a path north from Messina, Sicily—there, where ships had wrecked in the throes of Scylla and Charybdis and Aeneas had guided his Trojan countryman; there where the plates clashed, where Etna spewed its fire nearby and Aeolus unleashed his winds. It was at the end of September of 1347 that it reached Messina, and by October had spread through the rest of Sicily. By December it had reached the islands of Sardinia, Corsica, Elba, coming ashore at Genoa in late December. It moved quickly in January of 1348 into Pisa and then Venice. Florence, Bologna and Modena in March. Through Perugia and Padua in April and then into lovely Orvieto in late April and May, where I visited my friend Virginia Igonda. In May it passed into Siena and then into Rimini. It seemed to be traveling the old Roman road—Via Flaminia (though another outbreak of it will come up from the south from Naples to Rome in August). In June, it arrived in Parma, an ancient city nestled in the Po River Valley between Bologna and Milan.

In those days, cities were virtual kingdoms in Italy, and Parma was such a city-kingdom. Its rulership was much sought over and contested. One Francesco Petrarca—"Petrarch" to us—had arrived there in 1341 from Rome, where he had just been crowned with the laurel wreath as poet-laureate of that city. (It was Petrarch who made this a symbol of lasting triumph.) He had spent his time in Rome like any good tourist, ogling the sights of the Imperial City and walking the streets with Giovanni Colona—a Dominican monk—until they both collapsed with exhaustion on the roof of the ruins of the Baths of Diocletian and there, talked of many things: A conversation which would later be recorded in letters to Fra Giovanni from Parma and come down to us today as an eloquent narrative of his visit to Rome and his theory on the origin of the arts.

Petrarch was only one of millions who suffered great losses from Yersinia Pestis. He would lose his son, his grandson and the love of his life—a woman named Laura whom he may never have spoken to, but who lives in his sonnets to her. As the plague raged in Parma, the poet wrote to his brother, who lived in a monastery in Montrieux. His brother was the only survivor out of thirty-five people there, and had remained, alone with his dog, to guard and tend the monastery.

Parma ~ 1348

MY BROTHER! MY BROTHER! MY BROTHER! A new beginning to a letter, though used by Marcus Tullius [Cicero] fourteen hundred years ago. Alas! my beloved brother, what shall I say? How shall I begin? Whither shall I turn? On all sides is sorrow; everywhere is fear. I would, my brother, that I had never been born, or, at least, had died before these times. How will posterity believe that there has been a time when without the lightnings of heaven or the fires of earth, without wars or other visible slaughter, not this or that part of the earth, but well-nigh the whole globe, has remained without inhabitants. When has any such thing been even heard or seen; in what annals has it ever been read that houses were left vacant, cities deserted, the country neglected, the fields too small for the dead and a fearful and universal solitude over the whole earth?. . . Oh happy people of the future, who have not known these miseries and perchance will class our testimony with the fables. We have, indeed, deserved these [punishments] and even greater; but our forefathers also have deserved them, and may our posterity not also merit the same . . .*

We know now, from Procopius, of at least one other time of such desolation, possibly from the same disease. While Petrarch, the poet, conveys the desolate feeling of those times, his friend Boccaccio writes more factually and concretely about Florence in the introduction to his classic work, *The Decameron*, read by every student in my high school when I was 16 and the work itself was nearly 1500 years old. It is a detailed portrait of Yersinia Pestis, upon arrival in the great city of Florence in that year of 1348.

I say, then, that in the year 1348 after the Son of God's fruitful incarnation, into the distinguished city of Florence, that most beautiful of Italian cities, there entered a deadly pestilence. Whether one believes that it came through the influence of the heavenly bodies or that God, justly angered by our iniquities, sent it for our correction, in any case it had begun several years earlier in the east and killed an

* Adapted from: George Deaux, *The Black Death 1347*. New York: Weybright and Talley, 1969.

innumerable mass of people, spreading steadily from place to place and growing as it moved west. . . .

There were dead bodies all over, and all were treated in pretty much the same manner by their neighbors, who were moved no less by fear that the corrupted bodies would infect them than by any pity they felt toward the deceased. They would drag the dead bodies out of their homes (either themselves or with the aid of porters, when they could get them) and leave them in front of their doors. In the morning great numbers of them could be seen by any passerby. At that time they were laid out and carried away on biers or, if none were available, on planks. Nor did a bier carry only one. Sometimes it carried two or three at a time, and there were occasions when a husband and wife, two or three brothers, or a father and son were carried off together. Any number of times two priests with a cross would be on the way to the church with someone and porters would fall in behind with two or three more biers, so that the priests, who thought they were on their way to bury one person, eventually found that they had six, eight or even more.

Nor were these dead honored with tears, lights or companions. Things sunk to the level that people were disposed of much as we would now dispose of a dead goat. Thus it became clear that what the wise had never learned to suffer with patience when, in the natural course of things, it struck less dramatically and less often, became a matter of indifference even to the simple, thanks to the sheer scale of this misfortune.

The amount of holy ground available for burials was insufficient for the huge quantity of corpses arriving at the church every day and even every hour, especially if they wished to follow the old custom and give every body its own place; so when all individual places in a churchyard were taken they dug huge trenches and put people in them by the hundreds like merchandise in the hold of a ship, then covered them over with a little dirt, until the ditch was filled to the top.

But I shall spare you a detailed description of the miseries visited upon us and simply mention that the ill winds blowing through our city did not spare the surrounding countryside. There, to say nothing of the towns (which were like smaller versions of the city), throughout the villages and fields the poor, miserable peasants and their families, who lacked the care of doctors or the aid of servants, died more like beasts than humans, day and night, on the roads and in their fields, And thus like the city-dwellers they became loose in their behavior and stopped taking care of their possessions and occupations, and all of them, once they began to anticipate their deaths, stopped caring about what they might do in the future with their beasts and lands and simply concentrated on consuming what they had. Thus their cattle, donkeys, sheep, goats, pigs, chickens and even their dogs, man's best friends, were driven off into the fields where the wheat stood abandoned, not merely unharvested but not even cut. These animals were allowed to roam where they pleased, and many, like rational beings, returned home each night after eating well during the day, without being encouraged to do so by a shepherd.

Enough about the countryside. Returning to the city, what more can be said except that the cruelty of heaven (and perhaps in part of humankind as well) was such that between March and July, thanks to the force of the plague and the fear that led the *healthy to abandon the sick, more than one hundred thousand people died within the walls of Florence. Before the deaths began, who would have imagined the city even held so many people? Oh, how many great palazzi, how many lovely houses, how many noble dwellings once full of families, of lords and ladies, were emptied down to the lowest servant? Oh, how many memorable pedigrees, ample estates and renowned fortunes were left without a worthy heir? How many valiant men, lovely ladies and handsome youths whom even Galen, Hippocrates and Aesculapius would have judged to be in perfect health, dined with their family, companions and friends in the morning and then in the evening with their ancestors in the other world.**

We should be grateful that he spared us "a more detailed description of the miseries." Modern demographic studies estimate the population of Florence in 1300 at 120,000 and by 1427 the number of people counted had fallen to around 37,000. However accurate the estimates are, it is undeniable that Florence suffered a huge, swift population loss. Deaths in New York City to that effect would be five and a half million people. In the United States, over two hundred million people. Boccaccio's account reminds us of a sad verity that is easily obscured in "good times": Civility and compassion are the luxury of comparatively prosperous and untroubled conditions.

I find it remarkable that in those dark days, such inspired individuals could emerge as Petrarch, Boccaccio and Dante, who was also writing in this period. They had to have been the most apocalyptic of times, yet beneath that wintry destruction, once again seeds had been sown that would blossom a century later into the Renaissance.

When Petrarch was born, in 1300, very few people could read and write, which may be why he valued his correspondents so. It is ironic that in our own time, the easier it becomes to communicate through computers and the internet, the less we have to say. The current fad is to "twitter" one's messages in 140 characters or less. Not words, *characters!* I like to observe to my friends that if Paul had twittered the Corinthians, there would be no New Testament as we know it. Nor, to the present-day Twitterers, would Petrarch's lengthy letters be anything but unnecessarily time-consuming. Yet consider the labor of writing with quill and precious ink. First to find the feather—"a good strong flight feather from the wing of a robust bird worked the best" as one source put it. Then trimming the point, and scratching away for hours. I am especially fond of this letter, which Petrarch wrote to his friend Lapo da Castiglionchio, an eminent scholar and lawyer, on the subject of a borrowed book.

Your Cicero has been in my possession four years and more. There is a good reason, though, for so long a delay; namely, the great scarcity of copyists who understand such work. It is a state of affairs that has resulted in an incredible loss to

---

* Translated by David Burr, History Department, Virginia Tech, Blacksburg, Virginia *Boccaccio.* http://www.history.vt.edu/Burr/Boccaccio.html. Accessed 12-14-09.

scholarship. Books that by their nature are a little hard to understand are no longer multiplied, and have ceased to be generally intelligible, and so have sunk into utter neglect, and in the end have perished. This age of ours consequently has let fall, bit by bit, some of the richest and sweetest fruits that the tree of knowledge has yielded; has thrown away the results of the vigils and labours of the most illustrious men of genius; things of more value, I am almost tempted to say, than anything else in the whole world. . . .

But I must return to your Cicero. I could not do without it, and the incompetence of the copyists would not let me possess it. What was left for me but to rely upon my own resources, and press these weary fingers and this worn and ragged pen into the service? The plan that I followed was this. . . . Not a single word did I read except as I wrote. But how is that, I hear someone say; did you write without knowing what it was that you were writing? Ah! but from the very first it was enough for me to know that it was a work of Tullius [Cicero], and an extremely rare one too. And then as soon as I was fairly started I found at every step so much sweetness and charm, and felt so strong a desire to advance, that the only difficulty which I experienced in reading and writing at the same time came from the fact that my pen could not cover the ground so rapidly as I wanted it to, whereas my expectation had been rather that it would outstrip my eyes, and that my ardour for writing would be chilled by the slowness of my reading. So the pen held back the eye, and the eye drove on the pen, and I covered page after page, delighting in my task, and committing many and many a passage to memory as I wrote. For just in proportion as the writing is slower than the reading does the passage make a deep impression and cling to the mind.

As a twenty-first century writer, this letter impressed me deeply. How intimately he must have experienced the Roman statesman who had lived nearly fourteen hundred years before him, just as Augustine had been inspired by Cicero at the age of 15 in Tagaste, North Africa. It is an intimacy of feeling and understanding that very few people experience among their contemporaries and friends, Facebook notwithstanding. In fact, at one point in his life, he addresses letters to Cicero as if he *were* a contemporary. Those letters survive as chronoscopes that can collapse time on a page. But isn't that the secret of all writing? This bending and folding of time into paper envelopes or CD sleeves or whatever the future will invent for it?

Petrarch made me want to read Cicero—the very fellow that Dad and I had cut from our lives by "stabbing Virgil," poor man. Once again I blessed the printing press for making it so easy to bring Cicero to hand in the Loeb Library Edition in a friend's library. I opened it to an essay addressed to his friend Atticus. These were the very letters that Petrarch was reading and, like Petrarch, I found it congenial to have someone discuss the onset of old age with me, as it is "coming on apace" (Cicero's words) for me too. When this was written, around 44 BC, Cicero was then 62 and Atticus, 65. He uses a style of dialogue in it that he no doubt learned from the Greeks, since he was well-educated in them and had been tutored in the style.*

* In fact, it is Cicero who is considered responsible for bringing Greek philosophy into mainstream Roman culture and developing a Latinized vocabulary for its philosophical terms.

I know your self-control, writes Cicero, and the even temper of your mind, and I am aware that you brought home from Athens not only a cognomen [surname] but culture and practical wisdom too. Nevertheless I suspect that you, at times, are quite seriously troubled by the same circumstances which are troubling me. . . .

However, at the present, I have determined to write something on old age to be dedicated to you, for I fain would lighten both for you and for me our common burden of old age, which, if not already pressing hard upon us, is surely coming on apace; and yet I have certain knowledge that you, at all events, are bearing and will continue to bear that burden, as you do all others, with a calm and philosophic mind.

This is a long piece in its entirety, almost fifty pages in the Loeb edition, which does not spare words or characters at all. It calls upon the comforts of the cultivated mind and spirit as the compensation of old age and is filled with anecdotes and memories of historical moments, very personally described and put into the mouth of Cato, as Plato had spoken in his dialogues through Socrates, though no doubt faithful as well to that mentor. I picture Petrarch pouring over this material, transcribing it faithfully with his quill pen, while being comforted by it in mind and heart.

✦ ✦ ✦

It was not until October and November of 1348 that Yersina Pestis reached the foothills of the Alps where it lingered until 1350. Bellinzona, being the crossroads that it was, could not escape it. The Ticinesi in their valleys had good reason to remain in their isolation, but this also meant that they were cut off from their winter work and their source for many of their necessary goods.

Shortly after that time, or perhaps at the end of it, the valleys were opened up again and yet a different kind of traveler made his way into their remote villages.

CIRCA 1350 ~ Brione, Ticino

GIOVANNI BARONZIO

THE COMMISSION TO PAINT THE FRESCO IN THE CHURCH OF ST. MARY of the Assumption may have saved the life of Giovanni Baronzio. The Black Death was particularly bad in Italy. (The people of Brione had been counseled not to travel south, even to Bellinzona.) His fellow painters in Giotto's Rimini school had thought him mad for taking up a commission in so out of the way place as this remote Alpine valley in the Ticino. "Who will ever see your work? Who cares there about the great Giovanni Baronzio?" It was true that he had just completed a very fine and prestigious commission by the Franciscans for the creation of the principal work for their monastery church of Villa Verucchio. This church was one of the most important institutions in their Mendicant Order, not far from the city of Rimini. It was the Franciscan order that had originally invited Giotto to Rimini. Baronzio's work was to celebrate the Malatesta rulers by virtue of its imposing presence, and to underline the fact that Saint Francis himself had stayed at the monastery. In his masterpiece, Baronzio had told the story of Christ's passion in the language he knew best, painting. In Ravenna, he had painted a fresco of the great poet Dante near a side door of San Francesco that opens into the little graveyard where the great poet is buried. He painted him as a pensive figure, seated with his hand on his chin, reading intently before a lectern. It seemed appropriate that he could express something of the poet in art, as Dante had expressed so much in the Italian language—the first writer to abandon Latin and speak directly to the people in their own vernacular.

The heavy rains when he arrived in the village of Brione caused him problems at first. Once the paint was laid, it would withstand water. But to begin on a wall that had been dampened by water would prove fatal to the final work, leading to discoloration and mold. So his first task had been to construct gutters and trenches to direct that water away from the wall. The mayor of Brione had complained that they hadn't hired a carpenter or a plumber and why was he wasting so much time? But the girl Maria, who had watched the process carefully when she brought him his mid-day meal, had calmed the flinty mayor with her reasonable explanation and saved him the unpleasantness of arguing with the town fathers. She was sitting now, watching him; ostensibly praying for an ailing child in the family after delivering the small repast prepared each day by women in the town. She seemed fascinated by the process. Her family excused the delay because they also were interested and felt that his work was a grace from God that honored them. Nothing quite so exciting had happened in the town since the building of the church, and that was only a distant memory.

Baronzio sighed at the irony of his efforts to keep the wall dry, when the next step was to dampen the wall with a layer of coarse lime plaster on which he had brushed the design in red earth pigment. The Italians had devised a way of working in sections, which they called giornate—a day's work. The colors held much better when worked on damp plaster in a smooth intonaco layer. He had just finished applying that and now began to apply the pigments, which he had diluted in water, to the wet plaster. This was the secret to insuring their permanence. Over time, Italian artists had discovered that fresco a secco, applying pigments to a dry wall, did not have the same durability and began to flake off as the years went by. Today he was painting the Virgin's robe.

At first the girl had sat very quietly in the back and never uttered a word inside the church. But each day she moved a little closer, still silent, until she was now on the closest bench and could see him perfectly. She no longer pretended to be praying, but watched him closely. He had taken up the habit of speaking to her as he worked. His voice was low and he never took his eyes off his work. He might have been in intimate conversation with Our Lady, Maria. There was a certain intimacy every painter felt with the figures coming into being beneath the brush. She had said at the beginning that her name was Maria and perhaps they had become overlaid—the inner one, the outer one. He felt her youth, her innocence, yet also her readiness to become a mother. There was that quiet expectancy about her. On the rare occasions that he turned to look toward her, her face was impassive, but her dark eyes were alert, taking in every movement of his brush, almost hungrily.

"Ah, now see this beautiful rich yellow I'm about to apply, how warm it is. Nothing quite disturbs the balance of a painting like conspicuous areas of a strong yellow, so that must be avoided. You want a golden, not a bright yellow. The pigment I am using here is made of yellow earth from Siena, not so far from my home in Rimini. It is the color of the Tuscan hills at evening. My mother was born there.

"This green I have used—we call it terra verte, green earth—is made from celadonite found in the neighborhood of Verona. Ah Verona! A beautiful city. Do you know its arena is almost as big as the Coliseum in Rome? My cousin Lorenzo, who was born there, calls it piccolo Roma. Little Rome. We Italian painters are very fortunate to have these materials so close at hand. For the robe of the apostle Mark I will use vermillion. We say that nothing has had a greater influence on painting than the invention of vermillion. It has completely changed the way we paint from the time we started using it about two hundred years ago. Yes, it is that new. But its red was so brilliant that we were naturally forced to find ways to increase the intensity of the other colors we use and the result is what you can plainly see here. A vividness and life-like beauty. It is a simple recipe really. You mix mercury with sulphur and heat them together. At just the right temperature, the black sulfide of mercury condenses in the top of the flask. The flask is broken and there you have your vermillion. Of course it must be ground to get the color, and the finer you grind it, the finer the color. My master used to say that if you ground it every day for twenty years, the color would still become finer and more handsome." He turned and smiled at her.

"Such is not true of the azure stone, which gives us the beautiful blue I have used for Our Lady's robe, as you see there where she is holding the Christ-child. The azure stone is a beautiful dark blue, and it must be ground just so to make the perfect color. This you don't heat or it will turn black. I break it up and grind it only until it is a coarse powder. That coarseness makes it a little harder to apply, and I had to use several coats to produce a solid blue. It must be done very skillfully, but you see how the crystals of it sparkle in her robe."

And so it went. He recreated for her a world that had ceased to exist, although he never told her so. The friends and relatives whom he conjured for her with his words—all gone. Victims of the disease that had decimated the cities he loved. But for a while, for Maria, they all lived again their vibrant lives in their thriving cities and it gave him back the heart he needed in order to paint.

Sometimes others from the village came and then he worked silently while they talked quietly among themselves. Only when he was alone with Maria, perhaps knowing that she wouldn't speak, did he revert to the role of master, instructing his apprentices. He wasn't sure why this was so and how a silent presence could be so full. Could touch him so.

He was working now on the Last Supper and her hungry eyes seemed even more alive when she saw the food taking shape in the pot, the flagon of wine, the bread. It was his hope that the finished work, if it could not provide food for their tables, would provide food for their souls.

It is not absolutely certain that it was Giovanni Baronzio who painted the frescos in Brione's Church of Mary of the Assumption, but it is clearly of the Rimini school of Giotto and bears the mark especially of Baronzio. It is an unusual Last Supper, at least to my eye. Not the twelve disciples sitting at a long table—like the head table at a conference where the speakers sit. Obviously in the upstairs room where Jesus and the disciples gathered for a last meal together, the scene would have been more intimate. The painter of this fresco has seated them at a round table and the food, even after 700 years, looks rich and succulent, the colors still bright. At the very center of this panel of the fresco is a large round serving bowl or pot, inside of which can clearly be seen a whole, cooked animal, which at first I thought to be a succulent piglet. Why is this detail so centrally placed when the key elements of the Last Supper are the bread and the wine? Perhaps it is not a pig but a lamb, symbolic of the coming sacrifice. Everything about the scene is unusual, in comparison to the much more familiar presentations of scenes in the life of Christ as they appear in the later art of Europe.

I am reminded of the very early pyramid texts in Egypt, at Sakkara, around 2000 BC. These texts are carved into the walls and have survived for millennia. The three-dimensional hieroglyphics created by a priest-sculptor were more than mere letters or syllables. They artistically depicted the quality of what they represented so well that it was thought that the dead could be nourished by them as by actual food. I wonder if that is what Giovanni Baronzio was doing with his sienna yellow and vermillion, his azure and his terra verte, "green earth." They were certainly nourishing Maria.

Circa 1350 ~ Pavia, Italy

ECCLESIASTIC SUPERBOWL: THE CANONS VS. THE HERMITS

AUGUSTINUS AURELIUS IS ON THE MOVE AGAIN. This time in the minds of the Hermits and the Canons. He has become rather like that electron that the early quantum physicists noted could be found here or there (though never in both places at the same time) depending on the eye of the observer.

After being safely delivered to Pavia by King Liutprand, Augustine had enjoyed a quiet repose in the Basilica of San Pietro in Ciel d'Oro—the Church of St. Peter of the Golden Sky—under the auspices of the Benedictines. They had been displaced by the Augustinian Canons Regular in 1221. Who, you might ask, were the Canons Regular? (As if there had might have been Irregular ones.) In this case, "regular" (from "regula" meaning "rule") were a community of canons living under what was defined as the Rule of St. Augustine. Erasmus, who was himself a canon regular, declared that the canons regular are a "median point" between the monks and the secular clergy.

As we noted earlier, Augustine had returned to Tagaste with his friends, establishing there a community that became the model for similar communities that followed. By 430 AD, when the Roman empire in Africa collapsed under the under the onslaught of the Vandal tribes, monks and clergy fled to Europe, carrying Augustine's style of communal living with them. The Augustinian order which developed was not at all like the humble and inspired gathering of friends in Cassiacum. I am reminded of Jung's statement, "Thank God I am Jung and not a Jungian." Had the revered corpse been able to speak at this moment, he might have made a similar comment.

Now, in the fourteenth century, both the Augustinian Canons of the Church and the Augustinian Hermit monks can lay claim to parts of Monica's long-errant son. He had been a bishop of Hippo, after all, so he was an active churchman while fulfilling that role in the tradition of the Canons. Yet he had also established the idea of living in ascetic community, a tradition which was being (theoretically) followed by the Hermit monks. Unfortunately, these two groups not only laid individual claims to Augustine's personality, but to his body as well. This proved a much more difficult debate to resolve.

When the General Chapter of the Augustinians met in Paris in 1327, the prior general of the order, Guglielmo of Cremona, was entrusted with the task of negotiating with the Canons Regular, who had settled in with the Benedictines in the Church at Pavia in 1221. Pope John XXII had granted the Hermits custody of Augustine's relics and even gave them permission to found a monastery next to San Pietro for 25 to 30 friars. They were granted the privilege of celebrating Mass along with the Augustinian Canons. This led to some very unholy wrangling. By 1331, the Hermits seemed to have won the upper hand in their claim to Augustine's Tomb. They slowly expanded their claim then to the physical territory of the basilica, while siphoning off funds designated for the Canons into their own pockets. The Canons responded to this encroachment by building a wall inside the church to protect their own interests. Pope Boniface IX had to intervene and assign halves of the church to each group. The actual location of the bones of Augustinus Aurelius, delivered with such care by Liutprand, had long since been forgotten, so each group claimed that their side held the holy relics.

Around the same time that Giovanni Baronzio was at work on the frescos in Brione, another artisan began the work on an *arca* to adorn the official tomb of the saint. Never mind that the Berber son of Monica had given up all of his possessions on his return to Tagaste. *His* possession had become a literal bone of contention between the Hermits and the Canons, and the *arca* had been commissioned by the Hermits to display in conspicuous form their praise (and proprietorship) of the saint. The *arca* was an elaborate and impressive piece in marble depicting the life of Augustinus Aurelius with no less than 50 bas-reliefs and 95 statuettes.

The religious rivalries were inextricably woven into the political rivalry between Milan and Pavia, both independent states ruled over by powerful dukes. This prolonged superbowl didn't hesitate to use the holy reputation of their saints as political footballs. Pavia's ruling families allied themselves with the powerful

Visconti family of Milan, and they rooted for the Canons, their team. The Hermits had adopted an anti-Visconti, Republican position and were rooted for by the Pope. Hard as it is to believe, these rivalries went back partly to the time of Liutprand in the eighth century, when he had secreted Augustinus Aurelius to Pavia, rather than to Milan, where the Milanese felt that they had the greater claim. Where, after all, was the saint converted and baptized but in Milan? But the Viscontis of Milan had a more current agenda to add to the old injury: They were in the midst of a new campaign to conquer Pavia. (This is what the various duchies *did* in those centuries. Conquer each other. "Italy" was still a long way off.) The *arca* had been conceived as an embodiment of the Pavinese resistance to Milan. When the Viscontis commissioned the sculpture of the Dominican saint, Peter the Martyr, in Milan, it had the rallying effect in Pavia of Sputnik in the 1950s. A sculpture dedicated to Augustine would surely be of greater honor and value and would cement, or rather marble-ize, the position of Pavia and the Hermits. At that time, there were only two free-standing sculptures to saints in existence.

The ancient Rule of life formally constituted for the Hermits around 1243 was inspired by Augustine's life with his family and companions in Cassiacum. It was continued on his return to Africa when he and his companions began their ascetic life of prayer and study. What developed into the Augustinian Rule reflected many of the ideas that were refined through those afternoon discussions in Cassiacum. Disciples are expected to be "of one mind and heart on the way towards God." Through his sermons as Bishop of Hippo, Augustine had taught that "nothing conquers except truth and the victory of truth is love." This echoes Augustine's declaration in Cassiacum of the importance of pursuit of truth through learning, balanced by the injunction to behave with love towards one another. The Augustinian rule is intended to apply to rich and poor, the powerful and the marginalised. Underlying it lies the belief that Love is not earned through human merit, but is the gift of God's grace, totally undeserved yet generously given—the epiphany that had come for Augustine in the garden of Milan.

Augustine wrote and spoke passionately of God's beauty and felt that it received sublime expression through music. "To sing once is to pray twice" he said and sacred music is one of his legacies. Contemporary Augustinian musical foundations include the famous Augustinerkirche in Vienna where orchestral masses by Mozart and Schubert are performed every week and the boys' choir at Sankt Florian in Austria (now over 1,000 years old) in a school conducted by Augustinian Canons.

Mt. Ventoux ~ April 26, 1336

ASCENT

Thus the superior man of devoted character heaps up small things in order to achieve something high and great.

Adapting itself to obstacles and bending around them, wood in the earth grows upward without haste and without rest. Thus too the superior man is devoted in character and never pauses in his progress.

— HEXAGRAM 46
Pushing Upward*

I END THIS GRIM CHAPTER OF OUR HISTORY on the ascending note of Petrarch's climb of Mont Ventoux in 1336, before the arrival of Yersinia Pestis but with a value to later readers which transcends it. The event is emblematic of the turn that European culture is taking at this time, out of a deathly darkness into a new birth, which will take place in that moribund city described by Boccaccio, Florence. Here, Lorenzo de Medici will reign over one of the most illustrious community of artists and philosophers in European history. Michelangelo, Leonardo Da Vinci, Marsilio Ficino and so many others.

Few men can ever have had a more varied experience or a wider range of interests than this restless traveller, the companion of cardinals and princes, the friend of great statesmen, the ambassador from the Lords of Milan to an Emperor, who was also the hermit of Vaucluse, the poet of Laura, the lover of country life known to a circle of devoted friends as " Silvanus," the indefatigable student, the great scholar to whom, more than to any other man, we owe the Revival of Learning in Europe.

— HENRY CALTHROP HOLLWAY-CALTHROP
Petrarch: His Life and Times

The fact that Mont Ventoux is sometimes called the Giant of Provence only proves to us that Provence is not a very mountainous region. Mont Ventoux, in the Department of Vaucluse, France is only a little over 6,000 feet (2,000 meters) in elevation. Neither is it the most beautiful of mountains. Its limestone peak has been swept bare of vegetation by the mighty mistral that blows through regularly with winds up to 200 mph (320 km/h), scouring its bald pate. It is a creature from the African-Eurasian plate encounter, but seems to have wandered off from the rest of the Alps and stands alone, the better to overlook the Rhone valley with a commanding presence, accentuated by a barren peak that gives the impression from a distance of being snow-capped all year round. In short, as Alps go, Mont Ventoux is an imposter. But it remains dear to history, and to the present, in spite of all those deficiencies.

* Translation and Commentary by Richard Wilhelm, translated by Cary Baynes

The steep climb up "Mount Baldy" from the village of Bédoin is the most grueling stretch of the Tour de France cycling race. There are ski runs on the northern side, but the elevation is uninspiring and the winds daunting. Yet consider the *view!* This is exactly what our friend Francesco Petrarca did in 1336, before the arrival of Yersina Pestis.

It is a bright day in April when Petrarch sets out with his brother Gherardo to ascend Mont Ventoux, "a steep and almost inaccessible mass of crags." On the way, they meet an old shepherd who tries to discourage them from proceeding further. He tells them that as a young man, he had been moved by a similar zeal, only to be met with a laborious effort yielding flesh and clothes torn from all of the rocks and brambles. No one before or since then, he insists, has ever dared the task. But the brothers press on. I won't say they are undaunted. Petrarch freely admits that he mostly sought ways to avoid the toil of a steep climb, finding lower paths which in the end are getting him nowhere.

To Dionisio da Borgo San Sepolcro
Malaucene, April 26

To-day I made the ascent of the highest mountain in this region, which is not improperly called Ventosum.* My only motive was the wish to see what so great an elevation had to offer. I have had the expedition in mind for many years; for, as you know, I have lived in this region from infancy. . . .

At the time fixed we left the house, and by evening reached Malaucene, which lies at the foot of the mountain, to the north. Having rested there a day, we finally made the ascent this morning, with no companions except two servants; and a most difficult task it was. The mountain is a very steep and almost inaccessible mass of stony soil. But, as the poet has well said, "Remorseless toil conquers all."

It was a long day, the air fine. We enjoyed the advantages of vigour of mind and strength and agility of body, and everything else essential to those engaged in such an undertaking and so had no other difficulties to face than those of the region itself. . . .We made ready for the ascent, and started off at a good pace. But, as usually happens, fatigue quickly followed upon our excessive exertion, and we soon came to a halt at the top of a certain cliff. . . .

While my brother chose a direct path straight up the ridge, I weakly took an easier one which really descended. When I was called back, and the right road was shown me, I replied that I hoped to find a better way round on the other side, and that I did not mind going farther if the path were only less steep. This was just an excuse for my laziness; and when the others had already reached a considerable height I was still wandering in the valleys. I had failed to find an easier path, and had only increased the distance and difficulty of the ascent. At last I became disgusted with the intricate way I had chosen, and resolved to ascend without more ado.

When I reached my brother, who, while waiting for me, had had ample opportunity for rest, I was tired and irritated. We walked along together for a time, but hardly had we passed the first spur when I forgot about the circuitous route which I had

* windy

just tried, and took a lower one again. Once more I followed an easy, roundabout path through winding valleys, only to find myself soon in my old difficulty. I was simply trying to avoid the exertion of the ascent; but no human ingenuity can alter the nature of things, or cause anything to reach a height by going down. Suffice it to say that, much to my vexation and my brother's amusement, I made this same mistake three times or more during a few hours.

After being frequently misled in this way, I finally sat down in a valley and transferred my winged thoughts from things corporeal to the immaterial, addressing myself as follows: "What thou hast repeatedly experienced today in the ascent of this mountain, happens to thee, as to many, in the journey toward the blessed life. But this is not so readily perceived by men, since the motions of the body are obvious and external while those of the soul are invisible and hidden.

Yes, the life which we call blessed is to be sought for on a high eminence, and strait is the way that leads to it. Many, also, are the hills that lie between, and we must ascend, by a glorious stairway, from strength to strength. At the top is at once the end of our struggles and the goal for which we are bound. All wish to reach this goal, but, as Ovid says, "To wish is little; we must long with the utmost eagerness to gain our end."

These thoughts stimulated both body and mind in a wonderful degree for facing the difficulties which yet remained. Oh, that I might traverse in spirit that other road for which I long day and night, even as today I overcame material obstacles by my bodily exertions! And I know not why it should not be far easier, since the swift immortal soul can reach its goal in the twinkling of an eye, without passing through space, while my progress today was necessarily slow, dependent as I was upon a failing body weighed down by heavy members.

One peak of the mountain, the highest of all, the country people call "Sonny," . . . for the peak in question would seem to be the father of all the surrounding ones. On its top is a little level place, and here we could at last rest our tired bodies.

. . . At first, owing to the unaccustomed quality of the air and the effect of the great sweep of view spread out before me, I stood like one dazed. I beheld the clouds under our feet. . . . I turned my eyes toward Italy, whither my heart most inclined. The Alps, rugged and snow-capped, seemed to rise close by, although they were really at a great distance.

. . . The sinking sun and the lengthening shadows of the mountain were already warning us that the time was near at hand when we must go. As if suddenly wakened from sleep, I turned about and gazed toward the west. I was unable to discern the summits of the Pyrenees, which form the barrier between France and Spain; not because of any intervening obstacle that I know of but owing simply to the insufficiency of our mortal vision. But I could see with the utmost clearness, off to the right, the mountains of the region about Lyons, and to the left the bay of Marseilles and the waters that lash the shores of Aigues Mortes, altho' all these places were so distant that it would require a journey of several days to reach them. Under our very eyes flowed the Rhone.

While I was thus dividing my thoughts, now turning my attention to some terrestrial object that lay before me, now raising my soul, as I had done my body, to *higher planes, it occurred to me to look into my copy of St. Augustine's* Confessions, *a gift that I owe to your love, and that I always have about me, in memory of both the author and the giver. I opened the compact little volume, small indeed in size, but of infinite charm, with the intention of reading whatever came to hand, for I could happen upon nothing that would be otherwise than edifying and devout. Now it chanced that the tenth book presented itself. My brother, waiting to hear something of St. Augustine's from my lips, stood attentively by. I call him, and God too, to witness that where I first fixed my eyes it was written:*

"And men go about to wonder at the heights of the mountains, and the mighty waves of the sea, and the wide sweep of rivers, and the circuit of the ocean, and the revolution of the stars, but themselves they consider not. . . ."

What I had there read I believed to be addressed to me and to no other, remembering that St. Augustine had once suspected the same thing in his own case . . . I thought in silence of the lack of good counsel in us mortals, who neglect what is noblest in ourselves, scatter our energies in all directions, and waste ourselves in a vain show, because we look about us for what is to be found only within. . . . How few, I thought, but are diverted from their path by the fear of difficulties or the love of ease! . . .

We came, long after dark, but with the full moon lending us its friendly light, to the little inn which we had left that morning before dawn.

The Augustine who ascends Mont Ventoux with Petrarch is not the same Augustine who is being fought over by the Canons and the Hermits of St. Peter of the Golden Sky or the Augustine fixed in marble in the elaborately sculpted *arca*. And neither would we recognize him as the son walking through the streets of Ostia with Monica. This is a different kind of migration that occurs in the minds of humans and the distance traveled is through time. The chronoscope here is again language. The moment in the garden in Milan that was the turning point in the life of Augustinus Aurelius and the realization of a mother's dream for Monica, will fund this moment for Petrarch over a thousand years later and irradiate it with some of its original light, which is now renewed with the light of Petrarch's moment and will reverberate on down the centuries to reach us here, like the light of a distant galaxy. Of course it will also be morphed and warped along the way into countless forms both good and bad, liberating and oppressive, beautiful and ugly. The most famous Augustinian, after Augustine himself, is still in the far-off future. The Augustinian monk, Martin Luther, will have a similar impact on the world in 1519, when he nails his 95 theses to the church wall in Wittenberg and launches the movement that will become Protestantism, in all the many forms that we see today.

And what of Monica, without whom—one way or another—there would be no St. Augustine? She had the good fortune to rest in peace for a time in Ostia, where she said good-bye to her son. In the sixth century, her faithful bones were moved to a hidden crypt there in the church of St. Aureus. In 1430, that will change when she is moved with great fanfare (and many miracles along the way) to Rome. Alas, no rest for the blessèd.

In exactly one hundred years after Yersinia Pestis had finally departed from Europe, Augustinus Aurelius will arrive in Monte Carasso. In 1450, an Augustinian church and monastery will be built on the flatlands. But the old church of San Bernardo will also be given new life as another painter, like Giovanni Baronzio, makes the trek through the chestnut grove where stone houses have been built now with access to the church. He will undertake the work of painting a series of scenes depicting the Work of the Days, some much closer to the lives of the people, depicting familiar experiences of planting, reaping and celebrations.

In July 1776, the people who live in the upper hamlet of Corte di Sotto will likely continue to attend their masses at San Bernardo church, while the people in the lower hamlets near the flatlands will attend masses at the Augustinian church. Auntie Giulietta and her family, like others of the village, will find themselves trekking to both as family members from different parts of the village are baptized, married and buried.

◆ ◆ ◆

"This is where we came in," as my parents would say in movie theaters. For some reason, we always arrived for movies late, my parents and I, and would sit through the beginning of the next showing. When we had reached a recognizable scene my mother would make this announcement—"This is where we came in"—and, much to the consternation of the people behind us, would rise and lead us out of the theater.

I hope you don't leave, however, because the best is yet to come. We are about to follow the Atlantic Ocean westward and eventually we will meet up with the farm in Marin. Which you now know is really a *ranch*.

✳ ✳ ✳ ✳

Grossi Farms ~ The Present

PUMPKINS

My friend Sally and I had a wonderful day yesterday. We had made plans for Sunday lunch in Glen Ellen. Although it was my day off, the Pumpkin Patch was in full swing. A perfect autumn day that made the colors of the vegetables vivid in the slanting autumn light and the opulence of pumpkins shone to perfection.

The parking lot was filled with cars and people moving in every direction. I had felt sorry for Ed with the burden that pumpkin season lays on him: Over a thousand children pour through the farm for weekday school tours and hordes of children and their families come through on weekends to pick their pumpkins. He already has a full plate served up by his nursery business with Susie. This means no day off for Farmer Ed. As soon as I approached the stand I saw that my worries were imaginary. There was Ed, in his wide-brimmed hat and dark glasses, holding forth to some customers about the varieties of garlic that he grew—the difference between Lorenz and Metechi—pausing to speak to some arriving children. "Would you like to pick some strawberries?" Or to others returning from the fields—"Well did you get more in your stomach or the basket?" He was happy as a clam and why not? *This is the harvest!*

After all the decisions of what to plant and what not to plant, the plowing and the cultivating, the threat posed by unseasonable heat in August, too much cold and damp in the Spring, the months of tending young plants toward their fullness—a lifetime of learning to do this well . . . Here in the warm spotlight of an October sun were the literal fruits of his labors. And people swarmed to share them. To *disfrutar* them as the Spanish for "enjoy" puts it. I stood and watched the scene, allowing it to etch itself in its memorable detail: brilliant yellow summer squash, the last of the pattypan and crookneck. The deep green of the zucchini and the dusty green of the Turk's Turban winter squash, next to the yellow-white spaghetti squash and the warm tan of the butternut. The brilliant peppers—jalapeño, Anaheim and bells were caught in their summer-to-fall transitions; a wizardry of color transformation from rich green to scarlet. And last, but by no means least, that most voluptuous of all fruits, the tomato. Voluptuous shady ladies, sun yellow banana legs, baskets of small orange yellow sungolds that taste like candy, can be eaten like popcorn, and are far more healthy than either. And for contrast to all this color, the shiny purple-black eggplants.

All I could think of, watching this, was an artist at the opening of his or her exhibit, displaying the product of months to years of creative labor, answering questions as to how he got just this, just that effect. Sally arrived at that moment and, equally charmed by the living canvas, grabbed her camera. "Yes, perfect! (squinting at a particular angle of vision). "Just sit right there on that hay bale next to the pumpkins. Great!" And then I got mine out to do the same thing. When I started off to look for Ed to tell him I was leaving, the golf cart came flying by me and Ed yelled into its wind "Be right back" as he took some happy customers on an impromptu tour.

If this is the season of Ed's delight, the same cannot be said for Susie. For her it is the season of dread and she greets it darkly, rolling her eyes heavenward. "If I survive pumpkin season it will be a miracle." "That-damn-Eddie where *is* he?" "Edd-*eeee!* Get those people out of the shade house. What are they doing *there?*" (This is the place where some of the nursery's more delicate trees are stored. Some of its crown jewels.) "There are *no* pumpkins in the shade house." "Eddie, these people are all over the place! You've got to get the stand people to *give them directions.*" She fretted and fumed as Ed chatted and exulted.

Unfortunately, she was right. I don't work on the weekends, but hearing her complaints, I had walked down to the stand to take a look for myself. It was unbelievable chaos. The bright red wheelbarrows, each sporting its clippers for the U-Pickers, were heading off in all directions. I dashed ahead to intercept a round little woman with her young daughter who was driving her wheelbarrow determinedly toward the strawberry fields, 180 degrees in the wrong direction. How can you mistake a strawberry for a pumpkin?

"Can I help you?" I said breathlessly when I reached her. "Are you looking for pumpkins?" She nodded grimly. I gave her the directions and pointed to the pumpkin field. I have to admit that the field is *not* very accessible this year. Rotation of crops may be the secret of good farming, but it can be the nemesis of the U-Pickers at Pumpkin Time. The patch was so far away that even I couldn't find it at first. "Just go back out the parking lot to the driveway and walk back down the driveway toward the road. Now see that dark field over there? The empty one? Well you walk to the end of that, —please watch out for the cars and nursery trucks—until you reach a footpath on the left. No, I'm sorry, you can't see it from here but it's there. Just walk down that with your wheelbarrow and you'll see it on the left. On the other side of that field. How far?—I really don't know. I'm not good at measuring distances. But not very far." The woman was peering across the field as if a jack-o-lantern might suddenly rise up to beckon her. That's the problem this year: not a flicker of orange can be seen from the road except with binoculars. Still clutching her wheelbarrow handles with determination, the little woman looked dubious. "Well I don't know. How long do you think it will take to walk it? I have frozen meat in the car."

I left her still pondering this difficult question while Sally and I headed off to Jack London's neighborhood to have lunch at the Glen Ellen Inn—over there on the quiet side of Sonoma Mountain!

PART IV

THE WAY WEST

This world was . . . divided into two parts: an old and a new. His home was in the Old World, in the world that was frail, worn-out, and full of years. Its people were worn-out, decrepit, old and weak and finished. In their ancient villages time stood still; in their old moss-grown cottages nothing happened which had not happened before; . . .

The New World was young and fresh, and full of splendor and riches beyond imagination. . . . To the New World all those emigrated who at home were poor and oppressed, all those who were harrassed and suffering, the destitute and those full of sorrow, the hunted ones and those full of despair.

— Vilhelm Moberg
The Emigrants (1949)

You talk about the wilderness and how empty the land was, even though to us the land was always full. . . . I look at the history books of [our] kids. They start in the east and come west, all of them, like that is the way history happened. . . . It teaches them to understand this country like they were on those boats and covered wagons. That's not the way it was to us. For us, this was a big land where people lived everywhere.

— Sioux Elder in
Neither Wolf nor Dog
by Kent Nerburn

Majorca to Monterey ~ 1749

MIGUEL ANTONIO

I CAME TO MAJORCA IN 1969 ALONG WITH THE TIDE of twenty-some vagabonds "Doing Europe" on the cheap. I can still see clearly the shining white tour boat we crossed on—the Tenerife. I went aboard in the dazzled state of the young adventurer to whom everything is a First. I was prepared to travel steerage, faithful to the budget tips in my Frommer's *Europe on $5 a Day*. But I was approached, along with two young women friends I had met, by the captain and two executive officers who chatted us up amiably and, in no time at all, had invited us to stay in officers' cabins, rather than sit up all night in steerage, slumped over our luggage. Young and naïve as we were, we felt like princesses riding pumpkin carriages. Long before midnight, the pumpkins lost their wheels. I'm not sure what the other girls did, but when my officer made his move to extract payment for this largesse, I pleaded headache or the vapors or some such and actually had a nice sleep like Goldilocks, even if I had missed Cinderella's ball.

Palma in those years had become an overnight tourist mecca and they couldn't throw the hotels up fast enough. Literally. One couple on the boat had complained that they had made their reservations months ago and had just found out that the hotel they were booked in still wasn't built—"so sorry." My fellow travelers and I cruised this ersatz Riviera of hotels and found one that fit our Frommer's budgets. We checked in, cheerfully oblivious to the fine details of the décor. But then it began to dawn on us that the place looked like a movie set with hastily applied plywood facades and lots of potted palms. The elevator didn't work, or perhaps there was no machinery behind the doors. When I went to open the door to the room we were sharing, the door knob came off in my hand.

Needless to say, I didn't warm to the place or its "old world charm" made yesterday or mañana. I couldn't wait to get out of town, and one of my destinations was Valldemosa, the place on the island where Chopin had lived with Georges Sand and written, among other things, the lovely Raindrop Prelude and twenty-three others from Opus 28. Although my favorite Chopin piano works are from Opus 10, composed in Vienna at the peak of his strength, the Raindrop Prelude captures the feel of rain that is both tender and melancholy; veiled and gray. Nothing at all like the Instant Tropical Paradise of my hotel and its surroundings.

I set out by bus into the mountains the next day, and arrived in a very different world. The temperatures dropped and the clouds gathered and the coastal beaches seemed like a memory from another life. Chopin and Georges Sand had lived here in a converted monk's cell in the Royal Carthusian monastery in the winter of 1838–1839. I liked the sound of the wind soughing through the pines more than the building itself with its cold stone interior and darkish passages. They came here to take refuge from the world and for Chopin's health, but this hardly seemed a healthful place to be in during winter. The monastery was built as a palace in the 14th century by King Sancho to take advantage of the clean air. It was given to the Carthusian monks in 1399.

Obviously Sand and Chopin came here to do exactly what all of the contemporary tourists are doing—finding a getaway in cheap and sunny Spain for the winter. Except that now, with the European Union, Spain isn't much cheaper than other European countries. If you Google Majorca you will get pages and pages of travel sites. One of my favorites is Monastic Fantastic Travel. The island is full of monasteries, most of which have been converted into tourist accommodations, just like the Royal Carthusian Monastery, née Royal Palace of King Sancho. One can combine contemplation with star-gazing: from a tour bus you can glimpse the beautiful home of Michael Douglas and Catherine Zeta-Jones. They have apparently resisted the temptation to convert a monastery.

But we are not stopping here in Majorca to take in the headline spots on the island. We are pausing in a place near the center of the island, neither beach nor mountain but a large plain, protected from the sea to the north and west by a range of limestone mountains. It is a fertile plain where almond and apricot, olive and carob trees grow. In spring it is a sea of almond blossoms. The time is the early 1700s and the place is the village of Petra. There is a monastery in this village, as there are throughout the island. It is the Franciscan Friary of San Bernadino, the present building founded in 1672.

About a hundred yards from the friary in the Carrer des Barracar neighborhood is the house of Antonio and Margarita and their two children, Juana María and Miguel. Antonio has a small farm and Miguel is coming of age to help his father with the work of planting and harvesting that has been the daily life here for centuries.

On a hill above the town is the shrine of *Mare de Déu de Bon Any*, which is Mallorquín for Mother of God of the Good Year. The farmers come to the shrine with their prayers to petition or give thanks to Mary for a good year. They are as intimate with her as they are humble and respectful in the big church of the Franciscan Brothers, offering up their prayers to La Purissima on the high altar and San Juan Capistrano, who stands with his foot on the Turk's head and banner in hand to the virgin's right. Special prayers are made in the many chapels along the side of the church dedicated to Santa Clara, San Antonio de Padua, Nuestra Señora de los Angeles, San Francisco Solano, San Buenaventura, San Miguel, Santa Rosa, San Gabriel, San Rafael, Santa Ana, San Diego de Alcalá and San Francisco. If you live in California, you will recognize these names and it is not a coincidence.

Little Miguel has a natural calling that has just grown up with him through his visits to the Brothers and the holy rituals of the townspeople—much as you would find it in small towns in Mexico today. Miguel has a sweet voice and has asked the Brothers to teach him Gregorian Chant as well as reading, writing and mathematics.

It is only a five minute walk to the church. From time to time, the Brothers allow him to be a cantor at church services. He is learning about the breeding of cattle and the care of the vineyards and olive trees. As one writer put it, it is a Biblical village and a Biblical life. Not so different from life in villages throughout the Mediterranean region. Their histories are intertwined and influenced by many of the same earlier cultures and traditions—Carthaginians, Greeks, Romans, Christians and Moors. The piety of the Majorcans is likely the result of a deeper imprint.

From 716, when the island was conquered by Abdallah, son of Musa (conqueror and one-time master of Tariq ibn Ziyad), the island was ruled by the "Moors" or North African Berber-Arabs, who had a walled city at Palma. The Arab conquerors were appreciative of its beauty and ruled over the region with benevolence. This halcyon period ended around 844 when the Vikings began to make their incursions and sacked the whole island.

The Jews of Muslim Spain, before the Berber invasions of the eleventh and twelfth centuries, were the successors to the great rabbinic centers of Baghdad and Jerusalem. The city of Palma and later Inca, in the center of the island, had large Jewish populations, which included Arabic-speaking Jews and Jews from French and Catalan lands who spoke the Romance languages. Many of the Jews here represented the cream of Jewish intellectual, cultural and spiritual life. Numerous royal charters to Majorca's Jews have survived. They confirmed their right to buy and sell land, property, and slaves, to engage in a wide variety of trades, to establish separate court systems and a communal system of tax collection and to freely practice their religion.

All of this changed in the eleventh century under the oppressive rule of the Almoravid Berber conquerors.* Neither Christians nor Jews were safe in the region until the "reconquest" of the island by James I of Aragon. James I, "King Jayme," was the son of Pedro I of Aragon, who was known for his protection of the Cathars. The Cathars were being pursued as heretics by the Catholic Church of the time in what became known as the Albigensian Crusade.

In the eleventh century, the Muslim Amir of the Balearic Islands maintained a friendly relationship with the Christian Count of Barcelona, Raymond Berenger I and made the remarkable concession that all the Christian clergy of Denia and the Balearic Islands were to be under the jurisdiction of the Bishop of Barcelona. Alas, this Amir was dethroned by one of his officers and the subsequent rulers were oppressive and piratical. Christian ships were no longer safe in the region. By the thirteenth century, in the time of King Jayme of Aragon, it was determined that Majorca must be conquered and its Arab population replaced with a Catalan population. Jayme was only 20 years old when this expedition was undertaken.

We see soldiers fighting in 1229 side by side with holy men, (if such unChristian

---

* The Almoravid Berbers were a later dynasty distinct from the Berbers who crossed into Spain under Tariq ibn Ziyad. They were desert nomads until the 11th century, when they came to power. Theirs was a more oppressive rule than their predecesors.

activities can be called holy. This was a period when Onward Christian Soldiers was not a metaphor for the holy life). Even St. Dominic, not sainted in that moment, entered Majorca with James and left his imprint there.

James I, referred to in the language as "En Jayme," engaged a tutor for his son, James II whose name was Ramon Llull, in English, Lull. Lull was born of a wealthy family in Palma in 1315. He was well-educated and became a writer and philosopher, known for writing the first major work of Catalan literature, which King Jayme had encouraged. His interests were wide-ranging and esoteric. In retrospect he is regarded as a pioneer in computation theory, influencing the later Gottfried Leibniz. He was conversant in Latin, Catalan, Occitan and Arabic. He led a troubadour's life until he became the administrative head of the future King James II of Majorca. Lull is described as "a medieval mystic and visionary who sought common ground between Christianity, Judaism and Islam."

The Christian reconquest of Majorca in 1226 occurred at a time of intense Christian activity throughout Europe. Francis of Assisi had died only three years before the conquest and a later-to-be-sainted Dominic had entered Majorca with King Jayme and the expedition. Ramon Lull has his conversion in the royal household of Jayme II (James II). So Christianity returns to the island as an intense flame which burns brightly in the ensuing traditions and pious spirits of the people. Faith rides in on a military campaign and soldiers can hardly be separated from the men of faith. It is said that Dominic had such an effect upon the soldiers that they wouldn't move without his orders. True or not, we will have reason to recall this historic moment and its circumstances when we look ahead to the later life of little Miguel.

For this, we must jump ahead five centuries and pick up the thread of Antonio and Margarita in the Carrer des Barracar. Their son Miguel, physically slight, is nevertheless mentally bright and actively absorbing the ambiance of the church and the island. By fifteen years old, he is certain that he has been called to a religious vocation and declares to his parents that he wants to be a priest. Giving up their only son to the priesthood is a real sacrifice for a farming family, but it is also an honor.

In 1729, Antonio and Margarita take their son to Palma and arrange with one of the priests of the cathedral for him to live at the priest's house. In return for board and lodging, Miguel will be tutored and learn how to recite the Divine Office in choir. He will begin the formal study of scholastic philosophy at the Friary of St. Francis, still one of the architectural gems of Majorca to be found in the center of the old city of Palma. (Quite a contrast to the modern architectural wonders I encountered in the new part of the town in 1969.)

By 1730, Miguel had made the decision to become a Franciscan, joining the mendicant order whose founder gave up all of his worldly possessions and practiced constant penance to be able to follow Christ more closely. Miguel donned the gray tunic and hood, the white knotted cord and the sandals of the Greyfriars and took on the menial tasks of their community while receiving spiritual guidance from the novice masters and learning about the history of the Franciscan order.

As a Franciscan, Miguel is now Friar Junipero Serra of the Order of Friars

Minor. For his proficiency in studies he is appointed lector of philosophy before his ordination to the priesthood. Later he will receive a doctorate in theology from the Lullian University in Palma de Majorca, where he will occupy the Duns Scotus chair of philosophy until 1749. Among his students will be Juan Crespí and Francisco Palou. Father Palou was also born in the village of Petra, in 1722.

The musical tradition at the Convento de San Francisco in Palma must have been as satisfying to Friar Junipero as it had been to the young Miguel. Twenty-five years after his departure from Palma, another young Majorcan, Juan Bautista Sancho, would become the choir director at the Convento in Palma. During the two years he spends in that position, Sancho will copy a considerable collection of music, including over 170 pages of over forty works including orchestral masses and a "bravura aria" from a popular opera of the time that had been converted for sacred use by imposing the texts *Laudate Dominum* from Psalm 116 and *Iam auditor celum* to create a rather demanding but beautiful aria that was sung as a Psalm for Vespers.

All of this music will be carried to New Spain in 1804 and will be the source of great interest to later musicologists. The survival of a number of such individual opera arias in Mexico City, (which was the original destination of the Franciscan missionaries) suggests that singers of the eighteenth century must have carried such unrelated individual arias with them, which had been converted to sacred texts, much as they would today, with the difference that all of these scores would have been hand-copied. Sancho's manuscripts show that he was a virtuoso keyboardist. The music issuing from the Mission San Antonio de Padua for the twenty-eight years of his service there must have been lovely. Father Serra would found this mission in the rugged and beautiful Santa Lucia mountains along the edge of the sea, south of the next mission at Carmel.

Seven of the early missionaries of California's missions were from Majorca and several of them leave their mark in an important way.

✦ ✦ ✦

It may be surprising to think that many of the seeds of a future California are being sown on this little Mediterranean island, before Jefferson, Adams and Franklin gather with the other members of the Congress in Philadelphia. It would have been even more surprising to the Spaniards of Serra's time, as we shall see. I think that it is important to have some sense of this place, Majorca, because undoubtedly some of its character will be imported into the so-called New World of California, like Sancho's music. Among the often brutal and even degenerate clerics whom we find in the history of the missions, the most positive contributions seem to come from many of these Mallorquins, which is not to say that they were free of the widespread abusive practices of the missions. Among the most important records that we now have of that era will come from the pens of Fathers Serra, Palou and Crespí.

Junipero née Miguel Serra was a natural choice as a candidate for a mission on the other side of the Atlantic. In his biography of Serra, Palou writes "His sermons were listened to with the greatest attention, even by literary men; his last sermon in Palma was so much appreciated, that a famous orator, not friendly to our Apostle, whispered at the close: 'this sermon is worth being printed in letters of gold.' The humble Fr. Junipero however, did not seek the applause of men in large cities. His only ambition was to preach the Christian doctrine in small towns to a rude peasantry and still more did he desire to go and bury his brilliant talents amongst the uncivilized children of the forest." But Majorcans were expressly kept from this vocation by the Church who categorized them in general as "unstable." This was likely due to the multi-ethnic-religious history of the island. Despite the activities of a Majorcan Franciscan in the late seventeenth century in initiating— in both Spain and New Spain—apostolic colleges for special missionary training and activity, the order had no missionary college in Majorca. Even though Rome approved, the Provincial superiors "alleged that their subjects were too inconstant and fickle in character to become model missionaries." This lack of confidence was presumably based upon the relatively large number of *conversos*—Jews who were forced to convert to Roman Catholicism in the fourteenth and fifteenth centuries or face exile.

It was mere chance, or more likely seen by the friars as a sign from God, blessing their endeavor, that made it possible to break the convention. Fr. Serra's student, Francisco Palou, had announced his own dream of a mission to New Spain, and both were able to go as substitutes, in places vacated at the last moment, thus bypassing the requirement of joining a missionary college on the Spanish mainland. Once the way was paved by Serra and Palóu in 1749, a number of Majorcans followed in order to enter the missionary field in New Spain. Among them were Fra. Serra's other student Juan Crespí, and the musician, Juan Sanchos.

♦ ♦ ♦

We have already met Father Serra and Father Palou at a later date, when they started their historical trek through Alta California, following the Spanish plan to establish Missions and Presidios along the way as had been done in Baja California. Serra moved to the area which is now Monterey in 1770, and there he founded Mission San Carlos Borroméo de Carmelo, where he remained as "Father Presidente" of the Alta California missions. In 1771, Serra relocated the mission to Carmel, which became known as "Mission Carmel" and served as his headquarters. Under his presidency were founded Mission San Antonio de Padua, Mission San Gabriel Arcángel, Mission San Luis Obispo de Tolosa, Mission San Juan Capistrano, Mission San Francisco de Asís, Mission Santa Clara de Asís, and Mission San Buenaventura—many names we can recognize as the chapels of his childhood church in Petra, Majorca. Serra was also present at the founding of the Presidio of Santa Barbara on April 21, 1782, but was prevented from locating the mission there because of the animosity of Governor Felipe de Neve.

Serra was often at odds with the military leaders and was outspoken in what he considered his defense of the spiritual life of the natives. In 1773, Serra traveled to Mexico City (a distance of some 1800 miles or almost 3000 kilometers) to complain to Viceroy Antonio María de Bucareli y Ursua of his difficulties with Pedro Fages, the military commander, and to argue for the removal of Fages as the Governor of California Nueva (New California). Bucareli ruled in Serra's favor on 30 of the 32 charges brought against Fages, and removed him from office in 1774, after which time Serra returned to California. It has been said that during the American Revolutionary War, Father Serra took up a collection from his mission parishes throughout California. The total money collected amounted to roughly $137, which was sent to General George Washington.

During the remaining three years of his life, he once more visited the missions from San Diego to San Francisco, traveling more than six hundred miles in the process, in order to confirm all who had been baptized. He suffered intensely from his crippled leg and from his chest, yet he would use no remedies. He confirmed 5,309 persons, who, with but a few exceptions, were Indians ("neophytes") converted during the fourteen years from 1770.

Mission San Carlos ~ August, 1784

THE DEATH OF FATHER SERRA

Thirty-five years after their fateful departure together from Palma, Majorca Father Serra enters his last days, chronicled here by his old friend and student, faithful assistant and biographer, Father Palou. Although it is written in the third person, it is from the pen of Palou and reflects the tenderness he felt for his mentor and the sense of holiness that surrounded Father Serra for the faithful of his flock of Spanish, Mexican and Indian converts.

> Although the Ven. President had not requested Fr. Palou's immediate presence, nevertheless he resolved to go, and finding that the boat was not to sail for some time, he started on foot, reaching the Mission of San Carlos, August 18th, to find his beloved Prelate very weak, though still able to walk every afternoon to the church, to teach catechism, to pray with his neophytes, and sing with them some verses in honor of the Assumption of the Blessed Virgin, as the church was then celebrating the octave of that feast.
>
> Fr. Palou, hearing Fr. Junipero's voice, and recognizing it as natural, said to a soldier near by: "It does not sound as if our Ven. President were very sick." But the soldier, who had known Fr. Junipero since 1769, answered: "Father, we cannot rely upon such a supposition. This Holy Father is indeed unwell; but when there is praying and singing to be done, he always appears well, although he may be nearly dead."
>
> Next day, Fr. Junipero requested Fr. Palou to sing mass in honor of St. Joseph, as he himself had been accustomed to do on the nineteenth of each month; and going to the choir, Fr. Junipero sang the responses, after which he recited aloud seven "Our

Fathers" and seven "Hail Marys" and in the afternoon he sang as usual in honor of the Blessed Virgin Mary.

The next Friday, he made the "Holy Way of the Cross," and afterwards treated of certain business appertaining to the missions. Fr. Palou found him pensive, in which state he always lived, especially since the expiration of his faculty for confirmation.

Five days after Fr. Palou's arrival, the packet-boat anchored in the harbor, and the royal surgeon hastened to Carmelo, to offer his services. He prescribed some burning applications, to which our Ven. Father replied: "Use as many of these remedies as you please." Not a murmur escaped his lips, though his sufferings were intense. He continued going about on foot, even distributing with his own hands food and clothes to the poor, naked Indians.

On the 25th he expressed regret that the Fathers of San Antonio and San Luis Obispo had not yet arrived; he feared his letters had not reached them, which was really the case, they having been forgotten at the Presidio of Monterey. Fr. Palou, without delay, dispatched a courier to these Fathers, and requested them to come immediately, if they wished to see their beloved alive; but, though no time was lost, the good Father of San Antonio arrived only for the funeral, and the Father from San Luis on the seventh day, for the Requiem Mass.

On the 26th, Fr. Junipero arose, weaker than usual, and said Fra. Serra had passed a bad night, and wished to be prepared for the worst. All day he was buried in the contemplation of God, admitting of no distractions; at night, he repeated in tears his general confession, after which he partook of a little broth, then requested to be left alone.

The next day, very early, Fr. Palou found him reciting matins, as he was accustomed to do every morning, even while traveling. Being asked how he felt, he responded that he was well. "However," said he, "consecrate a host, and reserve it." After mass, Fr. Palou again visited the dying saint, who said: "I wish to receive the Holy Viaticum, but I will go to the church." Fr. Palou tried to persuade him to the contrary, assuring him that his cell could be prepared for the occasion; the saintly Father replied: "No; as long as I can walk to the church, there is no reason why our Lord should be brought to me." Fr. Palou was obliged to yield. Unassisted, Fr. Junipero proceeded to church, which was about three hundred feet distant from his room; he was accompanied by the officer of the presidio, the soldiers and Indians all deeply moved, and many bathed in tears.

On reaching the sanctuary, he knelt before a little table prepared for the occasion. Fr. Palou repaired to the sacristy, to vest and prepare for the administration of the Holy Viaticum. Upon emanating from this place, and when about to incense the Most Holy Sacrament, to his great astonishment he heard Fr. Junipero, whose voice resounded as clear and sonorous as when in perfect health, repeating the "Tantum Ergo Sacramentum," whilst tears bedewed his cheeks. The Viaticum was then administered to him, with all the ceremonies of the Ritual; after which our saintly Father remained kneeling, absorbed in God. Thanksgiving being concluded, he returned to his room, accompanied by his sorrowing children, some of whom shed tears of devotion, others tears of sorrow, knowing that they were soon to be *deprived of a Father who so tenderly loved them. Alone in his room, he remained wholly wrapt in God.*

Shortly afterwards, Fr. Palou, observing the carpenter of the presidio coming towards the room of the Father, asked him what he wanted; he replied that Fr. Junipero had requested him to make his coffin, and he wished to know how he would like to have it made. Fr. Palou then told the carpenter to make one similar to that which he had made for Fr. Crespí.

Our Ven. Father spent the entire day seated in his chair, in profound silence, taking no other nourishment than a little broth. At night he felt much worse, and asked for Extreme Unction, which he received seated in his chair, reciting with those present the Litany of the Saints and the Seven Penitential Psalms. He slept none, but spent the greater part of the night on his knees, or resting on the boards of his bed. When urged to lie down, he said he felt easier as he was. A portion of the night he passed seated on the floor, supported by some of his devoted children, with whom his room was thronged all night. They were induced to be present by the great love they bore their spiritual father. The surgeon, having been interrogated as to his condition, replied that he seemed to suffer much from prostration, but that the blessed Father wished to die on the ground.

The next day, August 28th, he appeared to be much exhausted. The morning Fr. Serra spent seated in his chair, near his bed, which latter consisted of but hard, rough boards, covered with a blanket, which served the purpose rather as a coverlet. Even when traveling, Fr. Junipero used the bare ground, using his blanket as a pillow, embracing a large cross, which he brought from the College of San Fernando to lie on, and which he always carried with him. When not in bed, he placed the cross reverently on his pillow, and so spent his last night, refusing to go to bed.

At about ten o'clock, the officers of the frigate, with Captain Cañizares*, whom he had known since 1769, and the Chaplain, Diaz, came to visit the good Father, who received them most kindly, rising from his chair to embrace them, and ordered the bells to be rung. Having taken their seats, they narrated many incidents of their voyage, and the notable events which had transpired since they had last seen him, in '69. After listening to them for a time, he said: "I thank you, gentlemen, for coming so great a distance, and after so long a time, to throw a handful of earth over my poor body." Hearing him speak thus, those present were astonished at his answering so well; and, concealing their tears, the officers said: "Father, we trust in God that you will recover, and continue your spiritual conquest." The dying saint, who doubted not his approaching dissolution, answered: "Yes, yes; do for me this act of charity, and I shall be grateful to you"; then, turning towards Fr. Palou, said: "I desire to be buried in the church, close by Fr. Crespi. When the stone church is built, they will throw me where they like."

Shortly afterwards he requested Fr. Palou to sprinkle holy water in his room, and being asked if he felt any uneasiness of mind, he responded in the negative, and having remained silent for a time, he suddenly exclaimed, "a great fear has come over me, I am much in dread, read the recommendation for the dying aloud, that I may hear it."

---

* We met Capt. Cañizares as the pilot of the San Carlos who first took the long boat to explore San Francisco Bay in 1775, nine years before.

"I did so," says Palou, "in presence of the officers of the ship and their companions, Fr. Noriega, the surgeon and many others." During the recital our saintly Father seated in his chair, responded as if in perfect health. Scarcely had Fr. Palou finished, when the dying man full of joy, cried out: "Thanks be to God! Thanks be to God! the alarm has entirely left me, thanks be to God, there is nothing more to fear, such being the case, let us all go out. Much surprised every one left the room; animated by this triumph over hell, the captain of the ship said: 'Father President, your reverence will see what St. Anthony can do, I have asked him to cure you, and I hope he will accede to my prayer, so that you may continue to labor for the welfare of the unfortunate Indians." The Ven. Junipero's only answer was a sweet smile, by which all understood that he did not expect to recover. Seating himself near the table, he took his diurnal and began to recite from it.

When he had finished, Fr. Palou told him that it was after one o'clock, and requested him to take a cup of broth, which be did, and giving thanks he said, "let us go now to rest." He walked to his bed-room without assistance, took off his cloak and laid it upon his rough bed, and clasping his cross most reverently, seemed to be preparing himself for rest. Those present believed that he was going to sleep, as during the previous night he had not a single moment of rest.

The officers went to dine; but Fr. Palou remained, and feeling uneasy, entered his friend's bed-room shortly after, and approached his bed, finding Fr. Serra in a position corresponding to that in which he had been left, but he was already sleeping in the Lord. No sign of agony was present and there was nothing to indicate death, save that he was breathless. "We piously believed," says Palou, "that he slept in the Lord just before two o'clock, on the afternoon of the feast of St. Augustine, in the year 1784, and that he went to heaven to receive the reward of his apostolic labors."

Father Serra represents an important link in our six-degrees of separation, which—according to the rules I have made up for it—includes *places* as well as people. The island which gave birth to Serra and Palou, Crespí and Sanchos was shaped by those forces that brought the Mediterranean into being, like the other regions in our stories. It is connected to Tariq ibn Ziyad, through its conquest in his time by Musa's son. The Occitan elements in the culture and language reach into the Alpine region of *Piemonte,* just to the west of Ticino. The Cathars who are protected by Pedro or Peter the First, father of "En Jayme," also have a presence in Lombardy in the twelfth century, having come from Eastern Europe, perhaps even Persia. Cathar beliefs had some similarities with the beliefs of the Manichees who had drawn Augustine to them in his early years. The population and culture of Majorca was an amalgam of Jewish, Muslim and Christian traditions which held some of the finest threads of each, even through the periods of brutal oppression.

Fathers Serra and Palou seem prepared by this background to represent the natives they encounter in California in generally positive terms, unlike many of the other priests who describe them scornfully and treat them as less than human. It is in their bones that they truly believe that they can make life better for the natives through converting their souls and offering food and shelter. They may not have foreseen the degree to which they would require the labor of the natives and the level of enslavement that would result, not to mention the abusive treatment and the terrible diseases to which they succumb in tragic numbers.

Through the emigration of Father Serra and the other Franciscans, our stories are carried from the Mediterranean to the New World and another major character in our landscapes: the region around the Great Bay of San Francisco.

Ticino ~ 1803

MOMENTOUS TIMES

In the year 1803, Switzerland was on the threshold of a major change brought about by Napoleon Bonaparte. From the 13th century, Switzerland had been a loose confederation of states or cantons. The Confederation had drawn together and declared its neutrality in the 17th century to remain free of the endless European conflicts that raged beyond its borders and had drawn them into the protracted thirty year war of 1618 to 1648. Through the treaty at the end of that war, Switzerland—as the Helvetian Federation—was finally independent of the Holy Roman Empire. The 18th century was a period of relative peace and prosperity. But in 1798, Napoleon invaded Switzerland and established a centralized government, the Helvetian Republic, to replace the system of cantons. The Swiss were forced to abandon their neutrality and provide troops for France. The country became the battleground for Austrian and Russian armies trying, unsuccessfully, to dislodge the French. It was overrun with foreign troops, which further impoverished the country. The Helvetic Republic became increasingly unstable as its parliament was divided between the federalists and the centralists and this was rapidly drawing its citizens into a civil war. Napoleon intervened as the mediator of the Helvetic Republic and in March 1803, he passed the Act of Mediation. The cantonal system was restored, with the addition of six new cantons: Aargau, Graubünden, St Gallen, Thurgau, Ticino and Vaud.

The events of 1803 were bringing significant change to the isolated valleys of Ticino. Napoleon's invasion, followed by his Act of Mediation, allowed Ticino to separate itself from its German neighbors to the north and declare its existence as a separate canton. Another census would be ordered in 1808, this time by Napoleon. Its objective was not a counting of souls like Fr. Galli's *Status Animarum*, but a record to be used for the formation of a Swiss army of 16,000 men whom he would lead to defeat in the failed campaign of 1812. We have already observed that Giuseppe Dodini was successful in slipping through this net.

In the Monte Carasso hamlet of Poncetta, the love-struck Bernardo Grossi, (as I have depicted him) did indeed marry and in 1798, their son Domenico was born. He is the first Domenico in our narrative, not the last. Pietro's friend Bernardo Rambosio is married and his wife has just given birth in June to their daughter, Giovanna. And what of the baby of Giuseppa De Prati from the story? She has now grown up and married the fictional Auntie Giulietta's actual grandnephew, the lively five-year-old, Bernardo Antonio Morisoli. They live in the squadre of Corte di Sotto, one of the four hamlets of Monte Carasso. Their oldest son, Natale (born on Christmas Day) is now a lively three-year-old. While Auntie Guilietta is fictional, her descendents as I've described them here are real (quite an accomplishment for a fictional character to achieve), as are the Dodinis, whose story I have learned from Tony Quinn. (We are on a first name basis now because he has been so generous with his input.)

At the end of April, on the other side of the Atlantic, Thomas Jefferson concludes the Louisiana Purchase, virtually doubling the size of the United States. The politician in him has resisted the idea for several reasons—including his reluctance to acknowledge that France has any right to be in Louisiana in the first place, and his concern that it goes against his own belief in state's rights over a strong federal government; a view that would essentially make such an act unconstitutional. But his greater concern is the threat to the new nation of having Napoleon's France on their border.

The original focus of Jefferson's concern had been the port of New Orleans, which controlled the trade on the Mississippi River. Through it, the United States shipped agricultural goods such as flour, pork, bacon, lard, feathers, tobacco, cider, butter and cheese to and from the parts of the United States west of the Appalachians. Access to the port had been assured through a treaty signed with Spain in 1795, but Spain revoked the treaty in 1798. Once again, it was the machinations of Napoleon that turned the tide. In a secret treaty with Spain in 1800, Louisiana was returned to French rule.

Jefferson was apprised of these actions through his intelligence network and sent a representative, Robert Livingstone, to Paris to pursue the purchase of New Orleans. Livingstone's mission failed but was followed by the more quiet diplomatic efforts of a French nobleman living in the US who was close to Jefferson, Pierre Samuel du Pont de Nemours. (His son would become the founder of the DuPont de Nemours and Company which still bears his name today.) It was DuPont who conceived the idea of the larger purpose of purchasing the Louisiana Territory, arguing that it offered a way to block Napoleon's ambitions of a kingdom in North America, a prospect cherished especially by the French foreign minister Talleyrand. Napoleon was facing setbacks in Haiti where he had sent an expeditionary force to conquer the territory and reintroduce the slave trade, once again enslaving those blacks and mulattos who had been emancipated there in 1793-1794. This had sparked a revolutionary war which threatened to weaken France's hold on the Caribbean. Huge French losses due to war and yellow fever put an end to Napoleon's plans for a New World empire. Without the huge profits from sugar plantations in the Caribbean, Louisiana had little value to him

It is against this background that Jefferson sends James Monroe to France to negotiate for New Orleans. The negotiators were prepared to spend $10,000,000 just for New Orleans and its environs. They were astounded to be offered the entire Louisiana territory for $15,000,000. It stretched from the Gulf of Mexico to the basin of Hudson Bay to the north and extended from the Mississppi River to the Rocky Mountains. The treaty was signed on May 2, 1803 and it was announced to the American people by Jefferson on July 4th.

One can now imagine the enthusiasm of Jefferson the scientist for this vast new and unknown region that had become part of the original United States of America. Even France was unsure how much land it had sold. Almost immediately, Jefferson had Congress appropriate $2500 for an expedition into the new territory. He chose Meriwether Lewis to lead this expedition to study the Indian tribes, botany, geology, Western terrain and wildlife in the region, as well as to evaluate the potential interference of British and French Canadian hunters and trappers who were already operating in the area. Lewis chose William Clarke as his partner in the enterprise and set out from Pittsburgh on August 31, 1803 on the historic expedition to the Pacific that would change the nature of the country in dramatic ways.

Johann Augustus Sutter was six months old.

JOHANN AUGUSTUS

Beyond the mountains to the north of Ticino, just over the Swiss border in Kandern, in the Grand Duchy of Baden, Johann Augustus Sutter was born in the same fateful year of 1803. His father was a native Swiss from nearby Rünenberg, thirteen miles from Basel. Sutter's grandfather, Hans, had owned a paper mill in Basel, but when the company fell into debt, Hans moved his family to Kandern. There he took up a position as foreman in another small paper factory, a position which Johann's father inherited upon his death.

Johann Augustus attended high school in Neuchâtel, Switzerland and then briefly worked as an apprentice to a publisher. In the town of Burgdorf, near Bern, he worked as a grocery clerk, presumably to be near his new love, Anna Dübeld. A day after his shotgun marriage to Anna, his son Johann Augustus Jr. was born. Through the financial help of his mother-in-law, Sutter opened up his own business, a draper's shop and dry goods store in Burgdorf. As the business faltered, Johann was burdened with mounting debts and by 1834 he was facing the prospect of debtor's prison. He fled the country only one step ahead of his creditors, leaving his wife and five children behind in Switzerland. He secretly secured a passport, slipped into France and caught a ship in Le Havre for America. He was now John Sutter, complete with a military captaincy, which he seems to have invented. A new persona for a new life. Anna and her children were left to make it on their own. When her mother died, her own portion of the estate was seized to pay her husband's debts.

We will hear more of Johann Augustus soon.

California 1801

HUICMUSE AND MOTTIQUI

THE HUIMEN MIWOK SINGERS CHANT ON, *punctuating the ancient songs with their clapper sticks. These songs connect them with the Beginning. With the powers of the ancestors and the spirits. They are calling upon them now. There is more urgency in the voices. But fewer people gather in the Round House on this night. The fire itself seems diminished, as if unable to gather itself into a burning force against the night. Secretly, some wonder if the spirits have left them. Had they been vanquished by the spirits of the men across the bay? Were their songs more powerful? Their medicines stronger? Why were Huicmuse's people dying of illnesses that the white people could survive? He looked upon the small group that remained and thought not only of those who had died, but those who had taken the final trip across the water to the new gods. Huicmuse and Mottiqui cannot settle their minds, even in the presence of the sacred ritual which is the one fixed center of their changing lives. Their minds keep returning to the plans that will be carried out on the following morning.*

Unable to sleep, Huicmuse and Mottiqui sit in their hut, sorting slowly through the objects that have been as much a part of their daily lives as their hands and feet, as dawn and sunset. For Huicmuse, there are the bone and abalone fish hooks he has so painstakingly fashioned. The precious feathers he gathered for his ritual costume. He sits very still, letting the memory of those events return. Following the flickering color of birds like a creature of the woods himself, moving his net with the gentle grace of wind, so as not to startle the flicker, the woodpecker, or the magpie. He spoke softly to them, explaining that their gift of feathers would be honored by his people in their ceremonies. The prized tail-feather of the flicker would be woven into a beautiful headband. Should he take the feathers with him? He thinks of the countless beautiful mornings on the waters which he knows like the lines which criss-crossed Mottiqui's hands and his own. He cannot give up those places of his heart, but hadn't he seen his own people paddling their tule boats along the waters in the service of the white strangers? Surely those days of plying his boat through the rippling waters would not come to an end. They would need good fishermen like him who would provide food, which was so desperately needed. The oak trees had turned against them and withheld the acorns that were so essential to their diet. The fall had offered only a poor harvest and the supply had not lasted into spring.

Mottiqui holds up her prize basket and asks yet again of Huicmuse, "Is it not beautiful? See how tightly it is woven!" She is very proud of her baskets and she places in the largest one the bone awl she used to make them, along with Huicmuse's stone tools, flaked with just the right sharp edges for cutting fish and game, for scraping the skins and furs of animals. He holds out the palm of his hand to her, and his eyes ask a question that she understands. In his palm lay the carefully shaped obsidian arrowheads he had made and had once been so proud of. Weapons would not be welcome where they were going, yet he does not want to part with them. They are more than weapons; they are a kind of talisman for those who make them. She nods and takes them from him, hiding them in a small basket, where she has also put a precious shell necklace. This reminds her of the piece of deer antler that he has always used, along with the stone tool, in the working of his obsidian points. These too go into her basket. The digging stick with which she gathers plants and herbs are also set aside, along with their warm rabbit fur blankets and cloaks. Then they sit quietly in front of the hut, saying nothing, and waiting for the first light to show over the hills to the east. Then they will load their few things into the boat and silently slip away from the world they have known.

In the winter of 1801, something impelled Huicmuse and Mottiqui to leave their native village of Anamas in the Huimen territory for the restrictive life of Mission San Francisco de Asis, which was now known as Mission Dolores. Anthropologist Betty Goerke speculates on possible reasons: Had that winter been particularly difficult for the southern Coast Miwok peoples? Had the fall acorn harvest been too poor to feed them all? Had the heavy winter rains torn up the tule *kótchkas* in which they slept, or had the rains flooded those rancherías not on high ground?

We will never know exactly why a large number of the Huimen Miwok crossed the bay in 1801 to enter the Mission Dolores. By this time, they were familiar with both the advantages and the restrictions that were a part of mission life. A few years before, a quarter of the Native Americans at the mission had fled to escape the poor conditions, which included abuse, illness and unrest and sometimes led to death. Yet they were also a reliable source of food and other material advantages that the people lacked in their own villages. Some had truly been moved in spirit by the inspiration of Fr. Santa Maria of the San Carlos or other missionary priests.

In this year, Huicmuse—the child born in Anamas six years after the arrival of Fr. Santa Maria—had reached the age of twenty years old. The fabric of Miwok village life had remained intact through his early years, since the natives of Anamas and the other nearby Miwok villages did not immediately flock to Fr. Palou's new mission. Huicmuse learned the survival skills of his people—hunting and fishing, and the gathering of acorns in the fall. He had sat in evenings around the fire in the Round House, listening to the age-old stories, the songs, learning the dances by which his people had communicated with the spirits of their world for centuries. But now the traditional fabric of Miwok social and cultural life was being torn as others of their people had begun to follow in the wake of that first couple to a new life across the Golden Gate.

Out of spiritual enthusiasm, hunger, boredom or desire for Spanish goods, people were departing. Huicmuse, at twenty, was now united with Mottiqui and no doubt they had given thought to what their future would be, especially without those family members and friends who had taken up a new life in Mission Dolores. Many were leaving behind their villages simply to be reunited with family on the other side. Huicmuse and Mottiqui loaded up their tule raft with their most precious items—no doubt those for fishing and cooking, precious feathers, beaded necklaces and ritual objects—paddled slowly across the water to begin new lives with new names under the care of strangers.

They arrived in a completely different world, rectilinear as Betty Goerke points out in her excellent book *Chief Marin*. Rectangular buildings, straight streets, a regulated life. Gone were the curves and circles, the meandering paths of their organic homes and villages. But there were also things to wonder at.

The Mission Dolores had developed into a much more impressive structure over the twenty-five years since Fr. Palou's first Mass under the oak branches. Large redwood logs supported a tile roof and the adobe walls were four feet thick. Huicmuse and Mottique must have marveled at the brick floor, the doors with locks, the windows made of glass, the painted ceiling and the gold leaf altars. They would have felt more at home, however, with the chanting and singing of the Mass and the rituals with the chalice.

Surrounding the church now were an open plaza, a kitchen, a dispensary, workshops, storerooms and an orchard as well as living quarters for the priests, a barracks for the soldiers and adobe houses for some of the Indians—separate dormitories for the single men and women. It must have been a tower of Babel, with all of the languages that were being spoken. In addition to Spanish, at least four different Indian languages could be heard. The majority were Ohlone from the East Bay and the Peninsula. The Coast Miwok and Bay Miwok people from the hills east of Oakland spoke different languages.

The first two weeks of their new lives were spent in learning the catechism and prayers of their new religion, with one of their old friends from Anamas who had come before them and now spoke enough Spanish to act as translator.

On March 7, 1801, Huicmuse and Mottique were baptized as Marino and Marina and then married into their new faith.

The Golden Gate had been well and truly crossed.

RUNAWAYS

LIFE IN THE MISSION DOLORES MUST HAVE BEEN A VARIED EXPERIENCE, with events to inspire and events that must have caused humiliation and pain to the neophytes—the converted native people. A great deal depended on the character of the soldiers or priests who were in charge. The following excerpt is from an account of a trial held at the Presidio of San Francisco of Indian runaways that had been rounded up from across the bay, including several of Marino's people. Although the date is 1797, it gives some idea of the early native experience at Mission Dolores.

Tiburcio: He testified that after his wife and daughter died, on five separate occasions Father Danti ordered him whipped because he was crying. For these reasons he fled.

Marciano: He offered no other reason for fleeing than that he had become sick.

Macario: He testified that he fled because his wife and one child had died, no other reason than that.

Magín: He testified that he left due to his hunger and because they had put him in the stocks when he was sick, on orders from the alcalde.

Tarazón: He declared that he had no motive. Having been granted license to go on paseo to his land, he had felt inclined to stay.

Ostano: He testified that his motive for having fled was that his wife, one child, and two brothers had died, and because he had fought with another Indian who had been directing their work group.

Román: He testified that he left because his wife and a son had gone back to their land, because of the many whippings, and because he did not have anyone to feed him.

Claudio: He declares that he fled because he was continually fighting with his brother-in-law Casimiro and because the alcalde Valeriano was clubbing him every time he turned around, and when he was sick, this same Valeriano made him go to work.

José Manuel: He testified that when they went to bring wood from the mountains, Raymundo ordered them to bring him water. When he declared that he wouldn't do it, this same Ravmundo hit him with a heavy cane, rendering one hand useless. He showed his hand. It was a little puffed up but had movement. That was his reason for having left the mission.

Homobono: He testifies that his motive for fleeing was that his brother had died on the other shore, and when he cried for him at the mission they whipped him. Also, the alcalde Valeriano hit him with a heavy cane for having gone to look for mussels at the beach with Raymundo's permission.

Malquíedes: He declares that he had no more reason for fleeing than that he went to visit his mother, who was on the other shore.

Liborato: He testifies that he left because his mother, two brothers, and three nephews died, all of hunger. So that he would not also die of hunger, he left.

Migilo: He declared that his motive for fleeing was that Lorenzo, who had been at the house of La Sargenta, took him along with him.[*]

MARINO

THE WIND HAD COME UP IN THE GOLDEN GATE and waters that were ruffling in a slight breeze at dawn had turned into choppy waves. It didn't matter one bit to Marino. He leaned his muscled arms into the paddle and turned the small tule raft to the east, to lift up his face into a sun rising over the coastal hills and gave thanks that he was still alive, on the water, and free again. If the waves took him, well that would be good enough too: He would rather give himself up to the waters that had been his spirit's home all his life rather than to the diseased-infested prison of the mission.

[*] From *A Time of Little Choice: The Disintegration of Tribal Culture in the San Francisco Bay Area: 1769–1810* by Randall Milliken. Ballena Press Anthropological Papers, 1995.

His freedom was not perfect. It was temporary. But it gave him access to the fresh sea air and a chance to get some fish for Marina and himself. As he had hoped, his special skills were valuable to the white men. Even those who had boats did not trust themselves on these waters. So Marino was given the job of making deliveries of messages and goods from one place to another. He was even teaching Capt. Argüello how to read the tides and had made himself so valuable that he received more privileges than the others.

Marino had earned the respect of the padres by learning enough Spanish to help as translator for the Masses and other ceremonies. How stupid these people were who could speak no language other than their own and never tried to learn. Marino himself had learned the languages of the Ohlones years earlier so that his people could trade with theirs. How had God, the great Holy Spirit, made such foolish people who could build and make fine things but did not know how to use them? Their buildings were overcrowded. The padres had been so eager to draw his people to their God that they now overflowed the buildings and were living in a community of their own native houses near the orchard, which was fine by them. Except for one thing: The padres had refused to let them burn the huts. Marino had explained that this was their custom, when they became too soiled or infested to live in comfortably. In Anamas, it had been simple to solve this problem by burning the old and building afresh. The result of their ignorance was that his people were dying of the squalid conditions and of disease.

As he pulled the paddle through the water, he thought of many things and planned. He would get Marina and himself away from this pest hole. Not to Anamas, but farther north, to the native village at Olompali or Petaluma. The punishment for runaways was harsh and demeaning and the soldiers regularly went out in search of fugitives, so the coastal villages were no longer safe. He would have to be clever about it. But he could not afford to delay much longer with the peste, as the padres called it, ravaging his people with an illness they had never known and had no cure for.

But it was already too late. When he arrived back at the Mission with fresh fish for his wife, she was gone. Father Vicente, a good man who had become his friend and truly cared about his people, assured him that her soul had gone straight to Heaven and would now enjoy eternal life. Anything, Marino thought bitterly, would be better than her life had been here. After they had made the fateful crossing from their village, she had only lived sixteen more months. Her death only hardened his resolve.

Monterey ~ July 4, 1807

MARIANO VALLEJO

During the first weeks of his incarceration at the presidio, Marin gave signs of being reconciled to his fate, and it seemed that the words of Reverend Father Ramón Abella were making a deep impression upon his soul. By this artifice he succeeded in persuading Christians that he had taken a liking to them. As Father Abella was very insistent that the door be opened for him, and that he not be left shut up in the dark jail in which he had been placed, Don José Argüello gave in to the entreaties of the missionary and granted Marin permission to stroll about the vicinity of the presidio. Scarcely did the latter find himself at liberty than he stole a horse with a saddle and a bridle, crossed the bay on a balsa raft and went to rejoin his tribe. [*]

—From an 1849–1850 Report to the California Congress
by Gen. Mariano Vallejo

MARIANO VALLEJO IS THE FIRST TO REFER TO MARINO AS *MARIN* and he speaks of him as "the great chief of the tribe of Licatiut and other tribes [of Marin] and Sonoma." His account above is second-hand and written many years after the event. Although they are adversaries at times, Vallejo recognizes in Marin the qualities of a valiant and intelligent leader. A few of the missionaries insisted that the natives were too ignorant and primitive to have a hierarchy or to have any leaders. Vallejo could see otherwise.

According to Vallejo's report, after his escape Chief Marin went north to Petaluma to gather the scattered natives together and "thenceforth dedicated his most strenuous efforts to harass the troops in their hostile incursions into that part of the country." He reports that in around 1815, a military expedition, under Capt. Argüello (possibly Jose Argüello's son Luis), had proceeded north of San Francisco Bay to explore that area and on their return through the Petaluma Valley encountered a force of 600 Coast Miwok warriors led by Chief Marin. Overwhelmed by the superior fire power of their adversaries, the Indians fled but Argüello captured Marin and led him back to the Presidio, from which he soon escaped for a second time.

◆ ◆ ◆

Mariano Vallejo was eight years old when the encounter in Petaluma Valley took place. But his role in the future of California might have been assured by the propitious timing of his being born: The Fourth of July in Monterey in 1807. Not that any of the Spanish "Californios" paid attention to the date, but celebrations of his birthday were going on far to the east and he would later have occasion to celebrate the dual-occasion himself. He entered adolescence in good company. As a teenager, Mariano, his nephew Juan Bautista Alvarado (1809–1882), and José

[*] From *Chief Marin* by Betty Goerke

Castro (1808–1860) received special instruction from Governor Pablo Vicente de Solá. As it turns out, de Solá would not be remembered in the way his young students would. Vallejo's name will grace a city, Castro's name will live on in a colorful San Francisco neighborhood, and Alvarado will appear in countless place names. Vallejo counted among his ancestors a captain who served with Cortez, an admiral who was said to have been the commander of the ship that brought Columbus back to Spain as a prisoner and a great great-grandfather who was said to have served as a viceroy of New Spain. Truth or legend? Like most family stories, who can say? His father had been a lowly sergeant, although described as *sargento distinguido* at the Presidio of Monterey. He eventually became the *alcalde*, chief magistrate, of San Jose. In California, it is the new life, not the old one or the ancestors that count.

We will meet Mariano Vallejo again but I will tell you a little secret about him now: One day he will own my Copeland Creek and the fish who glided down that clear stream from Sonoma Mountain and fed Miwok and other natives for thousands of years will now be coursing through Vallejo's world. Impervious, of course, to all of these changes. They are just doing what their ancestors have done for millions of years before us.

California ~ 1817

MISSION SAN RAFAEL

At Mission Dolores, Indians continued to die in horrifying numbers throughout 1817. Demoralized and desperate, some Coast Miwok fled. Others were given passes to return to their homeland, in the hope that better weather would improve their health.

— BETTY GOERKE
Chief Marin

THE PESTE HAD BEEN FOLLOWED BY AN EPIDEMIC OF MEASLES that killed over three hundred Indians in the spring of 1806, a quarter of the Indian population. Syphilis wreaked havoc on the Spanish and Indian communities alike. Sherburne Cook, in *The Conflict Between the California Indian and White Civilization* observes that such a debilitating and lethal disease would not only have led to a decline in the population but also to a general moral and social disintegration. "The relations of the soldiers and the Indian women were notorious, despite the most energetic efforts of both officers and clergy to prevent immorality."

Deaths among the Coast Miwok at the Mission increased from 116 in 1815 to 161 in 1816. One option which the priests considered was sending their converts into the hills to a healthier environment, but that would undo the years of efforts in building the missions in the first place. By December 1817, only sixteen Huimen people had survived, a mere eleven percent of those who had been baptized at the mission. One of these was Huicmuse, now Marino.

The report of twenty-nine deaths on the north side of the bay persuaded the governor, Pablo Vicente de Solá, that a more drastic step must be taken. He sent priests into the area to perform last rites on the dying and to establish a hospital or *asistencia* in an area north of the Golden Gate in what is now San Rafael. It was also hoped that separating the Coast Miwoks from the soldiers of the Presidio would help stem the spread of syphilis among the Indians since, according to the report of Father Abella, the soldiers were responsible for it.

The governor had some serious political considerations as well. Russian presence was growing to the north, where they had built settlements on the Pacific coast at Port Rumianstev on Bodega Bay and Fort Ross, near a Kashaya Pomo village, collectively known as Colony Ross.

A NEW HOME

MOTTIQUE AND HUICMUSE HAD LEFT THEIR HOME in the village of Anamas in Huimen territory fifteen years before, and now Marin, as the soldiers called him, was making a similar journey to a new home, not far from his original home on the north side of the Golden Gate. He was a different man, with a different name and a different wife. He had married Juana, daughter of the chief of the people at Olompali, during one of his "voluntary absences" from the mission. The padres would never understand that for a man like Marin, his spirit could not be rounded up and harnessed by anyone, native or white. Deep inside of himself, Huicmuse still lived. A few drops of water in the chapel could never change that. He had said as much to a priest. "You have a horse that is a saddle horse and you have a horse you use for a buggy," he had told him. "If you hitch the saddle horse to the buggy, he will kick and not go. If you put the saddle on the buggy horse, he won't go either. We Indians are just like horses. We are used to living in woods and hills and don't want to live at a mission. In the hills we are free like stags and deer. At the mission we are captives, just like saddle and buggy horses."

But still, here he was. He could not deny that the Marin part of himself was real also. He took pleasure in the respect given to him by his own people in the mission and by soldiers like Luis Argüello. He was learning many new things, including the craft of boat-building, in which he had been employed at the mission. He knew that he was invaluable to the whites for his knowledge of the tides and currents and his ability to act as interpreter. Not to mention the fact that his people looked up to him and would follow his lead. Marin had used that position to advantage and was often able to win concessions for himself and protection for the Indians against the abuses of priests or soldiers.

The crossing that was being made in 1817 was not a happy one. The December rainy season was not a time to be making such a journey, but the situation was desperate and the governor had finally been persuaded to move some of his people to a healthier environment. The sick from San Jose Mission and Mission Dolores were being ferried across the bay, among them over 200 of his Coast Miwok people, accompanied by five soldiers and two priests in open launches and tule rafts. They were headed to a place just north of the Huimen lands in Aguasto territory. Marin knew it well from his early years, when they would come to this place for clamming. It was not a bad place at all, and anything would be better than the disease-ridden Mission Dolores. He had survived the worst and things might be better, so close to home, for himself and his people. Marin steered his way carefully through the marshlands to the mouth of the creek below Nanaguani.

Marin and the others from Mission Dolores had arrived at a place that we now know as being on San Rafael Bay, with the San Quentin peninsula to the south and Point San Pedro to the north. Nanaguani sat on a small rise above what we call San Rafael creek, in a warm and sunny valley protected from the coastal fog by oak-clad hills. To the north, San Rafael hill rises seven hundred feet to shelter the valley from the cold north winds. Natural springs flow from the hill to provide a source of fresh water. Coast Miwok had inhabited this beautiful location for five thousand years, with elk, deer, rabbits and birds to hunt in the hills, and ducks and geese in the marshes. Tan oak and valley oak provided an annual supply of acorns. Salmon and steelhead were plentiful in the creek. Shellfish and shrimp were easily harvested in the shallow waters off Point San Pedro. The plentiful supply of tule guaranteed material for their boats and homes. They could weave it into baskets and traps from willow growing along the creek.

Many of the people had come home to their own territory. But it would never be the same. And it would never again be theirs.

The San Rafael Mission complex was small in comparison to Mission Dolores, but its lands extended from the San Antonio Valley, at the south end of what is now the city of Petaluma, west to Bodega and Tomales Bay and south to Mill Valley. By 1820, the mission included a church, a residence for the padres, a building where the women and children lived when fathers were away on tasks for the mission, storehouses and workshops. The rest of the Indians lived in their traditional thatched huts.

The lack of a Presidio filled with soldiers and the employment of only one priest, removed a good deal of the conflict that had plagued the Mission Dolores and its complement of soldiers at the Presidio. The priest, Father Amorós, was on the whole a kindly man. He was certainly committed to his dual mission to gather souls for the church and lands for the Empire. He took off almost immediately into the surrounding villages to spread the word, to baptize, to offer last rites. He may in part have been upping the numbers of converts to his credit in the way teenagers go after Facebook friends with a committed zeal for the numbers. But my impression of him is that he truly felt that he was offering the native people the highest destiny for their spirits through his acts of consecration. It was fine with him if they continued their lives in their own villages with cleansed souls. He sometimes returned to hear confession and the converts were expected to attend major religious events at the mission, which on the whole they seemed pleased to do. But those converts who joined the mission community were expected to remain a part of it. This was not as onerous at San Rafael as it had been at the San Francisco Mission. Given the small numbers, the native converts were given more responsibilities and went off on their own to work in the fields or as vaqueros with the cattle or as boatmen, sometimes not returning for days. They were frequently given passes to visit in their own villages.

Problems arose when they didn't return or behaved in "insubordinate" ways. Father Amorós sometimes sent requests to the San Francisco Mission (they were only a sub-mission at the time) for additional soldiers to round-up the runaways or to restore order. The other serious problem for the new converts was the hostility of the non-mission Indians. In some cases, the hostilities were old ones that had existed between the native groups, but in others, the hostility was directed against the missions and all associated with them by natives who saw them as a threat to their lands and their lives. During this period, the missionaries themselves never initiated hostilities and seemed to approach the people in the villages with only good intentions so this number was fairly small. It remained small because the Spanish, when attacked, always overwhelmed their adversaries with fire-power. And yet, unfortunately, the perceived threat to their lands and lives did turn out, over time, to be real; less through hostile intention than through the sheer force of inexorable history bearing down upon them.

In 1822, Mexico won its independence from Spain and became the nominal ruler of those distant lands, some fifteen hundred miles north of Mexico City. But it was not until 1826 that the missions felt their reach when the Mexican governor of Alta California (which included all of the present U.S. state) issued an Emancipation Proclamation, almost as far-reaching as that of Lincoln, but not in the end to the hoped-for advantage of the native population. All Indians within the military districts of San Diego, Santa Barbara, and Monterey who were found qualified were freed from missionary rule and made eligible to become Mexican citizens. Those who wished to remain under mission tutelage were exempted from most forms of corporal punishment.

The governor's objective was to convert the mission towns into civic pueblos under secular rules. One half of the movable property was divided among the "emancipated persons," the Indians, and each head of family was to be given 400 square varas (about 350 square yards) of land. All of the rest were placed in the hands of the appointed magistrate, subject to the decisions of the federal government in Mexico City. The clergy were left in charge of Church properties which were provided for out of the remaining funds.

In 1831, Jose Figueroa—considered by most the greatest of the Mexican governors of Alta California—was appointed. He journeyed to California bringing in tow ten friars from the Franciscan College at Zacatecas. Under Figueroa, they were put in charge of the seven missions that lay to the north of the Mission of San Carlos. The College at Zacatecas was not the academic equivalent of the college of San Fernando in Mexico City. The new friars were considered by the Californios to be, in Betty Goerke's words, "coarser, more vulgar and less sophisticated" than the likes of Father Serra or Father Palou.* According to some writers, the fact that they were native Mexicans with darker skin meant that they received little cooperation from most of the white Spanish population and the Indian population tended to reflect their attitudes. Goerke notes that a historian of that period, Father Maynard Geiger, wrote that the Father who replaced Mercado at his former Mission Santa Clara "took care of the woman and children of Mercado, and had some children of his own by her." And at least one of the "white" administrators, former governor Juan Bautista Alvarado, looked upon Mercado with admiration as an excellent fencer and dancer. He said that the priest "knew how to tuck up his robes and dance exquisitely."** But a former soldier complained that he practiced bad habits that included gambling and drinking; this, in addition to the many half-breed children he left behind him at all the missions that he served.

Father Mercado became head of the San Rafael Mission following the death of Father Amorós in 1832, which was no doubt grieved by many of his people who had regarded him with affection. During these changing times at San Rafael, many of the Coast Miwok fled to the Russian establishment at Fort Ross where they received better treatment. Those who remained must have felt very bewildered by the events around them, after having lived under the orderly, productive and generally benign rule of Father Amorós. A new conflict was being acted out before them between two powerful antagonists: Father Mercado and the current Commandante of the San Francisco Presidio, General Mariano Vallejo.

TRANSFORMATIONS

HE SITS VERY STILL IN HIS BOAT AT THE EDGE OF THE MARSH, as he had been taught to do as a child. "Be patient like the heron," his father had said, "and then as quick when the fish appears." There were no schools then but the teachers were everywhere. Heron, Flicker, Rabbit, Eagle, Coyote . . . especially Coyote. From Coyote, one learned cleverness. How to survive. But from the heron, patience.

If he closes his eyes a little he can almost see them again. The women laughing among the reeds as they gather them for baskets. The men outdoing each other in their hunt for ducks. The children wading in the shallows, shouting gleefully with each shrimp they pluck from the water. Old women gathering herbs on the hillsides.

The hills are green after the winter rains. The orange poppies are in bloom. The air is filled with the calls of ducks and geese arriving from the south, rejoicing to be back in their mountains and ponds, telling their stories of distant places. The valley oaks are fringed with their pale green buds. In these moments, the world is changeless and he is Huicmuse. It is this person, Huicmuse—clever like Coyote—who has kept him alive.

Argüello and Vallejo congratulated him on being a free man. A white man's law had declared that freedom. But how could any man be free who lived behind closed

* See Goerke, *Chief Marin*, p.129.
** Ibid.

doors under a roof which shut out the light of the world? He had such a house and he had chosen to go indoors and live as Marin, just as Huicmuse had chosen to cross the bay with Mottiqui and become Marino.

But sometimes the Huicmuse within him rebels against Marin, especially when the priest or the soldiers treat him like a dumb beast instead of a man. Then he escapes to his people at Olompali or Petaluma or Sonoma. He has friends and relatives in all of these places. He sits in the sweat house with the men, sweating the poisons out of his skin, or he sits before the fire at night listening to the old men telling their stories. He joins in the ceremonies, the dances and Huicmuse is truly free. Sometimes he goes to the San Francisco Mission or south to San Jose or Santa Clara, to visit friends in these places. If he is lucky, Capt. Argüello will be planning another expedition and need his services as boatman and interpreter. If he is unlucky, the soldiers come for him.

But year after year, he can see that the old ways are disappearing and the villages are becoming more desolate. Many have been abandoned. There are not enough of them left to hunt for the rabbits whose fur they would use for capes in the cold weather or for the feathers of the flicker and the eagle to make their ceremonial headpieces and belts. Many Indians are raiding the missions now for the sole purpose of stealing clothes.

And now yet another change brings promises from soldiers and politicians which he knows will never be kept; just one more thing to confuse and abuse his people. "Freedom and property for all." Marin has been asked to help in the surveying of the mission's lands to identify the borders of the Coast Miwok territory, including the land of Huimen. Livestock is to be distributed to the mission's neophytes. But Marin is not fooled by all of these promises. He trusts the white men no more than he trusts the Pomo of Healdsburg and certain other groups that have been hostile to them in the past. But there is so much more the white men can take from them now and the stakes are so much higher.

Instead of distributing the livestock, many administrators and priests have ordered the slaughter of cattle to get hides and tallow to sell, with the profits going to a select few, and none of them Indians. Other animals have been "loaned out" to friends and relatives of the people of influence in the missions, so that when the time comes for distributing the cattle and horses, few will be found at the missions.

General Vallejo has assured them of his interest in their welfare. Marin had been part of a large group that traveled north with Vallejo, under the orders of Governor Figueroa, to establish a pueblo at Sonoma. Vallejo was clearly curious about what lay beyond the northern frontier of their territory. Marin traveled with Vallejo by boat while horses set out overland to meet them. But their two schooners had run aground near Novato Point in Omiomi territory. The Omiomi saw this as a hostile invasion of their land and ran out from the shore to shoot arrows at the ships. Vallejo's crewman fired back and some fifteen Indians were killed. The rest fled or hid under the water to escape detection. Marin had seen this again and again on his expeditions with the white men. For the most part, they were well-received, with their offerings of gifts and their claims of good will. But if the Indian groups greeted them with hostility, they were quickly cut down by guns or cannon.

The northern Coast Miwok of the Licatiut and Sonoma tribes, as well as the groups of Patwin and Pomo tribes, welcomed Vallejo and their chiefs accepted his gifts of glass beads, blankets and tobacco. As he approached Sonoma, thousands of Indians had turned out to greet him, including over a thousand warriors and two Indian chiefs. General Vallejo was gratified by this show of friendship among the northern tribes and was particularly pleased when the Patwin leader, Chief Solano, urged support for Vallejo among the gathered groups. But Marin had not been fooled by Solano's show of support for Vallejo. What he really wanted was Vallejo's support against a Wappo tribe to the north, the Satiyomis.

Vallejo was joined the next day by 500 Licatiut led by the soldier Rafael Garcia along with 200 Coast Miwok neophytes from the San Rafael Mission. In June of that year, 1835, Vallejo honored his new friendship with Chief Solano by providing him with the support of an eighty-two man armed force—his own ends were being served by this too—in a raid against the Yolo tribe near Sacramento. An American adventurer on this trip witnessed Chief Solano attacking a pregnant woman by lancing the child on her back and then ripping open her belly to pull out the fetus. The enraged American was on the verge of killing Solano when Vallejo intervened on behalf of his new friend. Later he acted differently, however, when he heard that Solano had kidnapped and sold thirty Indian children. Vallejo had returned the children and had Solano imprisoned.

The raid had been a success for Vallejo. He returned with some sixty-five captured men as well as women and children. The women were placed in the women's dormitory at the Sonoma mission and the men were divided among the local ranchers for labor and the children were sold into servitude. These practices became increasingly common.

Indians were leaving the missions in large numbers and many found locations around San Rafael to settle. Some camped in the lower part of San Rafael at Bay View and what is now Taylor Street. Others located near today's Dominican University and another tribe lived in the willows between Tamalpais Avenue, Mission Street, Grand Avenue and Fourth Street. According to this same account by Charles A. Lauff, who arrived in Bolinas in 1850, many were located at San Quentin's Point and McNear's Point in Eastern San Rafael. The rest settled in Miller Valley along Miller Creek and in the Nicasio Valley.

In 1835, a group of Indian neophytes from the mission went to Monterey to petition Gov. Figueroa for a section of former mission land known as Nicasio. The governor officially granted the land to the claimants in documents he sent to Vallejo, further stipulating that Vallejo must be careful "that nobody interrupts or obstructs the peaceful possession of these lands." Vallejo made a note at the bottom of the document that he had carried out these instructions.

The administrator of San Raphael at that time was Ignacio Martinez and with the help of his father-in-law, Captain William Richardson, he determined that the boundaries of Nicasio enclosed approximately eighty thousand acres, which was in fact a pittance compared to the lands the Indians had had before the arrival of the whites. Nevertheless, given the intelligence and sophistication of the native leader Teodorico, one of the few Indians at the San Raphael mission who could read and write Spanish, these people came out ahead of many of the others.

Marin chose to remain at the San Rafael Mission, coming and going as he chose, and there he died in 1839, having survived a small pox epidemic in 1838 which killed off many of his people. His wife Juana had died three years before. Chief Marin was buried with ceremony in the cemetery of the Mission. By agreement, he was given last rites as a Christian.

In 1850, Gen. Vallejo would petition the California congress to name a county after him, encompassing the land of Huimen where he was born. "He was a great chief of the Licatiut people," Vallejo declared, although in fact he was not of the Licatiut people at all, but of the Huimen people. Those distinctions, however, were long lost.

What remains is the imprint of his name on the most prosperous county in the most prosperous country in the world. California was not even a state when Marin was laid to rest in the mission cemetery.

✳ ✳ ✳ ✳

Grossi Farms ~ The Present

THE GREAT C# MINOR

A tired quietude this morning, deepened by sodden clouds that have enveloped Mr. Fields and an intense period of writing. Even the birds are silent. I have gotten out my iPod to listen to a beautiful rendering by the Tokyo String Quartet of Beethoven's C# Minor Quartet from 1826. Beethoven composed this piece on his sickbed in the last year of his life. He was 55 years old. His health was deteriorating. His great 9th Symphony with its soaring Ode to Joy at the end had been premiered in Vienna to a standing ovation. But by that time, as hard as it is to believe, Beethoven was deaf. He had to be turned to face the audience before he was aware of the enthusiastic response to his work.

The C# Minor quartet begins with a lovely melody that moves between major and minor in a gravely tender, even dolorous fugue, rising unexpectedly to moments of brightness. The chiaroscuro of sound—light so subtly blended with dark—adds a dimension that strikes me as uncommon in the composers who had preceded him and even in Beethoven's own earlier works.

I am caught by surprise also, picturing Beethoven in his ill-health, when the next movement arrives with uncomplicated gaiety. At times, the lively fifth movement could be music for a hoedown and I can see an Appalachian fiddler tapping his feet.

By the next movement, it returns to the melodic graciousness that is a hallmark of the finest baroque composers—Mozart, Haydn, early Beethoven—

as if paying tribute to his own roots. The last movement takes up the melancholy tone of the first movement, repeating the opening counterpoint of major and minor, but it opens into a triumphal voice that ends on the pure ascending notes of the violin to the final affirmation of three major chords.

Schubert remarked of the work, "After this, what is left for us to write?" Robert Schumann found in this and the other last quartets a "grandeur of which no words can express. They seem to me to stand . . . on the extreme boundary of all that has hitherto been attained by human art and imagination."

What did Beethoven find within himself that could rise to such heights from the depth of physical decline? It feels to me as if Beethoven is gathering up the strands of his whole life in this work and making meaning and beauty of it.

But that is the point that comes to me as I listen: The only true portrait of a musical person like Beethoven is the music itself. No description in words or even art can convey that, although the best biographies are surely by people who met the man first through his music.

On July 4th of 1826, as Beethoven is putting the finish touches to what he himself describes as his most perfect work, two other men are lying on their deathbed and will pass away on this day—the Fiftieth Anniversary of the Declaration of Independence—one in Quincy, Massachusetts and the other in Charlottesville, Virginia. Beethoven might be writing for them as well, putting the coda on dedicated, difficult, yet ultimately triumphant lives, iconic of their country: John Adams and Thomas Jefferson. The two men had been estranged for a time over political differences, but in recent years they had resumed their friendship through a rich correspondence. Adams wrote a letter to Jefferson in 1818 in which he said, "While you live, I seem to have a Bank at Monticello on which I can draw for a letter of friendship and entertainment when I please." John Adams was 90. His last words were—"Jefferson lives." But in fact Jefferson had died a few hours before at Monticello.

I believe that the same thing could be said of them that Schumann said of Beethoven: Their contributions "stand on the extreme boundary of all that has hitherto been attained."

* * * *

HATS

It's the hats.

Not the changing leaves.

Not the rain.

Not the drop in temperature. Not even the disappearance of the crane melons.

The sure sign of winter, the rune of finis, appears overnight and I'm not sure how the signal is carried. Morphic resonance perhaps.

One day I step out of the camper and make my way past the stacked redwood planter boxes, the plastic pots, the wire cages of former chickens, the Cotati

Farm truck and there it is. It's not even raining. It's not even cold. The sun is shining like summer.

But the hats have changed. It gives me a pang, a sense of loss, to see this remorseless sign that the old season is over, the summer of our joy. Jaunty straw sombreros, so distinct for each wearer, have been replaced by winter caps. They're wonderful hats, with the Sweetlane logo on them. I've worn mine even in Rome. But Sergio is so identifiable to me atop the forklift by the straw hat, round at the top with sides that slope downward. Oriental-style. He sits erect, bright, proud on the forklift, the straw dome perfectly aligned with the zenith of the sky, as if awaiting a message from the M-43 galaxy. His brother Gerardo rides atop the forks to their next destination, an equally upright figure but with a straw sombrero perfectly weathered and shaped to fit everything that is Gerardo—smiling, laughing, hard-working Gerardo, so like his brother yet distinctly different. Just look at the hats.

Sergio and Gerardo are the first ones I see each day because their loading station and potting area are not far from my camper. Today it is as if they had half-disappeared. Their heads have shrunk! And now I'm not sure who's driving the forklift. Is it Sergio or Gerardo? Or someone else?

The farm's season is sliding quickly behind us. I see a man walking with an amazingly quick, light step out of the barn. Who is he? A stranger among us. I search my mind quickly and it dawns on me in that heart-sinking moment that it is Ed. Not Farmer Ed anymore. Dark glasses gone. The trademark straw hat. Because with Ed, not only is his straw hat always distinctive of *him*, he has a different one each season with some particular flare that makes it possible to locate him in the distance, in the field, and to point him out to someone looking for him, *See out there? It's Ed.* One year he had a hat that was narrow in the front and long and wide in the back, shaped sort of like an avocado. No one in the world could have worn that hat but Ed. It *was* Ed. At least for that season.

Nothing I could say could express Ed's generosity like the day a couple came to the stand—I think he was a retired farmer. They were old friends of Ed's who had moved away. It was a hot summer day. Noonish. "How's it going Eddie. It's changed around here. What you up to?" That's always a cue for Ed to say "Hop on the golf cart. I'll give you a tour. But it's hot. Better get your hat." I realize now what a mournful note it was when the man admitted that he didn't *have* a hat. A sign that his season was over. Quick as a wink, Ed lifted the handsome hat off his head and said "Here. Take this one. I've got others."

I always missed that hat afterwards and the change slightly disrupted the season. I never saw it again. If I said to you, "Ed would give the shirt off his back," it wouldn't mean half as much as if I said "He'd give you the hat off his head!" But it's true.

* * * *

New York ~ 1830s

NEW YORKERS ALL: SIX NOBODIES

I HAD NEVER HEARD OF HENDERSON, NEW YORK, although it's only a little over 100 miles from where I grew up in Rochester. I see now on the map that you just go east on Route 104, following the coast of Lake Ontario for about eighty miles, then turn onto Route 3 and go north for another twenty-five. The population in 2000 was 1,377—not exactly a booming metropolis. The population couldn't have been very large two centuries ago when a family of Puritan stock was living there or even a few decades later when a family of Swedenborgians lived there. Out of the first family came a child named Mark, born in 1813, who spent most of his childhood near the lake—Lake Ontario—that was also part of my own childhood landscape, though I always wished we lived nearer for outings on hot summer days. When Mark was 12, his family moved to St. Clair, Michigan where his father became postmaster. His father died in 1828 and Mark left school at 16 to work as a clerk in the mercantile business back in Niagara County, New York. The Niagara area I do know. An aunt and uncle lived in Niagara Falls and it was a treat to visit them occasionally in the summers. Mark was a steady sort of chap and ambitious enough that he became a partner in a small firm, then a bookkeeper and finally manager for "James Rowland and Company."

The second boy, Daniel, who was raised in the Swedenborgian family, was born in 1846 and also moved with his family from Henderson, New York. He spent most of his childhood in Chicago, Illinois. The teachings of the Swedenborgian Church of New Jerusalem bred in him the belief that humans should strive to be of service to others. But he didn't get off to a very promising start in this enterprise. He failed his admissions tests for Harvard and Yale, and was unsuccessful in his bid to enter politics. Shifting to a new direction, he apprenticed to a draftsman in Chicago where he acquired the skills to become an architect.

Now Watervliet, New York is a place I *have* heard of although I know nothing about it. It is thirty miles from Saratoga Springs, where I attended Skidmore College, and it sits right across the Hudson from Troy, New York. Undoubtedly Troy was named for its ancient mythical precursor, whose perished glories were sung by Homer and Virgil. But it was not of Achilles or Aeneas that I was thinking when I first encountered it: Skidmore was a girls' school back then so we often went on dates with boys from RPI—the Rensselaer Polytechnic Institute. It was the closest source of social life.

There in Watervliet, on the stage road between Albany and Schenectady, a farmer and innkeeper named Josiah raised seven sons—a boon to any father in the occupation of farming. His son Amasa, born in 1824, was a mediocre student, but proved himself useful in business ventures with his brothers, selling horseradish in Schenectady and chestnuts in Albany—reminiscent of our young men in Ticino selling chestnuts in Milan. He was resourceful enough to finance a law education at

20 at a law firm in Albany with the proceeds from timber he had cleared near the railroad. Three years later, he was admitted to serve on the Supreme Court of New York, and moved to new offices in the same city.

Across the river from Watervliet in Troy, while Amasa is helping his brothers sell horseradish and chestnuts, a boy named Charles, two years older than Amasa, is delivering newspapers to earn money to help his father purchase a farm in Indiana. When the family moved there in 1836, Charles helped to clear and cultivate the land for two years before he went to work, first in a sawmill and then at a forge for eleven dollars a month (with board). During the winter, he attended the district school. Later he started his own forge, with moderate success.

I looked it up and found that this Troy was indeed named after Homer's Troy by a vote of the people in 1789. Classical names were in vogue after the revolutionary war, perhaps because the people felt caught up in the myth of a great battle, which swept through and changed their lives. To the west is Ithaca, named after the home of Odysseus, although it is reached from Troy with much less duress. Also in the region you will find Utica, named after a town near Carthage in North Africa, and Syracuse—the birthplace of Archimedes in Sicily. You see we are never very far away from those ancient roots, even if we don't know it.

The fifth New York nobody was not born in New York, but moved there to Oneonta from nearby Connecticut. I know Oneonta about as well as I know Watervliet. It's a town you pass through if you decide to take one of the scenic alternatives to the New York State Thruway. It is about 80 miles west of Albany. Collis was born in 1821, a year before Charles, in an unpropitiously named neighborhood of Harwinton, Connecticut: Poverty Hollow. He worked on Poverty Hollow Farm with his father and attended Poverty Hollow School. How to make a kid feel bad! He was apparently among the poorer of the Poverty Hollow students because one teacher described him as coming to school poorly dressed and poorly cared for "as his family is in dire circumstances." By the time he was 13, the family was so destitute that Collis and his older brother Solon were removed from the family to improve their condition and relieve the family's burden. So by the age of 14, Collis had left home to fend for himself, earning 84 dollars plus board and clothing for the entire year. He saved every penny and with his small savings started a clock business. His brother Solon married in 1840 and moved with his wife to Oneonta, New York where he built a large and successful store. Collis would join him there in 1842.

The sixth boy, Theodore, also a Connecticut Yankee, is born in 1826 in Bridgeport, Connecticut, about fifty miles from where Collis is born. His family makes the move to New York during his boyhood. To Troy in fact, where he will enter the Polytechnic Institute there—just across the bridge within walking distance of Amasa. Not that they ever met. Charles had probably left Troy when Theodore arrived with his family, but they still share the geographic connection. Theodore is studying engineering. Quite a handy subject for his chosen occupation, as it turns out. He later moved to the area where Mark had lived, Niagara County, where he worked on the Niagara Gorge and helped build the Erie Canal. This is where the story, albeit briefly, eddies into my own, since my family moved to a town on the Erie (now Barge) Canal when I was 13. I walked often along its beautiful banks, where mules had once plodded, towing their boats toward Albany or Buffalo.

In the mid-1830s, three of these six are living just across the Hudson river from each other, two in Troy and one in Watervliet. They are still just boys. Mark is now in his twenties and living at the other end of the state in Lockport, NY. Collis has left home and is slowly making his way to his brother in Oneonta. He is fending for himself across the border in Connecticut.

Meanwhile, the packet ship Sully docks at the south end of the river after its month-long trip from Le Havre. She is a 3-masted, square-rigged packet ship, built here in New York in 1827. Two years before she had carried a fine portrait painter, head of the National Academy of Design, who struck up a friendship with a fellow passenger on the subject of magnetism. The conversation was to put his avocation of inventing on the front burner. No one pays much attention to the two on this trip but one of them will later inscribe his name in the history books for the invention that results from that trip aboard the Sully. The painter's name is Samuel B. Morse and his invention is the telegraph.

Now another little noticed passenger on the Sully is among the passengers who disembark at the port at the south end of the Hudson: Johann Augustus Sutter. But now you can call him John.

California ~ 1839

JOHANN AUGUSTUS: FINAL DESTINATION

In Europe he had been a debt-ridden clerk with a hungry family, no future, and warrant servers baying at his heels. Now he was a debt-ridden entrepreneur with a bulldog, a malacca cane, eleven Sandwich Island natives, a fourteen-year-old Indian boy he had "purchased" (from Kit Carson, some said) . . ., a German cabinetmaker named Wetler, some flotsam from the beaches of San Francisco Bay to work for him, and a brain swirling with chancy ideas.

— DALE L. WALKER,
El Dorado

SUTTER, THE ROGUISH CHARACTER WHO HAD FLED HIS SWISS DEBTORS, will figure prominently in the history of the west and California in particular. He arrives in New York and essentially invents a new identity to cover up his financial failures. He also has the cleverness, daring and energy to pull it off. He has no doubt heard, on his arrival in New York, of the success of William Johnson in allying himself with the Iroquois nation in the late eighteenth century during the French and Indian War. Johnson had built up a reputation for himself as a capable diplomat with the natives and amassed sufficient lands of his own to live like royalty as Sir William Johnson. Sutter's dreams may have begun there of fashioning something like that for himself in the West. William Johnson, however, was a man of greater integrity and capacity, with a genuine concern for the native people of the Iroquois nation and a desire to serve as liaison between them and Britain. Sutter's interest is in himself.

After arriving in New York, Sutter heads west for Missouri where he establishes himself as a merchant and innkeeper for several years. His first language is German and his first associations are with the German community just outside of St. Louis. St. Louis is the "gateway to the west"; a seething hybrid of a city, where East and West met.

Sutter's dreams of starting an agricultural utopia in the West begin to be realized in 1838 when he joins a trapping party headed to the Pacific Coast. In October of that year, they arrive at Fort Vancouver, which is the Pacific headquarters of the Hudson Bay Company. He is not able to go immediately on to California, so he sails with a Hudson Bay ship for the Sandwich Islands, landing in Honolulu in December 1838. From there he sails to the Russian Colony in Sitka, Alaska and is finally able to continue on to Yerba Buena. (San Francisco is yet to be born on that spot.) He arrives on July 1, 1839, almost exactly 63 years after Fr. Palou had said his first Mass there and four months after the death of Chief Marin.

✦ ✦ ✦

It had not been an easy voyage from Sitka. They had been hounded by summer gales down the northwest coast and suffered from acute hunger as their supplies ran low. By the time the Clementine finally slips into San Francisco Bay, he has little strength or enthusiasm left to appreciate this final arrival at his destination. Certainly the vast bay spread out before them with its estuaries is an impressive and welcoming sight, after the rigors of the open sea. But the handful of small Mexican settlements along the bay are less so. The mission built by Father Palou was closed down when Mexico won its independence from Spain in 1822. The Presidio's cannons, which appear to guard the bay's entrance, are no longer in use. As they approach their anchorage on the sheltered side of the peninsula, Yerba Buena comes into view—a small settlement of a few adobe buildings and, to the south of that, the remnants of the Mission San Francisco de Asis, known as the Mission Dolores. A few old launches sailed by Indians can be seen on the bay, carrying produce collected from settlements along the shore.

The launches belong to William Richardson, the Port Captain. Richardson is a British Mariner who arrived in the area at age 27, just after Mexico had won its independence. Like Sutter, he has a gift for languages and his fluency in Spanish has made him an influential figure in the area. Richardson received the first land grant in the city for a rancho in the headlands across the water from the presidio. He had found a fresh water source there that he used to sell water to visiting vessels. He called it Rancho del Saucelito, meaning Ranch of the Little Willow Grove. While the claim was being contested by several parties, Richardson settled outside the Presidio, building the first permanent civilian home. He has laid out the street plan for the Yerba Buena pueblo and oversees maritime commerce as the Port Captain.

The hills around the bay are deep green with their redwood forests. The Indians maintain a small temescal or sweat lodge at the foot of present-day Sacramento Street. No one at the moment is familiar with John Augustus Sutter or the future street that will bear his name or the city that Sutter's son will one day found, Sacramento. The commandant of the Presidio is anything but welcoming to Sutter. He sends an officer and fifteen men to order him out, informing him that the official port of entry is eighty miles to the south in the provincial capital, Monterey.

Sutter presents his letters of introduction and insists that the Clementine is in no condition to return to the treacherous waters of the Pacific before being re-provisioned and repaired. He is given forty-eight hours before setting off to Monterey, arriving on the Fourth of July, 1839. He is just in time to be invited to join a celebration at the home of Thomas Larkin, a prominent merchant from Massachusetts who has been in the area for seven years. It is a party of elite Mexicans, "Californios," who are government officials, landholders or foreign merchants along with Americans, Scots, Englishmen and one Swiss. Larkin's neighbor, Gov. Juan Bautista Alvarado, is also present, celebrating the independence of the country that, unbeknown to him now, will soon bring about his downfall. In the meantime, he grants the young Swiss gentleman, John Sutter, a limited authority over an area inland, along the Sacramento River, enlisting him to curb the rustling of large numbers of horses by a group of Indians and white men who are running them from California to New Mexico. Sutter takes this as a general mandate over all matters in the region. Alvarado has indicated that after a year's residency in the area he can become a Mexican citizen and thereby be eligible for a land grant. Sutter's plans are progressing nicely.

At the end of July, joined by Capt. Richardson, Sutter is provided with a rowboat and crew to transport them across the bay to the mouth of the Sonoma slough, and then up to Gen. Vallejo's Sonoma embarcadero to his Rancho Petaluma. Vallejo's ranch, granted to him under Mexican law, stretches over tens of thousands of acres, bordered on the north end by my very own Copeland Creek. Thousands of cattle roam over this vast expanse, which will be enlarged in the next decade to include the Suisun, Yulupa and Agua Caliente grants—names that have been preserved in the present-day regions of San Francisco Bay. As the government's administrator in the region, Vallejo oversaw the secularization of Mission San Francisco de Solano, distributing its lands, its six thousand cattle, six thousand sheep and three thousand orchard trees to the pueblo of Sonoma and to the Indians in equal part.

Commandante Vallejo, at age 29, is young for his remarkable achievements and vast estate. He tries to discourage Sutter from settling in the Sacramento Valley and suggests Suisun, Mt. Diablo or the Napa Valley regions. Sutter is even offered a well-stocked Sonoma Valley ranch at a very favorable price. But the observant Sutter would later comment, "The hat must come off before the military guard, the flag staff, and the church and I preferred a country where I could keep mine on, and I preferred a country where I should be absolute master." He wants to keep his distance from Vallejo's authority.

From the Vallejo ranch, Sutter rides with one of Vallejo's vaqueros to the Russian outpost at Ft. Ross, governed by Baron Alexander Rotchev and his wife, Princess Gagarin. The Russian fort lies fifty miles northwest of the Vallejo rancho on the headlands north of Bodega Bay. Like all of the other places Sutter has visited, the Ross outpost depends on Indian labor. Sutter is impressed with the small scale industries and artisans that serve Fort Ross, including mechanics, blacksmiths, tailors, shoemakers and tanners. The wheat, barley, vegetables and livestock on the Russian farms provide food for Russian Alaska as well as their own needs. The settlement leaves Sutter with a model of what he hopes to create in the Sacramento Valley.

The rowboats leave shore in the early evening. The sea bronzed by a lowering sun, with white frills of foam where the gusts of wind that had come up in the late afternoon are swept along its surface. Their destination is the only ship anchored in San Francisco Bay—The Monsoon—a Boston trade ship under the command of Capt. George Vincent. The captain has invited the commanding officers of all vessels in port and the principle men on shore to a farewell dinner for the Swiss adventurer. Even in this frontier town at the far edge of the continent, none of them have been where he is about to go and it is likely they never expect to see him again. It is a convivial celebration that lasts far into the night. Taurus and Gemini have risen in the east, in the moonless sky. A new moon, they said, is good for beginnings. For Sutter, an empty slate to write upon with his own will and dreams. Jupiter and Mars, those planets of expansive energy, are moving in tandem through the sky, crossing the celestial points where his own Jupiter and Uranus had been traveling together at the moment of his birth in Germany. The gathering goes on until sunrise when he and his small party slip over the side, down the ladders to the Isabel and the other waiting boats.

Early in the morning of August 9th, Sutter sets sail with the 22 ton schooner Isabel, chartered in Yerba Buena; a smaller schooner, the Nicholas, which (according to Sutter) had formerly been a pleasure boat of the Sandwich Islands king; and a pinnace manned by unemployed sailors he has hired, along with Kanaka workers who had joined him in the Sandwich Islands.

The small flotilla is loaded with all of the implements, tools, weapons and trading items he will need to establish his new home. Sutter, in the pinnace, sails through the misty dawn, quietly up the bay past Angel Island and the southern tip of Mare Island, around Point Pinole through the Carquinez Strait. From there they head to the starboard shore where he stops to visit Don Ignacio Martinez, who has a large rancho in the Alhambra Valley, granted to him in 1824 for his services to the Spanish and Mexican governments as the original commandante of Yerba Buena. Sutter instructs his oarsman to pull into the beach fronting the pastures of Rancho Pinole, and with a modest amount of German accented Spanish and an exceptional amount of chutzpah, he outlines his future prospects for trade with Don Ignacio, offering beaver, furs, wheat, and feed for horses, sheep and cattle once he becomes established in his new land. It is a productive visit. Sutter is able to purchase cattle

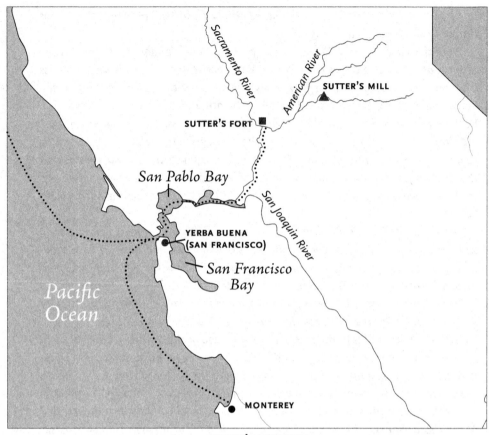

SUTTER'S JOURNEY

and horses that will be delivered as soon as he has found a location for his settlement.

From there they head northeast into Suisun Bay, an essentially uncharted territory—not for lack of previous travelers but for lack of reliable maps. They might have been in the Amazon for the maze of small islands in the boggy deltas of the Sacramento and San Joaquin Rivers. They have no way of identifying the entrance to the Sacramento River. They search the bayous and inlets along the entire northern shore of Suisun Bay and when they finally enter one of the swampy inlets, it turns out to be the wrong one, costing them two days as they retrace their route back to Suisun Bay. Then, as sundown comes on, Sutter looks for a place to spend the night and directs the pinnace to a small bay he has seen where they can safely shelter. Once inside it, the Sacramento River opens up before them.

The next day, the final leg of the trip begins. The spring flooding of the Mokelumne and Cosumnes Rivers, which join it from the east, have deposited loads of silt along the edges of the delta islands, forming raised levees, thick with tangled vegetation. The pinnace toils slowly upriver through the summer heat and clouds of mosquitos, past banks lined with cottonwoods, sycamores and elms. Wild grape and clematis vines hang from trees, and beneath them, a thick growth of berry vines, wild rose and poison oak. In places, the landscape opens up to reveal the sight of venerable oaks. The larger islands are home to elk, deer and antelope along with their predators, the wolves and coyotes. Grizzly bears still make their homes along these shores and countless waterbirds rise in great flocks as they pass. By night, they can't sleep, harassed by the clouds of mosquitoes. They have no doubt heard that Hudson Bay fur-traders, who passed this way before them in 1832, had carried malarial disease with them into the area and set off the first and worst California epidemic, which had killed thousands of Sacramento Valley Indians. The schooners fall farther and farther behind in the difficult waters and the pinnace moves cautiously forward.

Bunches of white feathers, hanging in the branches of trees, appear along the way as native prayers for food and good fishing. There is a sense of being watched. Then making a right turn on the river, a group of two hundred Indians appear along the banks, their bodies painted in black, red and yellow and making menacing gestures to what must have seemed an invading force of foreigners. Sutter tells the men to put away their guns. The pinnace is drawn onto the beach and Sutter steps out alone, calling out "A Dios," in the hopes that a mission Indian may be among them who knows the Spanish language. A man steps forward in response and Sutter is able to convey that they do not come in hostility, but that he is seeking to establish a home near there and would make a treaty of peace with them, and welcome them with gifts when they came to visit.

The Indian with whom he speaks agrees to go with Sutter and show him the land upriver. They sail on past the mouth of the American River and scout out the lower Feather River where he will later build his main homestead. They return then to enter the American River and a short way upstream, near the confluence with the Sacramento River, level land with grass and tall trees appears and Sutter announces that they will pitch camp and unload cargo on the south side of the river. Once the cargo has been unloaded and the tents have been pitched, the men from Yerba Buena approach Sutter anxiously to know when they may return. They have been made uneasy by their encounter with the Indians and the majority of them choose not to stay on. Sutter assures them all that they may return with the Isabel at sunrise of the next morning and settles up with them.

The next day dawns clear and the Isabel is quickly readied and on its way. As it departs, Sutter has set up his cannons near the shore and gives the departing vessel a traditional nine-gun salute. It is no doubt intended to send a message as well to the Indians nearby that the man who has just landed among them is not to be trifled with.

The young "Kanaka Bill" Davis at the helm of the Isabel is more than suitably impressed by this volley. He has the early maturity and foresight to see the moment in its far-reaching import.

"Having accomplished my purpose of landing Captain Sutter at the junction of the American and Sacramento rivers with his men and his freight, the following morning we left him there and headed the two vessels for Yerba Buena. As we moved away, Captain Sutter gave us a parting salute of nine guns—the first ever fired in that place—which produced a most remarkable effect. As the heavy report of the guns and the echoes died away, the camp of the little party was surrounded by hundreds of Indians, who were excited and astonished at the unusual sound. A *large number of deer, elk and other animals on the plains were startled, running to and fro, stopping to listen, their heads raised, full of curiosity and wonder. From the adjacent wood the howls of wolves and coyotes filled the air and immense flocks of waterfowl flew wildly over the camp.*

Standing on the deck of the Isabella, I witnessed this remarkable sight, which filled me with astonishment and admiration, and made an indelible impression on my mind. This salute was the first echo of civilization in the primitive wilderness so soon to become populated and developed into a great agricultural and commercial center. We returned the salute with nine cheers from the schooners, the vessels flying the American colors. The cheers were heartily responded to by the garrison, and thus we parted company."

YERBA BUENA ~ SAN FRANCISCO 1847

THE STATUS OF SOULS, AS CARRIED OUT BY FATHER GALLI, was inaugurated by the Council of Trent between 1545 and 1563. The first official year in California was 1847. The census was undertaken in late June at the start of summer. Unlike Father Galli, the census-takers remained anonymous. The small settlement of Yerba Buena that had grown up around the mission and the presidio after that first Mass under the oak branches had been christened San Francisco only five months before. Once again, the activity of naming and counting had created a new entity that was about to enter recorded history. It is much more detailed than Father Galli's Status Animarum. The people were counted by age, by gender, by race, by origin, by employment. The population of San Francisco, née Yerba Buena, was 459:

321 males
138 females
247 whites
26 indians
39 Sandwich Islanders
9 negroes
228 born in the U.S.
38 in California
5 in Canada
2 in Chile
22 in England
3 in France
27 in Germany
14 in Ireland
14 in Scotland
6 in Switzerland
4 at sea

* *75 Years in California*, William Heath Davis

And one each from Denmark, Malta, New Holland, New Zealand, Peru, Poland, Russia, Sweden and West Indies.

There were more people in Lavertezzo counted by Father Galli in 1776, than in San Francisco in 1847. But all that was soon, very soon, to change. It is easy to assume that gold made San Francisco what it is and that is partly, but only partly true. The counters of souls in 1847 added yet another category to their census: occupation or profession. Here is that list.

1 minister
3 doctors
3 lawyers
2 surveyors
1 school-teacher
11 agriculturalists
7 bakers
6 blacksmiths
1 brewer
6 brick-makers
7 butchers
2 cabinet-makers
26 carpenters
1 cigar-maker
13 clerks
3 coopers
1 gardener
5 grocers
2 gunsmiths
3 hotel keepers
20 laborers
4 masons
11 merchants
1 miner
1 morocco case maker
6 inland navigators
1 ocean navigator
1 painter
6 printers
1 saddler
4 shoemakers
1 silversmith
4 tailors
2 tanners
1 watchmaker
1 weaver

Four-fifths of the population of Yerba Buena/San Francisco were under 40, more than half of them between 20 and 40—the prime of life. Above 20, the vast majority were males, which accounts for the restless energy and enterprise of the growing new town. Their skills and professions were sufficiently diversified to meet the needs of a city. It was a remarkable concentration of talent in a small area.

Philadelphia ~ 1848

Mint U.S., Philadelphia, Dec. 11, 1848

SIR—On the 8th inst. we received, as I have already had the honour to inform you, the first deposit of gold from California. It was deposited by Mr. David Carter, who brought it from San Francisco, by the Isthmus route. It weighed 1804.59 ounces Troy; of which 1423.80 was from the lower surface mines, and 380.79 from those at Feather River. On the 9th inst., another deposit was sent, by the Secretary of War, which weighed 228 ounces.

The gold was of two sorts in external character, though apparently not different as to quality. The first, from the "dry diggings," was in grains, which averaged from one to two pennyweights; the other variety, from the swamps or margins of the streams, being in small flat spangles, of which, on an average, it would take six or seven to weigh one grain. Of these, by far the larger part of the deposits was composed.

The gold was melted in six parcels, and the loss by melting, due to the earthy and oxidable matter which disappears in this operation, averaged about 2 ½ per cent of the original weight. The loss thus reported is moderate, and shows that the gold had been carefully washed.

Assays of the melted gold were made with great care, and the results showed a variation in fineness from 892 to 897 thousandths, the average of the whole being 894. This is slightly below the standard fineness, which is 900.

The average value per ounce of the bullion, before melting, is $18.5-1/3; that of the same in bars, after melting, is $18.50.

The whole value of the gold in two deposits was $36,492, besides a few ounces reserved in the native state for the Secretary of War, at his request.

Very respectfully, your faithful servant,

R. M. Patterson, Director.

Hon. Robert J. Walker,
Secretary of the Treasury

California 1848

GOLD!

IT HAD BEGUN AND IT HAPPENED QUICKLY. Gold was reported on the property of John Augustus Sutter, about 150 miles from San Francisco. Flakes of it had been found in the millrace of the American River by his partner, James Marshall. Sutter and Marshall tried to keep the discovery secret, knowing full well the threat it would pose to New Helvetia, "New Switzerland," the colony he had founded in 1839.

Between 1847 and 1860, the population of the newborn San Francisco would skyrocket from 500 to almost 58,000 and continue growing by leaps and bounds. The English writer Thomas De Quincey thought the whole thing was a Yankee hoax and satirized it in an article written for *Hogg's Weekly Instructor* in 1852. Here is an excerpt that gives the flavor of how Calafia's isle was being regarded as it came to the attention of the larger world. Lines from the fanciful novel by the Spanish writer in 1500 echo through this nineteenth century moment: "The island everywhere abounds with gold and precious stones, and upon it no other metal was found."

From THOMAS DE QUINCEY'S "The Gold Swindle"

In the case of California, the most painful feature at the outset was the torpor manifested by all the governments of Christendom as to a phenomenon that was leading their countrymen by wholesale into ruin. Helpless and ignorant as that army of children, which in an early stage of the Crusades set forward by land for Palestine; knowing as little as those children of the horrors that besieged the road, or of the disappointments that would seal its terminus, supposing it ever to be reached; from every quarter of Europe rushed the excited ploughman and artisan, as vultures on a day of battle to the supper of carrion: and not a word of warning or advice from their government. . . .

The root of this conspiracy lay and lies (in all senses lies) up and down the United States. It is no affront, nor intended as such, to the American Union or to Mr. Barnum, if I say that this gigantic republic (which, by the seventh census, just now in the course of publication, has actually extended its territorial compass in a space of ten years from about two millions of square miles, which it had in 1840, to three and a quarter millions of square miles which it had reached last midsummer) produces a race of Barnums* on a pre-Adamite scale, corresponding in activity to its own enormous proportions. The idea of a Barnum does not at all pre-suppose an element of fraud. There are many honorable Barnums; but also there is a minority of fraudulent Barnums. All alike, good Barnums and bad Barnums, are character- ized by Titantic energy, such as would tear into ribbons a little island like ours, but

---

* Phineas Taylor Barnum (July 5, 1810 – April 7, 1891) was an American showman, businessman, scam artist and entertainer, remembered for promoting celebrated hoaxes and for founding the circus that became the Ringling Bros. and Barnum & Bailey Circus.

is able to pull fearlessly against a great bulk of a continent that the very moon finds it fatiguing to cross.

Now, it happened that the bad Barnums took charge of the California swindle. They stationed a first-rate liar in San Francisco, under whom, and accountable to whom, were several accomplished liars distributed all the way down to Panama, and thence to Chagres. All along the Atlantic seaboard, this gathering volley of lies and Californian "notions" raced with the speed of gunpowder trains up to New York, in which vast metropolis (confounded amongst its seven hundred thousand citizens) burrowed the central bureau of the swindle. Thence in ten days these poetic hoaxes crossed over to a line of repeating liars posted in Liverpool and London, from which cities, of course, the lies ran by telegraph in a few hours over the European continent, and thence by Tartar expresses overland to Indus and the Ganges.

Thomas De Quincy's satirical piece captures the "gold fever" of the times that quickly found its way to Britain and the European continent. Yet it is not as exaggerated as it may seem. There is very little humor in the circumstances that many found themselves in and we shall see that the events at Sutter's mill did indeed race across the Atlantic with wide-reaching effects that went even beyond the scale of De Quincy's imagination.

*** *** *** ***

Grossi Farms ~ The Present

LATE OCTOBER —SEASON'S END

A hot wind is blowing. Hot as the Sirocco out of north Africa. Two mornings in a row I have awakened to the smell of smoke. Yesterday there was a fire in Healdsburg. Is it still burning today? The fire alert is at its peak as temperatures soar into the 90s. Yet the old Chinese truth is written clear around me: the birth of new light is in midwinter. Its waning begins in midsummer. "By October-November, the light-giving power retreats and the dark power is again on the increase." Hot it may be but the summer is gone.

On the farm, this is no abstract truth. It is embedded in the soil. Soil the teacher. Soil the great mother. Soil the embodied yin.

Our dark earth returns to the surface under the blades of Alfonso's tractor. The old red international harvester is on the move and behind it, Ed follows in the huge yellow skiploader. This goes on against the background of the hubbub and color of pumpkin season and the happy flare of the last and brightest crop. When I teach dream classes, I divide a single line into four parts for the seasons. Under winter I put "seeding; germination" to remind people that, like sleep itself, winter is not without meaning for its essential contribution to the process of life. Simple, when you think of it that way. But when you also write death under the same segment, it is more difficult. Harder to believe that death is part of life. Are we the fruit or the seed of something that abides through the everlasting process?

Alfonso and Ed are preparing the ground for next week's planting of strawberries. They will be in a new place, a fresh field, even as a dozen small children laugh and play in the old strawberry fields which are still bearing their luscious fruit, happy faces stained with their red juice.

The fellows have seemed subdued. A little pensive. No truths are hidden for them. They are at the front edge of the plow and the first to feel the season's turn. In a month they will be looking for new work. Making new plans. All but Alfonso will be leaving the farm. Lazaro, with his usual mischief, says a goodbye to me at 1:30 PM. Shakes my hand solemnly. "You're leaving now?" I ask in surprise. "We're finished," he says. In the morning, when I asked him why he was so quiet, he told me he was sick. "It's my stomach," he said. "I ate something bad." He is a great prankster and I never know when to believe him. I shake his hand and say good-bye.

An hour later the truck returns with Lazaro at the wheel. Angel jumps down with a long yellow rope. Why am I still taken in by Lazaro?

"So what are you doing now?" I ask Angel. This season is over and Angel has completed his apprenticeship to Lazaro to near perfection. With a straight face he says "We're going to catch a bull that got loose in the field over there."

"Ah! Toreadors, eh?" Angel nods and then, in perfect imitation of his master, turns his head and slides his eyes backed toward me to see if I have been taken in. I haven't. He still has a ways to go. Maybe next year. But he has come out of his shell in these months. No longer the shy, inscrutable young man with the unsmiling face.

He reappears in the afternoon, holding up one of those balloons that can be twisted into shapes. This one is a bright yellow dog. I smile at the sight of it. "What are you going to do with your *perro*?" I ask. He holds it out toward me. "For me?" I say in surprise.

He nods. I take it and before I can thank him for this gallant little gift, he is gone.

✳ ✳ ✳ ✳

1853

There is a stir in peasant communities which have been the home
of unchangeableness itself for thousands of years.
To the earth folk, seeing their plots of land diminish while their offspring
increase, tidings have come of a vast land on another continent . . .

Into old gray cottages in tranquil hamlets where food is scarce
for folk living according to inherited customs and traditions,
a new restlessness is creeping over the threshold.
Rumors are spread, news is shared, information is carried from neighbor
to neighbor, through vales and valleys, parishes and counties.

— VILHELM MOBERG
The Emigrants

Ticino ~ 1853

TO GO OR TO STAY

TWO YOUNG MEN WALK SIDE BY SIDE *along the narrow, wooded path, lost in*
different thoughts. The taller one has a slender, sinewy build, with light brown hair
and hazel eyes that scan the landscape and welcome each new turn—familiar trees
and rocks, light and shadow—like an old friend. The busy river, the restless streams
which race off from its sides, burrowing under rocks or dropping suddenly over them
as a torrential waterfall, the trees which drink their strength from them. The smaller
one has a stocky build, a compact intensity, and his glance is mostly downward. If
his black eyes shoot upward toward the mountains, it is only in a furtive, resentful
glance at something menacing. They have both grown up within the shadows of
the granite walls which now surround them and rise steeply up on the sides of this
narrow defile. Nicolo, the taller cousin, sees them as protection from the harsh
winds. To Berto, they seem to get closer every year, as if to finally crush the last of
the life and light in him. Nicolo is the village mountain goat who always volunteers
to take messages and do errands across the Passo del Cocco and Val d'Osura into
the neighboring Versasca Valley to the village of Brione, where he has relatives. He
savors the wild alpine beauty from the soaring peaks and the sight of the clear azure
lakes that are suddenly revealed from their hidden glens. To Niccolo, this world
seems profligate in its beauty. But to Berto, it is a niggardly demon that would one
day rid itself of their presence. If Niccolo, the dreamer, sees only mountain peaks,
Berto sees his hungry brothers and sisters. His mother scrabbling to make do with
what little the harsh land will offer.

The young men are cousins, dispatched to deliver good news of a birth to family
members in the nearby village of Bignasco. Both have sisters there and nieces,
nephews, cousins. But they are returning with bad news, which always travels fast
along these trails. The border into Italy has been closed by General Radetsky. This

will cut off their lifeline. Their only source of revenue to supplement their meager subsistence in the valley. The first wave of men has gone and been turned back. These were men with guaranteed jobs they were returning to. What is worse, all Swiss living in northern Italy are being sent back. How did they think their people were going to survive? The situation in the valleys is growing increasingly desperate. When the winter comes on, Berto knows, there will not be enough food to feed them all if the men remain. Men who can do nothing, sealed in by the snows with the women, children and animals. Not to mention the loss of income from their usual jobs in the south.

News has been brought from Someo that booking agents are trying to recruit clients for their ships to travel to Australia to work in the gold mines. There has been a big strike there and trips are being made out every month, sometimes more than one. There is word that an English shipping company is about to start on the run too. The agents have painted a promising picture of ample work and opportunities. Several families had gathered around the fire in the Bignasco house to argue the pros and cons.

The older ones didn't like the idea of their villages and traditions being torn apart like this. Many of the young men, already growing restless with their confinement and their meager circumstances, were fired by the idea. It would be just for a short time, they argued. Only enough to earn some money to bring back to their families. Nothing different than they had already been doing in going to Italy each winter. "But it's so far away," many of the women had lamented. "It's across a whole sea. Not just like going over the hill and across the Magadino Plain." "It's a savage place, Australia," said one of the men who knew of such things. "It's been settled by criminals that the English wanted to get rid of. It's all back country. Bush. More primitive than here." "No no," the young men argued. "They've shown pictures of the place and a detailed description. It's civilized. It's got stores and banks and theaters . . . It's a good place. The younger ones of us could start a good life there. We can't do that here any more. We will send money back." The older women wept at the thought of this loss and their men looked grave.

Niccolo and Berto had just passed through Brontallo and it was the same. Everyone was outside in the small plaza, talking and arguing about the future. They had stopped to talk to their friend Battista Giacomini. The Giacominis were one of the big families there and Battista, at age twenty-six, was now one of the best butter-makers in their valley. His livelihood was not as threatened as those who counted on their younger men to go south to work. "I wouldn't mind going at all," Battista said. "It would really be something to see a new place like Australia or even America. But better the devil you know than the one you don't." Over time that sentiment would change.

Niccolo has mixed feeling about this. He is not eager to leave his mountain. The land that has been so much a part of him all of his life. Berto considers it a possibility. The desire to leave this place is strong in him. But there is family to think of. He sighs at the thought that the same conversations that lay behind him in Bignasco and Brontallo, now lay ahead of him in Menzonio. In fact they would soon be echoing through all of the valleys. Tomorrow or the next day, Niccolo would carry the news of the border closing and of the new baby in the Grandi house across the Val d'Oso to relatives in Brione and Sonogno. On his last trip, he had brought the news from Brione of a new baby in his cousin's house—a girl child, Caterina. That, at least, was good news. Or was it? Families this year were having a hard time feeding the children they already had.

They reach Ponto dell Merla and cross the bridge in silence, continuing single file up the path to their homes. They stop first at the Grandi house to deliver family messages and congratulations from relatives. As they draw near, the object of congratulations lets out a lusty howl. Salvatore Grandi, it seems, will be a strong and lively fellow. And won't he need it for what lies ahead of him!

◆ ◆ ◆

Not far from Bignasco in the Val Maggia is another of the very old villages of Ticino called Cevio. Although it lies some twenty-five kilometers from the lakeside town of Locarno, people have made their home here as far back as two thousand years ago. It lies near the intersection of two picturesque valleys, Val Bavona and Val Lavizarra to the north at Bignasco and to the west, the deep wooded Val Rovana, which divides into the Val di Bosco and the Val di Campo, each of which open into sunny bowls divided by a high ridge.

Across the central plaza is the imposing, three story Casa Pretorio, whose large smooth face is decorated top to bottom and side to side with coats of arms. Two houses face each other across the square belonging to two of the town's old families— the Martinoias and the Traversis. Not far up the road is the Dolcini house, and there is much coming and going between the three. The same conversation that was going on in the houses of nearby Bignasco is going on here. People are thinking of little else than the implications of the border closure at a time when people living in all the valleys are in dire economic straits. At the moment, Carlo Martinoa is sitting in the square with Caterina Traversi in deep conversation. She is upset at the direction that the conversation is taking because she has already set her heart on a future with her handsome young neighbor whom she has known from childhood. Carlo is telling her of some wild plans he has to go to America and make a home for them. She is thinking of Giuseppe Dolcini who ran off to Australia, abandoning his wife and family, never to return.

Those who go and those who stay. Niccolo and Berto are fictional, but the situation and the places are real. So are Battista Giacomini, Salvatore Grandi, and the girl-child who will one day become Caterina Buzzini. Carlo Martinoia will be one of the first to go to that land in America north of the great bay and he would be followed years later by Pietro and Michael Dolcini. We will meet them again later. I am sure that similar real scenes were being played out throughout the valleys of Ticino. Its closed worlds were about to open up in unexpected ways that will change the region forever. The amazing thing, of which no one is now aware, is that the heart of the dairy industry of Marin County is being born in these remote hamlets along their steep valleys.

Ticino, bordering Lombardy, was at times identified as the northern-most region of Italy and shared in its fortunes and misfortunes. It is not surprising that Caterina, for example, would identify herself as Italian in later life. In this year of her birth, she is. Except that there *is* no Italy as we know it today. The Italian region that had been united for centuries under Roman rule is now divided. The southern part is under Spanish rule, the mid-region under papal rule, and the northern Lombard region—including Ticino—is under the rule of the Austrian Hapsburgs.

When Napoleon invaded Switzerland in 1797 and replaced the Swiss Confederation with the Helvetic Republic, the people of Ticino saw this as an opportunity to break free of the German cantons to which they had been allied as part of the Swiss Confederation and declared their independence in 1803 only to lose it to the Austrians in 1815. The Ticinesi, like their Italian brethren, wanted no part of Austrian rule. By 1848, nationalist revolutions were foaming up around Europe and the Italians joined in with rebellions against their Austrian rulers. The Austrian ruler of Lombardy, Marshall Radetsky, received orders from the emperor to quell the Italian rebellion. In 1853, anti-Austrian riots had broken out in Milan. Radetsky suspected that rebels and money for their cause were crossing the border between Ticino and Lombardy so he imposed a blockade on the Ticino-Lombardy border and immediately expelled all Swiss—some five thousand men—from Northern Italy. This resulted, not only in a loss of the income from employment in Lombardy, but loss of access to an essential market for their timber, cheese and livestock. Even more essential was the grain that came from Lombardy to make their bread.

Around this same time, the mid-nineteenth century, conditions were further aggravated by blight to the potato crop and a serious disease that was decimating the livestock. It was a perfect storm that drove before it a wave of emigration as the only solution to the desperate conditions.

The story of that emigration from the Ticino has been told in detail by the Swiss historian, Georgio Cheda. He explains that it had come about through the activities of powerful shipping interests taking advantage of the repeal of the British Navigation Acts (1849) under which the United Kingdom had enjoyed preferential trade with British colonies. A group of German shipbuilding companies in Hamburg, linked to Swiss-French shipping companies, began building sailing ships specifically for the Australian run to carry German emigrants. The discovery of gold in Victoria in 1851 was a godsend for these companies and by 1853 they were looking for new pastures from which to recruit emigrants to fill their boats. By 1854-55, Oswald's Shipping Company of Basel was making three voyages a month to Australia. Early in 1854 these companies, joined by an English shipping company, James Baines, had begun targeting certain regions of the Ticino, particularly the Locarno Valley, in systematic, aggressive and very successful campaigns to recruit passengers. Much of the propaganda was conducted through advertisement in the local press and in certain towns, company representatives were sent to establish networks of agents.

By the spring of 1854, as a result of these activities, the region was gripped by gold fever. Some two thousand Ticinesi had arrived in Australia by the middle of 1855, after which this emigration fell off fairly sharply.

◆ ◆ ◆

In the little hamlet of Poncetta in Monte Carasso, we have a new Grossi coming of age, born in 1829 to Domenico the First. Domenico had met Maddelena Bregnoni, from the nearby town of Cugnasco where Giuseppe Dodini (originally of Lavertezzo) had met and married his Maria. Domenico and Maddelena were married and gave birth to a son with the wonderful name of "Michelangelo." Michelangelo is soon to start a family of his own with Teresa Guidotti, both descendants of old families from Monte Carasso whom we met earlier. All of these families are about to be caught up in the tightening web of history that afflicts the once peaceful valleys.

Hard times had come to Ticino.

◆ ◆ ◆

Ticino ~ Those who stay

FROM THE POSCIAVO NEWSPAPER ~ 1859

SOME SENSE OF THE IMPACT ON THE MASS MIGRATIONS TO AUSTRALIA, and later to California, appears in a newspaper in Posciavo, to the east of Bellinzona in another small pocket of Italian Switzerland. I find this very moving because it could have been written about any of the places and people who were "left behind." I'm thinking especially of many Mexican villages I passed through that had been purged of their men folk in this way. I am remembering the women of Chupicuaro and another village I visited often, Huecorio in Michoacan, where women had been left carrying on the hard work of farming on their small plots of land.

Oh how times have changed! At one time our menfolk found their greatest pleasure in cultivating the land and raising the animals: in autumn the chests were filled with grain, in the cellar a fine row of cheeses, the larder was well-supplied and the whole family was contented at seeing so much grace from God in the fruits of their own labours. Then when the harsh season approached the men and their older sons, rather than spending the winter in dreamy idleness, would go off to Lombardy as cobblers and casual labourers returning with the first swallows to hearth and home with a few quattrini in their purses. The young man who felt the urge married his neighbour's daughter, and the new families prospered under the guidance of their old parents. Ah! those were good times." (A peasant woman from Prada).

Yesterday morning on the main square of Poschiavo you could enjoy a new and moving spectacle. Gathered there was a new caravan of 31 men and youths preparing to leave for Australia. 24 of them are from Poschiavo, 5 from Brusio and 2 from Valtellina. Their relations and friends accompanied them this far to make their last painful farewells. The emigrants, a good many of whom are fathers with families, departed in tears. The hope of making a fortune did violence to their true feelings, and they left like those who, seeing the danger, grit their teeth and go forward to confront it.

What will they do, those women who are left isolated without their family and without a man's strong arm to support them? Who will plough the field, cut the hay, who will cut the wood and carry it, who will provide the materials to repair the decaying houses, who will go up into the mountains with the beasts?

Poor women! Poor Prada! cursed be the dream of gold! And do you suppose that those few who do come home again to their native valley will return with those simple and true values which they left behind in order to go and seek their fortune?) Their fathers are growing old: will the migrants want to go back to working in the fields again? Not too many of them.

These young people . . . do they think happiness just depends on gold? They dream only of gold and of lands of milk and honey and forget all else — even the duties they owe their parents, they forget the love of their brothers, they forget their native land. Australia! Australia! It's all they ever think about.

— from *Il Grigione Italiano*, 1859

✦ ✦ ✦

Wilkinson, Vermont 1853 ~ Those Who Go

TWO NEW ENGLAND BROTHERS

WE WILL ONLY TOUCH DOWN BRIEFLY HERE ON THE EAST COAST to look in on the Shafter family in Vermont. The grandsons of the young man who took up arms at 15 to fight at the Battle of Bunker Hill are themselves coming of age, although not as a "rabble at arms" as Kenneth Roberts described those early revolutionaries in his book of that name.

Young Oscar has by now graduated from Wesleyan University in Connecticut and has gone on to get his law degree from Harvard. After launching his law practice in Wilmington, Vermont in 1836, his star is rapidly rising. Or so it seems. Like his father and grandfather before him, Oscar was elected to the State Legislature and is now in the top ranks. He has been chosen by the Liberty party, first as their candidate for the U.S. Congress and then as their candidate for Governor. Having lost both of those races, he is now feeling a little despondent about his future. He takes some comfort in sharing a similar disappointment with his father, William. He writes to his father, "I am inclined to think if we had among us more *facility* of character, that we might some of us come to preferment; but as it is, it is some distinction to be pursued with *nominations* to high positions." His wife, Sarah—who will produce eleven children for him (not all of whom survive): ten daughters and one son—reassures him that he is still an extremely successful lawyer.

Oscar is so successful in fact that his reputation has reached all the way west to the firm of Halleck, Peachy, Billings and Park—at the top of the legal world in swiftly growing San Francisco. The firm can hardly keep up with this explosive growth. Its junior partner, Trenor Park, knew Oscar Shafter personally in Vermont and recommended him for the firm. The invitation to join the firm included a munificent salary that was generous even in those days. The timing is right. Oscar accepts. He assures Sarah that this will be a temporary arrangement to enrich their family's financial condition and assure the future for their children.

Oscar's brother James has followed in the family footsteps—an educated upright young man who is also making a name for himself in the law profession. Like his older brother, he has graduated from Wesleyan University in Connecticut and at the tender age of 20, was elected to the Vermont House of Representatives. As was the family habit, he rose to the top quickly and from 1842 to 1849, he served as Secretary of State. James, in fact, was the first to leave the state of his birth. In 1851, he moved to Wisconsin, and in no time was enjoying a similar political success in his new home as the Speaker of the State Assembly and in 1852, as Oscar was running unsuccessfully for governor, James was elected to Congress.

We leave Oscar, for the moment, in the midst of his packing on the night before his departure, as he writes in his diary. It is the plaintive note of all those who go, at the furthest edge of the invisible shore of home. It might have been written by Odysseus, about to leave his family behind in Ithaca.

Athens, Vermont.
Oct. 15, 1854

This is my last night with my family, my last at home. My trunk is packed, all the little details of preparation are over, my children have said their "good night," not joyously as usual, but with sobs and tears. The babe sleeps unconscious of the common grief. For one night more I sleep beneath the roof which I have reared and which covers those whose lives are mine. With the morning light comes the separation of me from mine. Though protracted, I hope in the mercy of God that it may not be final. My heart is burdened with a great woe, for my wife and little ones are inexpressibly dear to me, and the thoughts with which it struggles are better borne unuttered and in silence. As I was arranging my trunk, Emma slipt into it a piece of perforated paper with the following inscription wrought upon it by her own little hands—

"Hope for the best, dear Father. From Emma."

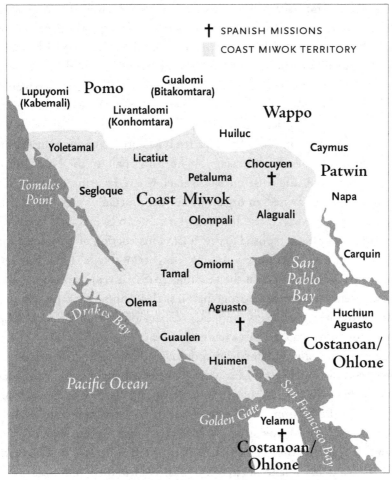

SPANISH MISSIONS

COAST MIWOK TERRITORY

Lupuyomi (Kabemali)

Pomo

Gualomi (Bitakomtara)

Livantalomi (Konhomtara)

Wappo

Huiluc

Yoletamal

Caymus

Licatiut

Chocuyen †

Patwin

Petaluma

Napa

Tomales Point

Segloque

Coast Miwok

Olompali

Alaguali

Omiomi

Tamal

San Pablo Bay

Carquin

Olema

Aguasto †

Huchiun Aguasto

Guaulen

Costanoan/ Ohlone

Huimen

Pacific Ocean

Drakes Bay

Golden Gate

Yelamu †

Costanoan/ Ohlone

San Francisco Bay

BAY AREA TRIBES AT THE TIME OF CONTACT

ADAPTED FROM ORIGINAL IN *CHIEF MARIN* BY BETTY GOERKE. HEYDAY BOOKS

California ~1853

MISSION IN DECLINE

IF WE LOOK BACK ON THE SHORT BUT SIGNIFICANT LIFE of Mission San Rafael where Chief Marin died in 1839 (shortly before the arrival of Sutter), we find that at the end of 1818 the number of Indian converts, or "neophytes" living there, was 386. These Indians planted fruit trees, beans, corn and grapes in what is now downtown San Rafael. The mission could be said to have reached its peak in 1828 when the number of neophytes in residence, under the zealous and relatively benign leadership of Father Amorós, was 1,140. Among those living there at the time was Maria Nicolasa, who was born in Yerba Buena at Mission Dolores around 1812, just after the arrival of Huicmuse and Mottiqui (then Marino and Marina). Her mother had come from the Coast Miwok village of Etchtamal in what is now Nicasio. She spoke both the Ohlone language of the tribes living in present-day

San Leandro, San Francisco and San Jose, as well as the San Rafael Miwok dialect.

Maria Nicolasa married the son of a Miwok couple from the Awani-wi village in the San Rafael area who had also come to live at the mission. Her husband was employed by the mission in washing and ironing the priest's clothes and he played the violin at Mass as a member of a seven-piece string orchestra, which would later be joined by the Miwok leader Teodorico, playing cello. (Elzeario had learned to play the violin from the priests at Mission Dolores.) We noted earlier that under the direction of Fr. Juan Bautista Sanchez from Majorca, Mission San Antonio de Padua was filled with beautiful music brought from Spain to the New World. We can imagine this too at the Mission San Rafael, where Fr. Amorós could sing the Mass and the mission owned an organ. In her description of this in Chief Marin, Betty Goerke tells us that "those Indians who came to San Rafael from Mission San Jose had already been exposed to the musical instruction of the talented Father Durán who taught the neophytes to sing Gregorian chants" (79). She cites an observation of P.E. Botta that "in the missions [the Natives] learn soon and easily to play violin, cello, etc. and to sing together in such a manner that they can perform the music of the Mass of a very complicated harmony, certainly better than the peasants of our lands would be able to do after years of study" (59).[*]

There were still many Indians who chose not to live at the Mission and some were openly hostile to it. Many Coast Miwok were living in places like the beautiful Ross Valley where the land supplied them plentifully with food. A group of local Indians attacked the Mission and burned several of the buildings. In 1824, a band of one thousand Coast Miwok attacked, seeking revenge for the death of an Indian at the hands of a soldier there. Corporal Rafael Garcia was rewarded for thwarting the attack with a grant of land north of Bolinas. We will meet him again later.

When Mexico won her independence from Spain and later ordered the secularization of the missions, there was another free-for-all land grab. After the closing of the San Rafael Mission, only Tinicasio, the Nicasio Rancheria, and Olompali—the Novato Rancheria that was owned and run by local chief Camilio Ynitia—remained of the dozens of Coast Miwok settlements and villages.

The original plan was that the 80,000 acres of Nicasio, for which Miwok leader Teodorico and the others had petitioned the governor, were to become their home under the care of Don Timoteo Murphy. The convolutions and deceptions around these acres of land declares the pervasive and corrupt madness that afflicts Westerners in the presence of vast stretches of native land. There is no single issue in which the vastly different cultures grind past each other with more deadly conflict and devastating results than the question of ownership of land, particularly since the concept was virtually nonexistent among the Pre-Columbian inhabitants. The native groups were certainly capable of preying upon one another at times and contesting prime spots of land resources, even stealing them. But they were

* Quoted in Chief Marin. Botta was an Italian scientist who otherwise had very little good to say about the Natives, which makes his comment all the more impressive.

outmatched in every way by the arrival of the Europeans, armed with their superior weapons and political maneuvers.

The strange thing to observe in this period of California's history is the complex and often contradictory character of people like Vallejo and Alvarado, among many. On the one hand, they appear at times to defend the Indians and to descry their mistreatment or outright swindling by others, while they proceed themselves to extract from them their land and their possessions, particularly the livestock, which are so obviously due to them by law. Depending on who is telling the story, the story's heroes are Vallejo or Alvarado or Timothy Murphy. Any and all of these become villains in other tellings of the story, which demonstrates the ambiguities of the times and the characters. The same can be said about most of the leading native characters as well, including Chief Marin. But by any account, the natives were the losers.

Timothy Murphy is in the category of those adventuresome Irishmen who were clever enough to become Mexican citizens in the opportune moment in order to meet the requirements for receiving a land grant. The first of these was the young Irishman from Dublin, John Thomas Reed, who arrived in San Francisco from Mexico in 1826 and built a cabin north of the Golden Gate. A resourceful fellow, he ran a ferry service that brought water, firewood and later lumber to Mexican families in the Presidio. When the San Rafael mission properties were divided up, he acquired 400 head of Mexican cattle and 60 horses for his Rancho de Corte Madera del Presidio—7,845 acres granted to him by the Mexican governor Jose Figueroa. The realm he had created for himself in the land of the Huimen will encompass Mill Valley, the Tiburon peninsula, Corte Madera, Larkspur (up to the creek), and Strawberry Point. Real estate worth a vast fortune today.

Timothy Murphy also came the long way round from Ireland. He was a huge man, "straight as an arrow and muscular as an ox," who worked in the meat-packing industry in London, Peru and Monterey and made his fortune trapping otter along the Monterey coast. He came to the San Francisco Bay area in 1837 and was made administrator of Mission San Rafael following the secularization.

In the most favorable accounts of "Timoteo" Murphy, he assisted the Indians under his care in relocating to their new land, referred to as the Nicasio Rancheria. He encouraged the Indians to practice the agricultural skills they had learned at the mission and helped them to sell the surplus wares made on their Nicasio Rancheria to customers in San Rafael, Sausalito, and Yerba Buena (San Francisco). Under his care the Indians had plenty to eat, in addition to American blankets, clothes, tools, and of course the acquisition of agricultural skills.

By this account, Timoteo Murphy championed a fair standard of living for the Nicasio people but in the end, they were done in by the corruption of the Mexican officials, the greed spawned by the gold rush, and the diseases for which they had no immunity. We are told, almost in passing, that in 1844 Timoteo Murphy, having become a Mexican citizen and Roman Catholic (a requirement for receiving land grants in California), was granted 22,000 acres of land at San Rafael, plus the ranchos of Las Gallinas, San Pedro, and Santa Margarita. He later acquired an extensive tract of land in Nicasio in 1849 or 1850. Nevertheless, Murphy clearly did help and advocate for the Indians in his care and has been remembered favorably in that context. The rodeos and fiestas he arranged for St. Rafael's Day in October became a popular event in the region with its feats of horsemanship and cattle branding along with the staple supply of gambling and booze. There was a bullfight in the afternoon and an evening dance at the Mission. By then, many of the Indians were excellent cowboys or "vaqueros." In a manner I have found still typical of Mexican fiestas in the smaller villages, these went on for days and food and drink was plentiful.

RANCHO NICASIO

THE MIWOK NAME FOR THE RANCHERIA AND LAND IN NICASIO was Tinicasio. It originally consisted of 56,807 acres granted to the Coast Miwok in 1835 by Gov. Figueroa. In the tangle of land ownership that followed, it was granted in 1848 to De La Guerra and Cooper.

The Rancho Nicasio land grant was the largest in all Marin so it was a plum coveted by many. The "official" grant was signed by Governor Pio Pico in 1845. Ten square leagues were granted to a Spanish nobleman, Pablo de la Guerra, for public service and six square leagues to captain Juan Bautista Roger Cooper in payment of $4,000 owed to him from the state treasury. Cooper was another of those clever Anglos who had become a Mexican Catholic in order to qualify for a land grant. The 16 leagues would have equaled 70,854+ acres, however it was later determined in a survey to be 56,621 acres.

General Vallejo and his nephew Juan Alvarado, both ex-governors, also had designs on the land. They conceived a plot to acquire and gain full title to it for themselves. Their plan was to dupe the Indian chiefs into signing away ownership, after they had managed to secure a legal conveyance to the Nicasio Indians, which had never been done. The chiefs signed away their ownership to Alvarado for $1000, which they never received. Once the plot was uncovered by the governor's secretary, the plan was foiled, since the grant to De la Guerra and Cooper had already been signed and no official document signed by the governor granting the Indians title was to be found and no payment had been made.

The only native Miwok who proved savvy enough to use the white man's system to hold on to some of his land was Camilo Ynitia, son of the Olompali chief who welcomed the first exploratory party of Spanish in the time of the San Carlos, 1775–76. How much had happened in two generations! Even Captain Ayala would have been amazed at the swift disappearance of the people whom he had encountered with such respect and good feeling.

Camilo had been educated at the mission and quickly caught on to the culture and ways of the invaders who had gained mastery over their lands. He earned the respect of people like William Heath Davis ("Kanaka Bill" of Sutter's crew), who found him intelligent and shrewd. Camilo formally petitioned the governor in 1843 for two square leagues of land in Olompali, where he had been born. Governor Micheltorena granted him the land "for his personal benefit and that of his family."* Camilo had carefully observed the rituals performed by his neighbors in claiming possession of their land. It was an ancient Roman juridical ceremony requiring witnesses. Gregorio Briones, Fernando Feliz and Mariano Vallejo's nephew Alvarado (later governor) performed this role and also helped him to measure out the official boundaries. Perhaps with equal ceremony, he used the bricks from the adobe house built by his father and the Spanish exploring party in 1775–76 to build his own house. It would later be added on to by Dr. Galen Burdell and his wife, Mary Black Burdell. It would be further added onto by their son James Burdell for his 26 room mansion. It would even survive a 1969 fire that destroyed the house and left only the original walls of Camilo's adobe. Those bricks fared far better than the Coast Miwok.

Camilo and the remainder of his tribe ran a successful operation at Rancheria Olompali, raising wheat which they sold to the Russians at Ft. Ross. After California became a state in 1852, and people like Sutter were tied up in the courts (the California Land Commission having called into question all Mexican land grants), Camilo Ynitia once again made a shrewd move. Rather than lose his land in the courts after expensive legal proceedings, he sold Olompali to James Black for $5,200 to be paid in installments, maintaining a 1,400 acre parcel which he called Apalococha.

Of the original 80,000 acre grant, the "last of the Nicasio Indians," Calistro, briefly held on to 30 acres. This parcel along Halleck Creek had been conveyed to them by Henry Halleck. In rather florid prose, the Marin Journal of 1887 reported that "Chief John Calistro finally gathered up all the remnants of Indian properties and with the proceeds purchased some thirty acres . . . thereafter making an attempt to uplift his people in a final struggle against the insidious voices of the white man. But this little band was surrounded by every kind of demoralizing influence and the settlers were too busy to banish the vagabonds preying upon them. It was soon necessary for the county to support these disheartened remnants of a once great race . . ."

At that point, the county appropriated $40 a month for their support, which came in addition to the wages they earned on ranches. There is an undated, handwritten "List of Indians Residing in Tinacasio," possibly from around 1871, (with a photocopy now in the Marin Library California room) that lists 27 Miwok men by name, 11 women and 15 children. A very spare census. One of the first anthropologists writing of the Miwok, Alfred Kroeber, gives the number of Coast Miwok pre-contact as being 2000. Later estimates are closer to 5000 Coast Miwok before contact. Between 1851–52, Kroeber cites a population of 250 and in 1880,

* Jack Mason, *Point Reyes: The Solemn Land*

sixty. Another report of that same year says that there were fewer than two dozen Miwok people living there in eight kothcka or red bark teepees. An old report in St. Mary's church from March 1884 said that "The Old Nicasio Rancheria, once a populous Indian village, has dwindled until only two natives are left, the mother and sister of Antone who was drowned recently." Census records from 1880 show 39 indians living in Nicasio and 95 in all of Marin County.*

Whatever the numbers were, miners and other settlers had sealed the fate of the native population, many of whom regarded them as an obstacle to the fulfillment of the future they dreamt of in the New World. To the north, in Mariposa County, conflict raged between Miwok, Chowchilla and Yokut tribes over the land now claimed by miners and settlers who put pressure on California's first governor, Peter Burnett, to solve the problem. Burnett's "State of the State" speech in 1851 articulated a commonly held sentiment across that invisible, ever shifting, Native American-European Immigrant frontier.

The white man, to whom time is money, and who labors hard all day to create the comforts of life, cannot sit up all night to watch his property; and after being robbed a few times, he becomes desperate, and resolves upon a war of extermination. This is the common feeling of our people who have lived upon the Indian frontier. The two races are kept asunder by so many causes, and having no ties of marriage or consanguinity to unite them, they must ever remain at enmity.

That a war of extermination will continue to be waged between the races until the Indian race becomes extinct must be expected. While we cannot anticipate this result but with painful regret, the inevitable destiny of the race is beyond the power or wisdom of man to avert.

The Native American counterpoint is eloquently expressed two decades later by Chief Joseph in what became known as the Nez Perce War over the same issues in far-off Montana territory.

I have carried a heavy load on my back since I was a boy. I realized then that we could not hold our own with the white men. We were like deer. They were like grizzly bears. We had a small country. Their country was large. We were contented to let things remain as the Great Spirit Chief made them. They were not, and would change the rivers and the mountains if they did not suit them.**

The two voices stand like bookends of that tumultuous period.

The Coast Miwok territory that had once stretched as far north as Bodega Bay, all of Marin County to the south and as far east as the town of Sonoma had disappeared in less than a century. Where once there were over six-hundred Miwok villages, like Huimen, over a hundred on the Point Reyes peninsula, a human tsunami had washed the land clean of its native population, who had enjoyed its bounty for thousands of years.

---

* See Goerke, p.215.
** Quoted in Chief Joseph: The Biography of a Great Indian by Chester Anders Fee. This passage is quoted in many places, but this work was the source for the PBS Special "The West."

San Francisco née Yerba Buena ~ 1853

THE REPORTER[*]

The first bells ring out over the town around half-past six, calling people to breakfast. These are soon joined by the thunderous tones of huge gongs and the two enter into a competitive duel of peremptory calls that would tempt the dead to rise up for a hearty breakfast of beefsteak and potatoes and coffee at Delmonico's. And anyway, this is San Francisco. Nobody comes here in the One Thousand Eight Hundred and Fifty-third year of our Lord to lie in bed in the mornings, even after being up all night. The city is a giant anthill by the sea—industrious and in constant motion. Of course what passes for industry here might not pass for industry elsewhere, as it includes gaming, some friendly swindling, bargaining for lots, panning for gold, and promenading in the plaza. Our Eastern reporter, eager to have a look at this new city and report to the world about what has only been rumor, is up and out with the rest of them. The thick early morning fog over the city doesn't seem to dampen anyone's spirits.

One thing about this town, it has no shortage of restaurants to provide a hearty breakfast. On the plaza, you have the United States and California restaurants that serve up the beefsteak and potatoes with a good cup of coffee for $1. Or you can just walk along Montgomery Street where venders have erected stands that cater to the constant flow of sailors along the waterfront, or the miners who have just come in from the mountains. Hot coffee, cakes, sweetmeats and plenty of things to look at while you eat. The streets that run down to the water are crowded with people of an outlandish variety. Our reporter observes solemn Chinese standing in front of their businesses taking in the scene with an impassive gaze. Peruvians and Chileans walk among them in brown ponchos and the German and Frenchman have their uniquely recognizable look and language. Even the English being spoken is full of variety from the slow drawls of the Texans, the Kentuckians, the Carolinians and Virginians, to the distinct speech of the New Yorkers and Down-easters.

The most prominent businesses in town are right there on the plaza—Dennison's Exchange, the Parker House and close by, what our reporter calls the canvas hell of the Eldorado. The Parker House was originally built by Robert Parker as a hotel, but was soon converted to a casino as the gambling craze swept San Francisco. A large room downstairs contains three tables for faro, two for monte, one for roulette and a seventh for any other game desired. Professional gamblers are paid $10,000 a month for the privilege of conducting their games in this room. A smaller room behind the bar goes for $3,500 a month. The appropriately named Jack Gamble leases the entire second floor for $60,000 and all the rooms are outfitted for games of chance. It has been estimated that at the peak of the California Gold Rush upward of half a million dollars was stacked on the tables of the Parker House on any given day.

In spite of its sober and respectable name, the Dennison Exchange next door is dedicated with equal zeal to the goddess Chance. Across the way are the smaller gambling houses, the Veranda and the Aguila d'Oro. Also on Portsmouth Square—

---

[*] Bayard Taylor was sent west from New York by Horace Greeley to report first-hand on what were only fantastic rumors at the time.

the Bella Union, the Empire, the Arcade, the Varsouvienne, the Mazourka, the Ward House, the St. Charles, the Alhambra, La Souciedad, the Fontine House and the Rendezvous. As the names so colorfully illustrate, multiculturalism and equal opportunity are alive and well already in San Francisco. Several of the establishments with French names are owned and operated by gambling syndicates from France.

The plaza of Portsmouth Square is the true center of town where business is conducted, amusement found, bargains and exchanges made, and the young men and women display themselves in the age-old ritual of the promenade. Naval officers and miners, gamblers and merchants stand in small knots of conversation, gossip and negotiations. Fortunes are being won and lost on street corners as much as they are in the mines and gaming halls. It is a raw and robust energy set loose on the very edge of a new continent. Although, in truth, it is not the continent that is new but the people.

Adding to the spirited energy of the town are the animals, from horses to wild bulls. You might see a wild bull racing down Kearny Street with two lariat-twirling vaqueros hot on its trail as the streets are hastily cleared to make way for them. By late-morning, the mist that had enshrouded the town at dawn has finally burned off to reveal the blue of bay and sea and the green of the headlands to the north. By noon, the wind has shifted and comes rushing out of the northwest picking up speed through a gap in the hills that opens toward the Golden Gate. All morning long a loud continuo of hammerings has provided its background sound to the morning's business as the ceaseless building of the town goes on around it. But now their relentless din is once again overtaken by the blare of bells and gongs calling people to the mid-day dinner.

By 2:00, the streets have emptied and the restaurants have filled again for the serious meal of the day. The choices have been made between Tortoni's, the Alhambra, the French restaurants on the plaza and on Dupont street, the extensive German establishment on Pacific street, the Fonda Peruana, the Italian Confectionery, or three Chinese houses, announced by their long three-cornered flags of yellow silk. These are renowned for their excellent cuisine and the fact that meals are $1 each, all-you-can-eat. Kong Sung's house is near the water, Whang-Tong's in Sacramento Street, and Tong-Ling's in Jackson street. Our reporter will write of them—"There the grave Celestials serve up their chow-chow and curry, besides many genuine English dishes; their tea and coffee cannot be surpassed." The well-heeled New Yorkers, nostalgic for home and ready to splurge, will likely head to Delmonico's, the Western version of New York's own.

Our reporter has chosen to walk down Kearney Street with some friends to the two-story wooden house on the corner of Jackson. The street level of the house is a market and the reporter stops to take in the details of the sight. Cabbage heads at $2 can be seen in the window and in the corner, a bin of Sandwich Island squashes. Quarters of beef and mutton hang along the walls. He continues up a dark, narrow flight of steps to a long, low room of about twenty tables in two rows already filled up with diners. The walls and ceiling are of white muslin and the floor is covered with oil cloth. They finally find places to insert themselves and are given the written bill of fare:

Soups.

Mock Turtle - $0 75

    St. Julien 1 00

Fish.

    Boiled Salmon Trout, Anchovy sauce...... 1 75

Entrees.

    Fillet of Beef, mushroom sauce 1 75

    Veal Cutlets, breaded........................ 1 00

    Mutton Chop................................ 1 00

    Lobster Salad............................... 2 00

    Sirloin of Venison 1 50

    Baked Macaroni............................ 0 75

    Beef Tongue, sauce piquante................. 1 00

    Leg Mutton, caper Sauce..................... 1 00

    Corned Beef, Cabbage...................... 1 00

    Ham and Tongues........................... 0 75

The plates are small but the cuisine is tasty, especially to miners who have been living in the wilds. The reporter observes that one acquires a prodigious appetite in California, as if to feed the insatiable energy of the city itself. "For two months after my arrival, my sensations were those of a famished wolf." A meal in moderation here will cost about $5.

Heavy with the mid-day meal, people settle down inside to work or play, in gambling houses or places of business. The wind stirs up a dust in the town that is unpleasant and the brilliant landscape of the late morning retreats behind a veil of dusty air. Only the waterfront remains active with the arrival of vessels, bearing their consignments to the town's merchants. Sometimes the wind keeps up until sunset and blows colder so that a warm overcoat is needed. The plaza is nearly deserted.

When night falls, the city is transformed. Viewed from the ships at anchor it is a magical sight. The makeshift houses along its sloping streets are still mostly of canvas, glowing like Chinese lanterns from the lamps within. This transforms them, our reporter notes, "to dwellings of solid light. Seated on the slopes of its three hills, the tents pitched among the chaparral to the very summits, it is . . . like an amphitheatre of fire. Here and there shine out brilliant points from the decoy-lamps of the gaming houses; and through the indistinct murmur of the streets comes by fits the sound of music from their hot and crowded precincts. The picture has in it something unreal and fantastic; it impresses one like the cities of the magic lantern, which a motion of the hand can build or annihilate."

The Reporter, being a reporter, knows that he will not have a true portrait of San Francisco until he has zoomed in from this perspective onto the innards of the gaming-houses. Like modern casinos, the gambling emporiums are open day and night, and after dark are thick with patrons. Eldorado is the likely place to get the full effect, being the most crowded and the most central. He is lucky even to squeeze through the door. One cannot match his marvelous prose descriptions:

There are about eight tables in the room, all of which are thronged; copper-hued Kanakas, Mexicans rolled in their sarapes and Peruvians thrust through their ponchos, stand shoulder to shoulder with the brown and bearded American miners. The stakes are generally small, though when the bettor gets into "a streak of luck," as it is called, they are allowed to double until all is lost or the bank breaks. Along the end of the room is a spacious bar, supplied with all kinds of bad liquors, and in a sort of gallery, suspended under the ceiling, a female violinist tasks her talent and strength of muscle to minister to the excitement of play.

At the Verandah he finds a musician who has a set of Pandean pipes fastened at his chin, a drum on his back, which he beats with sticks at his elbows, and cymbals in his hands. At the Aguila de Oro, a full band of Ethiopian serenaders "and at the other hells, violins, guitars or wheezy accordions."

Dwellings of solid light, hell holes of devilish dark, the chiaroscuro of a brave and feckless new world, still so flimsy in its wood, canvas and muslim walls that a "motion of the hand can build or annihilate it." *

Like faithful lovers, the gamblers will follow the miners to Sacramento, Columbia, Nevada City and the other mining towns, many of which will crumble to dust or fall asleep when the miners and the gamblers move on. Who would imagine that so reckless and roguish and flimsy a place as the San Francisco we see through the eyes of Bayard Taylor and other observers of the time could possibly throw down roots, solidify and flourish. Yet remarkably, when our reporter returns to the city four months later, he finds a very different place. In his words:

Of all the marvelous phases of the history of the Present, the growth of San Francisco is one which will most tax belief of the Future. Its parallel was never known, and shall never be beheld again. I speak only of what I saw with my own eyes.

When I landed there, a little more than four months before, I found a scattering town of tents and canvas houses, with a show of frame buildings on one or two streets and a population of about six thousand. Now, on my last visit, I saw around me an actual metropolis, displaying street after street of well-built edifices, filled with an active and enterprising people and exhibiting every mark of permanent commercial prosperity.

Then, the town was limited to the curves of the Bay fronting the anchorage and bottom of the hills. Now, it stretched to the topmost heights, followed the shore around point after point, and sending back a long arm through a gap in the hills, took hold of the Golden Gate and was building its warehouses on the open strait and almost fronting the blue horizon of the Pacific.

Then, the gold-seeking sojourner lodged in muslin rooms and canvas garrets . . . and ate his simple though substantial fare from pine boards. Now, lofty hotels, gaudy with verandas and balconies, were met with in all quarters, furnished with home luxury, and aristocratic restaurants presented daily their long bills of fare, rich with the choicest technicalities of the Parisian cuisine.

Then, vessels were coming in day after day, to lie deserted and useless at their anchorage. Now scarce a day passed, but some cluster of sails bound outward through the Golden Gate, took their way to all corners of the Pacific. Like the

* Adapted from Bayard Taylor's account in *The Western Gate*

magic seed of the Indian juggler, which grew, blossomed and bore fruit before the eyes of his spectators, San Francisco seemed to have accomplished in a day the growth of half a century.

When I first landed in California, bewildered and amazed by what seemed an unnatural standard of prices, I formed the opinion that there would be before long a great crash in speculation. Things, it appeared then, had reached the crisis, and it was pronounced impossible that they could remain stationary.

This might have been a very natural idea at the time, but the subsequent course of affairs proved it to be incorrect. Lands, rents, goods and subsistence continued steadily to advance in cost, and as the credit system had been meanwhile prudently contracted, the character of the business done was the more real and substantial. . . .

Prices will never fall to the same standard as in the Atlantic States. Fortunes will always be made by the sober, intelligent, industrious, and energetic; but no one who is either too careless, too spiritless or too ignorant to succeed at home, need trouble himself about emigrating. The same general rule holds good, as well here as elsewhere, and it is all the better for human nature that it is so.

A LOSER'S GOLD

AND WHAT OF THE SMALL PLUCKY BAND WE LEFT BEHIND offering up its nine-gun salute to the *Isabella* and the *Nicholas?* What of Sutter's dreams of empire and his New Helvetia—a transported Switzerland, friendlier to his outsized style? My father told me that some of our own forbears from Switzerland went west to join Sutter at Sutter's Mill. How did his settlement evolve from a few tents to the most famous establishment of its time in California? He was systematic and for all his daring and bravura, his approach was as carefully designed as a Swiss watch, even if—in the end—his Swiss gift for industry and invention did not extend to the Swiss gift for business and finance.

We recall that before he left Yerba Buena, Sutter had received an assent from Gov. Alvarado that after one year's residence he could become a Mexican citizen and thus be eligible for a land grant. He became a citizen on August 29, 1849 and the following year received title to 48,827 acres of land (198 sq. km), which he had selected very carefully. His New Helvetia, the New Switzerland that would redeem him from the old, was born on that date. Remember, too, that he had made arrangements in advance with Gen. Vallejo—before he had even set out to find the land—for the purchase of cattle, horses and sheep. He had courted the local Indians with the promise of "peaceful coexistence" and gifts during his very first encounter, just as he had instilled a terrible respect with his booming cannon. These opening gestures bore fruit as his future work force. His acts of kindness to the Miwoks, Nisenan and Maidu who became part of his work enterprise secured the loyalty of many of his workers, just as his cruel forms of punishment for transgressions large and small created lifelong enemies among them. Cruelties that were not withheld from erring white workers as well. He was an equal-opportunity employer/oppressor, particularly harsh in his punishment of the stealing of livestock, which was as common in California as cattle-rustling was in other parts of the west.

In 1840 he began building a fort to protect New Helvetia. He employed 350 Nisenan and Miwok Indians to guard the fort. By now there were large herds of cattle and horses grazing in the fields. Hunters were sent regularly to the mountains for fur pelts and elk hides. Within the walls rose a distillery, flour mill and bakery as well as a blacksmith and carpenter shop. A boat launch was created to carry freight and passengers between Sutter's Fort and San Francisco Bay.

In 1841 Sutter fulfilled his next plan of seeding his agricultural Utopia by creating the Hock Farm on the West Bank of the Feather River near Marysville, just south of what would become Yuba City. Here he intended to retire and to relocate his wife and children. It was a large-scale agricultural settlement composed of grain, cattle, orchards and vineyards. Hock Farm, named after the nearby Nisenan Hok Rancheria, would supply food for Sutter's Fort. Sutter himself had no experience of farming, any more than he had experience of anything else he had done. He was self-taught in all the things that he did, and he recruited immigrants from the United States, Switzerland and Germany to help him make it work.

In the same year, 1841, Sutter fulfilled another dream by buying the Russian settlements of Ross and Bodega, which he had so admired, for $32,000, secured by a mortgage on New Helvetia. By 1844, Sutter's Fort was nearly completed and his reputation and importance had spread far and wide as more and more settlers were arriving from the difficult trip west. It would be the destination of the ill-fated Donner Party, forty of whom perished in a winter storm during the treacherous crossing of the Sierras. The remaining thirty-seven were snowbound from November until February when, near to death from weather and hunger, they were brought to Sutter's Fort. He put them up there until they were healthy and able to move on, as he did for so many other parties arriving from all directions, including Kit Carson and John C. Fremont.

In 1847, Sutter contracted with James Marshall to build a sawmill on the south fork of the American River. It was almost completed when James Marshall discovered gold in the tail race on January 28, 1848. The strike of great fortune that would make hundreds of '49ers rich, was a strike of great disaster for Johann Augustus Sutter and would leave him destitute. Everything changed from the moment the first glitter of gold appeared in the water.

Sutter and Marshall tried to keep the news quiet but that was impossible. His workmen quit to look for gold, just as tens of thousands of new arrivals poured into New Helvetia, helping themselves to Sutter's land, crops and livestock. He was powerless before them. He tried to become a merchant to the miners, but his partners cheated him and soon his creditors were deviling him.

As the peaceful valley of the Miwok, Maidu and Nisenan Indians had been invaded by Sutter and eventually destroyed by all that he had brought in his wake, so Sutter was now being invaded by the gold-seekers. His fortunes had turned and his debtors were closing in. In a desperate move to protect his holdings, he deeded his remaining land to his son, John Sutter Jr., who had arrived from Switzerland in 1848. But much to his consternation, Sutter Jr. turned his focus to the laying out of the Sacramento town site in January 1849, rather than building up the local city center at Sutterville. In late 1849, Sutter sold his fort for $7,000.

In another desperate move, Sutter had tried to secure his rights to the property by signing a treaty with the local Nisenan and Maidu Indians, which officially ceded the land to him and, he hoped, would give him legal title. But he was told by the new American government in Monterey that "the United States government did not recognize the right of Indians to lease, sell, or rent their lands."

John Sutter's life, like that of so many people in these times, is a study in contrast and contradiction; of larger than life failures and accomplishments. In 1849, the same year that his life in New Switzerland began to unravel, he helped frame the California Constitution as a member of the Monterey Convention. The United States had won the Mexican War and California was now about to join the union of the United States. The Treaty of Guadalupe Hidalgo that secured California's independence from Spain, had also indirectly brought his personal downfall as his proprietorship of extensive lands granted by the Mexican government were now called into question by the new powers in Washington: Squatters who had overrun his land took him to court over the legality of his titles.

In 1850, after 16 years of separation in which his family had been left to fend for themselves back in Switzerland, they now came to take up their life with him in what had been a promising future for them all. His wife, daughter Eliza, and sons Emil Victor and William Alphonse arrived at last in Sacramento. He retired with his family to Hock Farm, to escape the chaos produced by gold fever at the Fort. The family enjoyed a few years peace together in their lovely redwood farm home, among the gardens, orchards and vineyards that Sutter had so successfully cultivated there.

The U.S. Land Commission decided in Sutter's favor in 1857, but a year later the Supreme Court declared portions of his title invalid. Rustlers were stealing his livestock and a final blow was dealt when a group of men set fire to his house, which was completely destroyed by the blaze. This sent Sutter and his wife to Washington, D.C. to seek restitution from the U.S. Congress for the loss of his lands. Meeting no success in this effort, they decided to settle down in the Moravian town of Lilitz, Pennsylvania. Sutter continued his battle from there. On June 16, 1880, Congress adjourned before passing a bill that would give him $50,000 in restitution. Unfortunately, Sutter died two days later and his wife died the following January.

* * * *

Grossi Farms ~ The Present

MAMA AND THE EGGPLANT

Home. A puddle on the plastic where the skylight leaked onto the bed. The mattress wet. Susie said it rained heavily for three days. Tuesday's school visits were cancelled.

Good to be back in Mr. Fields. Quiet.

I stepped outside the camper at evening to watch a beautiful sunset and walk down to fill my water jugs. I lingered before getting in the camper and saw a familiar tan vehicle negotiating the mud in my direction.

"Can I help you? Are you looking for somebody?" I said when he drove up. As if there was anybody else here but the birds and rabbits. "What's the address?"

"6617" Ed came right back.

"Sorry. I'm 6618."

"Balsam's mother picked some vegetables here today. She sent over some food she cooked. Can you join us?"

Balsam's mother just flew up from Los Angeles. It's odd because she usually doesn't come until Christmas and it's still October. "Please," she asked her son. "Send me a ticket now."

"She came because of the eggplant. I'm sure of it," Susie said. "She wanted to get here before Eddie plows it under. Balsam's mother is Persian and speaks no English. But she's clearly a woman of the soil."

"I'll tell you two words she *does* know," Eddie adds. "PLOW UNDER. Say those two words and she grabs her heart as if she were going to die on the spot." Balsam, a friend of the Grossi's, had brought his mother by last year about this time. She saw Ed on the tractor disking under the last eggplant and went running after him into the field, screaming for him to stop. "We've dubbed her the Vegetable Rescue Squad" Ed explains, as he describes how she ran behind him picking up eggplants that the blade had missed. "Why would you do this to an eggplant that has gone to such trouble to come to fruition?" That's Balsam's rough translation of her tirade.

Now, Mama knew, it was time: Ed would soon be climbing onto his deadly tractor again. "Please, my son. Send me a ticket."

"Of course she's welcome!" Susie said, ever generous. "She can have anything she wants. But we've just had a big rain here and this is adobe soil. Give her good boots." She arrived in good strong construction boots below her bowed legs. An old woman from an old country, as Susie put it. "She got taller and taller as she went down the rows because the wet black adobe soil sticks to the boots in ever-increasing layers." Susie and Balsam periodically took her aside to scrape off the mud, then she was off again, chattering, gesticulating, shaking her head. "What's she saying Balsam?" Susie asked.

"She's saying 'Such a waste. All those beautiful vegetables. She's never seen a garden like this. Ed is such a good farmer. Why would he waste it?" Mama was bent double, scuttling along between the rows, examining every fallen fruit.

"No no!" Susie kept urging. "Those have gone bad! Pick the fresh ones from the vines." But Mama was emphatic. Ed could sell those to customers. "See this 'bad tomato'? Just cut that bottom part off and its perfect. Why waste it?"

Not only did she happily harvest fallen eggplant, but also little ones that could never mature this season. "Not those!" Susie said. "They're not ripe. Too small." Mama's eyes glittered. Through Balsam's translation she explained to Susie how they could be stuffed and baked.

She tenderly lifted an eggplant flower for Susie to see. "Look," she said through her son. "This plant still has life in it. It can still produce fruit." Susie was relating this all to me, miming the facial expressions and gestures so perfectly that Mama appeared in full detail before my eyes. "It's just frigging confused," Ed muttered underneath his breath. He was thinking of the March heat wave and the early summer cold.

At some point, Mama spied the fallen fence, battered by the rain, that had once held the Italian black beans, favored by so many customers. We'd seen the last of those two weeks ago, at least. Mustang Sally had nearly fainted with shock and dismay when I gave her the bad news. Mustang Sally is a delightful senior citizen who drives a bright red mustang and cherishes our Italian black beans. Mama too was ecstatic. She knew these beans. They have them in her country and there is just nothing like them. She clambered over the fallen fence and started filling her bucket with another fallen crop.

"No Mom! Those are old. Tough. No good any more. Tell her Balsam." But Mama shook her head vehemently and her fingers scrabbled on along the fallen fence. Susie found her the last sprigs of dill. She turned to her son. "Buy wild salmon. Now we have dill. We must have salmon."

It was not only Ed's fallen fruits that were harvested. One of our most plentifully growing weeds, malva or "cheese plant," came under her happy harvesting. "But that's just a weed," Susie protested. Mama carefully showed her that you find the youngest leaves of the plant, remove those and use the stalk like celery.

Then to the figs. More ecstasy.

Nearby were the concord grape vines that grew along the lathe house by the old vegetable stand. Only a few grapes were left and Susie picked them and offered them to Mama. She put the round, succulent fruit into her mouth, closing her eyes to savor its sweetness. When she had drawn the last nectar out of it, she opened her eyes and spit the seed in a perfect arc toward the grass. "I loved it," Susie said. "Not too many people know how to handle seeded grapes like that anymore."

When they had finished and headed back toward the house, they passed under the walnut tree that grows on the edge of the Grossi's backyard. Once again, Mama fell to her knees with unmistakable cries of happiness and began picking through the fallen nuts, Susie continuing to provide her with new receptacles for her booty. "No Mom! Don't pick those off the ground. Take fresh ones from the tree."

"But the minute she heard me say Don't take the ones on the ground she started to pick through them faster, her hands moving a mile a minute." Susie laughed, miming her rapid strokes like a frantic swimmer, head bowed low. When she rose, Mama carefully explained through Balsam how to stuff the figs with these walnuts and bake them. "We could have made a cookbook out of all the recipes she gave us for everything she touched."

This story was told by Susie as we sat down to the feast that Mama had made from her afternoon pickings and sent over to Susie and Eddie. I have never had beans so tender. The inner black bean had grown to the size of a baby lima and was deliciously meaty and sweet. It had been cooked with her salvaged tomatoes and the tender stalks of *malva*.

"Balsam says she's got this little pressure cooker—just three or four quarts—that she brought with her. She cooks *everything* in it." More tomatoes had been chopped fine with some of Ed's parsley into a savory salsa, all served with rice. It was delicious.

After dinner, Susie drove me back to Mr. Fields in the golf cart, still talking about the gifts from Mama and her remarkable knowledge of things of the earth and how to use them in all phases of their season, making the most of every little thing in a delicious way.

"We've got to preserve this and the people like Mama," she said. "It's so important. If we can understand other cultures in this way, we can understand other people. Maybe really see ourselves under it all as one."

She's got a point, I think, climbing into Mr. Fields. We all have to eat. But how many people understand food like Mama does and the few people who still live directly off the earth. Certainly not I, raised on Bird's Eye frozen vegetables from the supermarket. But little by little, I'm learning.

PART V

POINT REYES

The peninsula measures 28 miles from stem to stern and, at its widest—between the lighthouse and the San Andreas Fault zone—about 12 miles. Its total area is just over 110 square miles, yet it touches oceanic waters along a span of fully 63 miles, about half-and-half rocky shore and sandy beach.

— Claire Peaslee
"Point Reyes on the Edge"
Bay Nature, July 16, 2012

The broken shore now called the Marin Peninsula is really two peninsulas. . . . The main peninsula . . . is the Marin Peninsula proper. It stretches from north to south, toward other land which it almost touches (but nowhere does), thereby helping form a large bay mothered by the sea. . . . But on the seaside of Marin is a different story; there, attached to Marin but not simply part of it, is the rival, Point Reyes, stretching east to west, out into the open sea.

— Arthur Quinn
Broken Shore: The Marin Peninsula in California History

ARRIVALS

THOSE WHO GO. AND THOSE WHO STAY. It is not surprising that so many of those-who-go went to California. California is a vagrant if ever there was one. This land of immigrants with its remarkably diverse population was itself an immigrant. It came together from its diverse parts and coalesced into solid units like the populations of its major cities.

The truth is that for most of history, California wasn't there. In fact it wasn't anywhere. The story of California is beautifully told in John McPhee's book *Assembling California.*

> The continent ended far to the east, the continental shelf as well. Where California has come to be, there was only blue sea reaching down some miles to ocean-crustal rock which was moving, as it does, into subduction zones to be consumed. Ocean floors with an aggregate area many times the size of the present Pacific were made at spreading centers, moved around a curve of the earth, and melted in trenches before there was ever so much as a kilogram of California. Then, a piece at a time—according to present theory—parts began to assemble.

California had to get itself organized, magnetize itself with the Gold Rush, make up its mind whether it wanted to be Spanish, Russian, British or this brash newfangled thing, American, and attract some topflight scientists before it was willing to tell its story. Like all stories, it keeps changing but here it is for now.

It begins as the Smartville arc—a collection of islands, thrust up from the deep during the Jurassic era, some 200 to 170 million years ago—around mid-December on our calendar. It looks something like Japan. The Smartville block is named after the town of Smartville, California not too far from Timbuktoo and Sucker Flat. Does that help? You'll think I made those up but I didn't. Timbuktoo is a ghost town in Yuba County, northern California, very likely sharing with its African namesake the feature of being a remote nowhere. Sucker Flat is close by. The names speak volumes about what some of the first settlers thought of the place. And Smartville? It could have been an early name for Berkeley, but it is actually near Grass Valley, where some of my own ancestors settled and Johann Augustus Sutter had his ephemeral kingdom. It is due east of Mendocino on the coast, but that wasn't always so. Back in the earliest Triassic time, it is far out to sea and the continental shelf is back in Idaho and Nevada.

In John McPhee's geologic tale, when Smartville "docks" in the Jurassic, it closes a trench east of Sacramento and opens up a new one west of Davis in another tectonic fender bender which dramatically alters the landscape. Just as the Smartville block is settled in for a bit, a new intruder arrives, sailing in from the west to dock against Smartville and cause a bit of a crumple there as the force of collision drives it 40,000 feet under the Great Valley. That crumple is the coastal mountains and the intruder is known as the Pacific Plate. Our stories so far have taken place in the landscape formed by a similar incursion of plate upon plate as Africa rolled over Eurasia. The energy bursting out of that seam, whether authored by Poseidon or Aeolus or more ancient and forgotten gods, gave rise to the exceptional Mediterranean cultures and individuals who crossed the Atlantic in the memories of thousands of immigrants. All of our stories, rooted in their particular landscapes, are drawn from those deep forces. Dominic Grossi will not be aware when he arrives that for a time, his life will straddle that seam and his family's future will lie on both sides.

If the Smartville block and the Coast Ophiolite (the wedge of the coastal range) come to port like giant ocean-liners, one of the latest migrants, the Point Reyes peninsula —which forms the eastern edge of the Pacific plate—has been compared to a great whale, slowly swimming north. Its nose, in fact, is aimed northwest, toward Alaska. Its humped back is filigreed with bishop pine and cypress. Its rounded tail sits between the Pacific and Drake's Bay. It swims imperceptibly forward in time through alternating thick mists and open skies. It is a creature independent of the Smartville and Coastal blocks, yet for now it is joined at the hip along Bear Valley.

On the seaward side is another companion, in a migrant pattern of its own that warms and cools the stolid leviathan of land made of rock and tree. While this western companion is more insubstantial, a thing made entirely of air, its presence is felt far to the east as it sends chills over the inland valleys: It is the North Pacific High, which glides above the sea a thousand miles to the west, following the rhythms of its own companion, the sun. It migrates south with the sun in winter and settles off the coast of Mexico. This is really the earth's journey, tilting like a dervish, spinning on its axis. As the tilting North Pole shifts back toward the sun, the Pacific High returns north with the snowbirds from Florida and Mexico, to settle down near the 38th latitude, just off the coast of Point Reyes taking up once again with its companion, the whale.

The North Pacific High is a mass of cool air, amorphous perhaps but influential. It gains size and pressure on its northern trip. As it slides into position alongside the whale, the Point Reyes peninsula, it generates the spring winds. Once it settles down off the coast, its sheer mass stabilizes the weather and protects the coast from Pacific storms like a giant invisible buffer. When the days grow shorter and the sun begins its retreat south, the Pacific High will go with it, leaving the whale's flank opened to the onslaught of winter storms. This rhythmic movement affects the ocean temperatures and current, as well as the air and the land.

So these are the first arrivals—those blocks of land that have slowly come to port, one by one. The most recent of *these* arrivals is that sharp-snouted coyote-looking Point Reyes Peninsula. (It swims like a whale but is shaped like a coyote, as some writers have noted.) And there is where we pick up the story again. While you can't quite see it today, the place where Point Reyes has come to rest against the hip of the Coast Ophalite and the Smartville Block is a very real, if invisible, boundary. Geologists know it as the San Andreas Fault. The Ticinesi farmers know it as the Olema Valley and to the north of that, Tomales Bay.

East of the fault line is the land of Nicasio, with its complicated history during the rise and fall of the San Rafael Mission. West of that, the Point Reyes peninsula has its own complex and even more convoluted real estate history. The common actor who appears in both dramas is Rafael Garcia, soldier at the San Rafael Mission, who was awarded a grant of land for his "service" in driving off hostile Indians in an attack on the mission. For this deed, Garcia—a mere corporal—is awarded almost 9,000 acres by the government in Monterey. The Tomales y Baulines Rancho lies right at the juncture of Nicasio and the Point Reyes peninsula. This begins one of the longest and messiest legal battles over land in the history of Marin.

LAND BARONS

They were talking about property. We were talking about the land. . . .
Your people came from Europe because they wanted property for their
own . . . to farm and raise the food to live. They had worked for other
people who had claimed all the property and took all the things they
raised. They never had anything because they had no property. . . .
That is what was behind the whole idea of America as a new country
across the ocean. To get property of their own.

— Sioux Elder in
Neither Wolf nor Dog
KENT NERBURN

PEOPLE FROM THE "OLD WORLD"—OR PEOPLE LIKE ME who were raised in the densely populated Northeast United States—cannot imagine what it was like for the first Europeans to come upon a vast, pristine landscape that was unmapped, unnamed, uncharted and seemed ready for the taking, notwithstanding the presence of an indigenous population. It was 2500 miles from Boston—far out of sight and out of mind for those first settlers. The Winnili, in the course of their centuries-long journey, traveled around 800 miles or 1200 kilometers. According to historical records, the first European didn't cross the Rockies until 1793 when a Scottish explorer, Sir Alexander MacKenzie, crossed the Canadian Rockies. Intrepid fur traders like Kit Carson, Jedediah Smith and Jim Bridger—"Mountain Men"—entered the Rockies after 1802 and Lewis and Clark were dispatched by Jefferson two years later. The first wagon train crossed the Rockies in 1832 but parties of settlers didn't cross in earnest until the 1840s when thousands began the difficult journey along the Oregon trail.

In the beginning of European presence, as we have seen, vast acres of California land belonged to the Missions, which the Spanish had established up and down the coast. Mexico took possession of California in 1821, after it had won its independence from Spain. Enormous land grants (ranchos) were doled out to Mexican loyalists, continuing the tradition of such grants by Spain. California is also a long way from Mexico City (over two thousand miles), so those "loyalists," as we've seen, were often part rogue and cunning adventurer, loyal only to their own fortunes.

The first Point Reyes land grant was awarded to our corporal in the Mexican Army, Rafael Garcia who thwarted the attack on the San Rafael mission by hostile Miwok. The requirements were simple and like so many things today, it was a matter of getting the paperwork and bureaucratic details right. He had completed the necessary ten years of service in the army and correctly filed his petition in a timely fashion. Suddenly, in March 1836, he was a *latifundista*—owner of a ranch of two leagues or 8,911 acres. This is twice the size of the current city of San Francisco. Not bad for a corporal. Rising to the grandeur of the occasion, he named it Rancho Tomales y Baulenes. It extended from Tomales Bay to the Bolinas Lagoon. Something like that. When you are so far from the bureaucratic center and a vast, largely unseen territory has just fallen into your country's hands, there is not much time for small details. Garcia never surveyed his property and there were never any official boundaries recorded. It meant little to Garcia that three hundred years before him an Englishman (Sir Francis Drake) had stepped ashore and declared the land for England and "Ta ta for now."

Garcia had actually moved onto the land two years before he officially owned it. According to what law there was in this Wild West, Garcia was prohibited from allowing someone other than himself to take possession of the land. But one can feel lonely on 9000 acres, so he invited his brother-in-law—Georgio Briones—to take possession of a part of it. Briones, with as quick an eye for profit as his brother-in-law, filed a corrected deed in 1843 showing himself as having lived on the land since 1836 and therefore entitled to ownership. The petition was approved and he was given legal title.

In 1836, another land grant was awarded to a similarly enterprising fellow: an Irishman named James Berry. Not a very Mexican name, but he had had the foresight to become a Mexican citizen and join the Mexican army so he met the qualifications for land baron. He was awarded approximately 38,000 acres in the Olema Valley. The equivalent of 60 square miles, this would be over 8 times the size of San Francisco, about 3 times the size of Manhattan. Now one could be *very* lonely in a place that size, but Berry had no intention of making his home there, in spite of the legal requirement to do so. He did comply with the Mexican law by building a home and stocking his ranch with cattle. He hired Garcia to run them.

Berry had only begun his fencing match with the Mexican land laws. Two years after purchasing the property under an agreement not to sell it off, he sold 9000 acres to a sea captain, Joseph Snook. Had the authorities been aware of this, he would have lost his title to the land, so Berry kept the transaction secret. Whether he had an agreement to that effect with Snook, I don't know. Gentlemen's agreements didn't hold up well among these first real estate owners. But they weren't exactly gentlemen in the first place. Snook wanted title to his land and the only way he could do this, he discovered, was by denouncing Berry's ownership on the grounds that he had not complied with the requirement to occupy the land. He seems to have had Berry's approval for this but how Berry escaped losing all of his property on this basis is unclear. The end result was that Snook became the owner of 8,878 acres of Berry's rancho, which he stocked with 59 head of cattle. Seems reasonably spacious at 100 plus acres a head for grazing. He hired Rafael Garcia, at $12 a month, to oversee his new holding.

Since James Berry *bought* the land illegally, it shouldn't be surprising that he sold it in the same way. Three months later he sold it to Antonio Maria Osio, who was already the owner of the Angel Island Land Grant and administrator of the custom house in Monterey. If this sounds like a macroscale version of the Monopoly Game, it was. Osio was after Park Place: He wanted *all* of Point Reyes Peninsula land.

Don Antonio Maria Osio was a government official originally from San Jose del Cabo at the tip of the Baja peninsula. The Mexican government granted him Angel Island in 1839, where the San Carlos had anchored in 1776, on the condition that he be allowed to build a fort there if needed. Osio raised cattle on the island, with his herd growing to more than 500 head by 1846. The cattle were transported to San Francisco in boats owned and operated by William Richarsdon, who then owned most of the Marin peninsula and lived in Sausalito—the Place of the Little Willow Grove, as he had named it. Richardson's Bay still carries his name today. (This is the same Richardson who tried to send Sutter packing when he first arrived in San Francisco Bay.)

In 1840, Osio won his petition for the remaining Point Reyes land. It had taken three years, but it was worth the wait. He was awarded an additional 48,829 acres. This is over 78 square miles, or 200 square kilometers—twice the size of the Isle of Jersey in the UK, with a population of 90,000. It was slightly larger than Washington, DC with a population today of over half a million.

Unlike Berry, Osio moved his family to Point Reyes and continued to lead a respectable life, commuting some 150 miles to Monterey—sans train, plane or car! He served as a Justice of the Superior Court there from 1840 to 1845 and as a substitute congressman in 1843. He became a San Rafael judge in 1845.

Osio obviously had access to official records and knew "the law." It didn't take him long to discover the shenanigans of Garcia, Berry and Snook. Garcia was profiting more than $12 a month for overseeing Berry's property. Once his brother-in-law was settled in, Garcia moved onto Berry's property and built a house there, proudly naming it Rancho al Punta de Estero. Berry sidestepped this problem by running his cattle on Snook's property. Everything was working out fine until Osio bought the property from Snook and arrived to find Berry using the land.

Osio sued Berry in 1844 and won. (No surprise there.) The judge made the very logical recommendation that everyone should just move back to their own land. Wasn't this reasonable? But instead of displacing Garcia, Berry just gave that land to a friend, Stephen Smith, in return for some debts. Garcia remained on the land owned by Smith and everyone was happy. That was until the United States became the proud new owner of all of California, after defeating the Mexicans in the Mexican-American War. After Santa Ana's defeat at the famous Battle of the Alamo in San Antonio in 1836, the United States claimed Texas in 1845. The Mexican-American war lasted from 1846-1848 and resulted in that famous Treaty of Guadalupe Hidalgo, in which Mexico ceded the territories of Alta California (California) and Santa Fe de Nuevo Mexico (New Mexico).

Osio returned to Baja California, selling his land to a prominent geologist, politician and investor from San Francisco, Dr. Andrew Randall. Like Osio, Randall had served as customs inspector in Monterey, after he arrived in California in 1849 from Rhode Island. He also served as postmaster, won a seat in California's first legislature, and founded the California Academy of Sciences. In short, Randall brought a level of respectability to life on the whale's back or the coyote's snout, if you prefer. He hired a foreman and built a house for his wife and four children on his new land, although he rarely occupied it. He also bought the land that Berry had traded to Smith. Mind you, Smith had duly sold the land to a man named Bethuel Phelps for $15,000, who turned around and sold it to Randall for $150,000. Randall had to borrow the money, but it seemed a good investment at the time—as the refrain goes. By 1854, his 35,520 acre property was valued at $178, 365 including the land—at $2 an acre—buildings, wild and tame horses, cattle and sheep.

Unfortunately, making profit off of land is as addictive as blackjack or coke. Who would not be intoxicated by the heady fumes of profit filling the air in the mid-1850s? Andrew Randall went on to buy other huge tracts of land throughout California and lost his shirt when a financial depression swept the country. Now the *real* drama begins over the ownership of the Point Reyes land.

In 1844, ranchers on Point Reyes were asking the Mexican government to sort out the confusion created by those first transactions but any progress made by the Mexican government in this effort ended abruptly with the Treaty of Guadalupe Hidalgo.

In 1851, the United States passed a law requiring the grantees to prove ownership of their land. (You may recall that this is where Sutter's downfall began.) It was an expensive process. Rafael Garcia managed to provide the necessary proof of ownership, but in his typically cavalier fashion, he began selling it, contingent upon his receiving the title. By the time he had officially received that document, he had sold almost all of it off for less than $2 an acre.

Randall was even less fortunate. By the time Randall's ownership was made official in 1855, he was deeply in debt and facing legal action from his creditors. When Joseph Hetherington sued, Randall refused to answer the judge's questions, fled and as a result was cited for contempt of court. The matter was settled with great finality a year later in a San Francisco hotel when Hetherington approached Randall with a gun and shot him to death. Two days later he was hanged by the

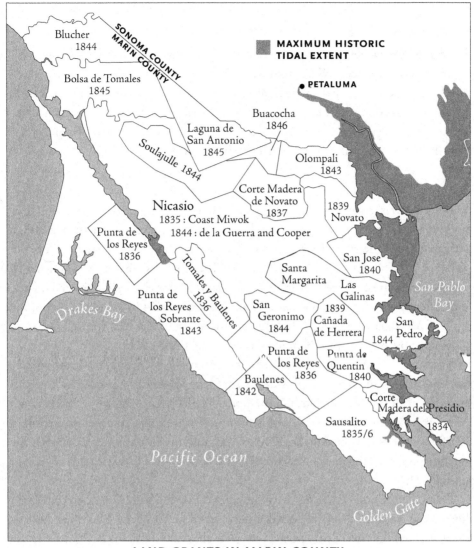

LAND GRANTS IN MARIN COUNTY
ADAPTED FROM ORIGINAL IN *CHIEF MARIN* BY BETTY GOERKE. HEYDAY BOOKS

city's Vigilance Committee (read there "citizen sanctioned vigilantes") before a cheering crowd. Life has never been dull in San Francisco.

Sadly, Randall's wife was pregnant with their fifth child and now saddled with a debt of $237,000 and several pending lawsuits. The land was foreclosed and sold. Multiple times, in fact, by the crafty local Marin County sheriff, G.N. Vischer. He sold the deed for the same property to three purchasers. Two other purchasers sued and won the same property through the courts. The Point Reyes Land Circus was thriving. There were now five legitimate owners of the same piece of land, all enriching the local sheriff.

It was one thing to discover the illegal theft. It was another thing to sort out the actual ownership in the courts. Four of them joined forces to hire a lawyer for that purpose but the fifth, Dr. Robert McMillan, was wealthy enough to hire a lawyer independently, and San Francisco's finest at that. This was his own lawyer from the firm of Shafter, Shafter, Park and Heydenfelt—Vermont lawyer Oscar Shafter. Yes, the man whom we left packing his suitcase and saying a poignant good-bye to his family, is now in place in San Francisco. He is a senior partner in the firm along with his brother James (hence the Shafter and Shafter added to the firm name). He is recognized as one of California's foremost title litigation experts. Not a bad job to have in those days. Now the stage is well and truly set and the denouement of the Point Reyes land drama can begin. The Shafters are here.

◆ ◆ ◆

No one was surprised that the courts found in favor of McMillan. They might have been more surprised to know that two months earlier McMillan had transferred the title of two-thirds of his Point Reyes land to the law firm in exchange for $50,000. Easy come, easy go. The Shafters' firm moved quickly to acquire as much of the rest of Point Reyes land as possible. They purchased the remainder of Randall's widow's land at an auction for $14,000 and the remaining third of McMillan's land for $20,000. The majority of the beautiful 75,000 acre peninsula now belonged to them for the sum total of $84,000.

The only land that remained out of their control was Garcia's. But time, money and legal know-how was on their side. In 1859, the Shafter firm proceeded to claim the original Berry ranch, including the portions of Garcia's land. The battle raged for six years and cost Garcia all of his money. It was finally resolved on February 21, 1866. Garcia died ten days later. There was now an exact boundary between the remaining Garcia land and the Shafter land: Olema Creek. His hacienda remained in Shafter hands.

Once again, a widow was left with the ruins of her husband's life. Loretta Garcia divided the remaining rancho between herself and her children. She came close to losing it when the sheriff threatened to take it all away to pay her $396 debt at the grocery store. In 1873, a young blacksmith named Ambrosio Correra approached the 60 year old Loretta and asked her to marry him. She might have been tempted, given her circumstances, but she was not interested in marrying the young man. An argument ensued and Correra shot Loretta in front of her adopted six-year old daughter. Correra tried to burn the house and then fled to a neighboring home where he confessed his crime and shot himself. At least this time it was over love and not land.

The Garcia children sold most of what little land they retained, some of it to the Shafters, at discount prices. The oldest son Juan worked as a butcher, wagon-master and bar-tender for Camp Taylor guests, but his weakness for gambling got the best of him and he died penniless. Son Felix was a constable and owned the Olema Saloon, which he lost when he got behind on the mortgage debt. He also died penniless. The other children died young or left the area. The empire of the first Point Reyes rancheros had come to an end. The Shafter Dairy Empire was about to begin.

THE SHAFTERS

THE SHAFTER EMPIRE

(from the California Milk Advisory Board)

. . . Brothers Oscar and James Shafter, prominent and energetic businessmen with keen foresight, developed Point Reyes to be the leading dairy region not only in California but in the entire West. Both brothers were prominent attorneys from Vermont before they moved to San Francisco. In 1857, during a twisted legal battle in which five men claimed ownership of Point Reyes, the Shafter legal team won the territory for their client, Dr. Robert McMillan. In return, McMillan sold the highly regarded property to the firm. In total, the Shafter brothers bought almost the entire peninsula for less than $85,000.

Oscar and James Shafter, along with Oscar's son-in-law, Charles Howard, promptly established their home ranch on the property (home of the present day Murphy Ranch) and wrote leases to the Steele, Laird, and other dairies already established on the territory. Howard became the most active member at the ranches, providing hands-on management of ranch construction and dairy operation.

The family resolved to keep the property together and pursue a tenant system. Each ranch was named a letter of the alphabet, starting at the tip of Point Reyes (A Ranch). Under Howard's stewardship, the dairies doubled in number. By 1870, Shafter-Howard owned 20 dairies with plans to add seven more from the ones previously leased. Typically, tenants leased the ranches from one to three years. The tenant rented the cows ($20-$25 per cow, annually), buildings and land, but provided their own home furnishings, dairy and farm implements, horses and pigs.

By 1866, the Point Reyes dairies led the field in production. Although the family experimented with producing cheese, they felt the land was better adapted to making butter. Consequently, they pursued their goal to produce the finest quality butter in great quantities for San Francisco.

Certainly, the market existed. Demand in the rapidly growing city was so great that the inferior butter from South America and the East Coast was still being imported. But this product was no comparison to the Point Reyes standards. As one contemporary journalist reported, ". . . the grass growing in the fields on Monday is the butter on the city tables on Sunday."

The Shafter and Howard ranches became famous as examples of well-organized, clean and successful dairies producing the highest quality products. In 1875, the Marin County Journal reported that the excellent quality of Point Reyes' butter resulted from the advantages of the peninsula's climate, "coupled with the evident enterprise and liberality of the owners of the land in improvements, and the wide-awake spirit of the tenants in efforts to out-vie each other in the quality of their products have given to the Point Reyes butter a most enviable reputation in the markets." No doubt, competition among the prospering farms existed. Many of the tenants immigrated from Sweden, Ireland, Germany, Switzerland and Portugal, each bringing their desire for success to the new territory.

At the height of the Shafter and Howard Empire, 31 dairy ranches were in operation. For each location, a reasonably flat site was chosen that was central to the grazing area and had a nearby spring to supply water for both the ranch house and the cows in the corral. Because it rarely rained, milking was done outdoors in a well-drained, central corral. Each milker took charge of a string of cows (between 20-25) and could milk them in two hours.

. . . By 1880, the demand for the Point Reyes butter was so great that dairies around the area were counterfeiting it. Empty Point Reyes butter boxes left by the commission merchants would be repacked with "common" butter and sold at a higher price. Upon learning this, Shafter and Howard trademarked their butter and stamped the letters P.R. on each package made at their ranches. This step to protect the quality and authenticity of their products may be one of the first forms of branding of a consumer product in California.

The Shafter and Howard families owned most of Point Reyes for 82 years, from 1857-1939. During that time, the operation of the ranches changed little, except for modernization in technology and transportation. The eventual sale of the ranches, between 1919 to 1939, was done in three transactions, ten years apart from each other. Most of the ranches were sold to tenants, resulting in increased prosperity and pride. Moreover, dairy production increased through herd improvements and physical modernization unhindered by a distant landlord. Indeed, a new way of life swept through the dairies at Point Reyes.

OSCAR

NEW ENGLAND ROOTS

JACK MASON MUSEUM COLLECTION

Oscar Lovell Shafter, ca. 1865

OSCAR SHAFTER IS LIKE ONE OF THOSE transition creatures of the Pleistocene who wakes up in a world of water and somewhere along the way finds itself moving in a completely different medium, as if it had been swept off to another planet. While this was a common experience for those who emigrated from Europe to America, or from the cultured East to the Wild West, Oscar was endowed with the gift of vividly recounting that experience in his letters. We can see a similarity to John Adams. Both are New England farmers, yet active in the affairs of their state. Both are devoted to their wives and families, faithfully writing long letters home when they are away. Each is caught up in the larger drama unfolding with the new nation. Oscar has the sensibility and reflective nature of Ralph Waldo Emerson, who is nearly his contemporary, born 16 years earlier. Yet Oscar's contributions to San Francisco and Point Reyes, for which he is most remembered, are both adventurous and practical.

We may remember that Oscar's grandfather, James Shafter, fought at the Battles of Bunker Hill, Bennington, and Saratoga, and did service on the Canadian frontier as well as serving as a member of the Vermont Legislature for twenty-five years. His son William Shafter, Oscar's father, was a member of the Vermont Constitutional Convention of 1836, County Judge for several years, and also a member of the State Legislature. William's wife Mary Lovell Shafter has been described as "a woman of superior mind and character, of majestic mien." She died when Oscar was fourteen, leaving behind a deep imprint on his heart and mind. Throughout his life, he could not speak of her without emotion. William, along with his political activities, was a hardworking New England farmer with a small tract of land on which he raised stock, cultivated a garden, and prepared his own supply of wood in the winter. William and Mary had seven children—two daughters and five sons—who lived to maturity. They no doubt each took their part in sharing the responsibilities of milking, tending the garden and caring for the stock.

Oscar Lovell Shafter, their first child, was born at Athens, Vermont on October 19, 1812. At any early age he expressed an interest in a college education, which his father opposed but his mother favored. She was persuasive enough that he was sent for preparatory studies to the Wilbraham Academy in Massachusetts. He graduated from Wesleyan University in Connecticut in 1834 and later entered Harvard Law School.

Oscar advanced rapidly in his profession. He practiced law in Wilmington, Vermont and was elected to the State Legislature. In spite of his own reluctance, he became the chosen candidate of the Liberty party for Member of Congress, Governor and United States senator, although he failed to win those elections. In 1840, Oscar married Sarah Riddle and they began their life together there in Wilmington and started their family. It is at this point that we will pick up Oscar and Sarah's story. I let Oscar tell it, because in doing so, he is telling the story of hundreds like him who will go West, not to mine gold but to build a city and a new life. He is our 19th century Petrarch, true to the epistolary tradition of Cicero and so many others who painted detailed and lasting portraits of their era in letters.

The first letters I have selected are written to his wife and children while he is serving away from home in other parts of the state. They give a clear picture of the life of his family, very much in the New England tradition. We see a man contented with what he has, not ambitious to travel or climb aggressively to high office after his involuntary candidacies. He imagines no other life than this one, and prays only for the continued health and flourishing of his wife and children. What lies ahead is something he never imagines.

Wilmington, Vermont ~ 1850

THE VERMONT FARMER-LAWYER

Wilmington, Vt., May 6, 1850.

My Dear Sister:

I have just returned from a long and laborious session of our County Court, and am now on this rainy yet still blessed Sabbath enjoying the endearments of my own family, the quiet of my own home. . . . I find that . . . the vitality which ebbs from the head floods invariably to the heart, and it is so now, in a greater degree than ever before. To this I can assign no other cause than your late letter to father, which I brought home with me and which I and Sarah have just finished reading in the hearing of our children. Emma, now in her eighth summer, understood and enjoyed it rarely. Mary (Laurette), who is half as old, listened very attentively and laughed repeatedly as though she was tickled, but on being asked the cause of her merriment, uniformly broke down in her attempts to give it. Hugh, who is now in his eleventh month, lay on his back in his mother's lap, with heels high in air, and if he didn't understand the letter, he at least added somewhat to the interest of the occasion. He is just the boy that I have been praying for these eight years past: straight in the back, deep in the chest, heavy in what he sits on, clear and full in his eye of blue-grey, with a head of the size of a half-grown pumpkin, but so formed and mounted as not to "ring hollow" under even the highest tests of phrenology. His hair is nut brown, like that of the uncle from whom he takes his name, and he is in short one of the best specimens of the gender that I have ever seen.

. . . What magic there is in names. "Hugh" is a word that used to be uttered in our hearing by our mother, dead long years ago. We uttered it ourselves as far back as we can either of us well remember. It was one of the home words in a family now disbanded and scattered. It is one of the oldest events that memory retains, that a brother answered to the name.

Well, years have elapsed since I uttered it in his hearing and he answered to it in mine. In the meantime I have founded a hearth of my own and have peopled it with wife and children. But they were all strangers to the old places—the old names—and the thousand and one old associations. The Michigander [his brother Hugh] was often talked of and talked about in our new circle, but neither he nor any one who bore his name had ever been talked to there. It had never been yelled out there by merry voices to one who owned the name —the responsive yell had not been heard there,—until a few short months since I applied the name to a little ten-pound immortal, in the hearing of my wife and children, as my father had done before me, to my babe's uncle, in the hearing of his wife, our mother, and of you and me, his children. And then, with a heart swelling with many old memories, I registered it in the Book. But now there is no name that I pronounce oftener than "Hugh"—none that I hear uttered half so often. And latterly it is answered to, and with a power of lungs that makes all ring again as of old. . . ..

May God in his mercy spare to you your children!

We came very near losing Emma this spring. She had a very sudden and violent attack of lung fever. I sent for Edminston; he saved her, and that was all. At the time Alice died, [a daughter previously lost] Mary would have gone, too, but for him.

I built me a house last summer on my farm of twenty-five acres, and am spending quite a portion of my earnings, as I have been for some years past, in improving and adorning... My professional business is good, and has grown more and more lucrative every year since I came to this place. At present I have all, and more even, than I can attend to personally. . . .

Tell Hugh that I have a very productive farm—a noble yoke of four-year-old oxen that would do his eyes good to see—a cow that makes 400 pounds of superb butter in a year —a colt of my own raising now three years old, worth $200 —a blood mare of great speed and power that is now with foal by the best horse in New England—a pair of Suffolk pigs for which I paid $25 at three months old, and a yardful of blooded hens;—but, over and above all, a boy at last, perfect in structure, rigged out with most remarkable appointments, hopeful in promise; and that we call him Hugh, in memory of his uncle and of the old times, places and thoughts with which his uncle is in my mind identified. . . .

Your aff. brother,
O. L. Shafter.

Many years later, it is Oscar's daughter Emma who will gather his letters and diary entries into a book. She writes an introduction to the next letter in the third person, although it was written to her as a child.

"In 1852 Mr. Shafter wrote the first letter addressed to one of his children—the beginning of a family correspondence faithfully carried on during each period of separation, and to which we are to be indebted not only for vivid pictures of the life about him, but for its unconscious portrayal of a wonderful human personality."

(Oscar L. Shafter to his daughter Emma.)

Newfane, Oct. 2, 1852.

My Dear Daughter:
This is the first letter, I believe, that I have ever written to you, but considering the character of my business, and the frequent and somewhat protracted absences from home which it occasions, it in all probability, if my life and yours are spared, will not be the last. I have just received your letter of yesterday's date; it is the first you have ever written me; but I hope a series will follow, relieving the exhaustion of professional labor, and strengthening a father's heart with the welcome proofs of his daughter's love.

I hope that little Maude will be able to walk when I return. Kiss her for her father, to encourage her in her efforts.

Tell your little brother from his father, that he will probably not see me coming up the walk for more than a week, but I shall come home as soon as the judges here tell me I can go. He must be a good boy, be kind to his sisters, and mind his mother, drink his milk without crying, and act like a man, so far as a small boy can be expected to. You must all of you jump every day, except little Maude, and hold your shoulders back whether you stand or sit. Tell Mary that she must read out of some book that she can understand, every day; if she does not, she will, I am afraid, forget all that she learned at school last summer. You are the oldest of the children and must be careful to set a good example before them. You must be kind to them and try to do them all the good you can. I hope you are making proficiency in your music, but remember that, after all, reading, writing and arithmetic and other branches of solid and useful learning are more important than the piano.

It is time that you commenced a systematic course of reading. I have bought a large library for the benefit of my children, and when I come I will select such books for you as I think it will be best for you to read.

. . . You must keep this, my first letter to you, for it will interest you perhaps in after life, when your father is no longer with you. The few mementoes of my mother that I have in my possession are more dear to me than rubies.

Be a good girl and write to me next week some time. Tell all the news, and particularly about the sick.

Your affectionate father,
O. L. Shafter.

THE ISTHMUS JOURNEY

There were three routes to California from the East Coast. A man could go across the continent, presumably on his own two feet if he had to. He could take a ship for the long, uncomfortable and dangerous voyage around Cape Horn, or he could make the "pleasant voyage to Panama, stroll across the fifty miles of Isthmus to the Pacific and, after another easy sea voyage, find himself in San Fransisco." So read the advertisements of the day. The trip wasn't quite like this . . .

— FESSENDEN NOTT OTIS
The History of the Panama Railroad

Emma: "MR. SHAFTER'S call to San Francisco, to join the great law firm of Halleck, Peachy, Billings & Park, in the capacity of an assistant, came in the year 1854. Although he had disdained high political preference, the monetary consideration offered (a salary of $10,000 per year), was too generous for a thrifty New Englander to ignore. It was for the sake of his family, and because this offered the chance to put them forever beyond the reach of want, through one year's work, that he closed with this engagement, which was to carry him so far away. The whole world is closely linked together in these days, but in the early eighteen-fifties, to reach California, by land or sea, involved a voyage far more perilous and uncertain, and almost as long in point of time, as it now requires to encircle the globe." What drew Oscar from the bosom of his family and set him upon such a treacherous journey into the unknown is the same impulse that will draw thousands of men out of small Mexican and Ticinesi villages; indeed villages throughout the world, even to this day.

The Panama Canal, which allowed ships to pass from the Atlantic to the Pacific across the Isthmus of Panama, was not completed until 1914. The rails of the "First Trans-continental Railroad" were not joined until 1869, when the ceremonial Last Spike was driven at Promontory Summit, Utah, after track was laid over a 1,756-mile (2,826-km) gap between Sacramento and Omaha, Nebraska/Council Bluffs, Iowa by the Union Pacific Railroad and Central Pacific Railroad. Before that time, there were three ways to reach California: 2500 miles overland, across the Rocky Mountains; sailing the 15,000 mile journey around Cape Horn at the tip of South America, which took three to six months; and through the Isthmus of Panama, 7,000 miles through the Panama jungle. All of these journeys were difficult, yet so many of our forebears made them, as did the early emigrants from Ticino.

The trail through Panama was wild country. The natives must have been very surprised when this deluge of white folk began trudging through their neighborhood. Many were quick to take advantage of the opportunity. But like every wild passage in the world, from the Silk Road to the caravan routes to Timbuktu, travelers were vulnerable, and ripe for the picking. Nevertheless, in the final seven years of the Gold Rush, 250,000 people made the Isthmus journey to California.

Several of those travelers have written about this passage, including Jessie Benton Fremont, wife of John C. Fremont, who made the trip with her daughter. But since we have already met Oscar Shafter and will be meeting him again, I turn to his descriptive prose to give us a portrait of what the first Ticinesi experienced before the cross-country railroad was built. We should remember that Oscar Shafter and Jessie Benton Fremont had the advantage of being more prosperous than many of the immigrants from Europe and of having been spared the rigors of a long voyage in the steerage compartment of a ship crossing the Atlantic. But that doesn't dim their courage and character in enduring the trials of this one.

Oscar writes his first letter to his wife when he arrives in New York City, ready to make that long and difficult journey that will bring so many people through the Golden Gate in the wake of the San Carlos, which had been the first European vessel to enter, less than a century before. How things have changed!

New York, Oct. 19, 1854.

Dear Sarah,

I sail to-morrow for Panama in the steamship North Star. She is one of the staunchest and finest sea-going steamers afloat. She was built by Cornelius Vanderbilt and is the same in which he made his recent pleasure trip to Europe, an affair about which so much was said in the newspapers. . . .

We land at Aspinwall* and go by Railroad 38 miles and then by mules 11 miles to Panama on the Pacific, thence by the steamer Golden Age to San Francisco. . . .

A new arrangement has been made in the steamboat lines to California. A steamer, and as I suppose, a mail, leaves weekly instead of once a fortnight as heretofore. There will be a mail leave here on the 29th, and by that mail either you or Emma or both must write. I shall receive the letter in one week after my arrival in California.

. . . Remember me to Grandpa and Grandma and give a father's love to all the dear children.

From your affectionate husband,

O. L. S.

Oct. 24, 1854. At Sea

Dear Sarah :

According to arrangement we left New York Friday the 20th at 2 o'clock P.M. precisely. . . . The vessel is unmoored, the signal guns are fired, and the stately craft moves slowly from the dock. . . .

The ship sets out on its southern course, which will take it between the islands of Cuba and San Domingo on what was called the "Windward Course," through very rough seas on the way to its first stop in Aspinwall.

The sea was very rough, and the vessel rolled and pitched badly. A large proportion of the passengers were afflicted with seasickness. I was not exempt from it, and what is more I didn't expect to be. I cast up my accounts in about an hour after coming on deck, ate nothing at all during the day, staid in my berth most of the time flat

* Colon, Panama

on my back with nothing to do but listen to the jar of the machinery, the creaking of the bulkheads and the roar of waters. At night I stript and went supperless to bed. . . . In the morning on coming on deck found that the wind had increased during the night and the tribulation of the waters was very considerably augmented. We were crossing the Gulf Stream, which on our line of travel was some 40 miles wide.

Five days later, about 400 miles off Charleston, South Carolina, Oscar recovers from his seasickness and is able to eat a little. He discovers that the butter is rancid, which is not a cheerful prospect so early in the trip. Through his eyes, we begin to see the experiences of other passengers aboard the ship.

It was too rancid for any civilized use except soap-boiling, so gave it up. Judging from appearances, the cargo of butter will not be materially lightened during the voyage. Slept well during the night, though the heat below deck begins to be somewhat oppressive.

Monday morning: . . . On coming on deck this morning I noticed a passenger, a German, chained to a stanchion. They said that he was delirious during the night and made proclamation that he was going to Panama by land. He was a young man, apparently about 25 years old, and looked quite respectable. They unchained him and took him down into the steerage. I soon after heard that he had been living on the Isthmus and was taken down with the Chagres fever. Last night he died, about dark. I slept up on deck, and at midnight the poor German was borne past us in silence by the crew, and without a tear or a prayer was launched from the stern of the vessel into the deep! . . .

Our 19th century reincarnation of Petrarch has prepared for this trip by buying a portable writing desk in New York that is large enough to hold his diary, "a half dozen quires of paper, inkstand, wafers etc" and seats himself by day in shady spot on deck. As the journey continues southward the heat increases.

I slept on deck last night, and a glorious night's rest I made of it, too, though I slept but very little. . . . Friends were sitting or standing in groups about the deck, talking in suppressed voices or silently communing with their own hearts and with the great sublimities of the heavens and the sea. The North Star and the constellation of the Great Dipper that revolves around it, are well down to the water, and the luminaries of another firmament are rising in the South. The vessel speeds on. The groups break up, one by one, and those that formed them retire to their berths, or, like me, camp on deck beneath the stars. The watch is set, and now all are asleep but me. I cannot sleep. I do not desire it. . . .

Quite a proportion of the passengers are women and children, and the larger proportion of the male passengers is made up of old Californians who are going back with their families. . . . There has been a good deal of seasickness among them, and some of the cases have been quite distressing. There is one little boy about seven years old who has been afflicted with the malady ever since we left New York, and with great severity. He has eaten nothing for days now, and is greatly debilitated. . . . His parents are seated beside him with faces filled with anxious solicitude.

There are wives aboard who are going unattended and alone to join their husbands in California. Some of them have children with them, and now that the seasickness is over with they seem to be as undaunted and chipper as the rest. There are three Catholic nuns aboard, and two Catholic priests. The nuns are called "Sisters of Charity," the order with which Evangeline connected herself after the conclusion of her wanderings, as you will remember.** The passengers are mostly young; scarcely one is past middle age. They are well dressed, and all demean themselves with propriety. I have seen no disorder as yet on board. . . .

Wednesday morning, Oct. 25.

. . . We have now accomplished about one half the distance to Aspinwall from New York. The little boy of whom I have before spoken is on deck again to-day, and the doctor says he is affected with intermittent fever. He is looking badly now,—almost deathly. It would indeed be a sad thing for the child's parents should he die, for he is all they have, and it would be doubly mournful should he die at sea, with the inevitable consequence of a watery grave.

. . . There are some very fine singers aboard, of whom, however, I am not one; but still a half dozen of us are singing, in the center of a large circle, songs of the sea and of the land, but more especially of the homes that we have left behind us. . . . Thus with song and jest and tale and sigh, and maybe now and then with an unbidden tear, night wears apace. It is now 10 o'clock. The mate has just pointed out to me the Island of Cuba to the west. I can see nothing however but a low black bank of cloud apparently skirting the horizon. To-morrow it will be out of sight.

The travelers reach Aspinwall at one a.m. in the morning of October 28th and are ferried in railroad cars to the "Summit." This begins the second and most challenging phase, overland across the wilds of Panama. The town—located in the republic of New Granada—has sprung into being as a result of the discovery of gold in California, reminding us again of the far-flung reverberations of the findings at Sutter's Mill.

At Sea, Nov. 1, 1854.

Aspinwall is a miserable hole. I stopt at the "St. Nicholas' . . ., [and] with a large number of other passengers, put our names on to its books. We called for breakfast. The landlord yelled to a half dozen of half naked natives, and they took their fishing tackle and made for the wharves. In about a half hour they returned with some 20 fish that would weigh perhaps a half pound apiece. Some very equivocal looking meat was procured from a butcher's stall over the way... I asked the landlord, who was a native as yellow as saffron and as greasy as a fried sausage, for some water to wash. He pointed to a back yard and out I went. The dining room opened directly into this said yard, and such a scene of brutal aboriginal filth as that yard exhibited I never witnessed before. It beat my hog yard all hollow. Broken bottles, decayed vegetables, fishes' heads and entrails, bones, and every description of rubbish and

---

* Oscar is referring to Longfellow's epic poem of that name. The heroine joins the Sisters of Mercy (not Sisters of Charity).

offal were collected there in cartloads, and then the daily rains and the burning suns had reduced the whole to a mass of the most loathsome and nauseating putridity. The noxious and revolting stench penetrated the dining room and every part of the house. But I washed, after a fashion, and after waiting a while we were summoned to breakfast.

. . . Then came the meat—they called it beefsteak. . . . I sliced off a fair-sized and as I supposed savory morsel, and swept it into my mouth with the voracity of a hungry pike. But that piece of meat I never swallowed. Immediately after taking it into my mouth I had occasion to rise suddenly from the table. By two or three rapid bounds I reached the back yard above named, and all I have to say is that when I returned I must have weighed less by a number of pounds. . . .

At 10 o'clock the train started, and by 5 P. M. we reached the "Summit." The distance is but 38 miles and you will see that our rate of travel must have been slow. The road is full of short curves, and the grade is generally very heavy, but when completed it will doubtless be the great thoroughfare between the Atlantic States and the Pacific until a railroad shall have been built across the continent to the North. . . .

The whole country is in a state of nature. . . . After leaving the seacoast it is wild, broken, and mountainous, and now, in the rainy season, is traversed by dashing, roaring brooks, tributaries of the Chagres River. And all these hills and the ravines and gullies between them are covered with a dense and gigantic vegetation far outrivalling, in size and in the depth of its green, the forest scenery of the North. Though unimproved, the country is not uninhabited. There are detached houses all along the line of the road... Four rude posts stuck in the ground forming a square, and the square covered with a roof of thatch, is the mode in which they are generally constructed. . . .

At the Summit the Railroad ended, and the rest of the journey to Panama, a distance of 11 miles, was to be performed on mules. When we left Aspinwall the expectation was that we should reach Panama that night; but on reaching the Summit we met the passengers from San Francisco by the steamer Golden Gate, who were bound for New York. They represented the road as being very bad. It was further currently reported that the banditti with which the road has been infested at times, had attacked, robbed and killed one of the passengers. These circumstances, together with the lateness of the hour, brought us at once to the conclusion to stop at the Summit over night, and the passengers by the Golden Gate were compelled to stay there also.

That night no one of the 1000 wayfarers that made up our number will ever forget. Fancy a clearing of say 25 acres in the midst of a dense tropical forest. In this clearing there are a half dozen native huts partially inclosed at the sides, and each hut is supplied with a bar at which every description of bad liquor is retailed at exorbitant prices. Each hut also spreads a table covered with stewed monkey, boiled mule, mouldy bread, and everything else almost that is revolting to the taste and stomach of a civilized man. There are no sleeping accommodations except what are afforded by the unlighted and unventilated cocklofts of these huts, but all together would not afford room for 200 persons to lie down. The clearing referred to, the rains and the tramping of men have turned into a great mortar-bed. At every step you go half-leg deep into the adhesive mud, and sometimes up to the knees and perhaps higher. And here are 1000 whites, men, women and children, gathered from the four winds and speaking in the dialects of half the civilized nations of the globe. There are perhaps, in addition to these, 1000 naked or half-naked natives of both sexes and of all ages and sizes, and they have in charge perhaps 1000 mules which they are seeking to hire out to us for the next day's journey to Panama.

. . . The business of eating was not completed till past midnight. The drinking did not stop at all. Such a scene of bacchanalian and brutal rioting I never witnessed before. The floors were covered with drunken men or with those who slept the perturbed and fitful sleep of exhaustion. The women and children were piled, one top of the other, in the lofts. As for myself, after eating a little boiled rice, I and my two friends started for a pile of boards which we discovered in a back yard. We smoothed and widened the top of the pile by repacking it, spread our blankets upon it, lay down and covered up, and if we didn't sleep much we rested quite comfortably, all things considered. We paid $1.50 for our supper, and those who lay on the floors in the huts had to pay $2 for the privilege. We cheated the landlord out of our lodging by camping out.

By 5 o'clock we were up and breakfasted upon a plumcake that Howe brought from home with him, and then we were employed for about two hours in selecting and pricing mules. In the end, after a deal of haggling and chaffering, we secured three as promising mules as were to be seen, then mounted, and took at once to the mule-path that led to Panama. At least 200 of the passengers had started before us, but we passed the larger portion of them . . . and arrived at Panama at 11:30 a.m. in fine spirits. We stopt at the Louisian Hotel.

We staid at Panama [City] until the next day, Tuesday the 31st of October. While there I busied myself in surveying the town and the country round about. There is very much in it to interest an untraveled New Englander. The city stands directly upon the seashore, and is surrounded by a wall built for the purposes of defense by the Spanish government a century and a half ago. These defenses are said to have cost $20,000,000, but are now greatly dilapidated by decay and neglect. The houses within the walls are all of stone and are apparently as ancient as the wall. Many of them are now in ruins, and those that are still inhabited are under the law of deterioration and decay. . . . Even the convents and the vast and magnificent cathedrals will soon be but disjointed piles of stone and mortar. . . .

On Tuesday, Oct. 31st, the passengers were embarked on board small boats and were carried in them to the steamer Golden Gate, lying at anchor about 4 miles from shore. The water was so shallow that the boats could not be brought within 3 or 4 rods of dry land, and the passengers were taken to the boats on the backs of the natives. Some of the passengers—and there were women in the number—dispensed with the services of the natives; some of them tumbled down in the surf and all of them got pretty thoroughly drenched with salt water. In a half hour we were all safely landed, however, on the deck of the Golden Gate. She is one of the most splendid steamships afloat, and notwithstanding the number of her passengers there is ample room for them all.

It is now Sunday, Nov 5th. We are about 1500 miles to the north of Panama, and in an hour or two shall drop anchor in the harbor of Acapulco, staying there about 24 hours to take on coal and water. We have so far had a most delightful voyage. This ocean has in our judgment earned anew its title to the name it bears. We have for the most of the time been within sight of shore and are now within a mile of it.

We have had religious services on board to-day, conducted by two Episcopal clergymen according to the forms of their church and attended by pretty much all on board. I shall seal up and dispatch this letter from Acapulco.

You must not infer, from the account I have given of my tribulations on the Isthmus, that I was very much disturbed by them, for in fact I was not disturbed or unsettled by them at all. I in fact enjoyed my ludicrous experiences there very much. It was very much like a trip into Texas a-fishing, only a good deal more so. A new country with its strange and gorgeous scenery, strange forms, naked or clothed in varied and outlandish costumes, a people whose manners and customs and entire social life were the opposites of all that I had been accustomed to, were enough to make me indifferent to muddy boots, a wet hide and an empty belly. . . .

From your affectionate husband,

O. L. Shafter.

The transformation of Oscar Shafter from New England gentleman farmer/lawyer into the rough and ready Point Reyes rancher has begun. He is discovering in himself a taste for adventure and wild places that might never have been revealed had he not received the letter of invitation to join the San Francisco firm. He is also showing his talent as a travel writer and keen observer as he treats us to an early portrait of the town that will become Mexico's premier tourist mecca—Acapulco.

At Sea, Nov. —, 1854.

Dear Sarah :

When I closed my last letter we were nearing the port of Acapulco. It was on Sunday the 5th of November, and we cast anchor about dark. The harbor is of great interest and of considerable commercial importance. The coast is rockbound and generally unindented with bays and inlets,—so much so, indeed, that Acapulco is the first port north of Panama, a distance of 2000 miles, where vessels can flee for refuge from the storms that sometimes sweep the Pacific. The entrance to the harbor is through a rent in the high mountain range that skirts the sea. The opening is not more than 15 or 20 rods wide, and leads into a port covering perhaps 1000 acres and surrounded on all sides by wild, precipitous mountains that rise to the clouds.

The town of Acapulco is built upon a little slip of comparatively level ground lying at the foot of these mountains and between them and the waters of the bay. The town is defended towards the sea by a fortress built upon a point of land to the south. It is built of stone and was erected by the Spanish government before the Revolution by which Mexico achieved its independence in 1820. We stopt at Acapulco for the purpose of taking in coal and water. All the coal consumed by the steamers on this coast is brought from the Atlantic States and around Cape Horn. There is a large supply of it at Acapulco, amounting I should think to many thousand tons. . . .

About 9 o'clock in the evening another death occurred on board. The man was from Arkansas and died from neglect and the Panama fever. He was taken on Thursday at the dinner table, grew worse rapidly and steadily, and died at the time above named, and there were none but strangers around him in his last moments. He was carried on to the hurricane deck, and in the morning about break of day his remains were sent ashore for interment. Such is life!

It was announced that the ship would sail at 8 o'clock, and at 6 a party of us started in a boat for the shore to deposit our letters with the American Consul and see the town. It is built very much in the style of architecture that prevails at the Isthmus, but the sides of the houses are generally closed up by a series of small poles lashed together and standing on end. We visited the market-place and found 100 to 200 Indian women squatted on their hams, busily engaged in selling chickens, yams, bread-fruit, bananas, red peppers, onions, etc. Their stocks were very small but their prices were very high. I notice the State to which Acapulco belongs is now in rebellion against the Mexican government under the leadership of Alvarado.

Santa Anna, the emperor of Mexico, has now a large force in the mountains to the East, which it is understood is marching or about to march to the attack of this city and the fortress by which it is defended.

After remaining awhile on shore we returned to the ship. The signal gun was fired at 8 o'clock and soon all those who had gone on shore were again on shipboard. At 11 o'clock the anchor was weighed and in a few moments we were out of the harbor and again afloat upon the open sea.

Wednesday, Nov. 8. From Acapulco so far the voyage has been delightful. A calm sea, mild and balmy breezes, the towering summits of the mountains in the distance, full moons at night floating in deep unfathomable blue, music, reading and pleasant discourse with very pleasant people, have relieved the voyage so far of its tedium; but still I shall be glad when it is ended. This morning we were in the latitude of Cape St. Lucas and now are over 100 miles to the north of it. We have already left the torrid zone behind us, with its burning days and glorious nights, and as hour by hour we progress farther and still farther to the North, the climate becomes more and more like that to which I have been accustomed. . . .

Thursday, Nov. 9. We are now about 1500 miles from San Francisco, but if nothing befalls us we shall arrive there on Monday or Tuesday next. . . .

This afternoon and immediately after dinner, on coming on deck a cry was raised by the steerage passengers of "A whale! A whale!" And sure enough, only a few rods from the vessel there was a veritable whale spouting and blowing and every now and then heaving half his diameter above the surface of the water. In a few moments three others were discovered, forming what the whalemen call a "school" . . . The sight of these monsters of the deep gave great satisfaction to the passengers, most of whom saw them for the first time. Ask Hugh if he would not have liked to have been with his father and seen the great whales which pleased the little boys and girls so much?

Friday, Nov. 10. It is now noon. The land is again in sight and it is only some 10 miles off. We have sailed 200 miles in the last 24 hours, and have fallen in with another school of whales more numerous than the other, and there is a large vessel some distance ahead and standing directly across our course, which is understood to be an American whaler.

Saturday, November 11. At noon to-day we were within 480 miles of San Francisco and the prospect now is that we shall arrive there Monday morning next. Though the voyage has been a pleasant one, yet no one will regret its conclusion.

* * * *

OSCAR SHAFTER ~ SAN FRANCISCO LAWYER

As we saw through the eyes of our excellent reporter, Bayard Taylor, San Francisco by 1853 was growing by leaps and bounds, changing itself from a wild western outpost into a real city. The sudden boom brought about by the Gold Rush reached its peak in that year and was followed by a depression in 1854. Still ahead lay the challenge to establish and enforce laws in a previously lawless region, particularly with regard to land ownership—the hopeless imbroglio that had developed from the time of Rafael Garcia. The Shafters were the major players in sorting this out and, as a result, became the major landowners, defining a new era on the Point Reyes Peninsula that would last for decades.

Oscar Shafter plays several roles for us here. His letters to his family are those of a keen observer of his city, at the center of its growth. They provide a first-hand account of what Point Reyes is like when the emigrants from Ticino begin to arrive. In a more personal vein, he also offers us a view of the trials suffered by men from Europe, Asia and the East Coast of America who left their families behind. Communication was often long delayed so that news of adversities back home and the death of loved ones arrived long after the event.

Again, the story that Oscar tells us through his letters is the story of countless people who made such journeys. Yes, even back to Odysseus, struggling to return to Ithaca where his wife and son are faithfully waiting.

Wednesday, Nov. 15, 1854

Dear Sarah,

I am in San Francisco safe and sound and without having experienced an alarm even on the passage. We arrived here on Monday the 13th at 5 o'clock P. M., having been on the way 23 days and 15 hours from New York, one of the shortest, and I believe they say the shortest passage on record. . . .

The goal is reached. I feel as though I was commencing life anew and that all the probationary steps to success had to be taken over again. During the 2 or 3 days I have been here I have been introduced to a great many of the leading men in the city by the politeness of the gentlemen connected with the firm. There is an immense bustle, an incalculable hurrying to and fro in the streets. It surpasses belief almost the wonderful changes that have been wrought here in a few years on the face of the earth, and like changes are now actively in progress on all sides. The population is about 60,000 already, and it is made up of emigrants from all nations. There are a great many Chinese in the State and in the city, and with their half shaven heads, long queues hanging down to their heels and outlandish dresses, they present an exceedingly whimsical appearance to newcomers. But the controlling element in the population is the Yankee. He by his energy and intelligence subordinates everything to himself and impresses upon everything his own image.

I am very anxious to hear from you, and shall be much chagrined if the boat that will arrive here on the 22nd does not bring a letter from you or my dear little daughter Emma. You must not allow a mail to leave without sending me a letter. Has Mary got along with her writing so that she can put in a word to her father ? Perhaps she understands writing enough to put in an entire letter. As for Hugh, he for a year or two longer cannot be expected to make much more than his mark, I suppose... and remember his father, who in the meantime will not forget any of you or forget to love you.

From your affectionate husband,

    O.L.S.

Next, we see through Oscar's eyes the changes that have taken place in a mere seven years since the census of 1847 when the population of Yerba Buena/San Francisco was 459 people. The population has skyrocketed to 60,000, and the people are very different from those that Sutter met on his arrival. Yet we are also seeing how the energy and industry of that original population laid the foundation of a dynamic city.*

San Francisco, Nov. 23, 1854.

Dear Sarah:

The steamer leaves here day after to-morrow for the Isthmus. There is no regular mail however, but mindful of my promise, the spirit of which was to write you by every opportunity of so doing, I shall send this to New York by express.

. . . As I told you in my last I am boarding with Mr. Park. . . . My daily routine is already fully established and is as follows: I get up at half past seven in the morning, breakfast at 8; then go to work, spending the day at the office or in court; at 5 o'clock we have dinner; then return to the office, remain there until half past 11, and then go home and go to bed. When home, at dinner, Mrs. Park and myself and John take a bout at the piano, singing the songs we used to sing in the dear land from which we all came. I find the exercise a great relief, not only in the perplexities incident necessarily to my position in a country whose laws I am obliged to rapidly master, but a relief for the sadness induced by absence from those I love. . . .

I am full of pluck and full of hope as I can hold, and determined to avail myself of all the facilities I enjoy for accomplishing the ends for which alone I came. The firm is very wealthy and is doing an immense business—the largest in the city and the largest in the State.

. . . This is a strange city, filled with a strange population. Seven times has the city been laid in ashes by fire, and now it has a population of 60,000 souls, the majority of whom live in princes' houses and do business in shops and warehouses of which the oldest and most populous city might well be proud. The male portion of the population are men in the prime of life; there are no old men, no cripples and no idlers, for none but the vigorous and active would come to this remote country. It would not do for any others to come.

* According to statistics reported by the Secretary of State to the California Legislature in 1853, the population of San Francisco in 1852, which at that time included San Mateo County, was about 36,000 people, and about 19,000 foreign residents.

There is a great deal of frankness and cordiality among the citizens and denizens in their intercourse with each other, and the energy and speed with which they do things is a marvel. I have been introduced to a great many since I have been here and have not yet met the first man who did not display singular intelligence in discourse, and not one who was not a keen and rapid thinker, and precise and rapid talker. . . . The women are beginning to come, wives and daughters, and the old settlers all say that they bring blessings with them. Churches have been built and several are now in process of erection. Sabbath schools have been founded, homes have been established, and numberless other local changes have taken place within the last year or two which the old residents attribute to the advent of women among them. I never was in a city where more importance was attached to dress, never indeed, where there was half so much importance attached to it among men. All the business men are clad in the richest materials, made in the latest styles, and in their personal habits they are fastidiously neat. I have been told by those who know that an ill-dressed man is little likely to succeed in business, whatever his business may be.

The women appear in the streets clad in the most costly apparel. Montgomery Street in this respect outshines Broadway even. Silks of the richest fabric and the most expensive pattern are uniformly worn in the streets. This is a city of dust emphatically, and this may account for the fact above named, as silk is less affected by dust than woolen would be and the climate is altogether too varied for cotton.

There is a great deal of galloping to and fro on horseback; this habit the conquerors have learned from the conquered. The Mexicans all but live in the saddle, and there are no finer saddle horses in the world than here. The mountainous character of the country, and the fact that the roads are generally bad, explain why traveling on horseback is the favorite mode of locomotion.

Your affectionate husband,

O. L. Shafter.

In spite of the distance he has traveled, the new world he has entered and the heavy burden of his work, Oscar remains an attentive father, still deeply attached to his family. His thoughts are still on his return within the year.

Oscar L. Shafter to his daughter Emma.

San Francisco, Dec. 5, 1854.

My Dear Daughter:

. . Your letter interested me very much, and the few lines added by your mother were very, very welcome. I read it over repeatedly and ever with increasing interest. Then the little boy not only remembers his father, but dreams about him and cries on his account when he wakes? Well, I came very near crying myself when I read it, but tell the dear little fellow that he must keep up a stout heart, and before a great many moons his father will come home and put an end at once to his tears and his dreams. Mary you say is as "fliety" (flighty) as ever. Well, I trust she will grow less and less so as she grows older. Little girls cannot be expected to have so much control of their limbs as those that are older, and I doubt not that in her case sobriety and

all desirable decorum of manner will come with years. I am glad that she has made so much improvement in writing, and hope that by frequent practice in writing to her father, she will retain and improve upon what she has already learned.

I am much pleased to hear that Hugh intends to learn all he can this winter. . . . I have no doubt but he will very soon get so that he can read anything, and will be able even to write long letters to his father, who loves him and all of you so much.

I trust that you do not fail to write in your Diary every night before going to bed. . . . I hope further that your resolutions to learn all you can this winter are as strong as Hugh's at least. He is a little boy and may forget his good resolutions or fail to act upon them, but you are of an age now to bear constantly in mind your good resolves, forgetting them not for a moment even, and of an age to carry them into effect with unfailing and unflagging constancy and perseverance.

Then little Alice has got so that she can laugh when she is tickled? I am glad to hear that she knows more than when I left. If she is as bright a baby as I believe her to be, she will very soon be able to do not only her share of the laughing, but her part of the tickling also. She will be a great delight to you all as she grows, and it will be a great delight to me to hear of all the little proofs she shall give from day to day that she has got the root of the matter in her. I devoutly hope, with the rest of you, that this little Alice will live, and that by one of those blessed illusions by which the hearts of the sorrowing and stricken are so often visited and comforted, her lost sisters of the same name will in her be again restored to us. When the babe has got along far enough, you must tell her about her father and teach her to lisp his name.

And now good bye. Love to Mary, Hugh and the baby and to your dear mother. . . .

O. L. SHAFTER.

San Francisco, Dec. 14, 1854.

My Dear Wife :

. . . To my little son I am sending a paper filled with pictures, and that it may appear more fully that it is intended for him, I have directed it to him. . . . The next time I write, I shall write to him, I think. How would he like to have a great long letter from his father? Will he keep it, and keep it always? . . . And the first letter that my son shall write me will be ever preserved in remembrance of him. I carry that pincushion the girls gave me in my vestpocket; the pins are not all gone yet, and I intend that some of them, at least, shall recross the Isthmus with me. I take it out half a dozen times a day for the purpose merely of looking at Hugh's jacket on one side of it. It does me quite as much good as it does to look at his daguerreotype, and the entire article is associated further in my mind with the affectionate regard and filial forethought of my little girls.* . . .

And now, good bye. In a week I shall speak to you again. Kiss the dear children all round on my account, and give my warm regards to father and mother and Mr. D. How are things in the pig-pen and at the barn ?

From your affectionate husband,

O. L. SHAFTER.

* One side of this little pocket pincushion was covered with a scrap of the cloth from which a jacket was made which he was accustomed to see on the little boy.

A Letter to Little Hugh.

San Francisco, Dec. 18, 1854.

My Dear Son:

When I wrote by the last steamer to your Mother, I told her that by the next mail I should write to you, and I am now about to do as I promised. I find it the more pleasant to talk to you in this way, for the reason that there are no little boys here for me to play with or talk to. I think there are not many boys here, or if there are, their mothers keep them at home, I must believe, for but very few indeed are seen in the streets.

The men who have left their homes and come out to this far off country, have left their little children behind them to do chores and look after things in their absence. But I have no doubt but that they often think about them day and night, and want very much to see them. . . .

I sent you a paper by the last mail filled full of all sorts of pictures showing how people earn their bread by digging gold way back among the mountains. The men who dig the gold are called miners, and when they get their pockets filled with gold, they come down to this city and sell it to men here who are called bankers, who give them money for it; and then the good miners send their money home to their wives and children, and the wicked miners go off and spend their money in gambling and for rum. . . . By studying those pictures you will get a very good idea of how the miners live and carry on their business. I hope you will keep the paper very carefully until I come home. . . .

Well, my letter is most done,—the first I ever wrote to you; but if I live and have the use of my fingers it shall not be the last. When you get to be a little older, you will answer my letters, and oh! how much I shall be pleased to receive them, particularly the first one. You must keep this letter. It is not very interesting, I know, but then it is my first to you. Put it in your drawer and keep it, and when you have another from me, put it with the other, and so on, and you soon will have a great pile of them perhaps, and when you get to be a man, and your father is no longer with you, you will consider them as a great treasure to you, for the reason that they were written by him.

Give my love to your sisters and tell them I want to see them. I often look at your pictures. Do you ever look at mine? I have no doubt you do, if it isn't so very handsome. Kiss your mother for

Your affectionate father,

O.L. Shafter

San Francisco ~ 1855

LOSS

May God in his mercy spare to you your children!

THE SENTENCE ABOVE WAS WRITTEN BY OSCAR to his brother Hugh in Michigan, while Oscar was still in Vermont. He might have been writing in anticipation of this moment in April 1855. In 1850, for every thousand births in the United States, the infant mortality number averaged 216. Compare that to the year 2000 when that average was 5.7.* The suffering of families was greatly increased when they were separated, as Oscar and his family were.

Oscar and his wife have endured something all too common in their time, the death in infancy of two daughters, both of which they named Alice, according to a New England tradition. This third daughter, Alice, was less than three months old on Oscar's departure. As Emma observes in her comment on the next letter, Oscar is having an exceptionally prescient moment here, as her reply to him shows. Oscar had not received her letter when he wrote this one.

San Francisco, Feb. 14, 1855.

My Dear Wife:

The steamer has not arrived, and is now overdue. The mail will leave day after tomorrow, and with my customary foresight in the matter of writing to you by every mail, I have concluded to begin now, for fear if I should wait longer I might in the end be too late.

. . . How is the baby? A few nights since, as I was reading a beautiful poem of Edgar A. Poe's, I came across a passage of exceeding beauty and pathetic beyond measure, which in the twinkling of an eye brought the baby's little namesakes before me, that are slumbering in the churchyard. Time was forgotten, distance was transcended, and the grave yielded up for a moment the cherished dead. The little girls were again with me. I saw them as they were in life, except as they came to me together, and were clothed with the brighter radiance of heaven. The heart almost stood still as with closed eyes and suspended breath I dwelt upon and delayed the grateful illusion. But it tarried not long. The dream was soon over, and the painful reality of wasting and bitter bereavement was again present with me.

How is my son, and my elder daughters? I ask you though I shall get the answers before you will get the question. How is it with them? How is it? There is great emphasis in my thought as I put this question, too great to be expressed by any signs or symbols that I can make with my pen. Tell them to be and to continue to be kind and good to each other, to their mother and to all. Remember and write by every mail. Tell the children and believe yourself that my heart is with them and you.

Ever your affectionate husband,

---

* The toll was much greater for black families. In 1850, the infant mortality rate averaged 340 out of 1000 children born. In 2000, the average was 14.1.

O. L. Shafter.

Wilmington, Vt, Feb. 13, 1855.

My Dear Father:

Our little Allie is dead. What a change in a few days! Mother went down to the (photographer's) saloon and had her photograph taken the day she was buried. The funeral was here, at our house. The coffin was placed on the centre table, as was (Alice) Maudy's, and the sofa was where it was then. And we sat upon it with Grandpa and Grandma Riddle. Grandpa and Grandma Shafter were here, with Uncle Hall and his wife. It was hard to part with her. Father, it would have been a comfort for us and for you, too, to have been here. But, Father, we did everything that could be done for her. Hugh came up to her when she was laying cold and stiff, and said, see her little bare arms. This miniature is very natural, and looks exactly as she did when she was asleep. It will be a great comfort to you. We hope it will not get lost, for we shall want to see it again. Mother and I are going to write you a long letter by the next mail, she says.

Good bye, Father.

From your affectionate Daughter,

EMMA L. SHAFTER.

San Francisco, Feb. 19, 1855.

My Dear Wife :

From the Presidio in company with a friend I struck off toward the "Lone Mountain Cemetery." . . . After a smart walk of about a mile, we arrived on the ground. It is among the sand hills that have been formed by the action of the winds. The sand has all been borne from the beach upon which it has been thrown by the sea in vast quantities for ages and ages past, and under the mastery of the winds it has been thrown into a system of hillocks and hills that I cannot describe better than by applying to them the term billow. They are generally covered with a low chaparral of scrub oaks so dense as to be all but impenetrable and about as high as one's shoulder. Through the chaparral paths have been opened in all directions, and when lots have been taken the brush has been removed, leaving a few only of the more comely trees by way of ornament. The number of interments so far has been quite limited. The Cemetery, indeed, was not opened for them until about 6 months ago, but the great congregation destined to slumber in its bosom has already begun to be gathered, and the living here are already preparing the sepulchres in which they are at last to lie down.

. . . The Lone Mountain, a high, isolated peak, bounds the Cemetery on the south, and adds to the prevailing barrenness and solitude the impressive contribution of its own peculiar desolation.

From the Cemetery we went about three miles in a southeast direction to the Old Mission. I went into the old church, built of sun-dried brick, about 75 years ago. The construction is very inartificial and so is the finish, outside and in. There are a great many pictures on the walls, and though some have much merit as works of art, yet they generally were prepared to please the uninstructed taste of the native Indians.

The decorations of the High Altar were obviously selected and arranged with entire reference to the same purpose. There is a paling running across the church, dividing the Altar from the main body of the building and separating the worshipers from the officiating priests. When I went in there was a Sabbath School in progress. Two classes were reciting, or rather being taught orally to say the "Lord's Prayer." . . .

From the sombre old church I strayed out into the Catholic burying ground adjoining. There is about an acre in the enclosure; it is a graveyard in a flower garden. I never saw anything so beautiful. There was little of storied marble, there were but few traces of the sculptor's art to be seen; the monuments were almost all of wood, but tastefully fashioned, and neatly painted and lettered in half the languages of the globe. . . . While I was there a lady dressed in black came into the yard unattended. With a hurried step she sought a little grave, surrounded with a white paling and covered with a profusion of flowers. She knelt beside the grave and wept as though her heart were breaking. To me the bereaved mother stood revealed. Her sorrow was too hallowed for a stranger to gaze upon, and with moistened eye I turned and left the spot. A half hour's omnibus ride brought me back again to the City, refreshed and invigorated by my ramble.

This letter of Oscar's shows more uncanny prescience, as if he were seeing his own wife. Emma's letter had not yet arrived. It will take close to a month for Oscar to finally receive the news. And it may have taken nearly as long for his reply to reach the family. How difficult it must be for the family at home to go through such terrible loss without the support and comfort of husband and father.

San Francisco, March 17, 1855.

My Dear Wife :

This morning on coming to the office I found letters on my table, and a parcel which I was satisfied was a daguerreotype. I commenced with that—opened the case, laying aside the accompanying letter—and beheld my wife and babe. For 10 or 15 minutes I sat steadily contemplating the picture—the thought never occurred to me but that the babe was sleeping, and as I gazed upon the infant and my heart swelled high with a father's pride and a father's joy, and again as I noticed her likeness to the loved and lost, my heart failed me at the recollection of past bereavement, and trembled with fear lest it should be again renewed, in the future. But I turned at length to the letter. The first line—"our little Alice is dead"—told me by sharp and sudden revelation that the pride was but a mockery, the joy but a delusion, (and that the thing feared had already occurred). You have placed her beside her sisters. . . . The intelligence unmanned me for the moment and wrung me with a grief aggravated doubtless by the mood of mind in which I turned to Emma's letter, and yet more by my isolation here. . . .

We have three children left. May God in his mercy spare them to our affections and our hopes, and enable us to rear them in His nurture and admonition. . . . I am under circumstances where I cannot stop to mourn. The luxury of grief is an indulgence from which a stern and unforgiving necessity debars me. I must meet

*what is upon me and before me, how greatly soever the heart may be burdened,
and I am resolved to do it. . .*

*Give my regards to all, but especially to all those who are kind and good to you.
From your affectionate husband,*

O. L. SHAFTER.

In late 1853–1854, San Francisco became the victim of its own success, much
as happened with the successes of our own tech industry in recent times when the
"bubble" burst. The clipper ship vastly expanded trade with its speed and ships were
arriving with more merchandise than could be handled without a drop in prices.
Bankruptcies followed and the high rents charged for San Francisco's new fireproof
buildings could no longer be afforded. The crisis reached its peak in February 1855,
when Oscar writes of this in his diary and then in a letter to his wife in March.*

Diary
February 9, 1855

*There is great stagnation in business here; trade is dull; laborers are here
in numbers but they are more numerous than jobs; the rate of interest is high;
taxes are exorbitant; immigration has pretty much ceased and the rainy season is
emphatically dry. In consequence, the business of gold-washing in the mountains
is brought completely to a stand, real estate is depreciating rapidly, but is still high
enough to allow the good work of depreciation to go on for a long time to come.
Improvidence and unbounded prodigality in public and private life have hitherto
been the order of the day in commercial circles, and among businessmen generally
I understand that the work of retrenchment and reform has been commenced, and
the good old maxims of industry and frugality are coming into vogue, but those who
tabernacle in and around Montgomery Block live and spend and waste like little
archdukes. The time may come when even they will lavish less gold on their backs
and bellies.*

March 22, 1855

My Dear Wife :

*. . . I wrote to you in my last to the effect that I had made up my mind to stay
here longer than a year. I meant by that however nothing more than that such was
my then present purpose. I intend on that question to hold myself in the hollow of
my own hand so long as practicable, and it is not at all impossible or improbable
even that I shall in the end determine to return. If at the end of my year I can invest
my funds so as to be perfectly secure and at an eligible rate of interest, it will be
an inducement for me to tarry no longer. But there is so much of dishonesty and
dishonor here in every lane of life that there is serious risk in trusting any one. The
hard times have induced the exposure of much that has heretofore been successfully*

---

* Oscar writes a remarkably detailed and insightful description of the various events,
conditions and practices that brought on this crisis in a letter to E. Gorham Jr. in Emma's
book, *Life, diary and letters of Oscar Lovell Shafter*, p. 99, available online.

concealed, and have driven and are driving many, very many, to every description of venality and crime. The whole framework of society, the entire organization of things here, is distasteful to me. I am not homesick. I am in no wise discontented, nor am I affected with any regrets for having come here, except that I was away when my child died. . . .

Tell my little son that his father often thinks of him and often looks at his picture in which he is represented as sitting in a high chair between his sisters Emma and Mary. He and they must keep their feet dry, throw back their shoulders, sit up straight, and try every day to see which can outrun and outjump the other.

And now good bye. I shall write by the next mail.

O. L. Shafter.

The final blow falls. The invention of the telegraph by Samuel Morse and the first steps toward a Western Union company that are being taken in my own home town of Rochester, New York* make possible more rapid communications from the East Coast, although the Intercontinental Telegraph line doesn't open up until 1861. It is not only good news that travels swiftly but also news of tragedy.

San Francisco, April 12, 1855.

My Dear Wife :

There are two left for us to love and live for, and there are five dead for whom we must ever mourn. Oh Life! Oh my heart! Two hours ago a telegraphic dispatch was laid on my table. I tore it open and learned that our son was dead.

There is hardly any measure of calamity that could have fallen on me with such weight. I was stunned and dizzied by the awful blow, and for the last two hours have lived long years of common woe. He was my joy, my pride, my hope. From the hour of his birth my whole future has been filled with him, my plans have all had reference to him and have all centred in him. . . . He was all that parental fondness could desire in an only son.

I was far away from him when he died! I came here not for myself but for him and his sisters. It was a great grief for me to leave them, but I hoped and trusted that I should advance them, and above all, that whatever of evil fortune I should myself encounter, that I should be permitted to see them all again. Two of them I shall see no more! How often have I pictured to myself the hour of my return—my children—my son! (I cannot name his name) coming forth to meet me. . . . My boy, my boy is dead! Would that I could have died for him! I try to master my sorrow—to resist the tide of feeling that overwhelms me. But I cannot. . . .

. . . God bless you, and my dear children that remain.

Your affectionate husband,

O. L. Shafter.

✳ ✳ ✳ ✳

* Hiram Sibley, in Rochester, teams up with Samuel Morse to develop a telegraphic service out of Morse's invention. It begins as a collection of small companies, which will have a continental reach as Western Union in 1861. Sibley was its first president.

THE GREAT BAY THROUGH OSCAR'S EYES

OSCAR IS NOW TRIPLY BURDENED BY THE ABSENCE OF HIS FAMILY, the loss of two of his children, and the heavy demands of his work. These will take their toll, yet his growing love for this new world and his impulse to observe and chronicle it are not quelled. He continues with his reporter's eye to reveal the land and the history that are swiftly unfolding around him.

San Francisco, March 26, 1855.

My Dear Wife :

Last Saturday Mr. Billings told me that he was afraid I should hurt myself with hard work, and was so considerate as to ask me to take a jaunt with him into the country. At 5 o'clock his horses were at the door, and in two hours from that time we were 23 miles distant from the City, to the south at San Mateo, a point of land that juts out into the bay of San Francisco.

The day was devoted to music, reading and wandering. This AM we left at 7AM and at 9PM were again in town. Before this jaunt, I knew very little about the country from actual observation, but still a great deal had been told me of its wonderful fertility and beauty. I am now abundantly satisfied that there has been no misstatement.

The great feature in the landscape scenery here is the rare combination of all the elements of beauty and grandeur and sublimity which everywhere surround you. Take the country that I traversed on the trip above named as a sample. To the left was the Bay of San Francisco, running about 40 miles to the south of the City and having an average breadth of perhaps 10 miles, and its face was as calm and unruffled as a mirror.

On the opposite side of the Bay and at a distance of 3 or 4 miles from its western shore, there is a range of wild, rugged mountains, rising sheer from a fertile plain that extends from their base to the waters of the Bay, and on one side the formation is substantially the same with this exception: Along the base of the black, jagged Sierra, and parallel with it, there are low ranges called the "foothills." They are easy of ascent, smooth and round as the head of a monk, arable to their summits, covered with grass of a most luxuriant green, and then sink gently down to the level of the magnificent plain that stretches away to the waters of the Bay.

These hills and the plain are a perfect parterre of flowers. The sun went down and the wonderful valley was filled with the soft and mellow twilight. The air was as mild and balmy as the breath of Araby. Thousands of horses and cattle were spread out on the plain and the foothills. There were few or no fences to limit the freedom of their range or to show that the all-grasping Yankee had supplanted the Mexican Ranchero in the land.

The plain and the hillsides were dotted here and there with oaks whose dark green foliage contrasted most happily with the lighter hue of the sward. As we whirled on to the south, we every now and then passed the openings of transverse valleys that penetrated deep into the body of the Sierra. Into one of these valleys we strayed the next day; it is called the Canada. There are perhaps a thousand acres, filled with cattle, watered by a beautiful arroyo (brook) abounding with salmon trout, surrounded with hills of the true Titan breed, and the bottom lands of the valley are as rich as a garden. It is a place in which to live, die, and be buried. This is indeed, a glorious country !

In the end when the lawlessness and crime that now mar and dishonor it shall have passed away and the reign of order and of a passable righteousness shall have been established, it will be a land which its native born will never leave for any other that the sun shines on. But now, society here and the beings that constitute it, constantly remind one that man and nature are at war. We had a very pleasant trip indeed, and the change of scene, relaxation and exercise, brisk as it was, have done me a great deal of good after my exhaustive labors.

Before returning I hope to travel through the State pretty thoroughly. There is a fall of water in the Northern part which is reported to be 910 feet in height and there are two mountains rising directly from the plain to the height of 17,000 feet above the level of the sea. Then there is the Valley of Santa Rosa which is said to far exceed in fertility and beauty the one which I have described.

I shall see them all before I start for home.

The weather is delightful, and the earth has added marvelously to its beauty by the vesture of flowers in which it has arrayed itself. Business is painfully dull in all the departments except the Law; in that there is no want of activity. The great proportion of the work is done by four firms, of which this house is one. The suspension of the banks and private failures have added greatly to the current business, and all the business of this firm is now done by me alone with such incidental aid as I can get out of the clerks.

I am oppressed almost with the severity of my labors here, but there is no escape and so I submit to it. I have no time to write to you except what I steal from sleep. Most of my letters are written after 11 o'clock at night, but I would write after 4 in the morning before I would allow a mail to leave without carrying you a letter.

From your most affectionate husband,

O. L. Shafter.

In the following letter, Oscar gives his first impressions of Oakland, which will later become the site of his family's home and then his daughter Emma's home when she marries and has children of her own. He is obviously still preoccupied with the loss of his children.

San Francisco, April 30, 1855.

My Dear Wife:

Yesterday I went with a friend to Oakland on the opposite side of the bay. There are thousands of acres of level land there and exceedingly fertile, lying between the bay and the mountains, and it is covered with ancient and gigantic oaks standing from 40 to 60 feet apart, and the sward beneath is covered with a luxuriant growth of grass and flowers. Among these trees the town is built. Every variety of fruit and flower, including many tropical exotics, grow here in the greatest perfection, and as to the climate, it is an unending June. Children here do not die young—at least *rarely. The lady with whom I board told me yesterday that their children were very often sick before they came to this country, but that since their arrival, now some three years, no one of them has been unwell even. . . .*

Ambition with me is quite extinct. There are certain economical results which I think it important to secure, and then my professional career will end. The rest of life will be spent at home in that only companionship which I value, the companionship of my wife and remaining children. Give to the little girls their father's love. Tell them to remember the advice and directions I have heretofore given them and among other things not to be forgotten, tell them not to forget to write to me.

Your affectionate husband,

O. L. Shafter.

Diary.
December 22, 1854.

The true life is the life of the heart. The head is nothing, its ambitions, its achievements even, bring no abiding content; their highest successes are in this behalf but barren victories whose proudest trophies soon cease to minister even to the pride of him who won them. True enjoyment in this, as in the future life, consists alone in the indulgences of pure and chastened affection.

California was not immune to the growing division between the North and the South, which would soon erupt into the Civil War. Oscar declares for the North (not surprisingly) and a "free progressive spirit" for the state.

San Francisco, Jan'y 30, 1855.

Dear Father

. . . California will not be divided, nor will slavery be introduced. There are many who desire it, many who have not ceased to scheme for it and to labor for it, but the die is cast, the tide begins already to turn. Southern men and Southern ideas begin to wane. Sensible men begin to know and feel that the State has nothing to hope from the South, and at last comprehend that its good will be best subserved by bringing it into harmony with the liberal policy and free progressive spirit of the North. In 25 years, if no ill betide, the "primitive age" through which all new communities have to pass, will have fully transpired as to California, and then, if there is a terrestrial paradise on the face of the globe, it will be found here. Then a higher civilization with all its attendant refinements and humanities will have fully set in. All the air is balm. The land was made for delights. It is a land of mountains, and their auguries are always of good, and it enjoys all the accidents of a perfect clime.

Write. Your son,

O. L. SHAFTER

San Francisco, Feb. 14, 1855.

Mr. E. Gorham Jr.,
Wilmington, VT

My Dear Sir:

. . . The future of this State, I mean the great future, is unmistakable: but for some years to come, the State has got to suffer, and severely too, for the consequences of its own undue precocity. Everything has been overdone that relates to superstructure, and everything has been neglected that relates to foundation. The result is that the State is topheavy. Its cities are too numerous and too large. There are too many merchants for the miners, too many consumers for the producers.

Immigration has pretty much ceased, and with this the increased rates of fare from New York have had much to do. In the heedlessness of the earlier time, matters of general concern were sadly neglected, and the upshot of that was that all public officers were defaulters or the public revenues, where they were not stolen outright, were deplorably wasted and misapplied, and now every city is weighed down with its public debt, and the State even reels and staggers under its burthens. Its current expenses even are not defrayed now otherwise than by promises to pay in the shape of warrants on the Treasury, and they are hawked about to brokers at a discount of 30%. Real estate in this city continues to depreciate, and those having much foresight predict that it will continue to do so for some time to come. A great deal of property still held at high prices is entirely unproductive to its owners, and with the enormous taxes and the high rates of interest is fast eating itself up. When the lowest point of depression has been reached and the tide begins to turn, great fortunes will again be made in an hour by those who are lucky enough to take the tide as it begins to flood.

There is a great deal of want and suffering here,—I mean in the city,—for lack of employment, and among those, too, who never knew what it was to have a wish ungratified before they left their homes in the East. Some instances of that kind have come to my notice of a most touching character. There is a great deal of frankness and cordiality in social intercourse here, and friend spends money upon his friend as freely as he would spend it upon himself, but this is after all a mere surface appearance. There was never a community where self exalted its horn so much in fact as it does here. Men talk with their fellows in the streets but for a purpose; they bow and shake hands and laugh and smile, but ever with reference to a project, and he who should conclude that it was the result of a feeling of cordiality in exuberance, would in my judgment be very much mistaken. It is all the result of refined calculation relating to personal gain or personal advancement as unerringly as the needle relates to the pole. . . .

OSCAR L. SHAFTER

Around the end of April of the following year, Oscar writes a letter to his father that portrays the dizzying heights to which the affairs of San Francisco, and Oscar's legal practice, have reached. We can see him caught up in the velocity of the city's growth and mushrooming prosperity. We also see the challenges faced by a new nation as it addresses issues of international law. One such case of the time involved a Russian ship, the Sitka, taken by the British as a prize of war during the Crimean War being waged at the time.

[Letter to his father in Vermont.]
Ca. April-May 1855

Dear Father,

. . . I have nothing to occupy my attention but business, and I have been at it since and including the day of my arrival, at the rate of 15 hours a day on an average. The amounts in controversy here are told by "ten thousands"—"hundred thousands"—and "millions," and the questions involved are many of them of great interest and difficulty. I went right to work when I reached the office, to inform myself about all that was peculiar to the local law; it took me but a short time to do that. . . . There is an incalculable amount of litigation in prospect as well as in progress, and going by Atlantic standards, the rates of professional compensation are perfectly fabulous. $1,000, $5,000, $20,000 retainers are of frequent occurrence in the transactions of the firm with which I am connected. Park has told me, without solicitation, that I can come into the firm as soon as Halleck, who is no lawyer, retires; that he will do so, he thinks, in 6 months. Peachy is vastly rich,—above business,—engineering for the U. S. Senate, and will probably withdraw before long. At any rate at the end of the year I shall come into the firm, or demand and receive a compensation that will be in some proper proportion to the amounts received by the members of the firm. . . .

About a fortnight since the "Sitka" was brought in here by a British cruiser as prize of war. . . . As soon as I heard of it, I was given to understand that the firm would be employed by the British Consul, and that I must take charge of the question. The writ was served, but the subordinate officer in charge of the prize was dunce enough to be up with his anchor and put to sea. He ought to have kept his anchors down in justice to his own government, and have boldly challenged and defied the local jurisdiction. . . .

In the changes in the firm that are in prospect I have little doubt I shall find the opportunity that I am awaiting for Jim.* He is a better lawyer, a better talker, and a stronger and more available man than any one belonging to the firm, and they are all of them quite respectable, and Park is very smart and efficient,—more so than all the rest put together. I'll have Jim here in a year or two at the outside.

Your son,

O. L. SHAFTER

* His brother, James McMillan Shafter.

We can see in Oscar the germ of a thought to move his family into a healthier environment as well as his growing need to have them near him for emotional comfort. His daughter Emma is now twelve years old, and the letter she writes to him in April may have influenced his final decision to bring his family West.

Wilmington, Vt, April 12, 1855.

My Beloved Father:

. . . We were very much surprised that you have made up your mind to stay longer than one year. We have been counting the weeks and months that you have been gone, as they rolled along, and looked forward to the close of the few more months, and then you would be home. It does not seem as though we could stay here without you another winter. It will be so very lonesome. It seems as much as we could bear to stay through the summer, now little Hughy has left us. Oh! it seems so lonesome. For my part I wish we could go where you are, or you come where we are. It has been an unusually severe winter here; we have all had throat difficulties more or less all the time. The air is very changeable, snow and then rain, and we suppose that is what brings on the throat ails.

Mother has thought, since your last letter came, of going on to San Francisco, but does not want to go contrary to your advice. . . . For two or three mornings past Mary and I have taken our little and well-worn sled up in the orchard and slid way down. Hughy wanted mother to get him a new sled this winter, but he thought [decided] he had rather she would get him a wagon, for the baby. The poor little boy—he little thought then that he would not have a little sister to draw, or that when summer came he would be lying by the side of her in the churchyard. Yes, too true, they are lying side by side in the churchyard. . . .

I would like to know what you are doing now. You do not know how lonesome we are. There were five of us when you went away, and now there are only three. It seems too much like dividing the Spirit, to have you there and us here. . . .

Accept a mine, and a mine, and a mine of love from all of us.

From your affectionate daughter, Emma

In the following letter, Oscar gives his first impressions of Oakland, which will later become the site of his family's home and then his daughter Emma's home when she marries and has children of her own. He is obviously still preoccupied with the loss of his children.

San Francisco, April 30, 1855.

My Dear Wife:

Yesterday I went with a friend to Oakland on the opposite side of the bay. There are thousands of acres of level land there and exceedingly fertile, lying between the bay and the mountains, and it is covered with ancient and gigantic oaks standing from 40 to 60 feet apart, and the sward beneath is covered with a luxuriant growth of grass and flowers. Among these trees the town is built. Every variety of fruit and flower, including many tropical exotics, grow here in the greatest perfection, and as to the climate, it is an unending June. Children here do not die young—at least *rarely. The lady with whom I board told me yesterday that their children were very often sick before they came to this country, but that since their arrival, now some three years, no one of them has been unwell even. . . .*

Ambition with me is quite extinct. There are certain economical results which I think it important to secure, and then my professional career will end. The rest of life will be spent at home in that only companionship which I value, the companionship of my wife and remaining children. Give to the little girls their father's love. Tell them to remember the advice and directions I have heretofore given them and among other things not to be forgotten, tell them not to forget to write to me.

Your affectionate husband,

O. L. SHAFTER.

* * * *

San Francisco ~ 1856

FAMILY REUNION AND JAMES

IN THE END, IT WAS DECIDED THAT OSCAR WOULD STAY and that the family would join him. It doesn't come as a surprise, after reading of his growing attachment to the place and his developing fortunes on Point Reyes. He also succeeded in luring his brother James and later, his brother William, who will manage Point Reyes ranches.

Oscar L. Shafter to his Father.
San Francisco, Jan'y 1, 1856

DEAR FATHER: You have already been advised of the safe arrival of James and my family. James is boarding at the "Brannan House," and I, with the residue of the immigrants, am stopping with Park. We have very comfortable quarters, and are in all respects very pleasantly located. . . .

Jim "struck out" boldly on his first arrival. I was in court in a few days after his advent, and found him on his legs, spinning a yarn with admirable point and most marvelous volubility. I can see that his partner is very much pleased with him, though he has as yet said nothing to me on the subject. Mastick has all along been doing a capital business, and under Jim's leadership I have no doubt at all but their business will improve. He seems to be very much pleased with his condition and prospects.

With his typical prescience, Oscar writes to his father in the spring of 1856 to predict a shift in the state from mining to agriculture as the dominant industry.

San Francisco, April 4, 1856.

Dear Father:

. . . This is rapidly becoming an agricultural state and is destined to be a permanence in agriculture as marked as in the business of gold-mining. Already the importation of provisions is pretty much ended and the period is not very remote

when the products of our soil will be found in half the markets of the world.

Free soil* is beginning at length to exalt its cause in California. A paper has been established in this city which advocates that doctrine, and with great boldness and power. I gave the paper $100 the other day to help it over a sand bar on which it was in danger of grounding.

The Whig party is annihilated. It is without leaders and without organization and has all but forgotten its traditions and name. The Democratic party is hopelessly divided and is utterly demoralized. The better portion of its membership is deeply imbued with Republican opinions and there is here as elsewhere a half developed conviction among the politicians of the Democratic school, that the days of the Democratic party as now modeled and directed, are numbered. This notion I doubt not will be with them a great aid to virtue.

Jim is with us as you know, and his services are greatly commended by us all. Our business is still at high flood. My own function will hereafter be confined in the main to looking after questions of law in the District Courts and to cases in the Supreme Court. The jury business will be divided up between Williams, Park, and Jim.

The children are attending school and seem to enjoy themselves greatly. Sarah is well, and on the whole is, or at least maintains that she is, greatly pleased with life in California. . . .

Give my love to mother. We read her letter with great satisfaction and shall hope to hear from her and you often.

From your son,

O. L. SHAFTER.

Dear Father:

. . . I have just hired a house at $55 per month for one year. It is new and not quite complete, but we shall be in it in a week. Jim will board with us, I think. We are getting on very prosperously and hope we shall be able to return before a very great while. . . .

From your son,

O. L. Shafter.

California has now been a state of the union for six years and the increasing flow of people from East to West increases the transcontinental ties. The country as a whole is already feeling divisions over the slavery question and California has an increasing role to play in the national debate. The candidacy of John C. Fremont for president in 1856 is a tangible example of this transformation.

Fremont was one of the first to lead expeditions west along the Oregon Trail and the Sierra Nevada, employing Kit Carson as his guide. On his last expedition, he was seeking a trail across the mountains for a future railroad. Fremont was the first American to see Lake Tahoe. As a member of the Corps of Topographical Engineers, his maps and accounts of the west were critical in paving the way for

---

* The Free Soil party arose in New York State as a third party in the 1852 and 1856 elections. They objected to slavery, not on moral grounds of the Abolitionists, but on its threat to the dignity of labor and, in its extreme version, a threat to jobs.

future settlers. One of his reports would inspire Mormons to investigate Utah as a possible site for their future home.

Fremont was married to an exceptional woman, Jessie Benton, who was the daughter of Senator Thomas Benton, the chief voice for the Manifest Destiny policy. The couple would eventually settle in California. Fremont was one of the state's first senators and then the Republican presidential candidate under the party's Free Soil campaign for Free Farms over Slave Power, as they put it. This pointed up the regional differences between the homesteading farmers of the West and the Plantations of the South, which depended on their slave labor. Although Fremont was a controversial character, particularly for his military activities, he became a convenient rallying point for many Californians, including Oscar Shafter.

San Francisco historian John Ralston gave me some interesting insight into the Committee of Vigilance ("Vigilantes"), which Oscar described, founded in 1851. "It would appear that at the height of their influence in 1856, they had about 3,000 members—at least that is what the Sheriff told James Casey in jail when the Vigilantes aimed a cannon at the jail and demanded Casey, whom they later tried and hanged along with a gambler named Charles Cora, (whose case was not nearly so clear-cut). The 'contribution to security' depends on whom you asked; some citizens were bitterly anti-Vigilante, but on balance the Vigilantes probably did what they had to."

Oscar L. Shafter to his Father.
July 20, 1856.

Dear Father:

We had a great ratification meeting last night, and endorsed Fremont and Dayton, and the platform to the full. I have strong hopes that the Republican Ticket will carry the State. The railroad question will have immense influence. The people of this state have dwelt upon the subject of an Atlantic and Pacific Railroad until it has become a kind of mania with them. It is universally understood that nothing whatever is to be hoped from the Democratic Party, and that everything is to be feared from it so far as the Railroad is concerned.

The slavery question also presents itself with growing prominence to the California mind. The Northern Immigrants are an immense majority, and on the somewhat modified phases which the slavery issue now presents, their views and resolves are in entire harmony with those of their brethren in the East. Leading Democrats are crying out at last all over the State, "off with shackles," and the rank and file shout, "Amen." The great resurrection of the patriotic and the just, which prophet tongues have predicted for so many weary years, is being realized at last. Glory to God in the Highest, peace on earth and good will towards men. . . .

From your son,

O. L. SHAFTER.

San Francisco, Sept. 1, 1856.

Dear Father:

. . . The Fremont fever is on the increase here, and will soon be quite incurable. The State Convention has just adjourned. The meeting was numerously attended by the bone and sinew and was very enthusiastic. The nominations are very judicious and are made from a class of men who have hitherto stood aloof from politics. With proper effort the State can be carried for Fremont beyond doubt, and the indications are that there will be no lack of effort to accomplish that result.

The Vigilance Committee have adjourned but not disbanded. They have yet their organization, their arms and their Alarm Bell. Jim and I have stood aloof from the "Revolution" on principle, not being by any means persuaded that a case for civil war was presented. But the palliations of the outbreak are numerous, strong and manifest, and I think very likely that permanent good will result from it.

From your son,
O. L. SHAFTER.

✳ ✳ ✳ ✳

SAN FRANCISCO ~ 1858–1863

In a letter to his father in March 1858, Oscar gives us a rich portrait of the growth and maturing of San Francisco, from a wild and lawless place to the beginnings of a world-class city—"the Paris of the West." As we will see, Oscar and his brother James play no small part in this development. Here he gives expression to the experiences of thousands of immigrants, then and now, who come for a year and stay for a life.

San Francisco, March 20, 1858.

Dear Father:

I have now been in California three and one-half years, and in looking back it seems sometimes as though I had been here but a day, and again as though I had been here an age. I do not know how much longer I shall stay. There is not one man in ten in all California that has made up his mind definitely, in my judgment, to make it his permanent home; still I am equally well convinced that an immense majority of our population will never know any other.

Men come here, leaving their families behind them, and with an honest intention to return after a short tarrying. They engage in business, their business gradually extends and becomes more and more complicated with the business of others. They invest in real estate, and they are not ready to leave. They send for their wives and children, they come, a house is rented or bought. If bought, then a flower garden is started, a new house erected, a few fruit trees planted by the wall, young

Californians are in due time born to expectant sires, a circle of acquaintances,...has in the meantime been steadily extending, congratulates you upon the happy event. Long before this you have taken a pew in the Church to benefit your children and save yourself from the suspicion of having emigrated from some heathen clime; you have become interested in the welfare of that all-prevailing institution, the contribution box; you have a troublesome misgiving that if you were to leave the country the Genii of the box might pursue you as a fugitive from high social duty.

In short you have gradually and insensibly become identified with the people among whom you have been living, and your interests have become interwoven with theirs. You have at last, in spite of yourself, learned to think, and at last to say, "Were it not for the graves of the dead, and the love I bear the few that survive, all idea of return would be abandoned forever." But you have yourself passed through all these mental experiences, I apprehend, and therefore understand them

San Francisco is now, I believe, the best ordered city in the Union; its municipal affairs are administered with as much care, prudence and economy, as those of any New England town. The spirit of violence and disorder has not only been rebuked, but effectually quelled. A new class of men has come into notice, and attained to positions of influence and authority. The "chivalry," as we call the half-educated, inefficient, swaggering scions of the plantations, have in this city been unhorsed, and were it not for the patronage doled out to them from Washington they would have to take to the highway, to the poorhouse, or starve. It is here, in short, as it has been everywhere, where Northern and Southern men have met (outside of Congress) in the competitions and struggles of real life, the one nerved and armed by the whole course of early discipline, the other unfitted for the strife by the same cause.

Your son,

O. L. SHAFTER

OSCAR SHAFTER ~ POINT REYES RANCHER

By 1857, the Shafter legal team had entered into that convoluted legal battle in which five men claimed ownership of Point Reyes. It is here that we converge with our previous stories and lay the groundwork for those to follow.

The Shafters won the territory for their client, Dr. Robert McMillan. In return, McMillan had sold the highly regarded property to the firm. In total, the Shafter brothers bought almost the entire peninsula for less than $85,000.

In the following letters, Oscar gives us a detailed picture of what life was like on Point Reyes in the mid-nineteenth century: It was still the Wild West in ways, but under the new owners, it was undergoing the transition to a major ranching enterprise. We have a first-hand account of what was required, both in legal and livestock transactions, to make Point Reyes a model of agricultural success.

It is hard to believe that this is the man who wrote to his sister in 1850 that he had built a home on 25 acres and was content with his farm; the proud owner of "a noble yoke of four-year-old oxen, a cow that makes 400 pounds of superb butter in a year —a colt of my own raising now three years old, worth $200 —a blood mare of great speed and power that is now with foal by the best horse in New England—a pair of Suffolk pigs for which I paid $25 at three months old, and a yardful of blooded hens." He expressed no ambitions beyond his life at that time.

What a difference seven years brought.

San Francisco, Feb. 17, 1857.

Dear Father:

. . . Jim, Park, myself and two others have recently become the owners of the best cattle ranch in the State, containing about 50,000 acres. . . . You will readily find it on the map. It is situated on the "Punta de los Reyes," a peninsula jutting out into the Pacific just to the north of San Francisco. It is within three hours' sail of the City. The sea fogs keep up the feed the year round and as you will perceive, it is fenced by the Ocean. Jim and I went over there about a month since and are entirely satisfied with our investment. We are having some litigation about the title but have no doubt as to the result. Judge Heydenfeldt, who recently retired from the Supreme Bench, is one of the gentlemen associated with us in the operation. We were over at the Point about a week on the occasion referred to and had great sport among the ducks and wild geese. Their number is told by hundreds of thousands and there is little for the sportsman to do but load and fire. Corruption and venality continue to be the order of the day in high places but there is a public sentiment gradually forming, which before long will find expression. . . .

From your affectionate son,

O. L. Shafter.

(EMMA: This letter written to his Father, bears no date, but, from its context, is contemporaneous with the Frazer River excitement.*)

---

* Emma is referring to the discovery of gold in the Frazer Canyon of British Columbia, which set off another gold rush in 1858, which ended around 1860.

San Francisco,

Dear Father:

The State is now in a perfect commotion caused by the discovery of a new El Dorado at the North. What will be the upshot of the furor time will determine. Some 18,000 men have left the State during the last month and the cry is still "they go." It is settled to the satisfaction of the most incredulous that there is gold on Frazer River, but in what quantities remains to be determined. We expect a heavy immigration from the East and from Europe in consequence of this new allurement. I have written to Genl. Kellogg by the steamer of to-day.

We are in full possession of Point Reyes Ranch. We have put sheep that cost $2000 onto it, have let portions of it and shall probably let the remainder of it before long. We are about investing $4000 more in stock to be added to the sheep. Jim leaves to-day to attend a term of court in an adjacent county. We remain in good health and are bound to see the old country again. Don't work more than is good for your health, I pray you. From mother's letter to Julia I fear that you are too ambitious

From your son,

O.L.S.

San Francisco, Sept. 19, 1858.

Dear Father And Mother:

Three weeks ago I left town on a business trip to our Point Reyes Ranch and have just returned. It may perhaps interest you if I were to give you an account of my trip.

A steamer took me from the city to Point San Quentin where the State Prison is located. This point is on the Bay of San Pablo about 15 miles from town toward Sacramento . . . There are about 500 prisoners at the Point, engaged principally in brick making. The warden informs me that the number is steadily increasing. The convicts work in a valley outside of the prison walls and under the auspices of cannon loaded with grape and canister.

From the Point to San Rafael, a distance of about three miles, we were carried in a covered wagon drawn by four California mustangs. We have two saddle horses with a full set of accoutrements at San Rafael. I found one of the two in the stable looking very much as though he had been drawn through a knot hole.

The day before I arrived had been an election day, and this horse had been used incontinently by an enthusiastic acquaintance in hunting —voters. I sent accordingly for the other horse that was about three miles off at pasture, and started early the next morning on my further travel . . . The horse was a milk-white Indian pony, small, a little lazy but plucky. All of his appointments were according to the style of the country,—Mexican saddle, bridle, lariat and saddle bags. I sported a white hat that couldn't be jammed, a white woolen coat bought at a slopshop, buckskin pants and Mexican spurs on my heels that would weigh the better part of a pound each. After settling myself fairly in the saddle, the word was given and enforced by a slight touch of the spur and I was off.

The animal struck at once into the country gallop and on we went at that pace up the valleys and over the "divides" through a succession of gulches and canyons to the foot of Tomales Bay, a distance of 16 miles. I was now on our Berry Ranch of 8 square leagues [about 55 square miles]. The rest of the day was spent in riding round on this ranch, visiting points upon it that I had not seen before.

The next morning I hired the son of old Mexican ranchers to guide me over the mountains that separate the Berry from the Point Reyes Ranch, to the camp of a herdsman who with our license had established himself on a secluded part of the latter Ranch among the spurs that lead from the mountains referred to and at right angles with them, down to the shore of the ocean. There was a driving wind from the sea. The whole country round about was enveloped in a fog so dense that the eye could not penetrate it more than a dozen rods. For about two miles there was a clearly defined trail, but when we broke over the ridge it branched off into any number of cattle paths neither of which appeared more plausible than the others. The guide admitted on close questioning that he had never been to the camp but maintained that he was familiar with "the ground."

After we had beat about at a smart pace for about an hour we heard the bleating of sheep and following the sound we in a few moments were at the hut of the Nomad. It was in a deep black canyon, well protected from the ocean winds, but what had chiefly induced this Cossack of the Pacific to pitch his tent at that particular spot was a spring that afforded an ample supply of water for his family and herds. He was there with his wife and four daughters and all were employed in looking after his cattle and sheep.

That business is done chiefly on horseback. The cattle, left to themselves, are inclined to keep together, and the horsemen divide them into bands and keep them on separate ranges during the day. At night a signal is given by a yell or a blast on a horn and the cattle at once all start for the corral, where they are secure for the night from the attacks of bears and California lions. The above was the daily routine of my Tartar friend.

After finishing my business we started back, and a wild scamper we made of it. The young Mexicano undertook to show off his horsemanship and give me a telling specimen of the mad riding of his people. Running horses uphill is not unknown at home, but riding down hill at an angle of something like 45 degrees on a sharp gallop and along the edge of precipices at the same rate is not customary there. . . .

Regardless of peril and mindful only of the honor of my country I kept the nose of my mustang within about two feet of the hind quarters of the horse of my Mexican acquaintance until we drew rein at the place where we started out in the morning. The next day I arrived at the principal Ranch house on the Point Reyes, taking with me a man whom we had employed as a shepherd to look after our sheep. The next day I and the man took down a house and shed and for four days thereafter were employed in moving the material a distance of about five miles. Then we went to work and put up the buildings. They are to be occupied by the shepherd and stand on a part of the Ranch which we have reserved for sheep.

The sheep have improved greatly since we took them over there. We have leased some 20,000 or 25,000 acres to five different men. They are all of them men of capital,—sober, industrious, enterprising, and have their families with them. We have been somewhat choice in the matter of character in selecting from the numerous applicants for land, and have given the tenants good and encouraging contracts, deeming that the best policy in the long run. The ranch is undoubtedly the best grazing ranch in the State, and is now very valuable and will become immensely so in time. I was over there about a fortnight longer than I expected to be when I left home. My linen came short, and I was compelled to make a shift by turning a dirty shirt inside out; had I been compelled to stay a week longer I might have been obliged to make another shift by turning that shirt the other end up.

I witnessed an interesting spectacle while I was there. Some men who have some 400 wild horses pasturing on the ranch, held their annual marking of colts. They employed 3 Indian vaqueros or horsemen. The first step was to drive the animals, say 100 at a time, into the corral. The next step was to lasso the colts. This the Indians did from the saddle, throwing the riata on the jump and with all the precision of a rifle bullet. While one threw his riata over the colt's head, another would catch him by the hind leg while at full speed, and by skilful twitching the colt would be speedily thrown, and then followed the branding. The exhibitions of the circus are nothing to the displays of horsemanship that are witnessed every day on the California ranches. But the time came for leaving, and I left greatly invigorated in mind and body by my two weeks' labor, and arrived at home two days ago, the dirtiest specimen of humanity that has been seen in San Francisco since the memorable year 1849. I found my family all well. The baby did not know me, but she recovered the lost idea, however, without much difficulty. . . .

The news of the laying of the Atlantic cable was brought the other day by the steamer Sonora and was received with great rejoicings. It is doubtless the greatest news the globe has heard since it was announced that to "Castile and Aragon Columbus has given a new world."

But I must bring this long and somewhat rambling letter to a close

Write often.

From your son,

O. L. SHAFTER.

San Francisco, Oct. 19, 1858.

Dear Father:

. . . In our ranch suit we not only recovered the land but $4500 for the rents and profits. On the 31st of May last the sheriff put us in possession of the ranch and also levied on 400 head of cattle for the payment of the judgment belonging to G. P. Richards, one of the defendants. Last Saturday Jim and I went over to attend the sale. We were advised that Weller, the postmaster here and brother of the Governor, claimed to own the stock by a conveyance from Richards, made, we believe, with the design to defeat the collection of our judgment. We made up our minds to sell an undivided half of the cattle only and bought it accordingly at the rate of $15 for a half of each head. We had five Spaniards mounted on horseback to take possession of the animals as they were struck off to us, and when the sale ended we started them at once for Point Reyes, 30 miles distant.

It was a wild scene indeed. Such riding you never see or hear of in the East. The feats of the circus are tame in comparison. The vaqueros were everywhere at once—ahead—on either flank—in the rear, and all through the drove at the same time, now chasing a fugitive cow or calf down a hill on the keen jump at an angle of 45 degrees, fetching the beast up with the lasso thrown over the head, and then spearing the captious buck up the hill into the drove,—yelling, laughing, flying,—on they go again with the bellowing drove.

Weller will sue us for damages, I suppose. If he should we shall try hard to beat him; if he beats us we shall have the cattle wherewith to pay him and then shall get our execution renewed against Richards. In about a month a suit will be tried between us and Richards in which we claim further damages for the use of the Ranch after the other suit was brought; this use runs through an interval of 13 months, and we expect to recover $13,000.

About two months since a man brought an action against us for the purpose of collecting a mortgage on our Ranch of $25,000 given by the person under whom we claim and before the conveyance to us. The case has been recently determined in our favor. It will go to the Supreme Court, but we have no fears as to the result. We have two or three other suits on our hands involving some odds and ends of controversy of no great amount anyway. Our success in the principal suit has stirred up the rupacity of about half of the San Francisco bar and they are hawking at the property like so many kites, but we don't fear them and so far have routed them at all points. The title is impregnable in our judgment.

We are all well. I often wish that you and mother were out here where we could minister to you in your age. Could I have my most earnest wish gratified it would be so. Property here has taken a start in consequence of the Atlantic Cable and the Overland mail. It comes and goes twice a week and the last time beat the steamer from N. Y. by 48 hours. The people here are half frantic with joy. We feel nearer to our old homes, and a large immigration across the plains the coming year is a matter now of absolute certainty.

Our business is good and we do not neglect it in consequence of the ranching operations, either. Our home experience in agricultural operations stands us greatly instead. Jim and I have sole charge of the property.

Love to Mother and Mary and her children.

Your son,

O. L. SHAFTER.

One of the important things the Shafters did on Point Reyes was introduce new and fine breeds of cattle and sheep. As we can see from Oscar's next letter, this was a costly investment that only well-to-do ranchers like the Shafters could afford.

San Francisco, Dec. 19, 1859.

Dear Father:

Park arrived here by the steamer of the 5th inst. He brought two bulls, one a roan Durham 2 years old and full blood,—the other 9 months old, also pure Durham, color red and white. He brought also 4 pure French merino rams 7 months old. The animals all arrived in first rate condition. We kept them in the city a number of days on exhibition. A great many went to see them, and the bulls are admitted on all hands to be the best ever brought to this State. The bulls and sheep cost us here about $1400. We were offered for the youngest bull alone $1500, and we declined to take it. Jim has gone with the animals to the Ranch; he will be back in a day or two. About a month since we bought 400 ewes for the Ranch. The purchase was made in the vicinity of the city at a cost of $2000. We chartered a steamer to take them across the bay, and not having been out of the city for about six months, I concluded to go with them in person to the Ranch, about 40 miles distant by a route I had never before traveled.

At the end of the first day's drive and about dusk, we came across a little run of water which no amount of urging could induce the sheep to cross. Jo, the assistant I had with me, worked at them until dark, when we gave it up and pushed on for a night's lodging to a farmhouse about two miles further on and situated directly on the ocean. After a smart canter of 10 or 15 minutes we arrived at the Ranch, where we were very hospitably received. . . . In the morning we started out bright and early in pursuit. There were two gulches coming down from the Coast Range to the shore of the Ocean, which we had to cross to get on to the ground where the sheep were left, and down each of these gulches a miniature Mississippi was pouring like a mill race. Our horses however carried us across safely. We then scattered, and after beating about for a time found the flock about a mile from where we left them.

The next question was what to do with them. To cross the gulches on the regular trail was out of the question; to leave them where they were, awaiting the subsidence of the water—

[Emma's Note: "At this point the very interesting narrative breaks off, by reason of the loss of the remaining sheets of the letter; but it has been thought best to print the foregoing, leaving the reader to imagine the thrilling adventures that no doubt followed."]

San Francisco, née Yerba Buena, is beginning to get on solid footing and is on track now for a more consistent financial flourishing. In the next letter we see Oscar Shafter, as the business man, gauging the city's condition after his five years of residency there.

San Francisco, March 19, 1860.

Dear Father:

. . . *The rapid growth and general prosperity of this Coast has never been so assured as at the present hour. Since I have been here, now about five and one-half years, there have been no "expansions" and "contractions," no "inflations" and "collapsings." Those terms which I used to hear repeated so often in the East, are rarely used here and never as applicable to anything occurring around us. Business here rests in the main upon cash or bullion, or in so far as it may be done upon credit, the credit is made to repose upon tangible and available securities. All enterprises are checked and kept within safe and reasonable bounds by the constant action of these most powerful and salutary corrections. There has heretofore been great prodigality and recklessness in the conduct of public and private officers, and no lack of venality and corruption. By these means large state and municipal debts have been contracted. Within the last few years, however, a great change has taken place for the better, and the old debts are in course of liquidation. Had the State started out with a "Banking System," I believe that the great triumph that awaits it would have been postponed for a generation.*

About a month since we imported a two year old Durham heifer from Bennington. She cost us here $500. We were offered $1000 for her on the day she was landed. Everybody says she is the finest specimen of the Durham breed ever brought to this Coast. Our sheep are just beginning to lamb. Off of 1000 ewes we shall have at least 2000 lambs, . . .

CELEBRATIONS AND LAMENTATIONS

San Francisco, September 9, 1862

Dear Father:

To-day is the 11th Anniversary of the admission of California into the Union; and all the flags are flying, and all the trained bands are out in honor of the occasion. A whole Brigade has just passed Montgomery Block. While we are thus holding high carnival on our advent into the Union, the telegraph is in the very act of telling us in its long traveled whisper across the Continent, that the defenders of the Union are being scattered, and that the fabric of our Nationality is just tottering to its fall. . . .

Your son,

O. L. Shafter.

Oscar is here referring to the news that the armies of the North are suffering serious losses in their battles with Confederate troops under the leadership of Robert E. Lee. Eight days later, the Battle of Antietam would be the bloodiest battle on American soil in U.S. history. Twenty-three thousand men would die on both sides. As Oscar so eloquently states, the telegraph assured that even distant California would be kept apprised of the war's progress.

Oscar writes the next letter on July 4th, 1863, less than a century since John Adams had predicted that such celebrations would take place in honor of the Declaration of Independence, and the union of thirteen colonies into a nation. Adams could hardly imagine that the Union would be torn apart and its survival threatened in such a short time. On the other hand, he would no doubt have been surprised and gratified that the Union had grown by 32 states by the 4th of July, 1863.

THE 4ᵀᴴ OF JULY ~ 1863

San Francisco, July 4, 1863.

Dear Father:

Today is the 4th of July, and great preparations have been made by the citizens for the celebration of the day. The French, German, Irish, Mexican, English and Chinese among us are in the habit of celebrating their National holidays, and this puts our own people upon their pluck. Were it not for the spirit of rivalry thus engendered, I fear that the "Glorious Fourth" would be little glorified here. The people here are not deficient, however, in attachment to the Union, but it is "attachment" as distinguished from devotion. They find their account in the Union, and therefore they adhere to it. Northern men, on intelligent business considerations; Southern men, who have as a general thing little interest in the business or property of the Country, because they hope that the Union can in some way be made subservient to their own particular madness, to-wit: "niggers."

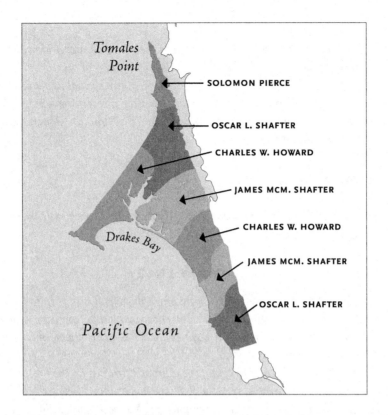

THE SHAFTER RANCHES ON POINT REYES

In this map from 1869, we see the Shafter ranches on
Point Reyes divided between Oscar, James and Charles
Webb Howard, Emma's husband.

*You will see by the papers that I am the nominee of the Republican Party for
the office of Judge of the Supreme Court. I have been told that there are many
Democrats of both stripes that will vote for me, and that the full vote of the
Republican Party will be cast for me I have no reason to doubt. I never engineered
for the nomination, nor ever asked for it, and but one person in the State ever spoke
to me upon the subject before the nomination was made.*

*I have been applied to since to take the stump, but have peremptorily refused
it. Since I have been here I have attended to nothing, striven for nothing, hoped
for nothing, and desired nothing outside of my profession. Inside of it I have simply
worked like a dog, performing more drudgery, I honestly believe, during that time,
than any other two lawyers in the State. The people have, or fancy they have
hitherto suffered greatly from incompetent, or dishonest, or partisan Judges, and
there is a general disposition just now to select men for judicial positions with some
reference to their qualifications.*

*I have no particular assurance in my own mind that I shall be elected, but that
a vote highly complimentary will be given me I have no doubt. I have never in my
life before now seen the time when I desired or would accept any office that would
withdraw me from, or interfere with the practice of my profession, but the reasons*

that have hitherto influenced me have been to a great degree met and overcome.

I am somewhat weary of the labors and endless solicitudes of practice, and at the same time am fully persuaded that active employment is essential to peace of mind and general well being, and furthermore that it is a duty, so on the whole I should have no difficulty in reconciling myself to a seat on the Supreme Bench, and in a word just now rather affect it. . . .

Your son,

O. L. SHAFTER

Oscar's wish was granted. He did end his distinguished career as a justice of the Supreme Court of California.

LAST DIARY ENTRY

April 13, 1867. After an interval of two and one half years it occurs to me to make another entry. Should I wait much longer, the chasm would become too wide to be bridged. We are well up with our court business, but not so far ahead of it as not to find present employment to the full.

Have been with a select party to Cisco, the railroad terminus for the present. Cisco will soon cease to be a terminus, but it will always have claims to the distinction of being the hyperborean center of the Sierra Nevada. We had sleigh riding and snow-balling, privileges that we had come to suppose, most regretfully, we should never enjoy again. The snow regions, to which the railroad furnishes an easy approach, will be a point of resort, I predict, until the Sierra shall cease to be "Nevada."*

Nov. 19, 1867. To-day I have made my will. Is it the last? I wait, trusting in God.

In 1869, Emma Shafter marries Charles Webb Howard, who becomes an active partner in the Point Reyes dairy ranches with Oscar and James. They divide up the ownership of the land between them.

There are no surviving letters or diary entries following the one above from November 1867. The pen of Oscar Shafter falls silent as his fine mind begins to unravel after years of overwork and personal losses. Shortly after the final diary entry he retires from public life. He travels with his wife Sarah to Florence and there his life comes to an end in 1873. It seems a poetic last place for a poetic soul. The following excerpt is from a letter that has survived, written to him by a friend on the Supreme Court, J.B. Crockett, in 1871.

FROM LETTER TO OSCAR IN FLORENCE from J.B. Crockett, Supreme Bench

. . . The crops promise well, and if the season continues favorable, will be very abundant. But there is an unprecedented stagnation in business. Times were never so dull in this State, and yet money is abundant and interest is lower than ever before. Ralston tells me that long loans are easily effected at 8 per cent per annum. But the railroad has broken down the merchants. It has brought us so near to N.

* snow-covered

Y. and Chicago, that our merchants no longer have a monopoly of the trade. Our markets are filled with Chicago hams, eggs, butter and poultry, and when a woman wants a silk dress or a fine bonnet, she sends to N. Y. for it. This is "rough" on the merchants; but is probably no disadvantage to the masses.

San Francisco is not growing; but Oakland is going ahead marvelously. You would scarcely recognize it with its beautifully paved streets, and its numerous new and elegant structures. The census reports its population at 11,000 and it is fast becoming one of the most beautiful little cities on the continent. I wish you were back in it, that we might crack a few more jokes on the ferryboat. I have some very good ones in store for you, when we meet. But I must stop, for fear you may say, "When will this blind man cease to prate?" But can't you oblige me with a letter in reply? I should be delighted to hear from you.

With kind regards to Mrs. Shafter and hoping soon to hear of your complete restoration to health, I remain

Yours truly,

J. B. CROCKETT

Oscar Lovell Shafter died in Florence on January 22, 1873. His 12 year old daughter, Fanny, born in California, died two weeks before Oscar's funeral. In spite of her losses, his wife Sarah Riddle Shafter lived on until 1900 in their Oakland house at 3701 Broadway, next door to her daughter Emma and Charles Howard. She was 77 years old.

SAN FRANCISCANS ALL:
FOUR SOMEBODIES AND A RAILROAD

IT IS TIME TO CATCH UP NOW ON FOUR OF OUR NEW YORKERS—"Nobodies All" in the 1830s when they were busy selling newspapers, horseradish, and general merchandise in small towns of the state.

Mark, from Hendersonville, had begun studying law in Lockport, New York in 1837 but then sold out in 1849 and left everything behind to head for the gold fields of California. He opened up a store in Placerville and hauled his goods down from Sacramento with an ox-team. The following year he opened up a wholesale grocery business with a partner.

Amasa married Jane Lathrop and moved to Port Washington in NorthernWisconsin. In 1852, his office and legal books burned, which left him nearly broke. In desperation, he sent his wife to live with her parents and went to California, landing in a mining village called Michigan Bluff. He joined the thousands of others in a hunt for gold, but had no success. Two of his brothers had also headed to California during the gold rush. He joined them in business in the mining region.

In four years, Amasa had garnered enough wealth and reputation there to move on successfully to a dry-goods store business in Sacramento. In 1857, he launched his political career as a Free Soil Party candidate for state Treasurer. Defeated in this election, he was nominated two years later by the party for governor, but was again defeated. I should mention that he was not known here as Amasa but by his more dignified middle name of Leland. Leland's defeats in politics only launched him onward toward greater and greater success. The party sent him as a candidate to the Chicago convention in 1860. While he did not come away from this convention with a political candidacy, what he did win was the friendship of one Abraham Lincoln, who had won the nomination for the presidency. Leland attended his inauguration in Washington and stayed on, apparently using his power and influence to affect national policies toward the Pacific coast.

Charles, who had moved to Indiana remember, also caught the gold bug and in 1850 went across the plains to California. He did his stint in the oil fields with similarly dismal results and, like Leland, decided after two years to establish a dry-goods store in Sacramento. He followed a similar trajectory to Leland's into politics and was elected to the state legislature in 1860 as a member of the Republican Party.

Collis also left his business in Oneonta in 1849 and set out for San Francisco with his wife and other 49ers."He reached the Isthmus of Panama but was detained for three months, along with many others headed for California, waiting for a northbound ship. Rather than do nothing during this time, he bought and sold merchandise, walking back and forth across the Isthmus 24 times in the process. He left for California with $1200 and arrived with $5000."*

In Sacramento, Collis—resourceful as ever—started a store out of a small tent. Not long afterward, he met Mark and the two industrious young men went into partnership together. They were so successful that by 1856, their firm was one of the wealthiest on the Pacific coast.

* * * *

THE RAILROAD

THE SCENE IS SET AND THE PLAYERS ARE IN PLACE. They are tempered by experience, hardship and long-distance journeys. They have caught the wave in California and prospered from it. But before we put them together for their final act, we need to say a word about the inception of something that would change the life of *Homo sapiens* in a most dramatic way and significantly change the course of migrations.

The time will come when people will travel in stages moved by steam engines from one city to another, almost as fast as birds can fly, 15 or 20 miles an hour.... A carriage will start from Washington in the morning, the passengers will breakfast at Baltimore, dine at Philadelphia, and sup in New York the same day.... Engines will drive boats 10 or 12 miles an hour, and there will be hundreds of steamers running on the Mississippi, as predicted years ago.

— OLIVER EVANS, 1800

Obviously railroads did not come into being overnight as the brainstorm of a single individual; not one invention but many, which had to be brought together through enormous leaps of organization, collaboration and money. It is in the iron rich country of Great Britain that the first significant steps are taken. Creating a "road" for a train to run on was one of the first steps. This was arguably done by a man named Beaumont who in 1630 designed and built wagon roads for English coal mines, over which horses could pull carts and wagons over heavy planks. The first steam engine arrived in the American colonies in 1753 . . . just the engine, mind you, as a source of energy. It was installed to pump water from a mine. Back in the Old Country, Parliament voted to establish a railway in Leeds—the Middleton Railway—which claims to be the oldest in the world. The one name I remember from this story is James Watt. In elementary school I had learned that James Watt invented the steam engine, Eli Whitney invented the cotton gin and Thomas Edison invented the light bulb, as if those three things had single-handedly brought about the industrial revolution.

* George Kraus, *High Road to Promontory*

Watt invents his steam engine in 1774—not the first, but the first "modern" stationery engine. Stationery is the operative word here. As a child, I thought this meant a locomotive, like the "engine" of a train. This engine didn't go anywhere, it just powered things before the combustion engine. His associate, a man named Murdoch, did get it to move a bit, giving it wheels so that it could toodle along at 6 to 8 miles per hour. We are obviously a long way still from the Atcheson, Topeka and the Santa Fe of 1950s song fame. The most movable thing that the steam engine powered was not a train but a boat, weighing two tons, which was built by an American—Oliver Evans—in 1800.

It is back in Leeds that the next move comes with the invention of a steam locomotive that runs on timber rails; probably the first actual "railroad" engine since a moving iron thing has now met up with a track. From now on things move along, literally, and in the same year a steam locomotive is built in Cornwall for the Welsh Penydarran Railroad, followed in three years by the very first passenger train which ran from Swansea to Mumbles on March 25th, 1807.

By the mid-1820s, we have a "locomotion" capable of pulling 90 tons of coal at 15mph. We might laugh at the slowness of it, but the men and beasts who had been responsible for the movement of that amount of coal would surely have rejoiced.

The first lines of rails are now being laid in the New England states in America and the first westward tracks are being laid between Baltimore and the Ohio River in Virginia. The first steam locomotive for the railroads arrives from England in 1829 but is too heavy to operate on the track that had been laid—twice as heavy as had been originally specified. Around that time, a fellow named Stephenson wins a competition in England with his own invention—a rather handsome thing of iron and wood called, fortuitously "The Rocket," which could carry 30 passengers at 30 miles per hour. Not bad.

Meanwhile, back home, workers at the West Point foundry in New York were putting the finishing touches on The Best Friend for the Charleston and Hamburg railroad. This is our own homegrown steam engine. As you can see, locomotives were named like the racehorses they were meant to emulate and then surpass. That custom would continue. Unfortunately, our Best Friend's boiler exploded after a year of service due to a reckless fireman, unexpectedly ending its, and his, career. Tom Thumb was built by Peter Cooper in New York in a mere six weeks. It hauled 36 passengers at 18 mph in August 1830.

Amasa would have been seven years old when the DeWitt Clinton appeared in his neighborhood on tracks running from Schenectady to Albany, the route on which he and his brothers would be traveling to sell their horseradish and chestnuts. The Brother Jonathon (1831) was the first locomotive in the world to have a four-wheel leading truck, designed by John B. Jervis for the Mohawk & Hudson Railroad.

Over the next two decades, refinements are continually being made to the new invention, but those efforts must be coupled with the equal challenge of finding land, financing and building the tracks on which the new contraptions would run. The first land-grant railroad (developed with the support of the government through granting of land) doesn't appear until 1855 in Illinois. The laying of track is beset by huge engineering challenges, particularly by building bridges on which something so heavy could run, like the first railroad bridge across the Mississippi River, which was completed between Rock Island, Illinois and Davenport, Iowa. Then there were the countless obstructions in its path, which the landscape presented. And the cost of it! Just imagine.

The story now moves forward as our four New York nobodies meet up in California. Without them, the next step could never have been taken on Point Reyes.

THEODORE

THEODORE D. JUDAH SET OUT FOR CALIFORNIA AT AGE 28 with his wife of six years. He did not go to dig for gold, but to put his education at Rensselaer Polytechnic Institute to work as the chief engineer of the Sacramento Valley Railroad, which would be built to operate between Sacramento and a mining district east of the town. Theodore was a young man of vision, energy and enthusiasm. Even as he worked on the Niagara Gorge and Erie Canal projects back east in New York, he had in mind a dream to construct a railroad that would connect the entire American continent, east to west. Now he was working in earnest to bring his wild dream into a reality. Through his initiative the California Legislature arranged for a convention to be held in San Francisco in September 1859 to look into the construction of the Pacific Railroad. The Convention delegates called upon Congress to take the necessary steps, at the national level, toward creating an organization to build the Pacific Railroad, expressing a collective preference among them for a central route. Once again, Theodore Judah was on hand to further their proposition and deliver their memorial to congress.

In November 1860, Theodore Judah authored a pamphlet that was distributed to financiers and politicians detailing a financial and geographical plan for the project.

"Being confident of having found a practicable line, I have devoted the past few months to explorations, resulting in the discovery of a route from the City of Sacramento to the Truckee River in a nearly direct line to Washoe, with a maximum grade of 100 feet to the mile. In view of the Pacific Railroad Bill, as matured in the last Congress, having been made the special order for the third Tuesday in next December, and inasmuch as the road in California most needs to be constructed by an organization effected under the laws of the state, it is proposed to organize a company in anticipation of the passage of the act by Congress."

Six months later, Theodore Judah followed up the distribution of the pamphlet with a meeting in Sacramento to consider the issues involved with the Pacific Railroad, specifically to discuss the route and funding. By this time, he had personally crossed the Sierras 23 times on foot or horseback to explore the possible options and was confident that the route he had outlined would be the best. The result of the meeting has been described as "nil." But that was not altogether the case.

COLLIS, MARK, CHARLES AND AMASA JOIN FORCES

WE LEFT COLLIS AS HE HAD DEPARTED FROM ONEONTA IN 1849, at age 22, with his wife and other 49ers and arrived three months later in San Francisco. You may remember that he met up with Mark here, for the first time, and they entered into a most satisfactory business partnership, selling miner's supplies and other hardware, both wholesale and retail, which were much in demand by the 49ers.

Collis Huntington was one of the men present at the meeting called by Theodore Judah in the Spring of 1861 to make his proposal and seek funding. Collis had not spoken up at the meeting or offered a subscription as some others did. At the end of it, Theodore approached him and solicited his opinion on the subject. That opinion was that the building of the Pacific Railroad could not be funded through voluntary contributions at a public meeting. That method might be adequate for a picnic or a Fourth of July celebration, Collis suggested, but it was totally inadequate for a project of this magnitude. He invited Theodore to call at his store some evening to discuss the matter further. Not surprisingly, the eager young Judah showed up the following evening and they talked late into the night. Collis Huntington promised to find among his acquaintances five men who could, along with Theodore and himself, finance the initial expenses of surveying the route and establishing an incorporated company to undertake the project.

Naturally the first person Collis Huntington turned to was his partner, Mark Hopkins, of the Henderson, New York Swedenborgian family. Enter also Amasa/ Leland Stanford, who had succeeded in his political vocation to become governor of California and a friend of Collis's. Charles, of Troy you will recall—that is Charles Crocker—is now a member of the state legislature as well as another of the leading merchants of Sacramento, with branch stores in other parts of the state. Charles is a self-made man who learned a good many things in his jobs as newspaper deliverer, saw-mill worker and eleven years working at a forge. He knew men and he knew iron, which qualified him to oversee the actual construction work of the railroad. This venture catapulted the four New York nobodies, who had already begun to gain significant recognition in the new state, into the lasting realm of the rich and famous as the Big Four, who would one day become neighbors in mansions atop Nob Hill, San Francisco.

In 1862, President Abraham Lincoln signs the Pacific Railway Act, which authorizes the construction of the first transcontinental railroad. Theodore Judah's vision to build a railroad across the Sierra Nevada mountains in California, and then to continue the railroad across the United States, is about to become reality.

History will record that the Central Pacific Railroad was financed by The Big Four: Collis Huntington, Leland Stanford, Charles Crocker and Mark Hopkins

But of more importance to our story is the change that this is about to bring about for the migrations of people across the continent. In 1855, Oscar still had to endure the grueling journey by way of Panama. But things are about to change, for the better, with the next wave of arrivals.

Point Reyes ~ 1869

JAMES BUILDS A HOUSE

The coast-line is broken at frequent intervals by the mouths of small streams, and at the available points at the mouths of these streams saw-mills are placed . . . for the redwood forests line the coast up to and beyond Humboldt Bay. . . . There are even mills which offer no lee to vessels loading; and here the adventurous schooner watches her opportunity. . . .

— CHARLES NORDHOFF
California, for health, pleasure, and residence: a book for travellers and settlers (1874)

JAMES MCMILLAN SHAFTER STOOD STARING INTO THE FOG, *as if the intensity of his gaze might part the curtain of mist and reveal the sight he was waiting for: a boat laden with redwood for the house he was about to build. The fog was so thick that he couldn't see his oxen only a few yards away, although he could hear their occasional snuffling sounds, and beyond them the low conversation of his Mexican workers, heard but not seen. From ahead of him came the murmur of Paper Mill Creek. The schooner was coming the long way round, out of San Francisco's Golden Gate, then north, entering Tomales Bay on a southward course again. James knew that this was the most treacherous stretch of coastline from Oregon to Mexico. Then the fifteen mile long bay had to be traversed to reach Paper Mill Creek. Many a vessel sailing along the coast had mistaken Tomales Bay for San Francisco Bay and headed toward shore full sail. Just before he had arrived here, an English clipper ship, the Oxford, had made that mistake and been wrecked. Its hull still stood rotting in the bay. A few years ago, the Sea Nymph, a beautiful clipper ship laden with a cargo of merchandise had sailed to its doom on the beach, a little north of Point Reyes, followed two years later by a Russian man-o-war that met the same end in the same place.*

A lighthouse was needed on the Point. He and Oscar and Charles—Emma's husband—had deeded 120 acres to the Government Lighthouse Service for its construction. Hopefully it would be ready next year. The revolving lens was now being cast in Paris. They were all heavily committed financially to the building of the North Coast Railway, but James saw this not only as a way to make good on another of their large investments—timber from the Russian River—but as an essential step in the growth of the whole region, connecting the vital life of San Francisco with the regions of the north, and opening up markets and transportation to the new transcontinental network.

His presence here was a ceremonial one. No one needed him to load the timber onto the wagon and guide it to his home site. But since business had brought him here, he couldn't resist presiding over this initial phase, like popping champagne for a ship's first voyage. He wished that Oscar was here to share the moment with him, as they had shared so many other significant events in their lives, yoked together like the oxen as they plowed the new land with their energy and wits. He wished too that he could seek Oscar's insights into what would be the greatest undertaking yet of the Shafter-Howard enterprises; greater even than all of their fine dairy ranches on Point Reyes: The building of a North Pacific Railroad. But if he had any lingering doubts, they were fading more rapidly than the mist over Paper Mill Creek. If the railroad ran from Sausalito to Tomales, as they were planning it, this whole roundabout trip by water would be unnecessary. They would have a way to exploit the huge lumber resource to the north, moving logs from the redwood forests by train to San Francisco Bay, and from there on barges across to the city. Their northernmost dairies on the peninsula could bring butter and pigs south on the train and then ferry them across the Bay from Sausalito to the Ferry Building in San Francisco. They could later extend the line up along the Russian River to Gualala, and make the whole trip by train.

James thoughts returned to the house he would build for his family—especially his wife Julia, who had been his faithful companion and colleague in their pioneering adventures, first in Wisconsin and now in California. He had married Julia Granville Hubbard in Montpelier in 1845, when he was 29 and she was 23. It said a lot about her that Julia was a graduate of Emma Willard, the first school in the country to provide girls the same educational opportunities given to boys. Back in 1814, Emma Hart Willard broke the mold. She believed young women deserved diverse subject matter and academic rigor in line with their ambitions and abilities. His oldest son Payne was now 23, James 18 and Julia, 10. Six years ago they had lost their son Chester at only nine years old. Those were difficult years. His brilliant brother Oscar had lost his mental faculties and resigned from the bench in 1867. He was now wandering the capitals of Europe with his wife Sarah, a mere shadow of the man he had once been. This house, the Oaks, was to be his own family's consolation for their losses and their hope for the future.

Against the blank backdrop of the fog, he let his inner eye move along the cypress and redwood lined drive that would one day make a tranquil entrance to their manor house. Emerging from the canopy, he could see the stately white mansion, as fine as the best in Vermont, with a pillared veranda wrapping around three sides of the house. Shuttered second story windows. He had a beautiful slab from a 150 year old oak which he was saving to use as a sideboard. From France, he had ordered a range for the kitchen, which he planned to embed in solid cement. Later he would build his own sawmill, sending lumber and firewood to Bolinas, where it could be lightered across the bar to ships heading into San Francisco.

All of this would be his legacy to his son Payne and the next generations of

Shafters. He was teaching Payne how to manage his Point Reyes empire. And all of this would begin right here, as soon as his lumber-bearing boat emerged from the fog. He heard sounds around him that could be elk or deer, and he had a sudden impulse to grab his gun and track it down. Hunting was one his great pleasures, along with fishing and swimming in the beautiful creeks on his land. But a different business was at hand and those pleasures would be deferred.

James McMillan Shafter was a robust and vigorous man and this must have been close to a peak moment of his life—the threshold of realizing his greatest dreams. The "peak" is so often the moment before, laden with its own flavor of dream and anticipation. James is 53 years old, a highly successful lawyer and rancher. In his new state—the third in which he has gained distinction—he has served in the state senate, where he also acted as President Pro Tem—and there are still important positions in state and county awaiting him in the future. He will be a delegate to the Constitutional Convention in 1878 and a judge in the San Francisco Superior Court; a member of the UC Board of Regents and President of the Agricultural Board. But now, he is building a house.

James and Oscar have profited enormously from being in on the ground floor of settling the land disputes in Point Reyes and being on hand to pick up defaulted properties at their lowest prices. But they have also managed things well. The Shafter-Howard enterprises now own 31 well-run dairies—the best in the state and perhaps even the country.

* * * *

Grossi Farms ~ Spring

RETURN!

Oh the joy of return to Mr. Fields and Spring as I have never seen it here. Especially after record-setting winter rains and flooding throughout three counties. My dear friend Sally Mahé drove me and my assorted baggage up here mid-day. I was in a serious state of exhaustion and my old nervous system was sending off alarms of wear and tear. My body was saying STOP. PLEASE. And only Mr. Fields could offer such a stopping place.

I was so happy that we finally had a day that started out sunny and held. Driving north from Mill Valley, the green green hills began around Novato, looking more like Ireland than California. I came through the farm on April 19th to drop some things off in Mr. Fields and see how he was faring. It's not possible to be in Mr. Fields during the winter rainy season because the back area of the farm is a lake of mud and water and Mr. Fields leaks. So I swathe him in bright blue tarpaulin and lock him up, always a sad moment. During those winter months, I do my travels and visitations and have a house-sitting job nearby. I had never seen the farm in April or noticed that the entrance is flanked by two Japanese cherry trees. Now here they stood in all of their splendor, two lush clouds of pink, and all along the dirt road that led to the farm, daffodils in bloom. I had walked very slowly on that April visit to take in this new sight of the farm in Spring. Fields of wild mustard where last there had been pumpkins and ahead of me, a green Sonoma Mountain.

Ed and Susie invited us for supper and we ate outside on the deck, taking in the view of Susie's beautiful Spring garden and beyond that, the sight of the camel-back summer hills turned emerald green. Later I would sit in Mr. Fields and marvel at the new sound: Water rushing in Copeland Creek!

As we enjoyed Susie's delicious meal, we heard the call of geese coming towards us from the north. As it got closer, a pair flew right over us and Ed said "There goes Thanksgiving and Christmas. Or is it Easter?"

"You better tell them the story, Eddie."

CHRISTMAS, THANKSGIVING AND EASTER

Once upon a time there were three large goose eggs in an abandoned nest behind the barn at Grossi Farms. They would soon become three fine little goslings, left to be raised by three unlikely parents: Farmer Ed, the Farmer's Wife Susie, and their friend Colleen. Colleen provided the incubator, which she had used for chicks of her own. Susie took on much of the care when the fledglings left their artificial nest and were let loose to roam the wide world of Grossi Farms. Farmer Ed, I'm sure, provided their names: Thanksgiving, Christmas and Easter.

From the time they could walk, they trailed devotedly behind one or another of their parents as they went about their daily chores. Susie bought them a brightly colored inflatable plastic swimming pool and filled it with water. They chirped and splashed and had such a wonderful time that when they had finally tired of the activity, the pool was nearly empty as the little goslings stepped out happily to dry their wings in the sun.

Something happened to Thanksgiving and then there were two: Christmas and Easter. They thrived and grew. But they couldn't fly. And let's face it, their foster parents weren't great role models for this.

One day, as Farmer Ed was leaving the farm to do errands—driving his pick-up slowly down the long dirt road that leads to the highway—he saw one of the geese-to-be trying strenuously to follow. He extended his arm out the window and, as if on cue, Christmas—or perhaps it was Easter—tentatively lifted his wings as some age-old instinct rose up in him. In moments, he was flying low beside Ed, the tip of his wing just off Ed's finger tips as he drove down the road.

I'm sure that I experienced what Easter must have felt on that morning when I first found myself gliding along on a borrowed two-wheel bicycle after a week spent mostly underneath it. But to fly! And how Ed must have felt when he shared this moment with his beautiful winged child.

"Why that's just like the movie 'Mother Goose!'" Sally said.

"Just like," he agreed, smiling fondly at the memory as we ate dinner on their deck. We listened to all the gathering birds of evening, looking out on the low hills of the neighboring ranch.

"Geese!" I had announced, when I first heard the honking.

"Christmas and Easter," Ed had corrected. "They come back every year. Only Thanksgiving is missing." And then he told his story.

But the story doesn't end with this graceful moment between man and bird. Both were so caught up in the joy of the spontaneous event that neither had thought ahead to the inevitable consequences. When Ed reached the highway and turned onto Petaluma Hill Road, the goose didn't know what to do, so fell uselessly back to the ground. But the ground was no longer the protected environment of Grossi Farm. It was the asphalt center of Petaluma Hill Road, the busiest highway this side of the Freeway. Pandemonium broke out as the cars coming from both directions threw on their brakes to avoid the sudden apparition. Ed leapt out of the truck to direct traffic, sort out the melee, and collect his foster child, grateful that the worst had not happened. Not yet.

He knew his own goose was cooked when an irate Colleen lashed into him for foolishly endangering their communal offspring. But there they were, in the bright spring sky. Christmas and Easter, home for the holidays.

✳ ✳ ✳ ✳

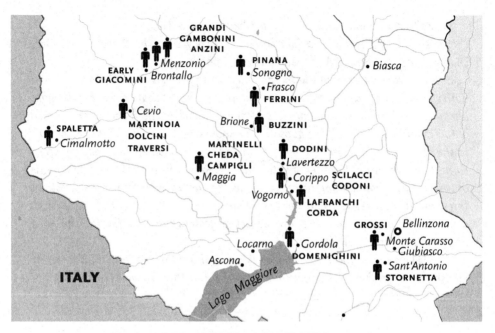

DEPARTURES FROM TICINO

Ticino ~ 1870

DEPARTURES

Ticino is opening up and emptying out as if a massive snowmelt in the high mountains had sent down a torrent that swept through the villages in a flood and carried away the bloom and vigor of its youth. The swift waters of change and desperation have driven them to the Atlantic, heaving westward on its rough seas. If, nearly a century later, another Father Galli had started from the furthest villages of the Val Maggia, where the cousins Nicolo and Berto once walked, he would have started out in their village of Menzonio, where the lusty babe, Salvatore Grandi, has now grown to young manhood. At age 16, along with his brother Louis, Charles and Giacomo Gambonini and the Anzini brothers, he heads off to the New World.

Traveling southeast along that valley, as it winds along the Maggia River toward Locarno, the village of Brontallo has given up several of its Giacominis, an old and big family there. In 1860, we find Antonio Jacomeni, (as spelled on the Census) probably from Brontallo, working on a ranch in Tomales.

Reaching Cevio, we have already seen that Carlo Martinoia and the Dolcini brothers—Pietro and Michael—were among the first to leave. There is a lovely little tributary off this path when it reaches Cevio—a side valley, the Val di Campo—which extends westward toward two small villages. The furthest village is Cimalmotto. From here, William Spaletta climbs the footpath that ascends from the village past a few huts on the left. Here, he likely pauses to look back over the rooftops of his town to the distant mountains, a much admired view and the last he will see of his village. He crosses a short valley into forest and then veers to the right

CARLO MARTINOIA
Courtesy of Sally Gale

LORENZO MARTINELLI

through the juniper wood of Alpe di Quadrella. What thoughts must he have had on that gentle descent among Alpen roses, juniper, and bilberry beneath a canopy of tall conifers. Regret? Hope? Joy? Apprehension? The path drops steeply out of the forest to an open area; with a small clutch of stone huts, where neighbors call out their farewells and wish him luck. He is soon crossing a small wooden bridge to the village of Corte Nuevo. More people here to watch his final passage through the valley. Perhaps a relative or two. But on he walks, out across the large, open meadowland and into another large forest. A narrow footpath takes him past hay barns and a small stream. Not long afterwards, he arrives at the village of Campo, spread over a grassy hillside, sun spilling across its sloping meadows. More farewells. Perhaps a bite to eat. Then he walks on through more forest and meadows to Cevio. He has reached the main path that will take him to Locarno on Lago Maggiore, and beyond that, the long, difficult path which will finally take him to California.

Along this well-trod route through the Val Maggia, over which generations of young Ticinesi had made their way to their winter jobs in Italy, these adventurous souls—like the pasture-seeking Winnili—pass the granite quarries of Cevio and Riveo and descend into the low-lying area of Maggia.

Maggia gives up some of the earliest emigrants to Marin. Lorenzo and Pietro Martinelli leave Maggia in the 1830s to work first as chimney sweeps in Paris, probably crossing the Alps to the north since the border to the south was closed. In the spring of 1854, they make their way to Le Havre to sail west aboard the Joseph Holmes, a Massachusetts-built ship sailing for New York. They travel on west after joining the Union Army under Gen. John C. Fremont and arrive with Fremont in California. Lorenzo serves as cook with two of Fremont's expeditions through the west, then makes the arduous trip back to Maggia in 1862 to marry Carolina Bonetti. A year later, Lorenzo returns to California to prepare the way for his wife to join him. He works at a Greek restaurant in San Francisco for six months, receiving in lieu of cash an acre of land between Montgomery Street and

San Francisco Bay. He sells this property in 1863 and leaves for the Mother Lode Gold Mining Country near Jackson and San Andreas, California.

Lorenzo and his brother Pietro join forces again, driving a team of 6 mules to ferry supplies to the miners, including cog-wheels, leather belting, food, tobacco and alcohol. When the owner of this very profitable business dies, the Martinelli brothers take it over, using their teams to supply the miners of California, Nevada, Idaho and Montana. But word of the success of other Ticinesi emigrants working in the dairy business in Marin, inspires them to establish their own dairy farm business there with a herd of cattle on the Devil's Gulch Ranch in Nicasio in 1866.

Lorenzo sends for his wife the next year after he has bought the ranch. When she arrives, she finds that Lorenzo and his brother had been living in a wilderness cabin, their dirty clothes piled up a most unwelcome sight. She almost returns right then and there to Maggia, but rolls up her sleeves and makes the best of it. She and Lorenzo will have nine children there. Ennio, born in 1868, will become the Marin County District Attorney and later, California State Senator.

Pietro eventually sells his half of the ranch to Lorenzo, who later moves to a ranch in Hicks Valley, then farther east to Old Lakeville Road, Petaluma. Lorenzo Martinelli will die on April 2, 1893 after suffering an aortic aneurysm while on his way to deliver butter to market in Petaluma in his horse-drawn carriage.

A decade after the Martinelli brothers depart from Maggia, Louis Cheda sets out from there as a teenager with Peter Campigli, sailing in 1864 on a vessel that takes them "around the horn," finally landing in Marin to take up jobs milking cows on dairy ranches owned or leased from Ticinesi from their own hometown. After a decade of saving up money earned, they return to Maggia to claim wives. Peter Campigli marries Isa Martinelli and Louis Cheda marries Isa's sister Nina and they return to West Marin to build their futures.

Stephen Martinelli makes his way out of Maggia in 1868, at the age of 17. Nine years later, in Watsonville—to the south of San Francisco—he will found the Martinelli Apple Juice company. This is a different branch of the Martinelli family on the same tree as Lorenzo and Lorenzo's son E.B. Martinelli. E.B.'s son Jordan will become a Superior Court Judge of Marin County.

Many more will follow out of Maggia, including Fridolino Lafranchi, who will take the same long journey in 1910 to play an important role in the new Marin being born after the Shafters, and Giovanni Corda from Vogorno.

From Maggia, it is an easy walk to Locarno. In fact the 28 kilometers from Bignasco is a flat, broad-bottomed landscape with only a small decline as the river flows toward Lago Maggiore. The swelling tide of émigrés emboldens others who might not have had the courage to take so bold a step. But word is trickling back that this is not another Australia. The land is good. Its promise is real.

✦ ✦ ✦

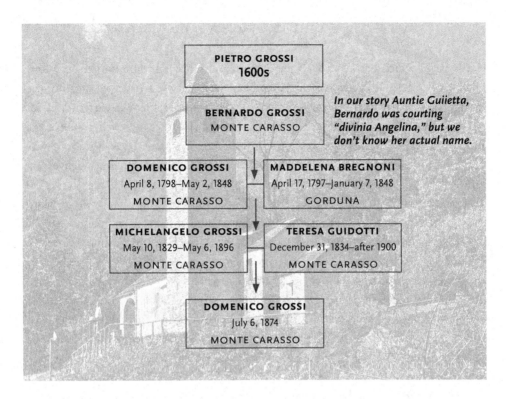

PIETRO GROSSI
1600s

BERNARDO GROSSI
MONTE CARASSO

In our story Auntie Guiietta,
Bernardo was courting
"divinia Angelina," but we
don't know her actual name.

DOMENICO GROSSI
April 8, 1798–May 2, 1848
MONTE CARASSO

MADDELENA BREGNONI
April 17, 1797–January 7, 1848
GORDUNA

MICHELANGELO GROSSI
May 10, 1829–May 6, 1896
MONTE CARASSO

TERESA GUIDOTTI
December 31, 1834–after 1900
MONTE CARASSO

DOMENICO GROSSI
July 6, 1874
MONTE CARASSO

Roughly two thousand Ticinesi had responded to the call for workers in Australia but the results did not live up to expectation and often left the families in a worse, rather than a better, financial situation. The voyage to Australia was expensive and the clauses of the contract were not respected by the agents. It was because of this that Germany prohibited the recruitment of emigrants in the country, which led the agencies to turn to Switzerland. The other cantons in Switzerland had put strict laws into effect to regulate the activities of these agencies, but Ticino had none and the agents operated with impunity there. The Australian venture not only set the families back some two million Swiss Francs, the cost of the journey, but the emigrants were not able to buy land or bring their wives and families over at a later time. The landscape was too barren for farming.

During that period, only a few hundred went to California but what they found there was truly a land of opportunity. The money they made in the goldfields could be invested in land and they could apply their natural skills of working with livestock and making fine quality butter and cheese. As we have seen earlier, there was a second yellow gold in San Francisco and that was butter, which was in high demand and could not be found anywhere in the city.

The stories of success were trickling back along with the beginning of emigrant funds returning to families in Ticino. California was making itself felt. If Ticino was closed off from the world in 1853, more and more things were opening it up in new ways. Roads were being built, more schools were being opened. Jobs were becoming available with the railroad. But life was still not easy for the Ticinesi.

In Monte Carasso, Michelangelo Grossi was coming of age during the difficult times that Ticino was facing. He had been born in the year of the great flood of the

Ticino River which had destroyed several houses on the plain. He was twenty-four when the border with Italy was closed and he surely felt the frustration of all of the young males deprived of their only access to winter employment to earn money for their families. He married into the Guidotti family, which we met earlier; one of the old families from the *squadre* of Poncetta in Monte Carasso. Teresa Guidotti was turning nineteen that year. We don't know their actual marriage date. Their oldest child, Pietro, was not born until September of 1867 when Michelangelo was 38 and Teresa was 35. Two years later, Maria Grossi was born and she would grow up to marry a Grossi from another line, Giovanni. Their third son Domenico, named after his grandfather, was born on July 6th of 1874. Their youngest child, Giuseppe, was born in 1876. Only one of them would leave home.

In the same year that Domenico is born, a child of a very different family is born two hundred miles to the south near Bologna, which lies on the old Roman Via Aemilia that connected with the Via Flaminia at Rimini and carried travelers north to the city of Mediolanum, later Milan. Guglielmo is born into the aristocratic Marconi family. We will encounter him later as Domenico and Guglielmo's stories converge in Point Reyes.

Carlo Martinoia, as the newly minted Charles Martin, is already living in West Marin in the 1850s, after a short stint working in the oil fields. By 1870, he is able to buy a large ranch in the Chileno Valley. He will become the 26th richest landowner in Marin. This legacy will be passed on to this daughter Anita, when she marries Pietro Dolcini. Charles will move down to San Diego to raise cattle.

* * * *

Point Reyes ~ 1870

THE RAILROAD STOP

BY THE 1870S, DAYS OF THE WIDE OPEN SPACES where the Miwok, Pomo and other tribes could freely move with the seasonal food supply are long gone. The days of the soldiers and padres whose sacred and secular law reigned over vast regions of California are gone. The days of the huge ranchos, granted by the Spanish crown or the Mexican government to often unlikely recipients, are gone. The measures of land are much smaller but no less valuable and no less fought over. What is needed now are not the vast expanses of grazing land for animals, but tidy little parcels for human habitation and small businesses. The railroad has brought this need to the forefront of Point Reyes and other places across America. Everywhere the train stops, a town of some description will spring into life. There are still fortunes to be made. The Shafter brothers may have stream-lined the legal system behind the land transactions, but when it comes to land, it is still the "wild west" in many ways. Now smaller players can become involved and that is what happens next on Point Reyes.

James Shafter, being in on the ground floor of the North Pacific Coast Railroad plans, had busily bought up lots around Olema, especially at sheriff's auctions, anticipating the town that would grow up there around the railroad stop. Unfortunately for him, by the time the railroad began operation in 1875, its route took it two miles from Olema—too far for passengers on foot to look for food or accommodations. The place that it did stop was only a cow pasture, and the tired and hungry passengers were met with disappointment if they had hoped for a hotel or restaurant.

Enter the dentist, Dr. Galen Burdell. Dr. Burdell, like Charles Howard and Jack Hamilton (the sons-in-law of Oscar and James whom you will soon meet), was a beneficiary by marriage who added to the blend his own entrepreneurial gifts. You may remember that Olompali was a Miwok village to which Chief Marin often retreated from the San Rafael Mission. In 1852, the resourceful Camilio Ynitia, last Miwok chief or headman at Olompali, sold his land to James Black for $5200. Black would later turn over 960 acres of the land to his only daughter Mary, who became Mrs. Burdell, the wife of the dentist. The North Pacific Coast train went right through this land, "Mary Burdell's cow pasture." Dr. Burdell quickly realized that this was a goldmine of its own and set about the business of dividing the land around the railroad stop into tracts for houses and businesses and leasing them out. He built a hotel and saloon across from the railroad station, and insured a monopoly on liquid gold—the sale of alcohol in his saloon—by forbidding its sale on any of the property he leased out for businesses.

By 1880, a vigorous town is in place with livery stable, blacksmith, butcher shop and school. In 1882, the town has a post office and in 1892 it is officially named Point Reyes Station.

There is a great deal of melodrama in the lives of James Black and Mary and

Galen Burdell, which must have provided a welcome diversion to the inhabitants of those large ranches, isolated and without television. Nearly every one of the fortunes made in the early days of California began with an intrepid adventurer like Rafael Garcia, Timothy Murphy, Oscar Shafter and James Black—not to mention the Irishmen, Portuguese and Ticinesi who would soon fill out the history and development of "the whale." Or "the coyote" if you prefer.

At the age of 20, James Black had shipped out from his native Scotland aboard a Hudson's Bay vessel. During the voyage, he contracted typhoid fever and was put ashore in Monterey. Black married the widow of Ignacio Pacheco—a Californio* who had been granted the San Jose Rancho—6,660 acres, which included part of Novato. James Black was poorly educated—he could read but barely write—and had married a woman higher on the social scale, from the esteemed Durante family. She was his second wife. Nevertheless, he had made a fortune in gold from the gold fields, which had allowed him to purchase most of the 8,900 acres of Olompali from Camilo Ynitia.

Galen Burdell had come to San Francisco the long way round past the Horn from New York, where he had received his medical education. His original destination was Brazil, but after a time in that country, word of the Gold Rush inspired him to travel north to San Francisco. He found passage as a ship's surgeon on the Dunsbury, arriving in San Francisco with a lucrative venture already to his credit: the invention of a tooth powder. After his marriage to Jack black's daughter Mary, a most unfortunate incident occurred. Maria Sais Black, James Black's first wife and Burdell's mother-in-law, died in Dr. Burdell's dental chair. No matter that he was absolved of the blame, Black was so enraged that he had both Burdell and his daughter Mary expunged from his will. He began drinking on grand scale and in 1869, was further degraded by a serious fall which resulted in a deep wound to the base of his skull. He later died of terrible convulsions.

The reading of the will took place at the Pacheco House, attended by Dr. Burdell as Mary waited outside. Jack Mason describes it in his book *Early Marin*: "Later that evening, he brought an attorney to read the will in a private suite of a San Rafael hotel. When the attorney left the room, Mary tore her father's signature off with her teeth, apparently swallowing it, since it was never found. She was arrested but quickly released, a story that was given sensational treatment in the San Francisco press."

In the end, Mary was vindicated after contesting the will in a probate court in 1870. As a result, Galen and Mary were now in possession of 20,000 acres ranging from Tomales Bay to San Pablo Bay. Large portions of Novato and Nicasio were included in this. Jack Mason again: "Here the retired dentist found ample outlets for

---

* The term "Californios" refers to the Spanish and Mexican inhabitants of California—
then *Alta California*, Upper California, to distinguish it from *Baja California*, Lower
California. Alta California was primarily populated with Spanish or Mexicans of Spanish
descent during the Mission Period when it was ruled by Spain, and later when it came
under Mexican rule, following Mexico's revolution against Spain. Baja California still
belongs to Mexico.

his inventive mind. On the San Pablo Bay he ran his own soil reclamation project. His orchards were of many kinds of fruit: apple, pear, quince, fig, pomegrante, persimmon, apricot, peach and plum. Fifty acres were planted in 30 varieties of grapes, a kind of experimental vineyard with 'a hint of noble wines to come.'" This was in addition to the 960 acres that James Burdell had given to his daughter on her wedding day, destined to become the new railroad town, Point Reyes Station, which would one day be called Home by arriving Ticinesi.

❋ ❋ ❋ ❋

DAIRYMEN ALL

IT IS THE LATE SPRING OF 1870, James McMillan Shafter's home in Olema is being completed. The Point Reyes lighthouse is being completed. Plans for the North Pacific Coast Railroad are proceeding apace. James and his family are still living in San Francisco and Payne is largely overseeing completion of the house in Olema, spending part of his time in Point Reyes. Son James Jr. has begun medical school. Julia, age 11, is still attending school in the city. They have two young Chinese servants who live in with them—Dun Ah and Waun Ah, as well as a gardener from Prussia, Frank Bochow.

Another count is underway. Nearly a century has passed since Father Galli toiled along the steep paths of the Versazca Valley. The Status Animarum has been replaced with the United States Census. Bear in mind that California has only been a state in the union for twenty years. This is its third U.S. census.

The Grandi brothers—Salvatore and Luigi, now Louis—have made the long trip from Menzonio and taken up residence in Nicasio township near what was once the Miwok settlement of Ecta-Tamal, birthplace of the mother of Maria Nicolasa, who was born in Mission Dolores at Yerba Buena in 1775, where she was baptized as Otilia. When Maria Nicolasa married the son of a Miwok couple from the Awani-wi village in the San Rafael area, they moved to the San Rafael Mission. It was her husband, you might recall, who was remembered for playing the violin (as well as washing the priest's clothes.)

This is the land also that was given to the local Miwok after the dissolution of the Mission at San Rafael by Vallejo. It was the last of the native villages, along with Olompali, which Teodorico and other leaders had fought for for their people. This was also land that had belonged to Timothy Murphy. So you see the disparate places and people in our larger story are beginning to converge here in Marin. It is a many-storied history on a beautiful land.

Salvatore and Louis Grandi are lodging with two other Swiss immigrants—Julio Giacomini 49 and Peter Anzini, age 35, from their home village of Menzonio. According to the 1870 census, the secular version of the Status Animarum, on a page of forty names, there are eight dwellings listed. All are dairy workers, with the exception of the eight women, who are listed as housekeepers. The dairy workers are divided into two categories: dairy workers and dairymen, the dairymen clearly being managers of higher status and earnings. Sixteen are from Italian Switzerland. Six are listed as Dairyman with "estates" valued at between $2500 and $6000 as compared to Louis Grandi's $400 or Julio Giacomini's $100. Others list no estate value at all. But consider that Louis Grandi is only 20 years old at this time and Salvatore, only 16. The prosperous dairymen are mostly in their 30s and have likely been here longer. The three Anzinis—Peter, J (illegible) and Antone—own 850 acres between them. The Martinelli brothers own 973, valued at $15,000. How the emigrants from Ticino are coming up in the world from those desolate conditions of 1853 and later!

The same year, a census was taken at Olema, listed in the township of Bolinas. There are 47 Ticinesi, all of the males working on dairies, out of 320 people living there. There are seven Chedas, among Swiss-Italian names.

Already, the Ticinesi are beginning to leave their mark on the Marin landscape, bringing with them the humble skills that had been essential to their survival along the steep valleys of southern Switzerland and will now bring them a share of California gold.

T. Anthony Quinn cites an article in the January 1870 *Marin County Journal*, which sounds a familiar note even today. It is the comment of an unemployed worker: "This county has reached a pretty pitch when a white man can't get a day's work—what white men ought to be getting 40 dollars a month for, greasy Swiss and Portugees do for fifteen in summer and grub in winter." Another complained about "them damned Chinese and other coolies, the Portugees and the Swiss."

Waxing eloquent on the Swiss and Portuguese question, a dairyman complained later the same year that "Swiss, Portuguese and Italians are ruining the dairy business by renting cows per head which white men, who have to expend something for Christian food, cannot afford to pay."

This opinion will change.

* * * *

1880 ~ POINT REYES STATION

In the late 1840s and 50s, Nicasio landowners who had followed in the wake of Timothy Murphy were cashing in on the acres of redwoods that covered many of the rolling hills of the Nicasio Valley and several sawmills were built on the valley floor, soon processing 15,000 to 30,000 feet per day. But the valley timber was exhausted by the end of the 1870s.

By 1880, that industry had been displaced by a booming dairy business, matching the successes of the Shafter-Howard enterprises to the west on Point Reyes. As Anne Papina writes in her book *Nicasio*, "By this time, nearly 30 dairies call Nicasio their home." In that year, we find a stream of families from the Val

Versasca. Salvatore Grandi and his compatriots from Menzonio—Charles and Giacomo Gambonini, along with a 19-year-old Domenico Conti—are sharing their household in Nicasio. Rooming with them are Vincenzo and Giuseppe (Joseph) Corda, from the village of Vogorno in the Verzasca Valley. Next door to them you will find Peter Cheda's family, and with them, Domenico Jacomeni, age 25, among many other Ticinesi living close by and working on dairy farms: Patocchi, Frizzi, Casarotti, Gargazoli, Pedroncini, Lafranchi, Dellamaria, Belgari . . . Battista and John Cerini from Giumaglio in the Val Maggia, are also working in Nicasio.

The Ticinesi have arrived in force. The dairy industry is growing, with record yields of butter and cheese coming from the dairy farms at Point Reyes throughout the late 19th century. Herds of Devons, Jerseys, Guernseys, and later Holsteins, numbering from 100 to 250 cows per ranch, have catapulted the Point Reyes enterprise to possibly the largest operation in the early years of the state. In 1867, Marin County produces 932,429 pounds of butter, the largest yield of butter in California.

Meanwhile, Galen Burdell has laid out his town of Point Reyes Station, where the railroad will pass. Four Ticinesi, including Louis and Salvatore Grandi, with Quinto Codoni and Peter Scilacci of Corippo, have started building up a business district in what is now called Point Reyes Station. In 1884, Salvatore and Wilford Darneal take over the store there from A.P. Whitney and build neat little cottages for his employees. Peter Scilacci is employed there until he leaves to start his own store in the same block and becomes "the competition." An interesting light is shed on these activities and the nature of the times by a lawsuit instigated by Galen Burdell against Salvatore Grandi. It has that quaint language of a legal document.

Department 2. Appeal from Superior Court. Marin County; T. J. Lennon, Judge.
Action by Galen Burdell against S. Grandi and another.
J. R. Brandon, for appellant E. B. Martiuelli, for respondents.

LORIGAN, J. This is an action of ejectment, wherein plaintiff seeks to recover possession of a lot of land in the town of Point Reyes Station, in Marin county, for an alleged breach of a condition subsequent imposed In a deed made by plaintiff to the predecessor in title of the defendants.

The court found:

That in June, 1883, plaintiff [Burdell] was the owner of a tract of land in Marin county, upon which the town of Point Reyes Station now stands. That upon said date, for the purpose of establishing and building up said town, he laid out said tract into blocks and lots and made sales of the latter to individuals.

That all deeds executed by plaintiff of lots therein contained the following clause:

"It is hereby expressly understood and agreed between the parties hereto and their respective heirs, executors, administrators and assigns, and all claiming or to claim under them, that this conveyance is made and received solely and expressly on the condition that no saloon, barroom, liquor store, beer hall or any place where intoxicating liquors, or beer shall be sold at retail, shall be opened, established, allowed or permitted to exist on the said premises conveyed or any part thereof; nor shall any liquor, beer, wine or Intoxicating drink be sold, bartered or exchanged thereon at retail without the express-permission in writing of the party of the first part, his heirs, executors or administrators, and that upon the breach of said condition the estate hereby granted shall Immediately cease, determine and be void and revert to the grantor, his heirs or assigns, together with all improvements which may have been erected on the premises."

... That in July, 1883, plaintiff, in consideration of the construction and erection of a store by one A. P. Whitney on a lot in said town (being the same premises Involved in this action), made a grant of said lot to him; the deed containing the condition and provision heretofore referred.

That said Whitney constructed and erected a store on the said premises, and thereafter by sundry mesne conveyances the title to said lot passed from said Whitney to the defendant S. Grandi, who in 1888 conveyed a portion thereof to his codefendant, Q. Codoni. That in March, 1902, the defendant Grandi, without the consent of plaintiff, opened and established a saloon on the portion of the lot retained by him for the sale of intoxicating liquors, and has since continued to conduct said saloon thereon and to sell Intoxicating liquors therein, without the consent of plaintiff. . . .

Well it goes on and on, of course, as those quaint documents tend to do. But the long and short of it is that Burdell had put a clause in all of his Point Reyes Station property leases and contracts that no "spirits" could be sold on the premises. Ever! This proviso was not motivated by Burdell's religious convictions regarding the evils of alcohol and calling for temperance, but quite the contrary. Saloons were the most popular businesses on the peninsula and Burdell wanted a monopoly so that his own saloon would be the single benefactor of the overwhelming thirst that comes from large, empty spaces. The original court had ruled against him because the purpose of the clause was so clearly to establish a monopoly. He also lost this appeal for the same reason.

You will notice that the properties in question have diminished considerably in size from tens of thousands of acres being shuffled in the time of Garcia and Berry to small lots and buildings. The Ticinesi are holding their own against the oldtimers here, defended in court by none other than Lorenzo Martinelli's son, E. B. Martinelli. Moreover, the Ticinesi are beginning to leave their mark on the Marin landscape, bringing with them the humble skills that had been essential to their survival along the steep valleys of southern Switzerland and will now bring them a share of California gold.

In 1883, the *Marin County Journal* finally publishes an editorial which vindicates the emigrant population and acknowledges their contribution:

Judging by their achievements in this country, the Swiss people are the most successful of all American citizens, whether native or adopted. Several of the very finest ranches in this county are owned by Swiss gentlemen. Some of them having been bought at figures as high as $50,000 to $75,000. And we can almost venture to say that not one of the owners of these splendid ranches brought any money to speak of to this county with him. They came here penniless boys. But they had good health, industrious habits and the frugality that is born in the Old World where labor has poorer remuneration than here.

These lads arriving here commence work in the humblest capacity on dairy ranches, usually being employed by their own countrymen, for they do not understand English, and one of their first efforts is to acquire the language of the country. Ten or twelve years pass, during which they grow to manhood, master our language, work steadily, and save their wages. They have no extravagant habits, no wild associates, no fast proclivities. They learn their business thoroughly, and before you know it they are capable of managing a large dairy themselves, and have money enough to lease or buy a ranch. We hold these Swiss citizens up before the young men of America as examples for them to follow.

While the ranks of the Ticinesi are expanding quickly, along with the Irish, the Portuguese and others in the immigrant tide in this year of 1880, it is reported that Captain Sebastian, a Nicasio Indian leader, has died at nearly 100 years of age. He had become a well-known figure in the area as a member of the last of the native Miwok as late as 1853—300 men who owned at least a territory of 100,000 acres.

By now, less than 30 years later, the last of the Nicasio Indians, as we noted earlier, have managed to briefly hold on to 30 acres of the original 80,000-acre grant. According to Marin historian Jack Mason, this 30-acre parcel along Halleck Creek was conveyed to them by Henry Halleck.* The *Marin Journal* Illustrated Edition of 1887 reports,

> Chief John Calistro finally gathered up all the remnants of Indian properties and with the proceeds purchased some thirty acres . . . , thereafter making an attempt to uplift his people in a final struggle against the insidious voices of the white man. But this little band was surrounded by every kind of demoralizing influence and the settlers were too busy to banish the vagabonds preying upon them. It was soon necessary for the county to support these disheartened remnants of a once great race . . .

According to Marin historian Charles Meret, the Nicasio tribelet dwindled to fewer than two dozen living in eight redwood bark teepees in 1880, each with a diameter of approximately eight feet.** Two remained in 1884 and "a few" in 1887.

From Nicasio.net: "The demise of the Coast Miwok civilization was due less to wicked villainy than to the clash of two disparate cultures that could not coexist, and yet it was due less to this disparate culture clash than to the secret weapon all foreigners brought, regardless of their motives: Deadly diseases for which the natives had no immunities."

* *Early Marin,* Jack Mason and Helen Van Cleave Park. 1971. Dewey Livingston clarifies that Halleck sold to W.J. Miller who then sold it to Calistro.
** Although the 1880 census reports 38 indians living in Nicasio, Meret may be reflecting the "visible community." In either case, the number is pitifully small.

There is a certain irony in the fact that the natives of those Ticino villages in the Maggia and Verzasca valleys are also dwindling, as they swell the census ranks in Marin. Unlike the indigenous Americans, they have a place to go and go they do. For the abundant native tribes of Marin and Sonoma, it would seem that the trail has ended in virtual extinction. (The last Coastal Miwok native speaker died in 1978.) But Betty Goerke tells us that this is not the case.

From *Chief Marin:*

The Coast Miwok have survived. In a small museum in Bolinas, the title of a 1993 Indian tribal exhibit announced: "We Are Still Here.". . . Although most of these survivors had moved to Pomo territory in Sonoma County's Santa Rosa, where many had intermarried with the Pomo and non-Indians, some people of Coast Miwok descent were still living on traditional Miwok land, for example, in Corte Madera, San Rafael, Novato, Petaluma, and the area of Tomales Bay, Bodega, and Bodega Bay.

A year before the museum exhibit opened, some 150 Coast Miwok survivors had come together in an emergency meeting at the home of Rita Carrillo [a descendant of Marino through her grandmother, Maria Copa]. They were assembling to oppose a proposal by the Cloverdale Pomo to build a marina, homes, a golf course, and a casino at Marshall, on the coast of Marin County, which was clearly former territory of the Coast Miwok.

In spite of their common heritage, many of the guests at Carrillo's home had not spoken with one another for more than fifty years, a consequence of what Greg Sarris referred to as an "angered history" between families. But they soon found their own close relatives in shared family photographs, realized their "connectedness, and saw it as a sign from the ancestors."*

As a result of this meeting, a group was formed called the Federated Coast Miwok, which consists of people of both Coast Miwok and Southern Pomo descent. In December 2000, the group gained federal recognition as a tribe and became the Federated Indians of Graton Rancheria.

---

* Greg Sarris, the newly elected chairman of this group and later Tribal Chairman, received his Ph.D. from Stanford University and went on to become an acclaimed author, screenwriter, producer, scholar, and professor at Sonoma State University. His many books include *Grand Avenue*, which later became an HBO mini-series produced by Robert Redford. See more about Sarris and the tribe today at http://greg-sarris.com/.

TRANSITIONS

IT IS A HOT, CLEAR DAY IN SAN FRANCISCO. A preview of the days ahead in September and October. Autumn is the best season in the city. At midsummer, temperatures can drop down into the 40s as the fogs hold sway.

In the Shafter house on Chestnut Street, an unusual quiet reigns, in spite of the coming and going of several guests and the presence of family members who have gathered there. James Shafter has taken to his bed. In the morning, the Reverend Emery of St. Peter's Episcopal Church came to have the "end of life" discussion with James. Two doctors have now arrived and are in consultation with the family over the turn that James' diabetes has taken and the general condition of the 76 year-old. It is not looking good.

James McMillan Shafter will not live to see those fine September and October days. Although he had been appointed to the Superior Court bench in 1890, at the age of 74, he was remembered in those years as bitter and cantankerous. His complaints about the dark office assigned to him won him better quarters in the courthouse. His complaints about the newspapers influencing jurors, won him the scorn of the famous Ambrose Bierce:

> *. . . the jaw*
> *That's always wagging with a word malign*
> *Nagging and scolding everyone in sight*
> *As harshly as a jaybird in a pine.*

His strident disapproval of the German bride that his son James brought home from Europe led to serious repercussions. James Jr. submitted to his father's will and divorced the woman. Soon afterward, her brother arrived from Germany and was eager for revenge at the offense to the family, correctly aiming his ire at the Judge. Fortified with whiskey and a revolver, he assailed Judge Shafter as he emerged from the elevator in the new city hall but his shots went wild. The athletic James, his age notwithstanding, wrestled his assailant to the floor and narrowly escaped being murdered. Justice Shafter had prevailed. James later married a professional pianist from Boston, Frances Rock Shafter.

James McMillan Shafter went out, not with a whimper, but with a bang.

* * * *

Monte Carasso, Ticino ~ December 1892

DOMENICO

EARLY DECEMBER IN TICINO, JUST BEFORE DAWN. The temperature is below freezing and it is possible they will have snow. Michelangelo Grossi is arranging the kindling and logs to start a fire in the grate. His wife Teresa moves like a sleepwalker through the familiar early morning motions of making the polenta. His son Domenico has gone out to get more wood from the woodpile. No one has spoken. Domenico is likely thinking that this is the last time he will perform this morning task, eat this morning breakfast, do the things that he has done daily for most of his seventeen years. His sister Maria appears at her mother's side, looking half-asleep, if indeed anyone has slept.

So many Ticino families have reenacted this scene, yet for them it is new. Raw. Teresa has exhausted all of her words, her arguments for her son to stay. And his arguments have always remained the same. It would be no different if he had gotten married to someone in one of the other villages. He would still be leaving home. It was natural. He is 17 years old. His mother insists that they would be able to see him if he lived in another village, but across the sea in America? Don't worry, he has promised, I will return and I can send money to help you. That is something I can't do from any other place in Ticino. You will be glad of it.

This is the scene I have imagined though we will never know exactly what took place among the family members on the morning of departure. We know she didn't want him to go. We know he said he would return.

December is a cold and dark month. Sometime in that first week, Domenico set off in the early morning with his cousins. Pietro Grossi, age 24. Luigi Grossi, who was his own age, and "L. Grossi" as he was listed on the manifest of La Burgogne, who was eleven years old.

It must have been very cold indeed when they reached St. Gotthard's Pass.

◆ ◆ ◆

The Gotthard Pass has been described as a "primeval massif" separating (or connecting) Northern and Southern Europe. The southern flank of the pass, the Tremola, was built between 1827 and 1830 and makes a steep hair-raising descent of over 3000 feet (1000 meters) down serpentine switchbacks from Airolo into the Schöllenen Gorge and the barren valley of the Urserenthal. In the nineteenth century it was traversed by Post Bus or by a stagecoach drawn by five horses.

The narrow valley of the Ticino rises from Lago Maggiore and the Lombard plain to reach the 7000 foot Pass. It descends on the other side through the valley of Reuss. The tracks through the path, on both the north and south sides, are very narrow and rugged, exposing the early travelers to great dangers. Early summer was a particularly difficult time to pass because it required fording the turbulent

Reuss, swollen with snowmelt during the early summer, in the narrow steep-sided Schöllenen Gorge (the Schöllenenschlucht), below Andermatt. The Devil's Bridge was constructed to avoid the drownings that occurred in this treacherous place.

A mule path across the pass was first mentioned about 1293 and some time after that we hear of a chapel and Hospice (toll house) at the summit. Centuries later, a carriage road was completed between 1820 and 1830. The final and most daring step, building a tunnel through the Gotthard was completed in 1882 and literally paved the way for trains to run between Milan and Lucerne, the end point of the pass on the north. It was a difficult and daring feat that is said to have cost the lives of some 200 workers.

Those early immigrants, Carlo Martinoia, Pietro and Michael Dolcini, and Salvatore Grandi would have made this treacherous crossing on foot, after leaving the stagecoach. Domenico Grossi and those who followed would have been able to travel by train. In every case, however, they must have felt palpably the turning point in their lives as the track descended out of their mountain homes, north to Le Havre. In his new country, he will be called "Dominic" by Americans, though he will remain Domenico among his family and Ticinesi friends. We will call him Dominic, for the new man he is about to become.

In the year 1892, the Shafter star is descending as Dominic Grossi's, and many other Ticinesi, are finally on the rise. The last Shafter brother, James, is making his departure from the landscape that he helped shape, as Dominic Grossi is slowly arriving on the scene. While Dominic makes the long, slow trip across the pass, then by the ship La Burgogne, then on the new railroad across America—the Shafter Empire is entering into its final phase of eclipse, making way for a new and more democratic Point Reyes dairy industry, although still with fortunes to be made by men of wits, energy and determination.

Point Reyes, Christmas Day 1892

ARRIVAL

IT IS LIKE LOOKING AT THE WORLD from the inside of a pearl—a seamless gray-white smoothness through the arc of sky to the haze of sea and land, suffused with a dull light. A darker white appears, outlined by a thread of shadow. A dot that quickly grows larger, flares out on cambered wings, separates the sky above and the firmament below with its perfect arbitrary flight. Large as an eagle but not an eagle. A condensation of sea and sky into purposeful flight. An osprey.

Suddenly it falls like a stone toward the water, but at the last minute veers off, having snatched from the sea a large fish which it now lifts upward into sky. It traces an invisible spiral and then with graceful deceleration, it disappears into the upper boughs of a tall pine.

Below, another dot perforates the whiteness with measured steps. A man is walking. He does not look back. Ever. None of them do. He belongs to this land now and is in community with this strange new bird. Harbinger of his future. Of his freedom. Other arrivals are yet to come, far into the future, and not all of them human ones. It is still half a century before fallow deer arrive, some of them pure white, and others brown or black, changing color like leaves and birds with the seasons. They are also migrants from the Mediterranean region, introduced into the Lagunitas area between 1842 and 1854. They have spread out now from Inverness Ridge to Bear Valley, a few further north and south. The shy and graceful axis deer also arrived from other parts in roughly the same period. A native of India.

WHERE EAST AND WEST MEET

1892–1893, Durgapur ~ East Bengal, India

A POND OF LIGHT

A FEW MONTHS AFTER THE DEATH OF JAMES SHAFTER and the life-changing voyage of Domenico Grossi to the New World, another life-changing experience will be seeded in the small village of Durgapur in East Bengal. Life-changing, that is, in the way that every pregnancy changes a woman and the members of her family. In this case, it is Sushila Devi, wife of the district postmaster, Nabin Chandra Datta. The postmaster could comfortably support his young daughter, Sunita, in that year and the son who would be born in the next. There will finally be three girls and two boys. Sushila Devi and Nabin Chandra will give thanks to Kanialal—Sri Krishna—for each one.

Yogesh Chandra Datta was born, according to custom, in his mother's village of Bekitaka. He was raised in Durgapur in their bamboo and mud house, just off the main road from Habiganji. The house is part of a larger compound. In the front of it is a very large pond that fills with the rippling light of sunshine and the voices of villagers who all share in its use. Beyond are lush fields, spread out to the horizon. If later Yogesh has memories of his early years, they will likely be filled with this green landscape, which suddenly disappears each year under the downfall of water brought by the rainy season. Then the fields and pond disappear under a glass-like sea that fills the eye in every direction and forces the villagers to travel about by boat, even to their neighbors' houses.

If Yogesh Chandra Datta has memories, they will also surely include those curious little boats made of clay, shaped like a pot, and only large enough for one person to paddle. He will remember spinning round and round for the sheer joy of it. As to other children? We do know that he views them as a spectator, puzzled by their odd antics.

"I just watched them playing and wondered what they saw in it. I felt very sedate and serene within. Outwardly I may have seemed like a little boy, but within I was never a little boy. I always felt that I didn't belong to this world. Everything seemed strange. It was a very strong feeling."

This slate of memory will be discarded, however, as Yogesh takes on a new identity and a new life, just as thousands of slates have been discarded in similar situations. Domenico, now Dominic, discards his own, as Yogesh will do. We can thank Sister Gargi for culling this information from the family of Yogesh. Of other things, he will speak more freely or they are simply things known about the place he grew up. So she writes—

In that peaceful village, where pumpkin vines grew over the thatched roof of mud houses, where fish could bask undisturbed on a riverbank, where the mustard-oil presses creaked in the early morning, where women winnowed padd, and cows

385

looked through windows—in that village Yogesh grew. And one could not grow up in an Indian village without becoming saturated with God. . . . In Durgapur, as in all other Indian villages. Men and women sang of God as they went about their daily tasks; Vaishnava monks came to the house for alms and sang of God or talked of Him; travelers passing through the village sang of Him; boatmen and cowherds sang of Him and the rural mailman walking all day long from house to house might sing that he was knocking at every door for the Lord to open it and appear before him . . . And there was the man who had taken a vow to repeat aloud the name of God continuously for twelve years. The practice had transformed him from an ordinary house-holder to a God-intoxicated saint. The Dattas had heard of him and asked him to come and stay for a week or so. There was not much conversation with him, but the name of God would ring through the Datta compound and charge the air. *

Chicago ~ 1893

CALIFORNIA BUILDING
WORLD'S COLUMBIAN EXPOSITION
OPENING DAY, MAY 1ST, 1893

Upon the occasion of the Opening of the World's Columbian Exposition, on May 1st, the California Colony gathered in their Moorish-Mission building, in Jackson Park, and with informal exercises celebrated the day.

The presentation of a handsome bear flag to the Commission was to be made by the Hon. James D. Phelan, on behalf of Pacific Parlor No. 10 of Native Sons of the Golden West.

— from an official pamphlet of the event

IT HAS BEEN SAID THAT WORLD'S FAIRS of the kind taking place in Chicago in the spring of 1893 originated in the French tradition of holding national exhibitions, which reached a peak during the industrial era with the French Industrial Exposition of 1844 held in Paris. This sparked other national industrial exhibitions in continental Europe and inspired Victoria's Prince Albert to hold in London the first real international exhibition on May 1, 1851 in Hyde Park's Crystal Palace. Prior to this Chicago Exhibition, two such international events have been held in the United States: one in Philadelphia in 1876, at the anniversary of the founding of the nation, and the other in New Orleans in 1884 as the Cotton Centennial, commemorating the first export shipment of cotton from the United States to England in 1784.

James D. Phelan of California is using this opportunity to extol the virtues of his new state to those older states of the Midwest and East. The World's Columbian Exposition, later often referred to as The Chicago World's Fair, is being held in Chicago in this year of 1893 to celebrate the 400th anniversary of

* From *A Heart Poured Out* by Marie Louise Burke.

Columbus's arrival in the New World in 1492. One of its great legacies, one might even call it an unintended consequence of this event, will be the profound effect it has on architecture and the arts. While Phelan has come here to sell California in Chicago, Chicago is selling him on a design he will later seek to carry out as Mayor of San Francisco. The persuasive figure in this process is none other than one of our early citizens from Hendersonville, New York. We have by now accounted for the Big Four—Charles Crocker, Mark Hopkins, Amasa Leland Stanford and Collis Huntingdon. But we have still to catch up with Daniel, the son of the Swedenborgian family, who has also become a very significant Somebody. In fact, the Chicago Columbian Exposition has, in large part, been designed by Daniel Burnham and his associate, Frederick Law Olmsted, as the model of what Burnham and his colleagues believe a city should be. It follows the Beaux Arts principles of design in its emphasis on symmetry, balance, and splendor in the classical style.

Architecture is not the only field that will be impacted by the events of the Chicago Columbia Exposition. A number of congresses will be held in conjunction with the exposition, including the World's Parliament of Religions, from September 11th to September 27th. It will be by far the largest of the conventions and the first attempt to create a global dialogue among various faiths. One voice in particular will be making its debut in America and will set off reverberations at least as large as the City Beautiful movement. The "wisdom of the East" is about to step onto the Main Stage of the World's Fair in Chicago to make a very significant debut in the person of Sri Vivekenanda, whose address draws wide attention.

Welcome Address ~ Chicago, Sept 11, 1893

SWAMI VIVEKANANDA

Sisters and Brothers of America,
It fills my heart with joy unspeakable to rise in response to the warm and cordial welcome which you have given us. I thank you in the name of the most ancient order of monks in the world; I thank you in the name of the mother of religions, and I thank you in the name of millions and millions of Hindu people of all classes and sects. . . .

The present convention, which is one of the most august assemblies ever held, is in itself a vindication, a declaration to the world of the wonderful doctrine preached in the Gita: "Whosoever comes to Me, through whatsoever form, I reach him; all men are struggling through paths which in the end lead to me." Sectarianism, bigotry, and its horrible descendant, fanaticism, have long possessed this beautiful earth. They have filled the earth with violence, drenched it often and often with human blood, destroyed civilization and sent whole nations to despair. Had it not been for these horrible demons, human society would be far more advanced than it is now. But their time is come; and I fervently hope that the bell that tolled this morning in honor of this convention may be the death-knell of all fanaticism, of all persecutions with the sword or with the pen, and of all uncharitable feelings between persons wending their way to the same goal.

WHO IS THIS MAN WHO HAS BURST SO SUDDENLY on the American scene and made such an impact on his audience in Chicago? Like Yogesh P. Datta, he is from Bengali in India. In this year of 1893, the year Yogesh is born, the man born Narendranath Dutta is thirty years old. Unlike Yogesh, who comes from a respectable, educated but not affluent family, Narendranath Dutta is born of an aristocratic family in Calcutta. His father is an attorney with liberal views on social and religious matters, although they are nevertheless a traditional Kayastha family, which means they are of a caste with dual status as Brahmin (highest sagely caste) and Kshatriya (warrior caste). The Kayastha were traditionally a caste of scribes. Narentranath's mother was a pious woman who prayed to Vireshwar Shiva of Varanasi to give her a son. Then in a dream, she saw Shiva rise from his meditation to announce to her that he would be born in the form of her son.

Raised in this rational and religious environment and reading voluminously, Vivekananda's mind developed and he became adept at meditation and entering into spiritual states. Like Yogesh, he was immersed in the spiritual life of India and was also impressed by the wandering ascetics and monks whom he encountered. His interests and studies were wide-ranging, but he took particular interest in Indian scriptural texts—the Vedas, Upanishads, Puranas, the Bhagavad-Gita, Ramayana and Mahabharata. His interest and aptitude in classical music was balanced by his love of sports and physical exercise.

Much of Vivekananda's education took place at home, but he later graduated in 1881 from a university in Calcutta with a Bachelor of Arts degree. He was regarded by his professors as a prodigy. A genius. In the end of that same year, 1881, he met one of India's best-known figures, the religious mystic Ramakrishnan, who later became his guru, or spiritual teacher.

In 1887, he took monastic vows and with those, the name Swami Vivekananda. A year later, at 24 years old, he took up the life of a wandering monk, traveling throughout India, visiting major centers of learning and exposing himself to the various religious and social traditions of his country. Like Siddhartha Buddha, the young man of affluent family came into contact with the suffering and poverty of India's masses. His two favorite books were the *Bhagavad Gita* and *The Imitation of Christ*.

Hearing of the World Parliament of Religions meeting in Chicago in 1893, he was moved to make the journey to America, by way of Japan. The response to his talk there was a standing ovation from seven thousand people that lasted a full two minutes.

Narendranath Dutta, now Swami Vivekananda, would go on to lecture in other American cities, including Detroit, Boston, and New York. He was offered the chair of Eastern Philosophy at Harvard University and a similar position at Columbia University, but declined both, saying that, as a wandering monk, such settled work in one place would be inconsistent with his vocation.

It would be seven years before he arrived in San Francisco.

1895 ~ Brione, Ticino

CATERINA

CATERINA BUZZINI IS SITTING IN THE CHURCH OF ST. MARY *of the Assumption in Brione, not far from where Maria had sat five hundred years before. Giovanni Baronzio would be pleased to see how well his fresco has survived through half a millennium. It has darkened with age and the colors are not so bright. It is chipped in a few places. Some of Maria's youthful innocence still shines from the virgin's face, though somewhat dimly. Caterina is not the youthful maiden that Maria was. She is a 43 year old widow with much on her mind. She looks at the fresco more closely now, as if she is seeing it for the first time. Or more accurately, for the last time. It is the only spot of color in the lives of many of the parishoners. What Caterina has in common with the young Maria and her family is . . . hunger. The town has built up since Maria's time and the noble Marcacci family from Locarno has built a castle here. To them, the town is "charming" and the landscape "magnificent." So she has heard. But to those less well endowed than the Marcacci family, it is a place where the struggle to stay alive and feed one's family is a losing one. Especially in those years when heavy rains come and ruin the harvest and livestock die of some strange disease. When every meal is polenta and little more.*

Caterina has no husband to work for her in Milan through the winter to bring back money to buy food in the markets. Her older step-children have struggles of their own and cannot be expected to support her. Now that her husband is gone, dead from pneumonia after a miserable winter when he was too ill to work and could not recover his health before the spring, she and her young son, Celeste, are on their own. Their cow has died and their goat looks to be on its last legs too. Another winter is unthinkable.

What Caterina is thinking about now, in between her fervent prayers to the virgin, is the letters that continue to arrive from relatives in California. She remembers Salvatore and Louis Grandi from Menzonio crowing about their plans to sail to America when she and Salvatore were sixteen years old. They had both been born in the same year—the year Radestsky had closed the border. The sixteen-year-old Salvatore had teasingly asked her to run away with him to make their fortunes in a new land full of opportunities. It was during the town's celebration of their Saint's day, always a grand event thanks to the generous contributions of the Marcacci family. In those villages, the feast days of their saints were events that everyone looked forward to, and people would travel a long way to attend one as lively as Brione's. It was on such a feast day, twenty-five years ago, that Salvatore had made his announcement. He and Louis were the first to go, back in 1869. The word was that they were prospering. Her brother-in-law had emigrated to Santa Barbara area, although she had yet to hear from him. Buzzini cousins of her late husband, from nearby Russo and Vergeletta, had also taken the big step and had found work in San Francisco. Joseph was a shoemaker and George was a liquor dealer. Salvatore and Louis were in a place called Marin, north of the city. They had a little store there. So why shouldn't she go too? They would help her find work. It wasn't as if she would be alone.

The church bell rang then and she knew that Celeste would be coming out of the school next to the church. She often met him and they walked home together. As they passed through the plaza, they met her step-daughter, Teresina. The 18 year old girl is also determined to make her way to America. She has dreams of meeting a husband there. Someone prosperous who could offer her a life far better than life in Ticino. But she would stay on until she had earned enough money for the trip, as her brother Giovanni was doing. Teresina's Mocettini cousins were also laying their plans. Antonio Mocettini was already in Santa Cruz, California.

There was a lot of tension in the village. Arguments about who should go and who should stay. Discord among siblings. Sorrow between lovers. As if hunger wasn't enough to trouble a town.

Marin ~ ca. 1898

THE TRAIN RIDE

CATERINA BUZZINI ARRIVED IN NEW YORK on October 24, 1897. She was then a forty-four year old widow, traveling with her seven year old son, Celeste. They likely settled in Point Reyes for a while. Years later, they will be living in Petaluma.

She promised this birthday gift to Celeste months ago and she knows that he has been counting the days. She had also promised to stop calling him Celeste and to use his American name, Charles. She tries to remember to do this because he was very resistant in the beginning to having his name changed along with everything else. But now that he has completed his first year of school and started into his second year, he doesn't want to be embarrassed by other children telling him that it is a girl's name. So Charles it must be, although she will not descend to calling him Charlie.

Caterina has packed a lunch for them both. The day is finally here. They will be riding the Picnic Train from Point Reyes Station to Cazadero. The new, longer route, which now extends beyond Tomales was opened in 1886 and carries passengers into the redwood forests near the Russian River. Charles especially wants to see a redwood tree. A friend at school had seen one as wide as their house and so tall that only the angels can see its tips. Well—so he said.

At 8 am, they board the train near the Place of the Little Willows, Saucelito—so named by Capt. Richardson when he had lived here. As the train starts up, it chugs along the rim of Richardson Bay, clickety-clacking over the wooden trestle as it crosses the water. To their left, had they known it, they are passing the place where Huicmuse-Marino was born in the Huimen village of Anamas, and to their right, the waters that crew members from the San Carlos had plied to reach the eagerly waiting natives, lining the shore to watch their approach.

The train passes on through their spectral presences, slowly gaining speed, and runs along the edge of a narrow inlet. To the east of that is the tip of a peninsula that reaches toward them like a cupped hand, proceeding in gentle rises and descents. Along the shore, low green cliffs drop down to the blue water. They pass two more small islands close to shore and then the mainland expands sharply eastward, with the silhouette of Ring Mountain in the distance as the train begins to veer westward. A valley opens up before them toward the northwest. Mill Valley, Belvedere, Tiburon . . . The lands of the Huimen are now spread out on either side of them, the tracks running parallel to where the Redwood Highway runs today. They pass to the west of Corte Madera and Larkspur, regions that were then covered by an extensive tidal marsh, intersected by waterways and little tidal islands. Tule and birds.

They angle now between King Mountain and Southern Height Ridge through the Ross Valley toward their first stop 10 miles from Sausalito in San Anselmo. After San Anselmo, the tracks divide at the foot of Red Hill, where a spur goes east to San Rafael. They have no thought of course for Father Amorós, Huicmuse and Mottique, Corporal Garcia and the father of Otilia-Maria Nicolasa who played the violin. They don't even know they existed.

The main line turns west toward the next stop, two miles on at Fairfax. Vineyards belonging to a Frenchman, Camille Grosjean, drift over the hills. The train is following along Corte Madera Creek to San Anselmo Creek, to Fairfax Creek just as the natives had. Fairfax Creek carves a valley between the peaks of White Hill and Loma Alto, forming a natural trail which had been followed by Coast Miwok for millennia, then wagons, and now the North Coast Railroad. In a few short decades it would become the traffic-laden Sir Francis Drake Boulevard.

Steep hillsides clad in spring green rise up beside them. Then they begin to rise too, curving in a loop to the north and then west as the train makes its serpentine ascent up White's Hill—the highest elevation of the trip at 525 feet. This had been the most difficult challenge for the engineers. Charles takes a seat on the opposite side where, beyond the train, empty space opens up and it seems, but for the noise, as if the train were flying through the air. He presses his nose against the glass and peers down for a sight of land beneath them. Yet he also likes to imagine them fleeing through the empty air away from schools and strangers who make fun of him. They pass through two tunnels and then hang suspended over two trestles. A hawk dips its wings in silent salute to them, fellow travelers of the heights. Then they descend into the lovely San Geronimo Valley.

After stops at Lagunitas, Camp Taylor and Tocaloma, they reach the shore of Tomales Bay and the bustling railroad town of Point Reyes Station. They could get off the train right here and be nearly home, but Charles is determined to see the whole countryside from Sausalito to Cazadero. There is time here to walk around a little and to get some small treat at the Grandi Store for Charles and to see friends "from home"—Salvatore and Louis. They always have news from Ticino—who has come; who is about to come; what they are doing now. It's as good as a newspaper, Grandi's store.

A calm and quiet settles over them again as they continue their train ride along the inland shore of Tomales Bay. Only a few passengers remain. They pass through sixteen miles of prime dairy country, along the towns of Tomales, Valley Ford, and Freestone before the great redwood forest begins at Howards. They pass the logging town of Duncan Mills, where many of the great redwoods will end their days to meet the region's population boom and where people like James Shafter were so *heavily invested, as many still are. This is the Russian River country—the heart of Kashaya Pomo territory for some five thousand years.*

The train follows along Austin Creek where they get off at the Elim Grove Hotel stop in the center of 500 acres of magnificent redwoods. They have not come to stop at the hotel but to fulfill Charles' dream of walking among the giant trees. They do this silently. As if they were tiptoeing down the aisle of a church. Then they return to the station, still without a word, to catch the returning train. Dusk is settling in. The trip from San Francisco was five hours, but it will not be so long this time. They will get off in Point Reyes Station and catch a stage home. Throughout the ride, Charles remains quiet. But on his face is a new expression, as if he had just visited friends. Catherine felt that the $5.00 spent on two excursion tickets, while a fortune to them, had been well spent.

✳ ✳ ✳ ✳

Bolinas, Point Reyes ~ August 1846 to the Present

MAKING WAVES

The whole of history could, indeed, be written as a drama of human nature reacting to invention. . . . And we live to-day in a time of accelerated inventiveness and innovation, when a decade modifies the material of inter-communication far more extensively than did any century before. . . . Within the present century, since 1900, there have been far more extensive changes in these things than occurred in the ten centuries before Christ. . . . In education and in the agencies of journalism and propaganda, there has been an increase of power at present incalculable, owing to vast strides in the means of intense world-wide information and suggestion.

— H.G. WELLS, 1919

DO YOU RECALL THAT DOUGHTY CORPORAL RAFAEL GARCIA, back in the days of "musical land grants," when the owners kept changing places? Garcia's original 8,863 acre Rancho Tomales y Baulenes was situated at the southern tip of the Point Reyes peninsula. This is the one area, other than the Pierce Ranch on the north end, that would not be subsumed by the Shafter-Howard dairy empire. It would remain a region whose inhabitants prefer to remain quietly independent, taking on the character of the land itself traveling slowly northward, independent of the North American plate.

Rafael Garcia was born in San Diego around 1790. His father likely arrived on one of the ships that sailed with the San Carlos on the ill-fated Sacred Expedition from San Blas, Mexico. The father of Gregorio Briones, his brother-in-law, came on that voyage in 1769 and then traveled north with Junipero Serra. Rafael Garcia also came north with one of Serra's expeditions and later commanded the military escort to the new mission San Rafael in 1817. He is middle-aged now. A sociable man, father of eight, rough-hewn, brutal; like Cain in the Garden of Eden, flawed, but vital to the human story.

He is standing at the western edge of his domain, watching the waves that break on the rocks in an endless, mesmerizing rhythm. He has walked out to the edge of a shale beach, extended by the summer tides, where he had often brought his children.

For Rafael Garcia, the edge of his world is the shale's edge, which drifts back and forth with the tides. But there are many layers in this place, some of them invisible, interpenetrating, that tell the Earth's story in a living calendar.

Underneath the waters beyond him, where only a pale light reaches from the afternoon sky, the man standing at the edge is a mere shadow, ephemeral and unrelated. A passing cloud. He is invisible to the myriad creatures who inhabit this region of the aqueous realm that is ninety-seven percent of the Earth's biosphere.

The layer of shale beneath Garcia's feet is a souvenir of a time spent docked next to Monterey during the granitic whale's slow northwesterly migration. A thousand to two thousand feet beneath him lies the granitic bedrock that formed, as naturalist Jules Evens puts it, "about the time that snakes slithered onto the scene and oaks and buckeyes began to bloom"; a day or two before Christmas on our calendar, 90 to 110 million years ago.*

Some ways behind Garcia is the settlement of adobe buildings he has built on his rancho. His family has grown and relatives have come to join him. It is the Mexican way. He has turned his own home and property here over to his brother-in-law, Gregorio Briones, and rounded up local Indians to help him build a new and bigger home for his family just west of Nelson's Hotel in Olema, where Theresa Buzzini will meet Dominic Grossi. All of it is his world now. Wild and beautiful. He is a keen hunter and the land abounds in wildlife. The other day, he had taken Captain Revere—on leave from his ship, the Portsmouth—on an elk hunt. The man from Massachusetts was awestruck at the sight of a herd of some 400 elk. "This is nothing," Garcia told him. "When I first came there were thousands and Stephen Richardson estimates that at one time there were millions. Maybe the largest elk herd in the world." Stephen is the son of William Richardson who first settled in the Place of the Little Willows, Sausalito.

Garcia invited Capt. Revere to spend the night with him before returning to his ship. He knew that the captain had fallen in love with the place and would return, even though he was full of stories of his native Massachusetts. He spoke proudly of his grandfather, Paul Revere, and the part he had played in the American revolution. Yet he was willing to leave that all behind for this wild beauty of Point Reyes.

Other invisible layers will develop in this place as the air itself becomes alive in new ways. In 1893, the young aristocrat born into the Marconi family near Bologna, in the same year as Domenico Grossi, is summering with his family in the Alpine foothills of northern Italy. A little over one hundred miles north, Domenico Grossi is laying plans for his departure from Monte Carasso. The new year will find Domenico working on the Pierce Ranch in Point Reyes, while Marconi continues to labor away on his secret experiments in the attic of his parents' home on their estate. One night

* I am indebted to Jules Evens for this scholarly and imaginative description and highly recommend his beautifully written *Natural History of the Point Reyes Peninsula*.

in December of that year—1894—as Domenico, now Dominic, is coming up on his second anniversary in his new home, Guglielmo Marconi will wake his mother and invite her into his attic laboratory to unveil the results of his mysterious experiments. He has constructed a device for sending and receiving Morse code across the room without wires. To his mother it seems an impossible act of magic. The wireless has been born. Radio.

By the turn of the century, Marconi's wireless signals will travel the airwaves across the Atlantic. Following the sinking of the Titanic on April 15, 1912, the radio operators on board the doomed liner, employees of Marconi's company, will make the radio communications essential to the rescue of survivors by the Carpathia.

World War I demonstrates the strategic importance of radio communication. The U.S. government assumes control over radio communication and in 1920, the Radio Corporation of America (RCA) is formed. In the 1920s, the Radio Corporation of America determines that the atmosphere above Point Reyes, at the continent's edge, is perfect for the transmission of radio signals in the Pacific. I RCA will build a transmitter just north of where Rafael Garcia is standing now as well as a new receiving station in Marshall, on the hill overlooking Tomales Bay.

There is yet another invisible layer above the waves that have rolled out from Guglielmo Marconi's attic room. Waves far more mysterious and still not fully understood. The French Jesuit priest-paleontologist Pierre Teilhard de Chardin will describe it in 1938 as the noösphere—"a living tissue of consciousness" that encloses the Earth; a sphere of human thought and intention above the atmosphere and biosphere with the power to create, to destroy and to heal. The Oxford Dictionary defines it as "the postulated sphere or stage of evolutionary development dominated by consciousness, the mind, and interpersonal relationships."

It is a layer toward which the New Age will turn much of its attention.

Not far from where Garcia is standing, another man, in another time, is taking in the landscape that was once Garcia's domain. He is tall and lean and fair as Garcia is shorter in stature, dark haired, dark eyed. For the tall man, a slow epiphany is unfolding. What he sees in this landscape—in the grasslands and the rolling hills— is a healing place. He pauses near the old RCA radio transmitter facility on the bluff overlooking the ocean and imagines a center for healing people and healing the earth. Unlike the rough and ready Corporal Garcia of another age, he is a graduate of Harvard and Yale. A visionary who has reached this continental edge, like the pioneers and adventurers before him, with a dream.

In 1976, he will join with two friends, child care worker Carolyn Brown and conservationist Burr Heneman, to enter into negotiations with RCA and the Trust for Public Lands for a 50-year lease on 60 acres at the southern end of what will be the Point Reyes National Seashore. Commonweal is born.

Commonweal will become a renowned retreat center for cancer patients, often in the terminal phase of the disease. Michael Lerner, working closely with Dr.

Naomi Remen, is facilitating communication among people bearing the terrible burden of their disease and the prospect of death. It will be featured in the 5-part PBS Documentary on "The Healing Mind" in 1993. Lerner will also found the New School here, "exploring nature, culture and consciousness." Like Marconi's radio waves, more communications of a different kind will stream out from the quiet, mostly hidden corner of Point Reyes, in the new medium of cyberspace. Lerner has a gift for listening and interviewing that is as valuable with writers and thinkers as with cancer patients. His thoughtful interviews with so many people at the metaphoric edge of thought—people like Angeles Arrien, Jacob Needleman, Joanna Macy, Fritjof Capra, Michael Pollan—will travel through cyberspace around the world, with a current online archive of over 200 videos. You can enjoy them almost anywhere on the globe at www.commonweal.org.

> As the new millennium dawns, much of the land around Garcia's settlement is still wild, although the community of Bolinas is growing—but not too fast. The population in 2000 is only about 2500. It is not that easy to reach and it doesn't welcome visitors. The New York Times has described it as "the Howard Hughes of towns." What once housed the Marconi Wireless Center is now the Commonweal administration building. In one secluded corner of the property, eight of the retreat center residents are walking a labyrinth that has been created out of white stones. Utah writer Terry Tempest Williams has written of this labyrinth in her 2008 book Finding Beauty in a Broken World.

> "My brother Steve had the privilege of working with Rachel Remen at Commonweal, where he attended the Commonweal Cancer Health Program in January 2004. Alongside the healing grace of Dr. Remen, Steve benefited from the practical and spiritual wisdom of Michael Lerner, Lenore Lefer, Waz Thomas, and the friendship of Jenepher Stowell. All made an extraordinary difference in how he lived with his illness and found an inner peace beyond cure. (403) . . .

> "In *Waiting for God*, Simone Weil writes, 'The beauty of the world is the mouth of a labyrinth.' . . .
> "My brother Steve has a dream of creating a labyrinth for Salt Lake City as part of the new Intermountain Healthcare complex. Since his diagnosis with lymphoma last year, he has found the labyrinth to be a walking meditation. He experienced this peace at Commonweal . . . . He believes a labyrinth could offer comfort to both cancer patients and their families, providing both exercise and a calming of the mind." (109–110)

In 1997, California Pacific Medical Center in San Francisco became the first hospital in the nation to install a labyrinth on its grounds as part of its healing mission.

There is one more layer to this scene that is the most important of all. It is not new. It is almost as old as the Earth: Soil. This is the essential layer of life. Kenyan Nobel laureate Wangari Maatthai calls it "the skin of the Earth." "We take the soil for granted," she says, "because it is there. It is everywhere. Except when it has been taken by the wind. The running water. And then you are left with bare rock and you realize that you can't do very much with bare rock."

Rob and Michelle Avis (www.vergepermaculture.ca): "A single teaspoon of soil can contain billions of microscopic bacteria, fungi, protozoa and nematodes. A handful of the same soil will contain numerous earthworms, arthropods, and other visible crawling creatures. Healthy soil is a complex community of life and actually supports the most biodiverse ecosystem on the planet."

Jeremy Narby (author of *Intelligence in Nature*): "A handful of terrestrial dirt contains more organized information than is on the surface of all the known planets."

Not far from the Commonweal labyrinth, a woman is at work, her hands deep in the soil of what was once a tangled, neglected garden waiting for just the right hands to heal and shape it. This is the other part of Michael Lerner's dream: the healing of the earth. He has found just the right people to take his permaculture project to the next level: Penny Livingstone Stark and her husband James. As she works, Penny is speaking to students who have come to learn from her as they help in Commonweal's Regeneration Garden.

"We don't grow plants," Penny says. "We grow soil and soil grows plants . . . We actually built up eight inches of topsoil in five years and now it's up to twelve inches.

Penny lays cardboard over a late garden and sprays it with water. On top of this she adds a layer of mulch. This is her recipe for "growing soil," along with techniques for "slowing water down" as she puts it. "This is arid land because water comes briefly, in heavy bursts, and runs off, carrying topsoil with it. We create catchments that slow the run-off and we gather every last bit of the water into storage tanks. For us, there is no drought.

"If you are looking at a system building topsoil, it takes six to nine hundred years to build one inch of topsoil. We, through mulching, built a foot of soil over about a ten year period. We know this," she laughs, "because the benches we built about 18 inches off the ground are now 6 inches off the ground.

This understanding of soil as the source of life is not new, like Marconi's waves or cyberspace. It is a very old knowledge that we are recovering. Hence the name "Regenerative Garden"; working with nature's own processes developed over 4.5 billion years. The Earth was working at all of that through January and February of our calendar year, slowly grinding and eroding rock and developing the bacteria in March that today we know is the essential active ingredient in healthy soil—the source of all life, because only here can plants take root that will feed millions of people and the animals, including those that are raised for food. According to the USDA, a teaspoon of healthy soil contains over a billion bacteria.

The secret, which farmers around the world are learning, is to return organic life to the soil. A reciprocal relationship: taking and giving back. I have watched Farmer Ed plow under the end of the vegetable crop each year for just this reason and then plant a winter cover crop. Penny and James, along with many of the dairy farmers on Point Reyes, have discovered that there are ways that cows and pigs and other animals that are their livelihood also play their role in this regeneration of the Earth if thoughtfully managed. Warren Weber's Star Route Farms in Bolinas is the oldest organic farm in California.

> Michael Lerner:
>
> In the 1990s, Penny and James had converted their three-quarter acre home into a permaculture oasis. They transformed a suburban backyard with a few trees into a dynamic living classroom...and a food forest garden teeming with fruits, vegetables, nuts, herbs, and berries. Gradually they began to notice an increase in the diversity of wildlife in their garden, a decrease in the amount of energy needed to produce food, as well as a decrease in the number of outside resources they needed to live in their home.
>
> Intrigued that the principles of permaculture could be applied to create such thriving and abundant living systems, in 1994 Penny and James co-founded the Permaculture Institute of Northern California (PINC).*

At Commonweal, Penny and James created a new organization, the Regenerative Design Institute (RDI), with the broad mission of serving as a catalyst for a revolution in the way humans relate to the natural world. "We envisioned a world in which people, inspired by nature, create and maintain healthy and abundant livelihoods that enhance fertility and biodiversity on the planet," reflected Penny. "We saw humans as a positive, healing presence on Earth, creating more abundance on the planet than would be possible without them. We dreamed of a world in which all people, inspired by nature, could live in a mutually enhancing relationship with the earth."

Penny's language, which I was reading on Commonweal's website, rang a bell. Thomas Berry came to mind, whom I had had the privilege of meeting on several occasions and admired very much as a deep and wise man and a great visionary. Thomas Berry gave the name Ecozoic to the geological era that would follow the 65 million year Cenozoic period we currently live in, which began with the last great extinction that included the disappearance of the dinosaurs. Earth's Fifth Mass Extinction. We are living in the midst of what scientists call the Sixth Extinction**, as the human population has mushroomed on the planet and unwittingly displaced so many natural habitats. I was recalling a description of "ecozoic" which I had just read on Allysyn Kiplinger's website "Ecozoic Times":

> "The term 'Ecozoic Era' was coined by Thomas Berry in conversation with Brian Swimme for their book *The Universe Story* in order to describe the geologic era

---

* From the Commonweal Garden website: http://www.regenerativedesign.org/garden/history

** From Stanford [University] News, June 19, 2015: "There is general agreement among scientists that extinction rates have reached levels unparalleled since the dinosaurs died out 66 million years ago. The new study, published in the journal *Science Advances*, shows that even with extremely conservative estimates, species are disappearing up to about 100 times faster than the normal rate between mass extinctions, known as the background rate."

that Earth is entering—when humans live in a mutually enhancing relationship with Earth and the Earth community." (The term Anthropocene, applied to our present epoch, would be to the Ecozoic Era as, for example, the Miocene was to the Cenozoic.)

Is it possible that the Earth Calendar's New Year—the Ecozoic Era—has already begun in that secluded corner of Point Reyes on Corporal Garcia's Rancho Tomales y Baulenes. In fact, it is beginning all over the world. People like Michael Lerner, Penny Livingstone and James Stark, quietly "making waves."

✳ ✳ ✳ ✳

Grossi Farms ~ The Present

STRAWBERRIES

THE FIRST THINGS TO COME INTO SEASON AT THE STAND are the strawberries. But they are also our longest running item and could last into September. Farmer Ed tried several varieties over the years and settled on Seascapes, which are reliably large and sweet.

I always put a few colorful baskets on my counter and they are hard to resist as the light spring sun pours down on them through the green mesh. But most people come for the U-Picks, not because they cost a little less but for the sheer joy of being in the fields. Our first regulars of the season arrive for this. There is an older couple who comes, looking as comfortable in their bodies as the canvas hats they wear that have known many seasons. I come to look forward to their arrival each year, like crocuses or daffodils, heralding a season. Then there is the young mother of the two little girls, Evelyn and Helen. Helen is a little towhead who rides in a backpack facing the world from behind. Her pretty little face could launch a thousand ships but her serious and watchful expression says that she would be too canny to fall for a fellow like Paris and stir up another Trojan War. Evelyn is old enough to walk, perhaps four to Helen's two, but her steps are tentative and shy. She has short, brown hair and a sweet face that I glimpse only in furtive little glances in my direction. Their mother Janet seems to have been doing this for a thousand years. One of those mothers who seems born into the role. I hand them all the ceremonial green plastic baskets and they disappear.

The fellows come to work long before me, at seven, so they are arriving from the fields with the first pickings. I hear them nearby singing. They have beautiful voices. I know that the loudest, full-hearted one is Lazaro and the other is Otún. Alfonso is too shy and conscientious to sing. It might seem unprofessional for the Field Foreman. But I hear his joking voice and know that they are all in good spirits, in spite of the hours of bending over, picking. I have tried this and an hour is too much for me. I have made coffee for them. They make a big show of testing it, shaking their heads and looking doubtful. Then Lazaro bursts into a smile and says "No Señora. It's very good!"

PART VI
ENDINGS & BEGINNINGS

Ticino ~ 1900

A NEW CENTURY

New York City is ablaze with electric lights, fireworks, and marching bands. The city's newspapers offer their visions of what life will be like in the new century: We will live longer. We will be taller, healthier and more beautiful in every way. And already some are thinking about the wonder of an entire New Millennium that lies relatively close by.

As the new century is dawning in Ticino, there is little to cheer about in the small villages of the Val Verzasca. Ticino remains dark. Impoverished and hungry. If there is a vision of the future for the young, it is Elsewhere. We have an account of a peasant woman living in the region of Brione after the turn of the century. Her account might well have come from decades, even centuries, before the new century began. This is the background against which women like Caterina and her step-daughter Teresina will contemplate their future and made the big decision to leave their valley.

CLEMENTINA RUSCONI'S STORY

A PEASANT'S LIFE IN THE BRIONE REGION[*]

MY MOTHER'S NAME WAS MARIA. There were ten of us, three brothers and seven sisters, making twelve in all with our parents. Now there are only two of us left, me and my sister Anna, who lives with me. Our mother died young, when I was eight and my sister five. In 15 years, she gave birth to ten children. People now say we lived that way because we were ignorant, but it is not true. We lived in extreme poverty. Anywhere it was possible to get a handful of grass, we would cut it. We were not ignorant, we just didn't have any money. For a day's labour, from sunrise to sunset, we were paid SFr 1.50 and, even when we could get that sort of work, eating polenta and cod was a luxury.

Once when my mother was seven months pregnant, she was haymaking in the woods above Pianesc, in the Brione area. On the way down, with a load of hay on her shoulders, she slipped and fell. She was very lucky, because her brother-in-law, who was a little farther down, managed to catch her, grabbing hold of her clothes and keeping her from going over the cliff. Fortunately, in those days they wore thick,

---

[*] Clementina Rusconi was one of 31 people from Val Verzasca interviewed by Franco Binda for his book *I vecchi e la montagna* (The old people and the mountain), published in 1983 by Armando Dadò. The interview was originally transcribed from the local dialect into Italian. Binda attempted to maintain the spontaneity and colour of the dialect, and therefore many of Rusconi's words and sayings have been kept. From www.swissinfo.ch

very heavy clothes that you couldn't tear even if you tried.

We would cut wild hay in the area known as Al Valee, above Daghéi, opposite Capelina (Val d'Osola). We worked in the shade. I would go with my sister and my brother Vincenzo, and our sister Lucia. At Al Valee there were no caves to shelter in, so we built a little hut. If the weather was fine, we were alright, but if it rained water came in everywhere. It was like one of those huts you see when they show pictures of primitive peoples in Africa. All in all, we were unaware of our precarious situation and were more contented than people are now. When we left, we took just a few necessities, as well as a blanket and an apron to put under our heads for a pillow, and we slept like logs. The night passed quickly. Pa did not come with us because of his asthma. He stayed in the village and told us to light a fire at night. This was to reassure him, a sign we were still alive.

Once, when I was not there, my sisters had begun to mow the grass on a steep section of slope and it was foggy. They lost their bearings and, instead of starting at the top as usual, moved out of the area and did not realise their mistake until evening, when they came up against the rocks. Sometimes people stole these from one another. They went to reserve them at night, even though it was against the customary rules.

When we got wet, we tried to dry ourselves round the fire, at midday or in the evening. If it rained, we did not leave the area immediately, hoping the weather would improve, but if we saw it was going to flood, we went back to the village. We did not use a scythe, just a sickle. There was a place here that was very difficult, very steep, and when we carried the hay down, the goat we took up with us for milk always walked along beside us. It never walked on the cliff side, but always let one of us walk on that side. It came with us on all our journeys because we petted it. It was fond of us. Goats are cautious animals. They never walk below you, always afraid of being swept down. This one, I remember, was called Topett. There was another we called Ghignom because it always seemed to be smiling. We also had a lamb that came with the goat. It always wanted to sleep with us, lying on our feet, but sometimes it urinated at night, soaking our mattress and our feet. Drinking water was also often a big problem. We looked for water dripping from a rock and left a container beneath it all day, so we would at least have plenty of water in the evening. Sometimes the water was so far from where we were working that we did not go to fetch it. So we could not even wash.

For us, shoes were a minor consideration. It did not bother us much, because we were used to going barefoot. In our family, we have always been lucky. We have never got bitten by vipers. I always used to say "i ma vanzóo i sirp". What does that mean? The vipers did not want me. Our dad always told us to strike the sickle on the rocks, then they would draw back into their holes. Then there was another saying that vipers run away from Christians. Of course, we used to pray in the evenings and recite the rosary, and among the other favours we asked was to be preserved from snakebites. The other danger—the greatest in fact—was that of falling. Lodovico had had a fall, but not when haymaking, on the alpine pasture, and also poor Tranquil Mocettini,* when he was very young. Considering the risks

---

* Teresa Buzzini Grossi's mother was a Mocettini ,"as noted on her death certificate.

we ran, we came out of it well enough. But if I were to live my life again, I would never go hay gathering!

Once people came from outside the valley to take revenge. They deliberately started a fire. The fire started around the Lögh, beyond the Posse de Soriröö, and burned all the area of Lögh as far as the Corona del Medée. It was forbidden to start fires, but on that occasion they did it at night, surreptitiously, to do harm. The fire spread as far as the Tenc pasture.

Such a plain and simple story, compared to the tall tales, often true, of the '49ers and the burgeoning fortunes and adventures of the emigrants in California. Yet for centuries this had been the life of "those who stayed" in places throughout the world—including Native Americans. The vengeful act of the people from outside Clementina's valley reminds me of similar things that were going on among the Miwok in California and other native groups that I have met or heard about. It was going on in the Elbe Valley among all of those small groups competing for land. Large, industrial societies have their own forms of these activities, often with more lethal and wide-ranging consequences.

In later years, when Ed's grandmother Teresina—later Teresa—Buzzini is entering her old age in Marin, the recollection that she will share with her grandchildren about the place of her birth is that it was "the lousiest place on earth" with never enough to eat. "If they had a varmint, they'd eat that." When the same grandchildren visited Ticino, they could hardly believe that such a picturesque place could have seemed so bleak a hundred years before.

San Francisco ~ 1900

THE UNINVITED GUEST

"'No monkey shines this year" appears to have been the order of the day issued by Police Chief Sullivan. The 1899 [New Year's Eve] celebration had been characterized by indiscriminate public kissing on the part of persons who had not been properly presented to each other. Chief Sullivan, the killjoy, planted five cops at each corner of Market Street and ten along each block. It was a cold, clear, windless (and comparatively kissless) night."

— *Nation's Business,* January, 1900

WHILE THE POLICE WERE ON KISS PATROL, an uninvited and unwelcome guest was about to arrive in San Francisco with the new century. *Yersina Pestis* is on the move again, emigrating to the New World using its favored mode of transportation, a rat aboard a ship. It arrives on the second day of the New Year, aboard the *Australia* out of Hong Kong. Manila, Honolulu and Hong Kong have already been swept by the Plague. Rats stealthily disembark in Chinatown, an unfortunate place to make their entrance. It will stir up the anti-Chinese sentiment already in place.*

The first Chinatown plague victim will not be identified until March, when the suspicious results of an autopsy will lead to further investigations by City Health Officer, Wilfred Kellogg, who tentatively identifies it as Bubonic Plague. With the first word of plague, police officers act quickly to cordon off Chinatown. Non-Chinese are ushered out, leaving the Chinese residents virtually imprisoned inside. This fuels the fears already rising in Chinatown with news of the Plague's devastation in Hong Kong and Honolulu and the appearance of dead rats on the roofs of buildings. Panic erupts. In the city, officials and newsmen greet the news of possible Plague in their city with ridicule, hoping to dispel any sense that this is to be taken seriously—a prospect that would be bad for tourism and business. Some in Chinatown, believing the scornful media and public denials, see the announcement of Plague as a further political attempt to discriminate against them and force the Exclusion Act. On top of this they are suffering the economic effects of losing wages from jobs and daily commerce with the city. It is a grim footnote that for this community, this year of 1900, beginning with the Chinese New Year in February, is the Year of the Rat in the Chinese calendar.

Soon after performing the autopsy, City Health Officer Kellogg boards a streetcar down Market street, carrying his lethal vial of microbes, which he literally ferries across to Angel Island to the headquarters of the quarantine officer, Dr. Joseph Kinyoun. He is relying on the skills of Dr. Kinyoun to make the final confirmation of his diagnosis. After all, it is Dr. Kinyoun's job to protect the homeland from invasion of infection through the Golden Gate.

◆ ◆ ◆

AN ISLAND STORY

ANGEL ISLAND. THE CHAMPAGNE IS JUST BEING POURED on the New Year's Eve of our Earth Year when Angel Island gains its independence from the mainland. That was occasioned by the end of the last Ice Age, when water from the melting glaciers, over four thousand years, filled what had been a narrow valley with low hills like those found all along the length of California today in the valleys of the Coast Ranges. The rivers flowed out of the Central Valley through the canyon that would become the Golden Gate—that narrow opening though which the gold of the setting sun poured at evening, leaving a trail of light across the bay. Over four thousand years, as the ocean waters rose, swelled by the melting ice sheets, the valley filled with water to become the great bay we see today, and the small hills became islands. During the Ice Age, while the waters were still lower, the Sacramento and San Joaquin rivers cut a deep channel which would become the Raccoon Strait that separate Angel Island from the rest of Marin County, especially Tiburon and Ring Mountain. For close to two millennia it was a hunting and fishing site for Coast Miwok. Chief Marin and his people

---

* I am indebted to Marilyn Chase for her excellent book, *The Barbary Plague*, which I highly recommend.

had easy access to it from his village of Anamas in the Huimen territory.

We may remember this island as the place where Captain Ayala brought the San Carlos to anchor in 1775, using it as his base to explore the bay and meet its inhabitants. It is Captain Ayala who gives it its name, Isla de Los Angeles. The island was then heavily forested with California oak, bay, and madrone, which would fall to the axe of '49ers who took up temporary residence there. Like the mainland after the arrival of the Spanish, it was used for cattle ranching.

During the Civil War, the U.S. army established a camp on the island, Camp Reynolds. Over the years, they reforested the island with eucalyptus trees. According to John Soennichsen, author of *From Miwoks to Missiles*, "Commanding officers on Angel Island, for one reason or another, had short tenures—one officer was in command for only two weeks, another for one month—and by 1886 Camp Reynolds had had no less than seventeen different commanding officers in twenty-three years. In that year, however, the procession of commanders came to a halt, for a time anyway, when command at Camp Reynolds passed to an officer who would remain in the position longer than any other. That was Angel Island's most famous commander, Colonel William R. Shafter."

Yes, he is one of *our* Shafters. Do you remember Oscar's letters to his brother Hugh in Michigan? William is Hugh's son, cousin to Emma and Julia, daughters of Oscar and James.

William Rufus Shafter comes down to us with mixed reviews by historians. He does not have the polish of Oscar and James, bestowed by their education at fine New England institutions. William was born in Galesburg, Michigan, a native of the Wild West, and has been described as "coarse and vulgar." But he is no less distinguished than his uncles and left an even greater mark on the national history as a warrior, like the grandfather whom he was named after—veteran of Bunker Hill and Saratoga. Soennichsen describes him as having "a 'mountainous frame' that would have immobilized most men." Less generous chroniclers describe him as fat, corpulent, a "floating tent." He weighed 225 pounds and was 5'11. "Shafter, however, had a reputation for being able to meet difficult situations, and had a penchant for 'hard work, firm discipline, brusqueness, volatility of temper and violence of language,'—on the frontier he had earned the nickname Pecos Bill,' [after the legendary Pecos Bill] as a hard-driving troop commander."

In 1861, William Shafter volunteered for service in the Civil War and earned the Medal of Honor for gallantry at the battle of Fair Oaks. He was captured at the Battle of Thompson's Station and spent 3 months in a Confederate prison. In April 1864, after his release, he was appointed colonel of the 17th Regiment of U.S. Colored Troops and led the regiment at the Battle of Nashville. After the Civil War, he led Buffalo soldiers in punishing campaigns against Indians in Texas, employing Shoshone scouts in tracking Apaches, even down into Mexico. He led the 24th Infantry, another United States Colored Troops regiment, in campaigns against the Cheyenne, Comanche, Kickapoo and Kiowa Indians in Texas. In 1890–91, he was in South Dakota helping to return Indians to Pine Ridge after the Wounded Knee massacre. By this point, Angel Island had become an infantry garrison for campaigns against the Native Americans of the West.

Although it is a lesser celebrated event in his life, William Shafter was also to play a role in the defense of the nation against disease, in spite of the fact that he often quarreled with the quarantine officers and dismissed a few from the island.

When a rumor began to circulate that a quarantine station was going to be built on Angel Island, the Army was far from happy. They argued for the importance of "keeping Angel Island and the Peninsular Island intact" to serve "the military purposes for which it is so convenient and indispensable." There was also the fact that this would entail the Treasury Department taking over a patch of land that had been theirs for 28 years.

Fear that disease could be introduced in San Francisco from a ship coming from Asia prevailed over the Army's opposition. The 1888 outbreak of smallpox in Hong Kong reinforced the need for a quarantine station other than the inadequate facilities then being used on the San Francisco waterfront. The Marine Hospital Service insisted that no more desirable place for a station could be found on the entire seaboard of this coast. Colonel Shafter submitted a letter, together with reports in opposition to the transfer of land from the Army to the Treasury Department but the project went ahead.

The first passengers who were placed in quarantine arrived on the ship *China* on April 27, 1891 with two cases of smallpox onboard. A new problem developed, which was brought to Col. Shafter's attention by a letter from the Army Post Surgeon, Major W.H. Gardner, warning that patients under quarantine, if not "rigidly guarded and isolated, will always be a menace to the health of this garrison." ... He had seen a party of women and children picnicking on the grounds. "These parties visit the island almost daily," he wrote, and added that it was impractical to maintain a twenty-four hour detail around the quarantine area. He argued for a tough, closed fence around the land side of the grounds, which could be done immediately and at small cost. It took two years to pass through the layers of bureaucracy but Col. Shafter finally got his fence. In the meantime, Shafter had to maintain a guard, which did not endear him to the quarantine officers, whom he is said to have dismissed from the island seven times. This is one of those occasions in which a fence would indeed have made better neighbors.

"Pecos Bill" left the island in 1896 to become the commander of the Department of California across the bay, with a promotion to brigadier-general. He later went on to command the Cuban invasion force in the Spanish-American War. Although this service earned him the sobriquet, the "Hero of Santiago," it was the least heroic episode of his career. He commanded the largest force of United States troops that had left American soil up to that time. But at age 63, weighing over 300 pounds and suffering from gout, it was doubtful that he was in the physical condition to meet the demands of this mission. He suffered badly from the tropical conditions and was unable to lead his men at the front as he wanted.

Confined to his headquarters and out of sight of the fighting, Shafter made several poor decisions. It seems ironic that one of the defeating elements was the disease that was rampant in the American army. Shafter left Cuba himself in September 1898 and was quarantined at Camp Wikoff on Long Island. Camp Wikoff was used to quarantine 29,000 soldiers, including Theodore Roosevelt and the Rough Riders at the conclusion of the Spanish-American War, to prevent the spread of yellow fever and other tropical diseases. Roosevelt arrived in mid-August for the six-week quarantine, so he likely overlapped with William Shafter. Shafter's star was descending as Roosevelt's was on the rise. In November of that same year, Roosevelt would be elected governor of New York State and exactly two years later in 1900, at Oyster Bay, not far away on Long Island from Camp Wikoff, Roosevelt would officially become vice-president of the United States. Shafter returned to his position at the Department of California, and then retired in 1901 to his sixty-acre farm adjoining his daughter's ranch near Bakersfield, California. By 1906, he was terribly overweight and he died at his daughter's home from an intestinal obstruction complicated by pneumonia. He was buried next to his wife at the Presidio in San Francisco, California.

◆ ◆ ◆

In 1900, not far from Ayala's anchorage on Angel Island, the Army built a hospital. It was known then as Hospital Cove, before the name was changed to Ayala cove. It is toward Hospital Cove and the newly built quarantine station that Wilfred Kellogg is heading on the ferry with his deadly little vial; to Joseph Kinyoun, who has just recently become director. Dr. Kinyoun had been the founder and first director of the United States' Hygienic Laboratory (1887–1899), the predecessor of the National Institutes of Health.

Early twentieth century San Francisco had something that fourteenth century Europe did not: Tools to recognize the microscopic footprint of the bacteria. In his microscope, Dr. Kinyoun confirms the identity of Yersina Pestis, but decides to run a secondary test to be sure. He inoculates test animals with the bacteria—a rat, two guinea pigs and a monkey. The results of this test would provide the final proof.

While the good news is that scientific methods in 1900 make it possible to identify Yersina, (although the means of its transmission is still not understood at this time), the bad news is that much of the population is still uninformed or skeptical about the reliability of these methods. Others have more calculated reasons for ignoring it: They do not want to see the yellow flag of pestilence hanging over their beautiful, booming city; their Paris of the Pacific. To say that it was bad for business is an understatement.

The newspapers have lampooned it from the beginning, ridiculing what they call the Bubonic Board of Health. *The San Francisco Bulletin* ran this rhyme—

Have you learned of the deadly bacillus

> *Scourge of a populous land*
> *Bacillus that threatens to kill us*
> *When found in a Chinaman's gland.*
> *Well the monkey is living and thriving*
>
> *The guinea pigs seem to be well,*
> *And the Health Board is daily contriving*
> *Excuses for having raised . . .*

After three days of quarantine there are no further reported cases. Pressures are rising to lift the quarantine. Chinese businessmen are threatening to sue the city for their losses. And the rat, the guinea pigs and the monkey live on. Under these pressures, the City Health Department lifts the quarantine. On March 8th, the ropes come down around Chinatown and the people rush into the streets in celebration, both in Chinatown and San Francisco. Normal life has resumed. The *Examiner* rejoiced with another satirical ditty, which they publish under the title "The Raising of the Quarantine":

> *Sweet Fong is at his post once more*
> *And cooking reigns supreme;*
> *Once more upon the kitchen range*
> *A wealth of viands steam,*
> *And joyful Plenty smiles again*
> *Where Famine's hand was laid;*
> *For, lo! The Board of Health has raised*
> *The Chinatown blockade.*

But the celebrations are premature. Two days later, on March 10th, the rat and the guinea pigs die on Angel Island, and the following day, the monkey. It is official: the plague has arrived in San Francisco. Other deaths follow in the city and the Plague will take its toll over the decade, but this does not prevent the continued denial of the city fathers. A "brazen cover-up" abetted by the governor.

From *The Chronicle* comes the headline—

> "THE PLAGUE PHANTOM; MORE BOUFFE BUSINESS
> BY THE HEALTH BOARD."

The following day,

> "NO PLAGUE IS FOUND."

And two days later, as the city celebrated St. Patrick's Day,

> "BUBONIC SCARE HAS COLLAPSED"

More plague cases are found. In April 1901, a clean-up campaign of Chinatown is undertaken, scouring almost 1,200 houses and 14,000 rooms. In 1903, a new governor takes office and vows to help the boards of health in every way. On February 29, 1904, a woman in the town of Concord, California, dies of plague, its last victim —for a while.

By this point, there have been 121 cases in San Francisco and 5 outside, with 122 deaths. San Francisco is very lucky compared to 14th century Europe. This good fortune is due in part to the fact that the breed of flea that bore the bacterium was a little different in San Francisco. The San Francisco flea species didn't transmit the plague in such a concentrated dose. The stomach of the Hong Kong flea had a slightly different anatomy that tended to collect plague germs into a ball of concentrated bacteria. The rodent control program was finally successful. The energetic response of the Health Department has proved worthwhile in spite of the local derision. Alas, Dr. Kinyoun resigned his position in 1901 after allegations that his conclusive bubonic plague diagnoses were scaremongering. Unfortunately, the appearance of further cases proved him correct. Only 200 people will die at the end of a decade.

The Paris of the Pacific goes on about its business.

YERBA BUENA GROWS UP

THE CITY IS NOW LIGHTED BY GAS AND ELECTRICITY, and local transit is carried on by cable and electric street-railways. There are some 135 churches, divided among almost all the leading denominations. St. Mary's Cathedral is serving a Roman Catholic congregation. Grace Church serves Episcopalians from its peak on Nob Hill. There are also Trinity Cathedral, Sherith Israel Synagogue, and Calvary Presbyterian and the First Unitarian churches. The Chinese have six large joss houses.

Educational institutions have been established including the Hastings College of Law, the Dental Department of the University of California, the medical and pharmaceutical departments of the same university, a training-school for nurses, and an industrial school. Technical training is offered at the Mechanics Institute, the Academy of Sciences and the Lick Mechanical Art School.

By 1895, the city is already renowned for its numerous libraries boasting some 500,000 volumes, including the Bancroft, the Free Public Library and the Sutro. There are 15 daily newspapers, 81 weekly, and numerous semiweekly, semimonthly, monthly and quarterly periodicals are published. Although the number of volumes (scrolls) in the ancient library at Alexandria (where Hypatia's father was the last director) cannot be known, estimates have been as high as 700,000 scrolls, the equivalent of more than 100,000 modern printed books. Even granting that the invention of the printing press in the 16th century is the major contributor to this change, it's rather remarkable that the wild city of Gold Rush immigrants that

Bayard Taylor had found just a little over 40 years before could have transformed itself into such an impressive center of learning.

The major cities of the world, through all of time, have had a single common requirement to achieve that status: excellent transportation. San Francisco's access, by both land and water, make it one of the most important commercial centers in America. Its railroads link it to the vast intercontinental system; the California and Nevada, the San Francisco and North Pacific Coast, and the Southern Pacific. Surrounded on three sides by water, vessels leave its port for all parts of the world.

In 1847, the population of Yerba Buena/San Francisco was 647 souls. By 1900—only 53 years later—the population has increased to 342,782—530 times its size in 1847. It is the ninth largest city in the United States and the only city west of the Mississippi, and of St. Louis to be listed among the twenty most populated cities in the U.S.

San Francisco ~ 1900

VIVEKANANDA

"I do not come to convert you to a new belief. I want you to keep your own belief; I want to make the Methodist a better Methodist; the Presbyterian a better Presbyterian; the Unitarian a better Unitarian. I want to teach you to live the truth, to reveal the light within your own soul."

— SRI VIVEKANANDA

AMONG THE ARRIVALS OF THE NEW CENTURY was the man who had made such an impression at the Parliament of the World's Religions in Chicago. That event, along with the success of his writings, had thrust him onto the world stage. Who can say what makes an audience ripe for such things. Perhaps it is the very success of the "things of this world" brought about by the Industrial Revolution, that makes people receptive to hearing about things *not* of this world. Perhaps it is the arrival of a new century, which scours the soul and prepares it in new ways. A lively spiritualism had run along invisible parallel tracks with the developing steam engines and railroads. If there were steel magnates larger than life, there were spiritual seers larger than death. The nineteenth century was abundant with mystics like Swedenborg (remember Mark's family in Henderson), Madame Blavatsky who launched Theosophy, the New England transcendentalists like Emerson and Thoreau, and the Eastern writers whom both men had much admired. Sri Vivekananda, like the Shafters, had caught a wave at its crest that had been rising for a while. He was by no means the last of the gurus from the East who would find welcome, like miners and bankers, in the New World.

By 1900, Vivekananda had drawn such celebrated admirers as William James, Josiah Royce, C. C. Everett, Dean of the Harvard School of Divinity, the French actress Sarah Bernhardt, and Madame Emma Calvé, the French opera singer who is about to become a hit of her own on the San Francisco stage. After his successful lecture tour in Europe and America, Vivekananda returned to India to an enthusiastic reception, addressing the social ills of his country, from the caste system to poverty and calling for an end to colonial rule. His lectures had a great influence on India's leaders, including Mahatma Gandhi. He was more leonine than ascetic in figure and in personality, more of this world than beyond it; all qualities that made him more palatable to the swift developing Western world and to San Franciscans in particular.

Vivekananda arrives in San Francisco on February 22nd, 1900 and is immediately caught up in a busy schedule of lectures and classes. Twice in Oakland he drew three thousand people. He must surely have come to the attention of Oscar's daughter Emma Shafter Howard, who was one of its active and prominent citizens at the time. By mid-March he was staying at 1719 Turk Street, San Francisco and from there, he founded one of several Vedanta Societies he seeded in America.

The Vedanta Society rounded out the city's ecumenical character. As noted among the earlier statistics of 1890, there were now 135 churches, divided among almost all the leading denominations.

Ticino ~ ca. January 19, 1901

TERESINA

TERESINA NEVER LOOKED BACK.

She knew that if she did, she would only see a blur where her village stood—hidden behind an early morning mist; the drear of winter. If she had, she would only have seen cold stone, hunger, the pall of a people cowed by poverty. Despair. She knew it well. It had been hers for years.

She carried very little with her and left very little behind. Her mother had died when she was young. Her stepmother and stepbrother had been gone for almost four years. They had left not long after the death of her father.

There was nothing behind her. There was everything ahead. There was hope.

New York ~ February 4, 1901

ELLIS ISLAND

A MONTH AGO, TERESINA WAS CERTAIN that nothing could be worse than the desperation of Brione. But that was before she boarded the La Bretagne on January 26th at Le Havre and descended into hell. When warned of the difficulties of the passage, she had shrugged it off. How long could 8 to 10 days be after all? The answer she now knew was forever. She couldn't decide now which was worse—the constant bone-shattering noise of the engines that bordered their compartment or the stench of vomit, excrement, and unwashed bodies. They were stowed away deep in the hull, crowded into a single large space with no portholes or decks. The ceiling was little over six feet high and the beds were stacked at two foot intervals, lining the walls. The thin mattresses were infested with lice. Bathroom facilities were inadequate and there was no ventilation. This miserable space rocked and swayed with the motion of the sea and most of the passengers suffered from sea sickness for at least part of the voyage. They sought relief on the upper deck when weather permitted.

Right now they were in the second day of a mid-Atlantic storm. The ship swung violently from one steep angle to another, tossing them about so that they grabbed for one another. The hatch of the lower deck had been locked and tied down to prevent it from flooding. People moaned, children cried, some screamed from the panic of claustrophobia. For food, there was only soggy bread and cured fish. Fresh water was available only in the upper deck, so thirst was now added to hunger. Some prayed for death. Teresina stayed close to the two friends she had traveled with from Ticino—Anna and Rosa. They had started out as friends from neighboring villages, but now—in the way of age-old ship journeys—they were more like sisters and clung to each other for comfort against adversity and the unknown. Together they kept the ember of hope alive for a better future in a far off place, even as their ship was drenched by the perilous waves.

On the tenth day, word reached them below that New York harbor had been sighted in the distance. People gathered up their few belongings and crowded onto the deck of the ship. Teresina and Anna pushed their way to the edge of the railing and Anna wept as the Statue of Liberty appeared out of the cold morning mist. "It's over," she cried. "We have arrived!" Teresina too felt the relief, but she neither wept nor laughed with joy as some were doing. She just stared at the tall buildings, the huge city coming slowly toward them. She felt a certain thrill at what awaited her. But it was a thrill laced with dread.

There was still a long way to go.

As it turned out, there was still a long time to wait right there on the deck of La Bretagne. Children fussed and cried. Parents caressed, cajoled or cursed. The ship docked at a pier on the Hudson River and they waited while the first and second class passengers—Americans and wealthy immigrants—underwent a quick, efficient onboard inspection before debarking and heading toward their destinations. The steerage passengers watched and waited, like prisoners, not knowing what to expect. It was cold on the deck. Hours went by. Many of the passengers had donned as many of their clothes as possible to increase warmth and have less to carry. But the clothes hung heavily as the hours went by. Many stood in small islands of bulky baggage. For once Teresina was grateful that she had almost nothing but the clothes on her back to contend with. Too much time to stare across the wide expanse of the Hudson River at the imposing building that held their fates. The success or failure of the journey would be determined there, on Ellis Island.

They finally boarded the ferry and another long wait followed before it began to move across the water. Teresina was impressed by the sight of the imposing red brick building. It was like some huge temple or castle. Its vast red and white brick exterior rose in layers, with tall arched windows in the lowest level, surmounted by multi-paned rectangular windows marking an upper floor. Above that rose four tall striped *towers like the belfries of a church at the corners of a central area, with gabled roofs to the side and a very large arched window facing them. There were more structural parts on the side that likely held hallways and offices. It was a very complicated building, Teresa thought, comparing it with the edifices of Brione, made mostly of stone. But of course there was Brione's church and its frescoes. While she paid little attention to them when she was there, she felt certain that these enormous building had no frescoes like hers. Not that she would miss them. No, not at all.*

San Francisco ~ December 1901

EMMA AND JULIA AT PIONEER HALL

In 1900, upper class, talented, energetic white women . . . are knocking at the door of social power and professional power in the United States. Women at the turn of the century . . . are beginning to come out from the shadow of men."

— LAURA WEXLER
From *The American Experience: America 1900*

My MOTHER SLIPPED THE MORTAL COIL in the summer of her 59th year from heart failure. That was in 1977 and the world has changed considerably since that time in ways that I'm sure would have intrigued her. My father lived on for 20 more years, seeking echoes of her spirit by rereading books they had read together. Not a bad idea. Sadly the last few years of his life were lost to Alzheimers. Everyone grieves at the passing of someone close to them, but in Dad's case, we were also relieved that he had been freed of that insidious predator.

The surprising thing to me was that once the grieving was past, I found that my father was given back to me in an unexpected way. There was no need to hold him in memory as that depleted and aging shadow of his former self. I had his whole life to choose from when I thought about him. He could be any age at any time or place, alive and vibrant in my mind's eye.

I am thinking about this now as I select a moment in the lives of the two cousins, Emma and Julia Shafter. I have chosen December 3rd, 1901. The place is San Francisco, Pioneer Hall, south of Market Street, near where the Moscone Convention Center sits today. The event is the Twenty-Sixth Fruit Growers' Convention, held under the auspices of the California State Board of Horticulture. Emma is 59, my mother's last age, but she is in the full bloom of health and activity as the wife of Charles Howard. Robust and substantial of figure, one can still see in her face the trace of the 12 year old writing to her father from Vermont. The round face and large round eyes. The full lower lip which curls upward to one side and gives her a quizzical look. She is doing the sorts of things my mother would love to have done in her life.

Julia is 42. Though she is not a tall woman, there is a dignity about her slender, erect form. She is now Julia Shafter Hamilton, for better or for worse. It is mostly worse. Neither woman has made a particularly happy marriage and both walk in the lights and shadows of their fathers, Oscar and James. In fact, at this moment they are staying at Julia's father's mansion on Chestnut Street.

TWENTY-SIXTH FRUIT-GROWERS' CONVENTION
HELD UNDER THE AUSPICES OF
THE CALIFORNIA STATE BOARD OF HORTICULTURE,
AT PIONEER HALL, SAN FRANCISCO, DECEMBER 3 TO 6, 1901.

Pursuant to call, a convention of fruit-growers, shippers, nurserymen, and others interested in horticulture and kindred pursuits in California, assembled in convention in Pioneer Hall, San Francisco.

DAY 1: TUESDAY, DECEMBER 3RD

The rain is coming down heavily in San Francisco, the southern tail of the North Pacific storm. Water is running in torrents down both sides of the Hyde Street hill but the cable car commuters are unfazed and the jaunty little vehicles ride up and down, hissing and splashing, from Fisherman's Wharf to Market Street.

Those attending the convention at Pioneer Hall arrive in carriages, which are now lined up along Fourth Street, waiting to debouch their passengers in front of the three story brick building. There is laughter and general good humor in spite of the downpour. This is San Francisco after all.

Julia and Emma have taken all of this into account and arrived early. Once out of the rain, they make their way through the elegant entry hall to the ladies' parlor, with its velvet sofas and divans. The first day of the Horticultural Convention coincides with the Opening Day of Congress in Washington.

In the Ladies Parlor of Pioneer Hall on that morning the women are discussing the floral display at the opening of Congress. One of the women had brought a newspaper in from the reading room and reads from that morning's San Francisco Call.

"A profusion of floral offerings, quite unusual in quantity, variety and in beauty, today transformed the Senate chamber into a veritable flower show. Almost every member of the body was the recipient of one or more of these evidences of the regard of his friends, and the atmosphere of the chamber was heavy with the odor of rare plants and blossoms. The display of chrysanthemums was notably beautiful, many of the specimens being of the choicest varieties." This was a subject of more than passing interest to participants in the Horticultural Conference.

Early arrivals among the men head to the large reading-room which contains several long tables covered with books and newspapers and large rocking chairs. Winter light comes in through the tall leaded windows and a warm fire burns at one end of the long room. The North Pacific storm is a subject of discussion and concern among men who have come down from the northern coastal areas of Marin and Sonoma. There is also a smoking-room and a billiard room upstairs, which stands empty at this early hour.

As the opening event approaches, people drift slowly into the great hall. This hall has seen so many lectures, meetings, dances and celebrations. Like the celebration on the evening of Admission Day, when the Forty-niners, their children and grandchildren had gathered for the festivities.

The hubbub dies down as the mayor approaches the podium to open the day's events. As Emma says, James Phelan is a man on the move, in many ways. But then so are most of the politicians in San Francisco. So were their fathers! San Francisco is coming into its own quickly and shaping itself as a world-class city. James Phelan sees himself as a key player at a key moment, the Pericles of the New World. He is well-read in the classics and well-traveled in the Old World. His vision for the city, like Plato's Republic, is based on new ideas that were inspired by the Columbian Exposition of 1893 in Chicago, where architect Daniel Burnham brought leading architects from the East, along with French sculptor Augustus Saint-Gaudens to build large-scale Beaux-Arts monuments with distinct Old World classical elements. Out of this came the City Beautiful movement and Phelan was one of its leading proponents. The goal of the movement was to create beauty, not for its own sake, but for the common good, as a way of promoting moral and civic virtue among the people.

Phelan has an aristocratic bearing, with a high forehead, hair parted to one side and slicked back, a mustache and a short, neatly trimmed beard. Emma and Julia listen intently as he describes a recent trip to the Paris Exhibition. He notes that at the Hotel Ritz, peaches were served in velvet pockets on a small board, like treasured jewels and charged for accordingly. This had convinced him that it would be possible to create a market in Europe for California fruits. He quoted a translation given to him by the Spanish consul of an article in a Valencia paper dated April 10, 1901.

"Spanish products are rapidly losing ground, and, unless our methods be brought into line with those of progressive nations, our wines, our oil, our fruits, and our vegetables will be condemned to home consumption. We have been astonished at the falling off in our exports of fruit and fresh vegetables to France, England, and Germany. The decrease for France, notwithstanding the enormously enlarged consumption created by the Paris exposition, was erroneously attributed to Italian competition. The rivalry really comes from the United States. California is now supplying the French, English, and German markets with fresh fruits and vegetables. The fruits are not offered at lower prices than our own, but they are presented neatly packed and in splendid condition.

"We can compete with America only by employing her methods—improved cultivation, harvesting, and packing, cold storage, and rapid, safe transportation. Otherwise, our exports will decline every day. Castile was once called the granary of Europe; yet we have lived to see foreign wheat, after paying heavy transportation taxes, protective duties, and an adverse premium of thirty-five per cent in exchange, competing with our home-grown cereals. Shall we live to see American oranges competing with ours on the Valencia market itself?"

There were appreciative affirmations from the audience. Julia and Emma exchange approving glances with one another and with Mrs. Sherman, who is sitting across the aisle from them. Mrs. Sherman's talk on the following day will address this very point and argue that it is the women on the farms who have been most responsible for this attention to the aesthetics of fruit packing. Her own talk will follow Julia's on Thursday, the third day of the conference. Julia's talk will follow Emma's. All of the women speakers would be grouped together in the morning.

DAY 2: DECEMBER 4, 1901

Arriving early, Emma joins a group of women gathered around a divan near the fireplace , where Maud Davis is reading aloud from the review by Blanche Parriter in The San Francisco Call *of the first performance of Tristan and Isolde. Emma has never lost the love of music that drew her to the piano as a child in Vermont. She and several friends had sat in her box at the Grand Opera House, enraptured by Wagner's music. But it was long. By now the audiences were prepared for that, after sitting through seven Wagner productions of the* Ring *cycle,* Die Fliegende Hollander, Tannhauser, Lohengrin *and* Die Meistersinger. *Emma had been able to attend only a few of them when her business took her to the city. It had by no means been a full house and she wondered if the length of the productions put people off. And as Blanche Parriter noted, the production was lacking on the feminine side.*

"Listen to this," Maud was saying.

"'I did not take my prayer-mat down to the opera-house last night to kneel and listen thus to Tristan and Isolde *as Wagner's young adorers in the Fatherland used to listen to the new* Lohengrin—*but I felt that one would have come in handily during the evening.'" The women all chuckled appreciatively. "'It is one of the world's love-poems, fitted to music of the most intimately beautiful sort, by the master musician at the peak of his power. Wagner's genius finds here its most characteristic expression, its ripest, noblest form, and in all music there is nothing so unapproachably lovely as some of its divine measures. . . . It is flooded with color, dazzling and yet most delicate, odorous half-tones—'"*

"What in the world are odorous half-tones?" Alice Grange interjected.

"Smelly sounds I suppose."

"Do go on Maud."

"'—and scarlet notes of passion color dreamed, . . .'"

"Scarlet notes! Passion color dreamed. Rubbish."

"'. . . and the flash of the brown of earth. Strange chromatic intervals dominate largely the melodic scheme of Tristan and Isolde, *and Wagner obtains thus the distinctive effect of the music-drama. The characteristic themes are almost all of this elusive char-acter, crystallizing the undertow of emotion, not personifying action.'"*

"The earth does not flash," Alice insisted.

"You have no appreciation for poetic language. It is very difficult to describe Wagner's music. I'd say she has described the indescribable quite well!"

"Go on, go on. What does she say about Van Dyck. I thought he was quite good."

"'Van Dyck was the Tristan, and was a stately and noble figure.'"

"Yes, he was," the ladies agreed.

"'He sang as Van Dyck has never sung here before, his voice holding out to the last colossal requirement of the role. Again his powerful dramatic faculty helped

to make an unforgettable portrait of the knight, and the whole measure of Van Dyck's attainment here is of the largest. Tristan is a long time dying—Van Dyck is credited with thirty-nine minutes as against the conventional forty—but the singer holds the interest in a truly remarkable fashion.'"

"What does she way about Reuss-Beice?"

"'Louise Reuss-Beice we must be thankful for, as without her the opera could not have been heard here. She is one of the few singers who can attempt the tremendous role and really did some surprisingly strong work last night; but the voice—hard, strained, shrill—hurts the ear, and one can only surmise what it may have been once and regret that its day has gone. But she has undoubted power, lifts to a fine climax and acts, if not always with fine art, at least with sincere and earnest intention. The effort of memory alone is immense, and altogether Reuss-Beice's work last night is entitled to a sincere respect.'"

"In other words, she was awful."

"Yes, but she put it so nicely, dear."

Emma left the debate in progress and crossed the hall to the reading room, more interested to hear what was being said there about the "Wagnerian drama" that was being enacted right in their own country, following the assassination of President McKinley and the sudden promotion of Theodore Roosevelt to president.

The room was crowded with people and seemed to have abandoned its habitual quietude. She looked around for her cousin Julia, but there was still no sign of her. As she tuned into the conversation it became immediately clear that no one was talking about horticulture. The San Francisco Call that morning had published the complete text of President Theodore Roosevelt's speech to congress. On the whole, the men were gratified that a leader in Washington was finally paying active attention to the needs of the Western states.

"Commenting upon the document, Senator Perkins said: 'It is a great message —able, clear, explicit, emphatic, and especially pleasing to the Pacific Coast, since everything the coast desires is indorsed and recommended by President Roosevelt. His strong references to Chinese exclusion, Irrigation, the Pacific cable and the Nicaragua canal are particularly satisfactory.' Senator Bard said of the message: 'It is very gratifying to the people of the Pacific Coast. Of all the public questions in which they have special interest, President Roosevelt shows a thorough knowledge and sound judgment.' Representative Needham said: 'It is a splendid message. Roosevelt is the first President who has ever treated fully those problems which are peculiarly 'Western.'"

There was hot debate, however, over the anti-trust legislation the president was calling for.

"This could hurt the railroad interests and it is the railroad companies that got us out of the depression."

"Wrong!" shouted one man. "It's the railroad companies that got us into the depression." A third more moderate voice chimed in:

"Railroads are the greatest invention of modern man. They have changed the face of the world and made us into one country, connected coast to coast. No doubt *about it—that has brought us great prosperity and raised the standard of living. But it was too much too fast. The railroad bubble burst and we are paying the price. But you can't blame it on the railroad companies."*

"And we couldn't have built those railroads without Coolie labor!" someone else insisted.

"Yes, but they are coming in by the droves now and they are taking American jobs just when they are most needed."

"They don't even speak the language or understand English. They just stay together in their Chinatowns and breed crime."

"Hold on now. We are a nation of immigrants and there are many Chinese citizens contributing mightily to the growth of this city. And as for crime, we are doing quite well on our own when it comes to breeding crime."

The conversation moved from there to the more hopeful note of what the building of the Nicaragua canal would mean to California. Emma was particularly appreciative of this, remembering the difficult journey through Panama when she was 12.

The conversation had finally come around to the most relevant topic—Roosevelt's proposals for irrigation and agriculture—when her cousin Julia arrived. Julia had been delayed by some business to attend to on Chestnut Street. Soon after, someone noted that the meeting was about to begin and those gathered in the Reading Room and the women in the parlor headed to the main hall.

The second day of the conference was devoted to presentations and discussions of the raisin and wine industries, as well as the appointment of a committee to consider Roosevelt's resolutions.

Emma Shafter Howard, on this December 4, 1901, had lived through two wars—the Civil War and the Spanish-American War, and two Depressions—the Panic of 1873 and the Great Depression of 1895. She was living through what must have seemed a very long, drawn out labor and birth of a nation and there were still only 45 states at the dawning of the 20th century. Oklahoma wouldn't become a state until 1907, and Arizona and New Mexico in 1912. Alaska and Hawaii don't join the Union until 1959.

Both the Panic of 1873 and 1895 were set off in part by the collapse caused by railroad overbuilding and overextension of finances. The Philadelphia and Reading Railroad declared bankruptcy in February of 1893. In both cases there was a run on the banks. The presence of the railroads facilitated the rapid movement of silver and many more mines were opened as a result. Silver and other metals began to flood the market. A series of droughts, particularly in the Midwest, left farmers without cash to pay their debts and the value of their land fell.

The unemployment rate rose from around 3% in 1892 to around 10% in 1893. Figures as high as 18% have been given for 1894 and in 1897, it was still close to 14%, falling to 12% in 1898. Finally, in 1900, it had dropped back to 5% and the nation was fully in recovery and began to prosper again.

As if wars and depressions were not enough to lower the spirits of the new country, in the course of Emma's lifetime three presidents had been assassinated: Abraham Lincoln in 1865, James Garfield in 1881, and the recently deceased William McKinley in 1901. As someone who remembers well the grief that gripped the country during the assassination of President John Kennedy, it is hard for me to imagine a people being dealt such blows in a single generation. Emma's generation. But after each successive economic and political blow, the nation seemed to come back stronger than ever.

DAY 3: DECEMBER 5, 1901

JULIA & EMMA SPEAK

Emma rose early on that Thursday morning to go over her paper. She was an experienced speaker and knew the importance of giving the appearance at least that the talk was spontaneous. It wasn't long and she had memorized it. Then she scanned the newspaper when it arrived over a light breakfast. Better not to eat too much before her talk. Julia came down and joined her for breakfast and they exchanged inconsequential conversation from that point on. Julia too would be speaking that morning.

Pioneer Hall was filling up quickly with fruit-growers, shippers, nurserymen, and others whose livelihoods were in some way touched by the state's horticulture industry. Emma and Julia sat side by side on this third day of the Twenty-sixth Fruit-Grower's Convention. Considering how far apart their homes were, one in Inverness on the far west of Marin County, the other across the Bay in Oakland, this was an uncommon proximity. A reminder, however, of their common heritage, the common landscape of Point Reyes, and the common interest they shared in its future.

It was exceptionally hot for a December day in the city. A rare absence of the morning fog that had cooled the streets and muffled the sounds. The ornate building on Fourth near Market, at the corner of Montgomery and Gold, shone in its glory. The cornerstone to this home for the Society for California Pioneers had been proudly laid forty years before to honor those members who had arrived before 1850 and their descendants.

Emma's talk, not surprisingly, dwelt on women in agriculture. But it also raised the issue of the separation of city and rural cultures. She took her father's philosophical tone, but also called upon his personal experience of city and country; of San Francisco and the wild Point Reyes peninsula. Emma articulates the fact that the new century will call for "the application of scientific methods and inventions to economics." Her special gifts of vision and organization appear in her active role in creating an agricultural and horticultural organization for women in California, and keeping abreast of similar developments in Europe, Argentina and Canada. She may have attended the meeting two years before in London of the Women's International Agricultural and Horticultural Union, after which the California Union is modeled. Emma has been busy and hers is an important voice!

WOMEN'S AGRICULTURAL AND HORTICULTURAL UNION OF CALIFORNIA.

By MRS. EMMA SHAFTER-HOWARD of Oakland.

The reactionary movement against subjective education as judged by results shows itself in various ways; in none more plainly than in the return to nature and the study of those elemental facts and factors which underlie the art of life and living.

The advancement of women in agriculture, like other evolutionary movements which call for the application of scientific methods and inventions to economics, is in line with truths and realities which result from the nature and relation of things. In this objective movement is involved the expansion and extension of the home idea as a progressive institution, vital to human society in all the phases of its growth.

This advancement is hindered by the gulf which separates the interests of city and country, especially among women; in the isolation of the country home apart from the so-called advantages of the town; and in the greater isolation of the city home in its lack of intelligence and sympathetic relation to its basis of supplies—the country.

It is largely the opportunity of women to throw out lines of mutual recognition and helpfulness, and to stimulate the home up-building of this State. "As a people are helped in their hearts to be brave in the face of difficulties, so they prosper."

. . . Women throughout the State have been asked to send their names and statements of their special work and methods to the corresponding secretary of the Women's Agricultural and Horticultural Union of California.

As this call is answered, there will be an increasing registration, which will lead to a bureau of information and exchange; and to a social organization based upon the natural conditions of our soil and its increase. . . .

About one hundred statements have been gathered, and represent various interests carried on by women, singly or in family relations. . . . It represents industrial effort in homestead extensions from one acre to one thousand acres, yielding support to many families, and better still, making of the family a community partnership. It also shows the tendency toward healthful growth in the diversions of home-making folk, in efforts to beautify and enrich barren surroundings on roadside and in garden.

Other countries are far in advance of us in opportunities for the training of young women as well as men upon these industrial lines—notably England and Denmark.

At the suggestion of the California delegate to the great International Convention of Women held in London, 1899, a Woman's International Agricultural and Horticultural Union was formed. Each of the ten countries represented pledged themselves to organization upon these lines and to report in turn to the International Union. English and Canadian women have organized. Belgium is about to do so—also Argentina.

At the Fruit-Growers' Convention held in San Francisco, in December last, a step was taken toward such organization in California. Its object as shown in the prospectus is: To circulate useful information, to compare methods of different districts and countries, and to encourage and stimulate (a) farming, dairying, stock-breeding, bee-keeping, poultry-keeping, etc.; (b) fruit and flower-growing for profit; (c) landscape gardening, arboriculture, forestry, the management of estates as employers and employed; (d) also the encouragement of working amateurs.

To this might well be added the words of Monsieur Henry, of the Societé Centrale d'Agriculture, at Brussels, speaking of the Union: "It has practical and social tendencies; 1. To afford enlightenment on the methods of different countries in the agricultural work of women; 2. To make popular such operations, and to retain the young girl in the country, and to provide her there with an honorable means of gaining her living." He also said of the woman taken from town to the country: "She will like it or she will be bored by it; she will only like it on the day *she learns to understand it.* If we could keep the women in the country, it is probable the men would be found there oftener. The projects you have introduced to us under this International Agricultural and Horticultural Union are vast, and their possible utility incontestable."

Meanwhile those who desire to register names and industrial interests will please send to Mrs. Emma Shafter-Howard, corresponding secretary, 1206 Alice Street, Oakland.

Julia's voice has the more practical tone of her father, James, though no less idealistic. Her call is for the gentleman class to return to the country and invest in farms there. She also encourages the present generation of successful farmers to prepare their children to carry on their heritage of farming, rather than send them to be educated in professions that will take them to the cities. She argues for the health and dignity of country life over "the smoke and fumes" of urban life. In many ways, she was anticipating issues that would not rise to the fore for decades to come. It would be voiced by the descendants of those "peasantry of Europe" who are now working on her farms.

NECESSITY FOR AGRICULTURAL EDUCATION.
Remarks by JULIA SHAFTER-HAMILTON of Marin County.

My ideas on farming are purely practical. I was left some eight years ago with 16,000 acres of land in Marin County to look after, and the conclusions I have had to reach were reached on a practical basis. I studied and learned and tried to understand. The Shafter ranches at Point Reyes are well known to all men interested in cattle in California, and I speak from the standpoint of a large landowner who sublets, and not as one running his own property.

One of the most serious questions with us is how to get men of superior knowledge to run ranches. What is the use of acquiring these superior conditions, if we cannot obtain men of superior knowledge? When I took my ranches I had to depend almost altogether on the peasantry of Europe, but I think we ought to bring our own children up to agricultural pursuits. Men are too anxious to get the money out of the land and expend it on the education of their children along professional lines, and are not willing to return anything to the land through the same channels—the education of their boys in agricultural pursuits.

It was too easy at the start to extract the money from the land, and thousands of dollars have been taken from it and turned into channels where none of it would return to the land. Boys have been taken from the farms and educated and employed in the cities in less remunerative, and in my judgment far less dignified, callings, for where is there a life with more freedom or more dignity than that of the farmer? Gentlemen, what are we to do in order to bring men of capital back to the country, where they will not be handicapped for lack of funds, in order to bring back the productiveness of the soil? Why is it that most men with capital are putting their sons into the overcrowded professions and mercantile lines, where there is so much failure, and where certainly the conditions do not bring about as normal, as healthy, and as dignified a life? Why are they not teaching them that from which they often have sprung?

My father made his money in his profession, but then returned to the occupation in which this rising generation's fathers were interested. Why is it that more gentlemen don't do this? . . . Why are men satisfied with such miserable, contemptible lives when they are in a crowded city, when they can have cleanliness, breath, and dignity just outside of the smoke and fumes of the city? I am a city woman myself, but I would not choose the city again. It is a place you can always come back to when you desire it.

These landowners should go back to the country and manage their property themselves. Another thing you city farmers should do is to take a human interest in the tenants you have on the farms. . . . The time of the embryonic state has passed and the time for growth has come, and I believe that if more of the city people would go to the country we would meet on a common ground and both be better off.

LUNCH AT THE PALACE

WHAT HAD STARTED THEM LAUGHING? Could one ever identify that single comment that sets in motion a wave of convulsion that reaches a crescendo of hysterical laughter? Julia and Emma leaned into their napkins to muffle their hilarity in this stately place—tears streaming down their cheeks. Was it just a release from the weight of the solemnities that had pressed down upon them for so long? And why is it that these fits of laughter strike us most irresistibly in churches, lecture halls and other places where they pose the greatest offense to rectitude, reverence and dignity?

On the last day of the conference, Emma and Julia had planned to finish off the event by taking tea at the Palace Hotel. It was a family custom among the Shafters to mark important events and conclusions with this age-old rite in the new and grandiose building built by William Ralston. No city monument bore a more lavish testament to the wealth of the railroad era and the fortunes that were made, less through the mining of gold than the mining of gold-miners. A most lucrative business.

The cause of the ladies' hilarity was easily identified in this case and this was not the first time it had offered comic release. Most every time that either of the families dined at the palace, someone recalled the spoof that had appeared in the Chronicle in 1877, purportedly written to the editor of a Hoboken newspaper by a visitor to San Francisco from that place. He had written that the hotel had been built on a colossal scale covering thousands of acres capable of housing a quarter of the city's population. The best room in the house, having the best view and highest elevation was number 24,999. The blocks in the vestibule were described as solid gold and the stairs mounted in silver. The hotel, the writer claimed, had 25,000 bellboys, with a number for each of the rooms.

In general, the writer had caught the spirit, if not the truth, of Ralston's dream. He had set out to outdo every hotel in America, counting on the completion of the Central Pacific Railroad across the country to deliver a herd of visitors each day to their fair city, from all parts of the country and even from all parts of the world. This would all be gravy on top of their regular clientele of local millionaires who had made their fortunes on San Francisco's mighty boom. The result was a hotel that spanned an entire city block (if not thousands of acres) and rose five elegant stories above a central palm court.

After tea, Julia and Emma went their separate ways. Julia had her usual pressing affairs in Inverness and would take the ferry to Point Reyes Station and then the stage coach from there to her home. Emma would stay on to see friends and do some business of her own in the city.

San Francisco ~ Same Day (December 6, 1901)

ROSA AND TERESA IN THE CITY

ROSA'S ENTHUSIASM WAS INFECTIOUS. "This city at Christmas time is like a giant amusement park full of free rides." Teresa looked at her skeptically. "You mean you didn't pay the cable car conductor? We better watch out for the polizia."

"You know what I mean." Teresa did know. They had ridden a cable car across the top of the city last night, right over Nob Hill. They had passed mansions, like palaces, that had been the homes of Mark Hopkins, Charles Crocker, Collis Huntington, and Amasa Leland Stanford. Of course they didn't know the names of the owners but they added to the fairy-tale quality of the night. Near the peak of Nob Hill was Grace Church. You could see the water on three sides where the lights of distant boats twinkled like fairy lights. In some places it was still gaslight, but in others, businesses had used the new electric lights, in color, for their decorations. It was like looking at colored stars from somewhere beyond the sky. For two women accustomed to the winter darkness of mountains, this was other-worldly.

Everything about Teresa's life now, if she stopped to think about it, was "otherworldly." She had arrived in February and in a short time, had found several of her countrymen in Point Reyes Station, especially Salvatore Grandi, who had done well for himself and his brother Louis. There was his name up in letters—The Grandi Store—as soon as she got off the train there. He helped her arrange a place to stay and in no time at all, she had a job at Nelson's Inn. Imagine! Teresa Buzzini with a job in a country where she couldn't even speak the language! But that was the story of so many of the people around her, especially dairymen who had just left their cows in Ticino to sit under cows in Point Reyes and do what they had done all of their lives.

Now, in just two weeks, on December 20*th*, she was going to be married. She had met Domenico Grossi at a Friday night event in town, when dairy workers were briefly let loose from their ranches to relax and enjoy a little entertainment. Olema was a lively place.

Waiting for the F Car that would finally take them down Market Street to the Ferry Building, Teresa and Rosa had watched elegant carriages and coachmen delivering their passengers like royalty to the Palace Hotel. What a city! They had stayed the night with a cousin of Rosa's who had an apartment in the city with what seemed to Teresa like a hundred relations, who kept coming and going while they slept through the night on old sofas that had obviously supported a platoon of visitors over time.

Perhaps it wasn't just Rosa's enthusiasm. Perhaps it was her own secret gaiety that Rosa was expressing. Rosa had insisted on this "shopping trip" in San Francisco, even though they had very little money for buying. Shopping meant looking into all of the windows, watching all of the people, walking through the elegant stores, and even a stroll through North Beach, where they listened to Italian being spoken, pretended they were in Milano, and then realizing that just to be themselves in San Francisco was the best thing of all.

They would take the ferry back to Point Reyes the next day. For Rosa and Teresa, even the ferry ride was like a carnival event. There had never been anything like that in Ticino, even at the gayest fiestas.

By 1899, after working like Jacob for seven years, Dominic had saved up enough money working at the Pierce Point Ranch* to rent his own ranch in Olema, not far from the Olema Inn—the latest incarnation of Nelson's Hotel. He was in a position to think of starting a family, now that he had a place of his own. In Olema, he was able to avail himself of the social life of the small communities, where many Ticinesi men and women gathered. It is not surprising that his eye fell on young Teresa Buzzini, working as a waitress at Nelson's Hotel. Once they had fallen into conversation—which of course always began with "where are you from"—they must have been amazed to realize that they were nearly neighbors in Ticino. Perhaps also

---

* The Shafters had invited Solomon Pierce, a friend from Vermont, to buy the ranch on the northern-most point of Point Reyes. It was considered the most well-run ranch on Point Reyes and the only one not owned by the Shafters. It has been preserved as a historic site for visitors.

that they were both born in July. Dominic was 27 and Teresa was 23. The courtship went quickly.

Dominic and Teresa married on December 30, 1901. I have to believe that there were many Ticinesi present to share in their celebration. The Verzasca and Maggia valleys had been joined—the villages of Brione and Monte Carasso had met across the sea.

Their first child Eda was born nine months later in the house in Olema, on the farm that they rented on the property of Payne Shafter.

JULIA AT THE FERRY

JULIA FELT LIGHTENED OF SPIRIT AS SHE WAITED IN LINE at the ferry building to buy her ticket. Emma had just delivered her there from The Palace and she waited tranquilly under a light rain. It had been good to be relieved for a while of the daily burdens and tasks, and to see herself as a woman of dignity and experience with something valuable to offer out of the years of responsibilities she had borne for her father's lands. Talking about her dairies made her feel that all was well, good things were going on, new furrows plowed for agriculture, for women, for California, for the country. It was easy to lose sight of this in the pressing issues of survival. But looking at her prospects in Inverness, from the distance of the city, and through the eyes of the participants in the Horticultural Conference, she was filled again with hope and optimism.

The city exuded this and it was richly distilled in the opulent hotel. But mostly her mind was empty now, watching the people around her, the gulls, the seals, the vibrant sounds of the city by the bay. Once again she marvelled at the diversity of its population, which came to her now in varied voices. The sharp sing-song of Chinese, undulating Spanish and Hawaiian vowels, the provocative descant of Italian. Two women stood a little behind her, speaking that language with a gay intensity. Sturdy peasant women she thought, making their new lives here. She was especially attuned to their voices because they had that particular intonation she heard so often on her ranches. Swiss-Italian, she thought. She turned briefly and smiled at them.

Things had not gone well for Julia. Julia and her brothers James and Payne were at their father's bedside when he died in August of 1892. The next day the newspapers extolled his civic contributions and noted his significant place in the financial world among the pantheon of San Francisco millionaires (which would be the billionaires of today). How wrong they were. Less than a year later, the *Examiner* printed a sobering correction in an article headed "Wealth Has Speedy Wings," in which they reported that James McMillan Shafter had died with his "lordly possessions reduced to the small end of nothing."

The weight and ignominy of this failure fell mostly on the youngest child, his daughter Julia. The oldest son, Payne, was now Squire Shafter comfortably ensconced in his mansion, The Oaks, which even sported a racetrack where he could put his thoroughbreds through their paces. The second son, James, was now a physician, successful in his own right. Julia's marriage to Alexander "Jack" Hamilton fit nicely into the family template of sons-in-law dedicated to the Shafters' Point Reyes interests. Jack Hamilton was manager of the Pierce Point Ranch but in reality the union was as unsuccessful as Emma's was to Charles Howard. Jack Hamilton was most content spending Julia's money and enjoying convivial pastimes with Payne, drinking and trotting his horses. He was no more help to Julia than her brother Payne was when the family's dire circumstances became clear. James leant a hand where he could.

In September of 1893, Julia was forced to make the public announcement that the Marin County sheriff would auction off the small ranches on North Bend that James had acquired in Garcia's time. Payne came up with $12,600 to buy the Olema Ranch that his father had bought at auction in 1871 for $7,526. There was considerable speculation about how so substantial a man as Judge Shafter could have been reduced to such straits. The *Examiner* laid the blame on a man named Milton Latham, an associate of Shafter's, who got the judge to put his name to notes floated to build a ferryboat to Sausalito, which was the terminus for his railroad. The *Chronicle* revealed that Judge Shafter had been advised to "cut his losses and get out when the railroad reached White's Hill, but because Milton Latham was in a hole, he chose to stand by him."

Julia publicly proclaimed that all of the interest payments on her father's debts were up-to-date and their financial situation was not as dire as it had been reported. "Lately I have sold $40,000 of property and proceeds have been used in paying off the debts. I have put the estate in better condition than it has known for twenty years. I have sacrificed no property, always sold at good prices. My brother Payne Shafter has his own estate of $100,000 with no encumbrances on it. I have 450 acres, which are valued at $25,000, so you see it is a mistake to say that we have been selling land because we need the money to live on. It has always been the Judge's pride to pay dollar for dollar, and so we have never allowed an obligation to go by default." Noble words indeed! But Julia's battle was just beginning and the disparity between Payne's comfortable and unencumbered estate worth $100,000 and her 450 acres worth $25,000 must have rankled, particularly when her husband was dissipating it so fast.

Julia and her brothers did agree in writing to make good on the huge debts when they could as well as paying interest on them in the meantime. In return for this, Jane Stanford O'Conner and Wells Fargo agreed not to foreclose on the Point Reyes land that James McMillan Shafter had put up as security. The communications between Payne and Julia during this period were bitter and altercations over their father's estate were many. In 1875, for example, their father had given Payne 2,235 acres of the old Berry rancho, with its lovely manor house, as a 30th birthday present "in consideration of his love, affection and $1." There is no sign that Julia was ever the recipient of such affectionate generosity. She was, however, chosen as executrix and she performed that role with passionate and sometimes scrappy determination in pursuit of the family's solvency and honor.

Payne managed to escape these family financial problems in 1895 when he signed an agreement relinquishing any claim to the estate, including the San Francisco mansion in return for $2500 in cash. Julia and James now worked together to sell enough property to pay off the creditors. Julia began to come up with imaginative plans to make their properties profitable. She published a brochure with maps of the 12,695 acre Point Reyes Tract and advertised that there was still a lime deposit on the land and a once flourishing charcoal industry which could easily be revived. There were nine ranches included and the price was $20 to $40 per acre, sold either as whole lots or in parts. "Cut it up into small holdings," she wrote, "erect a central creamery, . . . in conjunction with a cheese factory, or, better still, a condensed milk factory . . . and its present property is but a small promise of what is to come." She waxed similarly eloquent and optimistic about the three thousand acre South End Tract which ran westward from Olema to the ocean. "When the North Pacific Coast Railroad builds from Point Reyes Station to Bolinas (which it never did), it will pass this tract and the timber can be cut at a big profit for the San Francisco market." Spoken like a true daughter of James McMillan Shafter. She goes on, "To the westward of the ridge is dairyland. Glen and Wildcat Ranches are on this tract. 230 cows and an annual income of $3,875." The cost of this wonderful real estate opportunity was $100,000. There were no takers. She had more luck with the Inverness property, selling 100 acres of choice lots to Kate Johnson for $50 an acre. Unfortunately, the buyer died six weeks later on October 17, 1893. Julia had reached the point where the mansion on Chestnut Street, which her father had built in 1863, had to go on the market too. Her ad read:

"Grandest view in San Francisco; house 16 rooms, furnace; modern plumbing; stables; chickens houses etc. Grounds comprise 250 varas."

In Jack Mason's account of this period in *Point Reyes the Solemn Land*, he imagines Julia sitting there waiting for buyers, while she "retraced momentous events in her life that had taken place here: The tea party, for instance, in October of 1866, that the Argonaut had called 'among the most delightful of recent entertainments.' Cousin Mary Shafter had contributed musical selections. Among the invited were Mrs. Charles Crocker, Mrs. Mark Requa, Mrs. Theresa Fair, Mrs. James Mervyn Donahue, Mrs. J.C. Flood and Mrs. Emma Howard. Tea and refreshments 'were served by a number of Japanese and Chinese women appropriately attired.' On February 12, 1889, Julia had been married in this house with the Oriental motif again in evidence, Japanese lanterns illuminating the garden. The wedding was small, the reception large. Julia had greeted her guests in a white satin train richly brocaded, with diamonds and sapphires tucked in her coiffure. A wedding bell of blossoms hung between the double parlor. The bridegroom was a member of the Country Club that leased a part of her father's Point Reyes estate."

In 1898, James Jr. came to the assistance of Julia in organizing the Point Reyes Land and Dairy Company. Julia immediately set to work on its promotion. They launched the Sportsmen's Club to attract capital, selling shares at $2000. Each share representing 3 acres of land on Tomales Bay. A share gave the holder the privilege of 20 years of fishing and hunting rights over 16,000 acres. Julia's tenant ranchers were suddenly deputized as game commissioners and charged with protecting deer and quail in return for one day's quail hunting a week and one deer shoot a year. Unfortunately again, the Sportsmen's Club failed due to competition from a similar one founded in 1890 by her own menfolk. Mr. Shafter, her father, had leased hunting rights in 1890 to members of the Pacific Union Club of San Francisco. When the 5 year lease expired, Julia, in her role as executrix, refused to renew it. Her husband Alexander "Jack" Hamilton, however, was president of the Pacific Union Club and he threatened to sue her. In retaliation, Julia all but disowned him and on November 7th, 1895, he signed an agreement waiving any right to their community property. But her brother Payne stepped in at this point and sold 110 acres of his own land to the Club, including 30 acres of prime land close to The Oaks, less desirable for building but suitable for hunting and fishing. With a total price of $6000, the club got total use of Shafter roads into the area. The club members now took with enthusiasm to the development of their country estate. They too put out a Prospectus announcing the planned construction of a golf course, unsurpassed bridle paths and two championship tennis courts. Two swimming lakes would be created by damming streams and a clubhouse would be built with lounge, kitchen, dining room and bedrooms, surrounded by a wide veranda. The only thing which came to pass out of this was the clubhouse, which would eventually include stable and kennels. A son-in-law of Garcia's was hired as gamekeeper. Future guests would include Theodore Roosevelt and Ignace Paderewski.

The Country Club could be reached by the ferry to Sausalito from the city, where the North Pacific Coast Railroad, which had cost Judge Shafter his fortune, was waiting to deliver them to Point Reyes Station. From there they were driven by horse and wagon the two miles to Bear Valley. The Country Club lasted until the Great Depression, when it died along with the railroad and stage line. As Jack Mason wrote, "By 1934, the dream days were over."

Undaunted, Julia Shafter Hamilton persisted with her efforts. In March of 1906, she had a new scheme to advance the sale of 200 unsold lots in Inverness and a large section between Inverness and Bear Valley as well as 2700 acres on Inverness Ridge. The Inverness Land and Water Company was created for this purpose. She held back her own 300 acre Bayside Ranch, which she referred to as the Home Place, although it was a far cry from Payne's Home Place in Olema, The Oaks. She had great hopes now that her financial rescue was at hand.

✳ ✳ ✳ ✳

San Francisco, 1906

THE GREAT CARUSO

ENRICO CARUSO SAT DRAPED IN HIS FAVORITE SILK NIGHTGOWN sipping cognac. He was admiring the city. Admiring himself. Admiring Bizet for creating such a delicious role for him—Don Jose in his opera Carmen—*which he had performed so well this evening to enthusiastic audiences. He loved American audiences. They were so raucous in their appreciation. They had a kind of brute passion. Especially in San Francisco. Everything they said about the Wild West of America was true. Except this hotel—The Palace. It would not have been out of place in any of the European capitals where he had performed.*

After the performance, he and his friend, baritone Antonio Scotti, had celebrated with glasses of fine wine at the gaily decorated Garden Court of the Palace Hotel, amid palm trees and the night breezes from the Pacific. Then to Zinkand's Restaurant on O'Farrell for a delicious Italian meal. He felt sated now with wine, food and adulation. His valet Martino had retired for the night, leaving him this quiet moment to savor his triumphs and consider his surroundings. He had been given the finest suite in the hotel. It had a huge fireplace with a carved marble mantel, but the furnishings were not as fine as in other places he had stayed. Still, the hotel itself was grand and his suite had once been occupied by a U.S. president, Ulysses S. Grant. From the third floor, he could look down on the lights of the city, which still burned in many places, and beyond, he could see the glimmering red and green running lights of the ships in the harbor. It was a fine city, though it was no New York or Rome or even Napoli. Ah, Napoli. City of his birth, his home. He sighed in further appreciation of his good judgment. He was scheduled to sing in his beloved city, but a fiery eruption of Mt. Vesuvius had made him change his plans and get as far away as possible. By the time he reached San Francisco, the newspapers were full of the terrible disaster, which was still in progress. People were dying.* He shuddered at the thought.

What good luck it was that the Met had scheduled this tour. Such an undertaking— transporting all of those sets and costumes across this vast country. They had spared no expense and the result had put him as far away as possible from that demon volcano. As he had confided to the orchestra conductor on the long train trip west, "Maybe it was God's will after all that I should come this far." To prepare for the voyage into the Wild West of America, he had bought a pistol and fifty bullets, which he practiced loading and drawing on the train trip—when he wasn't playing poker in the dining car with other members of the company.

---

* In May 1905, a new eruption began, first with slow lava effusions and, since January 1906, with intermittent explosive activity (strombolian activity). On the 7th of April, 1906 the eruption reached the climax with lava fountains and earthquakes. The eruptive column of ash and gas reached the height of 13,000 m. The eruption ends in the last days of April. The volcano's eruption would kill 100 people by the following day and devastate areas around it. This was the same volcano that had destroyed Pompeii and Herculaneum in 79 BC, there in the region where two plates meet.

Tempers had flared at the afternoon rehearsal. His leading lady, Olive Fremstad, might have been a famed Wagnerian soprano but her anger at the clumsiness of the local stage hands led to an insulting outburst against him and turned her voice into a screech as she rehearsed her aria. She blamed HIM for the whole thing, claiming that his salary was so high that the Met couldn't afford to pay for good stage hands. Ridiculous! He had been paid much more than that in Mexico City! He came close to refusing to sing with her. He had also been unsettled by the fact that the critics had panned the Met's performance the evening before. He had not performed that night but he was anxious about their reviews tomorrow. Well, tomorrow was another day. Now, the Great Caruso would rest. It was after 3 a.m.

◆ ◆ ◆

At 3 a.m., as Caruso was finally putting himself to bed, James Hopper, a reporter for The San Francisco Call, was strolling home to his apartment on Post Street, taking in the scenes of the late night city, which struck him as particularly peaceful. Still, he felt a certain restlessness. The anticipated review of Caruso's performance had been delivered and would be printed in an early morning edition of the paper. Hopper and the reporter at The San Francisco Call wrote rave reviews. Hopper was looking forward to the full-page headline above his own: CARUSO MAKES DON JOSE THE LEADING ROLE. They found Fremstead too Wagnerian for the young, passionate Carmen and her weighing in at 200 pounds didn't help. But Caruso they loved. They had given him ten full minutes of curtain calls. As Hopper neared a livery stable, a horse bellowed and there was a large racket as the animals thrashed about for no reason. A little after 3, he too fell into his bed.

There would be no reviews on the morrow. At 5:12 a.m., after Caruso had drifted off into his satisfied sleep, he woke in terror to monstrous sounds of buildings crashing into one another. In the first moments, he thought perhaps it was Martino, coming to shake him awake. But then he felt his bed rocking and saw the chandelier swaying wildly, the chairs crashing into one another. He leapt out of bed and ran to the window, opening it to look out. Walls were falling everywhere and the earth continued to quake. When Caruso's conductor, Alfred Hertz rushed into the room, Caruso embraced him, crying hysterically "We are both doomed. We are both doomed." The maestro's one thought was for Caruso's voice. "Sing, Enrico, try to sing!" He was worried that the shock might damage the world's greatest voice. "Show the world that nothing could frighten the great Caruso." That did it. When the tenor burst into song, although it was only a few notes, they had the same rich velvet sound. But they did not quell the terror he felt. He ran to the door and was immediately overwhelmed by screaming such as he had never heard. He snatched up his watch, his diamond pin and his rings and rushed from the room and out onto the street, where hundreds were huddled together waiting for the next shock. When it remained quiet, the residents returned to the hotel, only to flee it again with another quaking. Finally, his valet Martino was able to return and pack Caruso's things in trunks to be removed with him. They would eventually make it out of the city with hundreds of fugitives crossing to Oakland on the ferry.

On Post Street, James Hopper heard a sound, "as of a snarl," and when he opened his eyes, the building was quivering with a vertical and rotary motion— jumping up and down and side to side. He saw the bureau head toward him from the far side of the room and then a piece of plaster fell on his head. As the quake continued, he was left without fear or horror. Without feeling. Just the clear thought, "It's the end," as past scenes of cataclysm swept through his mind: Pompei, Lisbon, Manila, St. Pierre, Vesuvius and, now, in a crashing climax—San Francisco.

The whale is on the move. It has lurched forward along the San Andreas fault that separates it from the North American Plate for 810 miles along the spine of California, passing through the center of San Francisco. The rupture is felt along the northern third of the fault, a distance of 296 miles. The Point Reyes peninsula jumps 15 feet in 40 seconds. It causes displacements of up to 28 feet. The shaking will be felt as far north as Oregon, as far south as Los Angeles and as far east as central Nevada. The cities of Santa Rosa to the north and San Jose to the south will have major destruction. The Salinas River is permanently shifting its course near the mouth, migrating six miles from its place between Moss Landing and Watsonville. Leland Stanford's university is in ruins.

In San Francisco, the fires caused by the quake will wreak as much havoc as the earthquake itself, perhaps more. Government officials will insist that fires are the main culprit and minimize the earthquake damage, and the death toll, which they reported as 375. Today's estimates are closer to 3,000 but the exact figure will never be known.

Pioneer Hall, where Emma Shafter Howard and Julia Shafter Hamilton held forth, is one of the first buildings to be destroyed.

In the San Francisco opera house, where the cream of San Francisco society and celebrity guests like John Barrymore had been seated in the elegant box seats only a few hours before, the world's largest chandelier came crashing down as the roof caved in. All of the Metropolitan Opera's sets and costumes, transported with such effort from New York, will go up in flames. The scene of the evening's triumph would vanish before first light. Former Mayor James Phelan, who had been in attendance for the performance, would write to a friend, noting that the roof had collapsed a few hours after the event and that they were "very thankful that the earthquake arrived too late to do us bodily harm."

James Hopper's final review of the whole night went like this: "I see [Caruso] stab, I hear Fremstad's scream, Caruso's wail of remorse, glutted passion and remorse commingled; I see his magnificent crawling movement to her as the curtain comes down. I see myself walking slowly back to my paper, the *Call*, a few steps away, and I am saying to myself: 'Surely, what I have felt tonight is the summit of human emotion.' And now when I think of that, I almost laugh."*

In a matter of moments, the Paris of the West had been reduced to ashes.

* From *The Great Earthquake and Firestorms of 1906: How San Francisco Nearly Destroyed Itself*, Philip L. Fradkin.

220,000 to 300,000 people, out of 410,000, were left homeless. Half of the people were evacuated across the bay to Oakland, while the rest were huddled together in Golden Gate Park, the Presidio, the Panhandle. Many took refuge under makeshift tents along the beaches between Ingleside and North Beach in camps that would remain in operation for two more years, as the city is rebuilt.

Not even the great mansions built by our four New Yorkers atop Nob Hill will escape the pitiless flames, which rage on without regard for wealth, power, beauty or fame. The man from the little town of Henderson, New York, who started out as a clerk in a mercantile business, had bequeathed his Nob Hill Mansion to the University of California on his death. Mark Hopkins' home had become an art institute and gallery. It housed several world famous paintings and some of the finest bronzes and statuary in the West. A crowd looked on in awe as flames began to engulf it and there was clearly no way to save it. A young officer called on several of the onlookers to help in the rescue of the best of the collection. No wagon was available in which to load its precious goods so pictures had to be cut from their frames and rolled up so that one man could carry several at a time. But the fire spread so quickly that the best they could do was move the finer marble pieces and some of the pictures to the lawn of the nearby Flood mansion. But the fire would later take them too. The city officials who had set up their camp at the huge nearly completed Fairmont Hotel, would be forced to evacuate. In the end, even Nob Hill would not be a place of escape. The monuments it held to the realized dreams of gold and American success, would be leveled as the city was destroyed.

Enrico Caruso had not, after all, escaped disaster. But he survived it, among the thousands of refugees who fled to Oakland on the ferries. Six years later, he would sing with the Met in New York as a benefit for the survivors of the Titanic. His voice held a sympathetic resonance.

JULIA AND EMMA

At the same moment that Caruso declares "We are doomed" to his valet and James Hopper awakes with the thought that the end of the world has come, Payne Shafter awakes in his room at the Oaks with the same words on his lips: "The world is coming to an end!"

For years to come, the epicenter will be recorded as having been at the head of Tomales Bay between Olema and Point Reyes station, close to the place where James Shafter once waited at Paper Mill Creek for the timbers to build his house. The bridge over the creek has jack-knifed. In fact, there is no larger footprint of the earthquake's rupture all along the fault than right there, where it runs along the Olema Valley and passes beneath Tomales Bay; in fact, right there on Payne Shafter's ranch. A Shafter dairy cow will enter into history for having been swallowed up by the gap in the earth. Later books will say that the story was an invention of Payne Shafter. But it is a good story and possible. Gaps as wide as 28 feet appeared in the landscape of Point Reyes. People will travel for miles, especially geologists, to see them. The greatest single movement of the April 18th quake takes place on what will become Francis Drake Boulevard, just south of Point Reyes Station.

A modest hotel topples into Tomales Bay. No one is injured. Another hotel meets the same fate in Bolinas. The quake passes right through Mary Burdell's cow pasture, which has become the booming Point Reyes Station. A fireman on the North Shore railroad is firing up his locomotive in preparation for the run to Sausalito as the locomotive and its four coaches start swaying back and forth. The fireman nimbly leaps to safety as the entire train rolls over on its side.

And for Julia Shafter Hamilton, who dreamed of a town of ten thousand on the site of Inverness? Her plan, remember, was to push the sale of 200 lots in Inverness and another 2700 acres on Inverness Ridge. Those last great hopes of a month before to finally pay off her father's debts and "save the ranch"—in this case many ranches—have been cruelly dashed by the vagabond plates. Newly-built homes in Inverness have been badly damaged, discouraging potential buyers from investing in its real estate. Her indebtedness grows, even as she continues to try to improve the town, piping in water and working herself as a clerk at its first school.

In her excellent book on Point Reyes, Gayle Baker describes the ever-active mind of Julia Shafter Hamilton as she addresses the needs of the crumbling Shafter ranches like the little Dutch boy holding his finger in the dike. "In addition to her attempts to develop Inverness, Julia considered other schemes, such as a condensed milk factory, timbering, the revival of the charcoal industry, a large-scale fishing enterprise, a limestone mine and an electric car transportation system." She has the visionary mind and determination of her father and uncle, but she has lived in the worst of times and she has borne from the start the burden of her father's debts. None of these things will pan out and in the end, she will be forced to sell off farmland in the Olema Valley to avoid bankruptcy.

In 1924, still hopeful, Julia borrows $160,000 against her ranches and by the fall of 1929, things seem to be looking better for the economy of the region. On this encouraging note, she borrows another $144,000.

Three weeks later the stock market crashes and all is lost. In the panic of the Depression, when she is late for her first payment, the bank gives her 15 days to sell all of her ranches. Within a week, she has sold them all off for $255,000 to real estate agent Leland Stanford Murphy, who also assumes payment on her debt.

Oscar's daughter Emma has fared no better. Her husband Charles Howard had promised Oscar to be a faithful steward of Shafter ranches, in return for owning a large portion, including some of the best pasture land and what would become the Home Ranch or Bear Valley Ranch (also W ranch). After Oscar's death, Charles took on the support of Sarah and her four adolescent girls, but his interest soon strayed in other directions than his Point Reyes property. He had his sights on becoming president of the Spring Valley Water Company, which he did. He made investments in Nevada silver mines, Russian River timber and railroad stock.

But the investments did not pay off as he had hoped. Unbeknown to Emma, he borrowed on his ranches to pay his mounting debts. She didn't learn the truth of their situation until the sheriff appeared at their door, threatening to sell all of the ranches at auction. For Emma, this betrayal of her father's legacy was a mortal blow; an unforgiveable breach of trust.

The financial disaster was averted but the family rift could never be repaired. It has been said that Emma blamed Charles for Oscar's death, claiming that his disappointment in Charles had led to her father's insanity. Charles had resentments of his own toward Emma and connived to get Oscar's widow, Sarah, to change her will in his favor. Once designated as heir, Charles formed an investment company with their children to which he left all of his assets.

It is not until 1908, when he dies, that Emma discovers that she has inherited nothing. She sues her children for her half of the estate, but her victory is a bitter one, permanently alienating them from her and leaving her with only heavily mortgaged land. Her son Oscar has gone to New York to become an aspiring songwriter. Her daughter Maud lives in Europe on her family allowance. Her son Fred Paxton is a gentleman farmer in Bear Valley. Her son Harold is in and out of mental hospitals and in trouble with the law. After her angry separation with Charles, she had sent three of her children back east to boarding schools and left the youngest, Harold, in the care of a nurse. It is not surprising that she had not gained their affection, although she continues to support Oscar and Maud into their adult years. At her death, the legal strife will continue among her four children. When the matter is finally settled in the courts and the lands evenly divided among the four, each will sell their portion to a wealthy San Franciscan named John Rapp.

Thus will end the Shafter Dairy Empire of Point Reyes. In T.S. Eliot's words, not with a bang but a whimper.

✳ ✳ ✳ ✳

Durgapur, India ca. 1906

INNER QUAKES

NOTHING COULD BE FURTHER FROM THE BRASH AND BRAWLING new metropolis at the western edge of North America, now shrouded in ash and mourning amid its ruins, than the quiet, rarefied air of the village of Durgapur in East Bengal where we met Yogesh Chandra Datta. The very air of India was saturated with a mystical sense, inhaled through daily life into the lives of the people. For Yogesh, the tectonic movements will be interior ones. As he would say later in his life, "Everything in India reminds one of God. Nature itself is permeated through and through with spirituality; for thousands of years people have thought of God, sung of him, meditated on him."

We may recall that Yogesh was born in the year that Vivekananda gave his famous speech at the World's Fair, attended by James Phelan, later mayor of San Francisco. When Yogesh is six years old, and the new century is dawning, Vivekananda is in San Francisco on a mission of bringing Vedanta to the West, following in the footsteps of the Spanish padres, who carried Christianity into the region with the same dedication. Vivekananda, however, is not trying to convert Westerners to Hinduism. His mission is more subtle—"I do not come", he says, "to convert you to a new belief. I want you to keep your own belief; I want to make the Methodist a better Methodist; the Presbyterian a better Presbyterian; the Unitarian a better Unitarian. I want to teach you to live the truth, to reveal the light within your own soul." In that year, he will found the San Francisco Vedanta Society.

Swami Vivekananda dies two years later on July 4, 1902 while the city he recently left is celebrating the nation's birthday. As rockets burst over the skies of San Francisco, something bursts in the sky of Vivekananda's mind.

Vivekananda died at ten minutes past nine p.m. on July 4, 1902 while he was meditating. According to his disciples, this was *Mahasamadhi*,* the "great Samadhi" granted to the holy one who is able to intentionally leave the body at the time of enlightenment. Afterward, his disciples recorded that they had noticed "a little blood" in the Swami's nostrils, about his mouth and in his eyes, which led the doctors to speculate that it was due to the rupture of a blood-vessel in the brain, although they could not confirm the cause of the death. His disciples were sure that *Brahmarandhra*, the aperture in the crown of the head, must have been pierced when he attained Mahasamadhi,

It is in this same place, Belur Math, that Mahatma Gandhi was heard later to say that his whole life was an effort to bring into actions the ideas of Vivekananda.

Vivekananda was thirty-nine years old.

◆ ◆ ◆

Somewhere around the time that Vesuvius was erupting and the San Andreas fault was quaking, a small but violent eruption occurred here too. The village of Durgapur, like any place on earth, was not without its dark side. A feud of some sort was going on against the principal of a nearby school and thugs had been paid to beat him. Mistaking his identity, they beat instead a respected Brahmin teacher of Bengali literature. The teacher was so deeply mortified by the incident that he lost his sanity and was no longer able to teach. His family had to move away, but the man remained in his house in a state of extreme poverty since he was without his livelihood. At this time, Yogesh is around nine years old. By the time he is old enough to attend the Junior High School, which was in the village where the Brahmin lived, the man is slowly recovering. Yogesh and some friends pay him a visit, out of respect, and there begins a mutually beneficial friendship. The relationship helps to restore the teacher's self-esteem and has a deep impact on

* A.P. Sen (2006), "Editor's Introduction," *The Indispensable Vivekananda*, p. 27.

Yogesh. The boy and the man enter into conversations on philosophy and religion and Yogesh is given free access to the man's extensive library. It is here that he comes upon a book by Aswini Kumar Datta—*Bhakti Yoga*. Yogesh would later describe the impact of his reading—

"It was as though a great storm passed through my mind. Many old thoughts were swept away, new thoughts came. I was shaken to the depth of my being."

I had a similar experience when I was 13 and spent a summer with my grandfather, who was a minister, teacher and philosopher of great depth. He too opened up his immense library to me and I came upon a book by P.D. Ouspensky called *Tertium Organum*. In my case, the world flew apart for me as I read excerpts from Kant's *Critique of Pure Reason*, with its assertion that time and space were only features of our own mind. I wandered around in a daze in this new world that was not at all as concrete as I had imagined. This book introduced me also to Jacob Boehme, when Grandpa drew my attention to a particularly beautiful mystical experience. I began right then reading philosophy, both Western and Eastern, in the early hours before I set off for school. Two years later, I encountered a wonderful teacher—my history teacher Mrs. Cross—who expanded those openings yet further. That relationship has continued to this day, and includes her husband Jack, their three children and grandchildren. This book is dedicated to her. That's how fertile a ground this age can be, if it isn't blasted to pieces by electronic noise and distraction of all sorts. Happily, I continue to encounter young people stepping into that holy ground who flower from out of those depths.

For Yogesh Datta, it is something more. It is closer to the experiences of Christian mystics like St. Theresa. As Yogesh will put it—"It was like being caught up in a raging flood, carried and turned over and over. I could not say what was happening, but the experience lasted for several days. Afterwards I felt absolute serenity and for weeks was in a state of joy. . . . The effect of reading that book never left me." Bhakti Yoga, after all, is the path toward a heart quaking with divine love.

◆ ◆ ◆

Yogesh is finishing high school when he first meets Vivekananda. Once again it is through a book, Vivekananda's *A Study of Religion*. He is touched to the core by language like these excerpted lines, selected by Sister Garga for her biography of him, *A Heart Poured Out*:

> Blessedness, eternal peace arising from perfect freedom, is the highest concept of religion, underlying all the ideas of God in Vedanta . . . Wherever anything shines, whether it is the light in the sun or our own consciousness, it is He. . . .
>
> The sum total of the universe is God Himself. . . . Upon Him the senses are painting chairs and tables and rooms and houses and worlds and suns and stars, and everything else.

Such experiences continue to infuse Yogesh's life and in his meditative states, "Swamiji" (Vivekanada) increasingly appears. Something is happening for him that could only happen in that India where the interior life is so alive for so many people. Although he has never met the man in person, Vivekananda becomes his teacher, speaking to him in dreams and meditation.

In 1919, Yogesh will become a member of the Ramakrishnan Order and begin his training at a monastery in Madras.

As you will see, all of these events are seeds for the new phase that is about to unfold for Point Reyes and the farm-that-is-a-ranch in Marin

PART VII

A FARM IN MARIN

When we came up here there was just the old house, all torn up, to live in with ten kids. The barns were hardly fit to use and needed a lot of repair because the ranch had been leased out to tenants and they had let everything go.

It was just kind of a mess, so we had to start making fences to keep the cattle where they belonged. We had a lot of building to do. All the buildings you see now we and my Dad built.

— James "Pop" Grossi

Ticino

WINNILI ON THE MOVE AGAIN

ONE BY ONE, THEY ARE COMING OUT OF THEIR REMOTE VALLEYS. Paul the Deacon's people. The Winnili, the Langobards, the Lombards . . . a small but steady strand of those earlier wanderers who finally found a home in the Alpine foothills and stayed, as others before them stayed behind, along the Elbe or in the mountains of northern Italy or the lands to its south. No longer eager for war, Winnili, but pasture-loving Winnili, wanting only to be left in peace. For centuries they have been people of Ticino—Lombards who likely mingled with early Celts, Swiss from the north, Italians from the south.

Now they are on the move again. The newest voyagers are about to become Americans. War and hunger are driving them west, across the sea, where they will dissolve into the mainstream of America. Or will they? Let us follow them into Marin, as we followed them southward into Italy, and see.

◆ ◆ ◆

The families we are following are only a handful of the number who emigrated from the mid-nineteenth century to the end of it. As we saw earlier, in the year of Salvatore Grandi's and Caterina Buzzini's birth—1853—the border was closed to Italy. Liberal sympathizers in Ticino were aiding the Italian "Risorgimento" movement seeking Italian unity. This was essentially an Austrian embargo between Ticino and Italy and the immediate return of some 5,000 Ticino workers employed in Lombardy was a severe blow to the valleys.

In those first emigrations to the goldfields of Australia, some 2000 Ticinesi from the Val Maggia and Val Verzasca made the long, expensive and disappointing trip to Australia. According to Swiss historian Giorgio Cheda, the Ticino coffers were emptied by some 2 million Swiss francs to pay for these voyages, with little return. In the beginning, only a few hundred went to California. The voyage to Australia in sailing ships dependent on wind conditions could take up to six months. (Before 1869, the trip to California was also long since ships had to go round Cape Horn and sail up the coast.) The only solution lay in the financing of a debt. Professor Cheda explains that when 10, 15 or 20 young people in a village decided to go to Australia, they would form a partnership and go to a notary, who would have them sign a contract with joint and collective liability. This caused some serious problems if, for example, one person died on the ship voyage before having earned anything, because that person's debt would have to be repaid by the others. This financial burden was borne by the families back in the villages, with their houses, cowsheds and land acting as collateral for the debt.

441

"In many cases," Cheda notes, "I have discovered that part of these debts were repaid, ten or fifteen or twenty years later, but with savings accumulated by their relatives who had emigrated to California."

After 1869, with the completion of the transcontinental railroad, the train trip from New York took a week to ten days. The entire trip, in the 1870s and '80s, would take about a month. Three weeks to cross the Atlantic and another week or so by train. This also made it more practical for Ticinesi in California, as they became more prosperous, to return to Ticino for visits, thus maintaining contacts between their valleys and what Cheda calls the Ticinesi "colonies" founded in California.

These colonies pointed to a major difference between the Australia and California emigrations: Of the 2000 Ticinesi who went to Australia over a two-year period, only around ten were women. The result was that they were not able to rebuild their families in Australia and the fabric was irrevocably torn. The emigration to California lasted many decades and in the subsequent waves of emigration, which included many of the women, the cost was borne by relatives working in California, rather than families in the villages.

Professor Cheda: "Then, many of those who emigrated to California were able to rebuild the kind of family life they had known in Ticino, on the ranches of the Salinas Valley, in Sonoma county, West Marin and so on, where full-scale 'colonies' were formed by groups of Ticinesi. The women were Ticinesi. The young men were Ticinesi, and if a young man could not return to Ticino to find a wife, he would write a letter inviting his mother or father to find him a promising young woman, then he would send her the money to join him in California and get married. As a result, many weddings were celebrated in San Francisco, or in Salinas or elsewhere, but still within the village community. So nuclei of Ticinesi peasants were reconstituted, but operating on a different geographical and economic basis from that of the Val Verzasca or the Val Maggia, because obviously the conditions in California were very different from those of their native valleys."*

27,000 people emigrated from Ticino to California in those years. Of these, a thousand had ranches. Since many, if not most, of the ranchers married Ticino women, close to 2,000 lived on ranches. Some were able to return to Ticino. And some, perhaps most, stayed. The ranchers and their families in West Marin were defining the landscape and its future.

* * * *

* From Dale Bechtel interview with Giorgio Cheda at swissinfo.ch

Grossi Farms ~ Summer

MALT EVENT WITH "POP"

ED HAS SENT ME DOWN TO THE STAND to pick out some melons and grapes for the event. I fill one box with plump green muscats and another with Crane melons and ambrosias. Also a big Texas yellow watermelon which, when cut open, would let out the noonday sun from its bright yellow-orange flesh.

As I arrange the grapes, I hear the thunderous roar of a big truck coming down the driveway. Who would be making tree deliveries on a Saturday morning? Then Ed appears, driving a Sweetlane Delivery Truck with the big red steel bar that looks like a piece of the Golden Gate Bridge and connects to a very long flatbed, which was now empty. "Is that for the grapes?" I ask. I can't imagine why we need this behemoth to drive to Novato but I welcome it as a new farm adventure. The event is a MALT (Marin Agricultural Land Trust) tour of his dad's ranch. About twenty people have forked out $25.00 for the event. "Why would people pay $25.00 to hear me talk?" his father had asked.

I am excited. Finally I am going to see the farm in Marin—make that "ranch"— that I have heard so much about. I have caught glimpses of Pop Grossi, as Susie and the nursery folks call him, when he has come to the farm to deliver apples or pears for sale in the stand. But those were brief encounters. This time he is going to tell his story and I am armed with a tape recorder.

As we head out with the long red bar and flatbed following grandly behind us, we suddenly dip off Highway 101 to the west. "We're taking the back way," Ed explains. As if I even knew what the front way was. Soon we have taken that fairy-tale crossing into another world as the wide, open grasslands of West Marin spread out toward the forested crest of Point Reyes. Hicks Valley Road appears off to the right and Ed says, "My school was down that road." I see nothing but waves of grass. A little ahead is the turn left onto the other part of Hicks Valley Road that will lead back toward Novato and Highway 101—a thing I discover later looking at the map. I realize then that we are driving through Camilio Ynitia's land—that clever bloke who managed to save a goodly parcel for the Last of the Miwokans. Ed went to school on that original Olompali land, granted in 1843. Before that, Huicmuse—Chief Marin—would have spent time here when he visited the village to the south and courted his second wife. Maybe even Sir Francis Drake passed this way when he was invited to meet the chief of the village here, according to surviving Miwok accounts. Now it is undulating grassland. Quiet. As if no one had passed this way before us.

The road begins to rise slightly. "When outsiders come here (he means me) what they see is a pretty landscape. What WE see is a watershed. That's very important to us." Ed still has the eyes of the land's ancestors, going back thousands of years. I'm afraid I am one of the first generations who didn't learn to Think Water. Not a very optimistic thought. The future will very likely need Ed's eyes rather than mine. Engineers, developers and architects have this special sight. But it shouldn't be a "niche skill" for the few. I'm learning some things. The Apartment Child is slowly growing up.

The landscape still seems wild at first although it begins to take on concrete angles as we enter the outskirts of a city—Novato. Before that happens, we turn into a little road and there is the house that Dominic and Teresa rebuilt. The farm in Marin that is really a ranch. This "Home Ranch" was bequeathed to Ed's father, Jim Grossi. The one Susie calls "Pop." It is a modest looking wood house that has been in the family for over 80 years. Next to it is a new addition. A separate unit where his father lives now. Ed's sister Beverly is living in the main house.

James "Pop" Grossi is there to meet us, still a handsome man with a quick wit at 92 years old. He asks if I want a cup of coffee when I join him in the kitchen. Ed is unloading the melons. I take this moment to ask a few questions about his father, Dominic Grossi. What did Dominic say about the "old country"? He never talked about it. What was the trip across country like and who were the people he traveled with? What happened to them? Pop shakes his head. "It's funny," he says. "But he never talked about anything before he landed in Sausalito on Christmas Day."

Pop has as many questions to ask about me. Am I married? How do I get along alone? He puts his arm around me and kisses the top of my head, as if to say if I get too lonely, he'll be available for company.

Dewey Livingston is the first to arrive. He will be doing the interview. I am almost as thrilled to meet Dewey as I am to meet Ed's Dad—Dominic and Teresa's second youngest son. Dewey is the foremost authority on the history of this area. I owe him credit for so much that I have learned about the Point Reyes Peninsula. He was a historian for the Park Service and has prepared studies of the early ranches of the area to help the Park Service identify places of historical value.

MALT volunteers arrive, ready to prepare coffee and treats for the guests. This is also the first time I have met Ed's sister Beverly, who comes out to greet the volunteers when they arrive. She is a tall lean woman with a stern face when I first catch sight of her. But as I engage her in conversation, her expression softens into a smile. She has just come off of a ten hour shift in the post office in Petaluma, where several million items a day pass through to be processed for Sonoma and Marin counties. It is not sternness but fatigue I have seen. She leans toward me confidingly and says, "You wait. You're going to get a whole lot of standard mail in the next few days." I feel privileged to be granted this inside information. She tells me that she has lots of pictures and has been creating scrapbooks of the family history which she promises to show me later.

People gather in a meeting-room-like area just off Pop's living quarters. As we go in, I get to meet Ed's brother, James Jr., Pop's eldest son. He is a handsome man, built more on the stocky side like his grandfather, Dominic. About 30 people, including family members, fill the room nicely. I set up my tape recorder. Ed makes a friendly announcement to people that his Dad's hearing isn't what it used to be so you better yell. I had already discovered that.

The talk will be followed by a tour of the ranch, and somewhere in there I want to slip in my visit with Beverly in the old Grossi house.

When the talk ends, Beverly signals to me and leads the way to the house where her grandparents lived. In this moment, Dominic and Teresa become real people to me. Here is the house that they built. I have seen a photograph taken not long after the last child was born, standing in front of this house. Teresa looks a little worn down by the intervening years of hard work, childbirth and raising ten children. Dominic, as usual, is dressed in a suit and looking like the scion of a great family, which in fact he is. Seeing the house now, I can hardly imagine that a family of ten children grew up here.

Beverly leads me into the old house, into a darkish room filled with photographs. Two thick albums sit on a large table –the family history and genealogy that she has assembled over several years. There is a wonderful picture of Dominic and Teresa with their ten children. And most poignant of all, a letter—translated from the Swiss Italian—which Dominic wrote to his sister back in Monte Carasso in 1913. He had put his business in order, he said, so that he could come back for Christmas. But when he told his family about this, they all cried so he really couldn't leave them. Would she please comfort their mother. And he enclosed $25.00. No doubt a lot of money in 1913. Especially in Monte Carasso. But not nearly so much as the fare to Switzerland and gifts for all the family would have cost him. From what I've heard of Dominic, he was thrifty in the extreme which is likely the source of his financial success. Perhaps the children did cry, but I imagine Dominic was particularly persuaded by the thought of the money that could be lost crossing the whole United States and the Atlantic. Not to mention the time! And how could he explain to them what it was like trying to run a thousand acre ranch, riding herd over sons and daughters to get all of the work done. Who would do this in his absence?

After our brief but illuminating visit, I catch up with Ed and Jim Jr. who are giving a tour of the milking barns. We explore the farm buildings and learn how they handled the milk from udder to market, listening to old family stories. We pass through a gate and follow Ed along the dirt road, up a gentle rise that leads to a little man-made lake created by the family in 1977. It's about 35ft. deep in the center and provides a source of water for the cows. We had just come past the cavernous old barn built by the Rinaldi brothers, who seem to have been the sought after barn builders of the time. After the barn had been built, Dominic decided that one end of it was taking up some valuable pasture space so he dismantled that and rebuilt it on the opposite side.

"You can do that if you have ten children," James Jr. quips, as he tells the story. He also tells us about the little one room school they had all attended and the teacher who rode her horse over from Nicasio each day. As we stand looking at the lake, Ed points out the densely wooded hillside above us and says "That's the way the teacher would have come." Twenty some heads turn upward and stare in mute awe. Finally someone says "Where? How did she do it?"

"It's not an easy ride," Ed admitted. The school teacher had gained new respect in everyone's eyes.

"POP" GROSSI TELLS HIS STORY

MY DAD CAME FROM SWITZERLAND WHEN HE WAS 17 YEARS OLD.
He landed in Sausalito on Christmas Day. Not being able to speak English, he had to find somebody who was able to talk the Swiss language. He was looking for a job in ranching work. They told him it was possible that he could find a job in Point Reyes. Then they told him to go to Fort Barry, up by the Golden Gate Bridge. The road used to go up from there to Point Reyes. They showed him where the road would go all the way around by the Golden Gate Bridge. All he had was his walking shoes so he left there and he walked it all the way. It was horse'n'buggy days. There were no cars. It was twenty-five miles.

When he got to the Grandi Store, he had to meet old man Grandi, who could speak the same language to him. Mr. Grandi had told him that in the Point Reyes area where the Shafter-Howard ranches were back then, they had a supervisor by the name of Hamilton. "When this man comes in to get the groceries for all the ranches out there, we'll introduce you to him and he might give you a job."

Those days they came in in small horse and buggies and most of the guys had those big ten gallon hats. So the gentleman came in and Grandi introduced him to my dad. He told him to hop in the buggy and he took him all the way out to Pierce Point. Out at the end of Tomales Bay. The last ranch out there.

My dad worked out there for him for seven years. He saved every little penny he could get out of $25 a month and he said he never had too much to eat. He'd kill an old animal and chop that up and that was their corn beef. They'd grow their own potatoes out there. His job was to milk cows and plant potatoes. So he worked there for those people for seven years, but then he wanted to go on his own.

There were two Grandi brothers as I recall and they helped him out. He rented a ranch down in Olema, across from Olema Farm, right in the back of the farmhouse and across the creek. That was 1400 acres. So Dad rented that for three years. My older sister Eda was born out there.

Dewey: If I understand this, the ranch he had in Olema must have been the Shafter ranch, which the Grandi Company had something to do with. They had some agreement with the Shafters. . . .

San Francisco Bay to Sausalito ~ The Present

THE FERRY RIDE

I have taken thousands of people across and to all of them my river has been nothing but a hindrance on their journey. They have travelled for money and business, to weddings and on pilgrimages; the river has been in their way and the ferryman was there to take them quickly across the obstacle. However . . . there have been a few . . . to whom the river was not an obstacle. They have heard its voice and listened to it . . .

— HERMAN HESSE
Siddhartha

San Francisco Bay enters most of our lives as an obstacle to pass over as quickly as traffic-choked bridges allow. . . . We remain largely oblivious to one of the most remarkable wild resources in urban North America. Beneath our wheels lies a world of interesting and outlandish life."

— ANDREW COHEN, "An introduction
to the San Francisco Bay estuary"
(savethebay.org)

MY GOD-DAUGHTER, JIMENA ROJAS HAY, HAS COME *to visit me for the first time. This means so much to me because she is the embodiment of all the years I spent in Mexico, introduced to the richness of that country through her grand-parents, Dr. Eduardo Hay, his wife, Yolanda Batiz de Hay and their daughter, Yolanda Hay Batiz—Jimena's mother and my comadre. Mexicans can bestow no greater honor than Comadre or Compadre. (Just think of "The Godfather" without the criminal element, as I mentioned earlier.) The Spanish conversations I am able to have with Alfonso, Lazaro and Otún are thanks to their patience in teaching me. Now, in a small way, I get to return that gift by showing Jimena my San Francisco.*

Today we are taking a ferry ride across this beautiful bay and then on to visit the giant redwood trees of Muir Woods. We sit at the back of the ferry to watch the city, silvered by sun and mist, slide slowly away from us as the green hills of Angel Island appear on the left. Presences surround: The San Carlos, anchored off the island as the pilot, Canizares, plies the longboat through the water, making the first European explorations of the vast estuary. Somewhere ahead of us, native Miwok descend the slope toward an encounter with Fr. Santa Maria and crew members from the San Carlos that will change their lives in every way. The very air is alive with amazement all around as Those-Who-Go meet Those-Who-Stay. Huicmuse and Mottiqui glide soundlessly through the water to our right toward their own fateful future at Mission Dolores. Huicmuse can have no idea that a new name given him by the Mission fathers will reverberate through both sides of the Golden Gate and across the world far into the future. Sutter and his small flotilla are also passing close to Angel Island but they will turn away from us and head east through the Raccoon Strait toward the maze of waters that will become his New World. His New Helvetia. More natives along the river banks. More fear and wonder.

Round the other side of the island, William Shafter is fuming because the army wants to build a quarantine station near his army base. City Health Officer Wilfred Kellogg is on his way toward us, carrying a vial of yersina pestis to be analyzed in the lab there. Presences thick upon the waters!

Jimena takes a selfie with the city behind us. A perfect shot. It flies from her iPhone to my waiting comadre in Mexico City, eagerly following our trip through her daughter's posts, then off to other friends and family in Mexico, as I will later send it to friends and family in the U.S. It will light up on screens, some hardly larger than the palm of a hand. Weightless. Insubstantial. A graph of light and shadow snatched out of a single moment; a tiny point on the turning globe in the vast universe, yet weighted with such significance for us. It carries within it the joy of Jimena's birth, for which I waited through the night in a hospital room with her grandmother, who as I write has just turned 96. All my memories of traveling Mexico with her mother are summoned by that photo.

We skim across the surface of the Bay. We ARE the skim on the surface of the bay. For three hundred feet below us lies a parallel universe, much richer and more populous than the one above. A universe as invisible to the passengers on the ferry as the quarks and their subatomic relatives that come at us from all directions from the Big Bang and the sun. About a hundred trillion are passing through our bodies every second as we go about our daily business. Parallel universes that exist side by side with us and are slowly coming into focus with our new eyes, our remarkably sensitive equipment.

Not far below the surface, thick schools of Northern anchovy flicker and dart, weaving among ribbons of sardines. Following close are striped bass who feed on the anchovies, while fishermen above use their best strategies to catch the bass. Chinook salmon and sturgeon will transit through the bay on their way from fresh waters to the sea. They will pursue the annual herring run as thousands upon thousands of the small fish wind themselves into a ball for protection against their predators. Native Miwok for millennia were an integral part of this moment, taking their cues from the birds and using their specially fashioned tools to break apart the living ball of herring, providing dried and smoked fish for their winters. Halibut and stickleback, pipefish and shiner perch swim among swarms of rockfish, blue and brown. Leopard sharks dwarf them all and among them glide the mammals, seals and porpoises, which breach the surface to human delight. Deeper down, tiny one-celled dinoflagellates give off their short bursts of light. Imagine! A single cell, winking at us like that across almost two billion years. August's children, sharing space in the bay with New Year's Eve "Children of the Last Hour of the Last Day." Creatures carrying on lives below us as they have from before the time of the dinosaurs. 90% of the creatures in the sea are bioluminescent, gliding through the dark with built-in flashlights.

Beyond the Golden Gate are the sea depths where the giant leatherback tortoises, weighing up to a ton, glide gracefully after the tasty iridescent jellyfish, having completed their long migration from Indonesian waters. These tortoises are small beside those creatures as long as a city bank but sleek and agile and smart: the whales who embark on migrations of their own from the Arctic to Baja California.

And in the mid-range of these waters, between 650 and 3,000 feet of sea depth, another migration has been discovered that is vertical rather than horizontal. We know it by its song, as creatures of those deep waters—shrimp and squid and other fish—migrate from the sea depths to the surface for their daily meal. The song we hear is the sound of billions of tons of life throughout the sea rising upward, like the thrumming of the earth when the wildebeest pass on the way to their feeding grounds. If all of this was happening above ground, Jurassic Park would seem tame. But it is all in the present, not some distant past, just as the light of million year old stars is reaching us each evening. They do not even slightly disturb the boatload of passengers above enjoying a peaceful Saturday afternoon.

Here are the hours and days of the Earth Year layered in space, together in time, from the tiny lamp-bearing dinoflagellates to the braided schools of fish, to the aerial fishermen who drop so gracefully from the skies, to the cellphone bearing hominids who ride their inventions hither and yon, apparently oblivious. Yet only we, the last minute children of Earth, can take the measure of them all. Capture them in thought and image, or a picture, like the one Jimena has just taken. Can sense and recite and depict our own deep history, just as Homer sang, with unseeing eyes, of Hector and Odysseus or as Virgil sang of Aeneas. Churches round the world recite messages from Paul the Apostle. Petrarch on Mt. Ventoux reads Augustine. Father Galli counts his flock in Ticino for our historical record. Americans on July 4th celebrate Jefferson and Adams and Franklin. Jimena and I today are adding a chapter to our story. Giving personal history to the landscape, the Bay, the city, just as each is giving history to us.

We reach Sausalito. The last people off the ferry.

SAUSALITO NEWS

Printing and Publishing Company, Sausalito

DEC 23 1892

Sausalito News is in its eighth year of publication.

A MERRY CHRISTMAS TO ALL

AS THIS TIME-HONORED FESTIVAL with its hallowed memories will have come and gone before we go to press again, such is the greeting the NEWS extends to the people of Marin county. American liberty was born on the 4th. of July, and the author of the Declaration of Independence, including the elder Adams died on that day; but these were common-place events compared to that which is significant of the eternal salvation of all the progeny of Adam and Eve.

Indeed, it is a veritable day of "peace on earth, good will to men," when children, grand-children and great-grand-children, return with hearts of gladness to gaze at the ancient hearthstone and once more gather around the festive board of the old homestead for a glorious time. It is as it should be, a day of blessed memory of Him, whose sorrows and suffering tend to soften the feeling and shorten the distance between the rich and the poor. It is the one day out of 365, that charity and genuine manhood grow strong enough to span the chasm between those who suffer and those who surfeit; and if this Christmas bridge across the gulf which separates wealth and poverty could be maintained, the knowledge of the extent of those who suffer in silence and die under the shadow of costly castles, would bring the poor and rich nearer to each other.

Next Sunday from a thousand ancient fanes the joyous bells will jingle the glad tidings and here in our own favored land, the cornucopia of the world, let the wealthy remember that the babe of Bethlehem sought and sounded the depths of hunger and misery; and that no worship is worthy which overlooks the poor widow and the fatherless in their affliction. In the lap of San Francisco alone, by steamboat and railroad lines, enough of the necessaries of life are poured daily to appease the hunger of a nation. The beautiful and costly residences that crown the heights around Sausalito, show to the world that we have men of large means in our midst.

To them, and to the wealthy, the world over, we say, wait not for the needy to knock at your doors; the worthiest of those who need your help, will not call upon you; go out and look for them as did the Saviour, and lend a liberal hand to the noble women, who are ever on the alert to find and feed the hungry and clothe the naked. In Sausalito, the gulf between the wealthy and the industrial classes is neither wide nor deep, and we are in favor of filling it in with material that will stay. To cordially shake the hand of the hod carrier and wharf sweeper, is full of comfort, even for one day; but to be recognized from the first day of January to the last of December, is more valuable than real estate, to a well regulated mind. If by liberality, kindness, courtesy and common sense, you shall succeed in perfecting a permanent armistice between broadcloth and rags and thus uncover the misery of the under world of our social life to those who know nothing of the sorrows of want and destitution, capital and labor will be brought to a more friendly understanding. You will feel better for having done so, and your flight to the Celestial city will be as rapid and straight as that of a bee from a buckwheat patch to its hive.

SAUSALITO LAND AND FERRY COMPANY

THE LANDS OF THE COMPANY, comprising 900 acres of choice building sites; half acre to 5 acre tracts; water front lots; the new subdivisions of Sausalito Heights and Waldo Point, and the other diversified valley and hillside portions of the five main sections of the property, contained in the east front of Woodward Valley and the Coyote Creek north frontage—are offered for sale by the Company. All sections are in easy reach of the North Pacific Coast Railroad, which traverses the Richardson Bay front for its whole length of some three miles.

Description of the property is almost unnecessary, as its unparalleled advantage of scenery, land and water, hill, valley and mountain; its pre air and health-giving climate, have attracted thousands to enjoy them. It has been compared to Lake Como for scenery by those who knew from when they spoke. It is nearer to SF than any other locality on the Bay.

MRS. H.A. COBB

It is with feelings of the most profound sorrow that THE NEWS is called upon to announce the death of Mrs. H.A. Cobb, which sad event occurred last Friday. From the beginning of her illness the gravest apprehensions disturbed the heart of her friends and neighbors, but hopes for the best results were entertained. They were destined to be shattered, as the fearful inroad of the disease marked its way and snapped the tender life cords, hour by hour sunder, until she sank into the rest in which there is no more worry, no more sorrow, but a glad awakening in that bright land where the supernal joys await her as the reward of a Christian life. The grave never closed over the remains of a braver, truer and nobler woman than Mrs. H.A. Cobb.

NOTICE!!!

The Sausalito Cemetery Association, having the Cemetery now in order for burials, parties having bodies of friends and relatives buried in the lands of the Sausalito Land and Ferry Company, outside the Sausalito Cemetery Tract, are hereby notified to remove the bodies within six months from this date, according to agreements made with this Company.

WANTED:

Two or three children to board, where they will have the comfort of a pleasant home. For particulars call or address MRS. A.M. STUART, Cremona Cottage, Waldo Point, Sausalito.

LOCAL ITEMS

A twelve-pound salmon was caught last Sunday in the lagoon on the old Throckmorton ranch.

Last Wednesday was the shortest day this year. Herrings are beginning to run.

A turkey-shoot will take place on New Year's Day.

A. Roman, a well-known caterer of San Francisco, was in Sausalito this week, with a view of starting a first-class French Restaurant.

Chattanooga, a thrilling story of the war. Everyone should read it. The new serial story by E. A. Mitchell, late of the U. S. A., in twenty-one chapters, commences in the NEWS, January 6 1893. Don't fail to subscribe and commence with Chapter 1.

Try the Mount Tamalpais Cough Syrup. Just arrived, new crop maple sugar at 4th and B streets, San Rafael. Try it.

BELVEDERE Land Company!

THE BELVEDERE PENINSULA

THIS COMPANY'S tract (formerly known as Kashawa Island) is situated in the immediate neighborhood of Tiburon, the ferry shipping point for the San Francisco and North Pacific Railroad. It is almost surrounded by the waters of the Bay of San Francisco, being connected only by a narrow Isthmus, owned and controlled by the Company, with the mainland. Swift and palatial steamers ply almost hourly between San Francisco and Tiburon. The trip from Belvedere to the city consumes only 35 minutes. The Company's buses connect with every boat.

Belvedere is laid out in villa lots of liberal dimensions, facing well-made avenues. The tract is covered with a fine growth of natural forest trees, sheltered from the severe trade winds, but with the heat of summer tempered by the neighborhood of the bay, the climate is absolute perfection.

The "El Monte," Hotel is now open for the winter season, under the proprietorship of J. E. Slinkey.

A young German mechanic, who lives and owns property in Sausalito, wants to get married. All communication to be addressed to "M. W.," care of Postoffice, Sausalito.

The property at Sea Point, belonging to W. R. Hearst, is on the market for sale.

The Christmas tree and festival of our public school will be held to-night at the school house.

The Christmas Festival at the Congregational Church, opposite the S. F. Y. C. House, will be held to-morrow Saturday night.

At the monthly meeting of the Sausalito Mutual Loan Association held last Monday night in Sausalito Hall, $1500 was loaned out at 25 cents per share premium.

A letter mailed to Europe or any foreign country will not be forwarded if unstamped.

Don't forgot the masquerade ball at San Rafael, Saturday evening, December 31, 1892.

Last Sunday a cow belonging to Mrs. Gardner, of Sausalito, was run over by an engine on the N. P. C. R. R. The animal's legs were severed. Constable Creed put the poor beast out of misery and Jake Dreyfuss took charge of the remains.

Heavy frosts prevailed throughout the county last week.

BREVITIES.

The Bachelor's ball last Wednesday evening in Sausalito Hall was well attended. The hall was beautifully decorated for the occasion, and everything passed off well. The music of Blanchard's orchestra was simply inspiring —so much so that the compositors and editors in the NEWS office adjoining the Hall, were perfectly entranced —more so when they caught a sly glimpse at the dear creatures being whirled round in the giddy waltz. Such luxuries! Ah me! are not for poor newspaper men.

POINT REYES STATION:

Quite a storm.

Winter has come.

Going to have a Ball.

The storm did some little damage Saturday night.

All the dairy men are happy over the storm and so are the sportsmen for quite a number of duck and snipe were bagged.

The salmon have started to run in the creek.

There is at present a small run of grilse [a young Atlantic salmon as it returns from the sea to fresh water for the first time] in Point Reyes Creek.

Last Sunday a jolly lot of anglers tried their luck at Point Reyes and although the majority of the boys went home with empty baskets there were a few among the gathering who enjoyed a good afternoon's sport.

Seaman John Olsen had his right leg fractured by a fall on board the schooner Ethel Buhne when off Point Reyes last Wednesday night.

Dr. Burdell is at the Lick House in San Francisco.

In the intestines of a fish caught last Sunday at Point Reyes were a number of small trout-fry not over an inch in length. Under the microscope the youngsters very much resembled the New Hampshire trout, a number of the young of which were placed in the headwaters of the Lagunitas Creek about June last.

The Country Club is having grand quail shooting at its preserve near Point Reyes. During the week upward of fifty dozen quail have been bagged, besides numbers of snipe and canvasback duck.

Sausalito ~ Christmas 1892

WHEN DOMINIC GROSSI STEPS OFF THE FERRY on Christmas Day in 1892, he finds a handsome town of some 1,500 people. He is seventeen years old and has just come halfway round the world by every means available in that time, from shoe leather to ship. He has enjoyed a privileged view of his new land from the windows of a cross-continental train. The narrow world of the Ticino valleys has exploded into endless spaces of water and sky, forests and grass lands. He has passed through New York and San Francisco, youthful cities like himself. He has gone from the poverty of Monte Carasso to the prosperity of Sausalito, where elegant residences dot the hill slopes among lush gardens and evergreens. Immediately before him, opposite the ferry on Water Street, is the Hotel Sausalito and Joe Garnier's French Restaurant. Next to that is the Sausalito News Office and nearby, the blacksmith's shop and a "Respectable Fortune Teller" who, for 50 cents, can tell your past, present and future with cards. He might be surprised to see this place compared to Lake Como in local advertisements. A place close to the region he has just left behind, as we have left it behind us in the stories of Monica and the Magister Comacini; the architects of ancient Rome.

William Richardson's Place of the Little Willows (Rancho Saucito, then Saucelito, then Sausalito) has changed a good deal since the days of Yerba Buena when Johann Augustus Sutter arrived. Before Sutter's arrival in 1839, Richardson had married the daughter of the Commandante of El Presidio, the Mexican military garrison in San Francisco, and was given a land grant of 19,571 acres (does this sound familiar?), which he named Rancho de Saucelito. It included the present southern and Western Marin County, with a hacienda on present day Caledonia Street in Sausalito. Typically for that time, it was a fortune easily won and as easily lost through lavish spending and debts.

In 1868, the greater part of these vast lands was sold to the Sausalito Land and Ferry Company. It is still all about land, as it was in the time of Garcia and Berry, then later the Shafters on Point Reyes. Now it is no longer about individual landowners but groups of nameless people, organizing into development and real estate companies. The stakes are higher than ever before as people pour into the new and larger towns and cities. Nineteen businessmen from offices on Montgomery Street in San Francisco formed the Sausalito Land and Ferry Company, becoming the first developers in Sausalito. They laid out streets and divided the land into lots. They bought a boat to ferry prospective buyers across from the city. The business enterprise did not really take off until the North Pacific Coast Railroad was built in 1875, which also took over the ferry service. As was the case with Point Reyes Station, the railroad passing through was like gold. Sausalito prospered and grew.

But Dominic Grossi is not staying in Sausalito. Ahead of him is that long walk to Point Reyes Station to find the Grandis and start his new life.

Point Reyes Station ~ 1892

TWO BROTHERS

THE TWO FICTIONAL COUSINS, NICOLO AND BERTO, who were delivering the news of the birth of Salvatore Grandi in Menzonio in 1853, might well have been the real brothers, Salvatore and Luigi Grandi sixteen years later when they came of age and made their own plans to leave their village. Menzonio is the most remote of the villages on our immigrant map, perched on a terrace above the Lavizzara River and surrounded by forest. Nevertheless, its history dates back at least to the thirteenth century. It is at its height when the Status Animarum is being taken in Ticino's valleys in 1776 and the Grandi family is flourishing there. But the political and economic conditions of the region over the next century cause many of its young men to seek their fortune in Australia or America. Famine and revolutions in Europe are driving people in vast numbers to emigrate. A Gold Rush in both places only fans the flames.

From 1820 to 1870, over seven and a half million immigrants came to the United States —more than the entire population of the country in 1810. When the potato crop in Ireland failed three years in succession, it led to a great famine there. Over 750,000 people starved to death and over two million Irish eventually moved to the United States. In the decade from 1845 to 1855, more than a million Germans fled to the United States to escape economic hardship and the political unrest caused by riots, rebellion and eventually a revolution in 1848.

With the vast numbers of German and Irish coming to America, hostility erupted. People in the protestant country settled by Puritans and Anglicans were threatened by the Catholicism of the Irish and many of the Germans. Ethnic and anti-Catholic rioting occurred in many northern cites. In Philadelphia in 1844, during a period of economic depression, Protestants, Catholics and local militia fought in the streets. 16 were killed, dozens were injured and over 40 buildings were demolished. "Nativist" political parties sprang up as Americans in low-paying jobs were threatened and sometimes replaced by immigrant groups willing to work for almost nothing in order to survive. The nativist parties also wanted to prevent foreign-born people from ever holding public office. Nevertheless, the burgeoning country was able to absorb the flood of immigrants to build its infrastructure and to provide labor for agriculture and industry.

After 1880, when larger steam-powered ocean-going ships replaced sailing ships, lower fares and greater mobility opened the way for more people to emigrate. In this wave of migration, nearly 25 million Europeans made the long trip.

Animals, birds, fish and even insects migrate toward sustainable sources of food. Native Americans, like many of the people of California, migrated seasonally for the same reason: for seafood at the coast in summer, acorns in the mountains in fall, and desert plants and animals in winter. While there were no political boundaries or land ownership to restrict their movements, each was bound by a certain territorial imperative. It was usually fatal to cross invisible boundaries into another's hunting grounds, whether it was tribes of lions in Africa, Assapitti and Winnili tribes vying in Europe, or the Crow and Sioux tribes of the Plains. Human societies may be much more complex, but at heart, the main causes of large migrations are the same. Survival.

The skin of the living earth is dynamic with vitality and movement as life burgeons and throbs irrepressibly across its landscapes, surging through conflict and catastrophe, adapting, dying out, growing back, "seeking new pastures" or "eager for war"; ultimately seeking preservation and sustenance in the rich depth of its seas, its fertile soils, its cloud-filled skies that carry life-giving oxygen and moisture. A vibrant blue and green mantled world like no other that we know of in the universe. Only in that last split second do we have the eyes and sensibility to see this, as so beautifully described by biologist Lewis Thomas in his 1974 book *Lives of a Cell*. "Viewed from the distance of the moon, the astonishing thing about the earth, catching the breath, is that it is alive. The photographs show the dry, pounded surface of the moon in the foreground, dry as an old bone. Aloft, floating free beneath the moist, gleaming, membrane of bright blue sky, is the rising earth, the only exuberant thing in this part of the cosmos."

Our two brothers, Salvatore and Louis Grandi are only a small ripple on that great tide but so important to the colony of Point Reyes that is coming to life and to Dominic Grossi who is on his way toward them. They had started out as dairymen living in Nicasio when they arrived and have become prosperous merchants by the time Dominic arrives in 1892. Salvatore has made important contributions to the town that was called Olema Station when it was founded in 1875. Like Sausalito, it was the beneficiary of the railroad and one of its important stops. The first store was built in 1883 and Salvatore Grandi purchased it in 1887 when it became the Grandi's Mercantile Company. Both brothers are married now and have several children between them, caught up in the Christmas festivities. Louis is living with his family on the 800 acre home ranch north of town. Salvatore still maintains a home in Nicasio with his family.

In 1906 the earthquake will strike Point Reyes and Grandi's brick building will collapse, to be replaced by what is now the Western Saloon. When Salvatore Grandi retires in 1908, he will sell his mercantile company to his nephew Reno. Reno, with his brother Ennio, will build a much larger Grandi Company, selling everything from cattle feed to housewares to pianos. The second story of the building will be a 20 room hotel and dance hall. Dwight D. Eisenhower will stay there in 1940. Reno, his brother Ennio and later his brother Oliver will run their operation together with their father Louis. In his last years, Louis will become vice-president of Novato's Central Valley Bank and his son Ennio will become president of the West Marin Bank. The last of Louis's children, Lydia, will marry John Bianchi who will run their ranch. John's sister Corinne will marry John Pelosi and their son Paul will marry Nancy D'Alesandro, who will become the first woman speaker of the US House of Representatives. Six degrees of separation between a remote alpine village perched on a terrace above a Swiss river to the very center of American power.

Like any store, Grandi's Mercantile is the hub of the town. It is also the welcome center for the Ticinesi arriving after their long voyage. They are greeted with open arms as they bring news of the valleys, and in return the arrivals are given a helping hand in starting a new life. As Dominic had been told, here in Point Reyes Station are people who speak the language. And here he will make his first contact with the Shafter family, as Julia's husband drives him out to the tip of the Point Reyes peninsula to the wild and beautiful Pierce Point Ranch, a place where coyote and bobcat and tule elk still roam its windswept landscape—so unlike the steep valleys that Dominic has known. He might as well be starting a new life on another planet.

◆ ◆ ◆

Our stories are beginning to weave together into a single strand. When Dominic arrives in December 1892, the Shafters are still in evidence, although their influence is waning. James Shafter had died the previous August, but to the unknowing eye, Shafter-Howard ranches are ostensibly thriving. It is Julia's husband Alexander "Jack" Hamilton whom Salvatore Grandi arranges for Dominic to meet when he arrives at Point Reyes after his 25 mile walk from Sausalito.

Few people are aware of the efforts of Julia and James behind the scenes, desperately trying to save their legacy. Julia, whom James Sr. had wisely appointed as his executrix, is putting into motion the first of her grand plans, which she presents in a very professional looking brochure, complete with maps. The brochure is promoting a 13,695 acre tract in Point Reyes, which includes nine ranches, touting its great investment promise. The struggle is on. She has been married to Jack Hamilton for three years, but behind this façade as well, the crevices are appearing.

Emma and Charles Howard are living on Alice Street in Oakland in the home presented to them by Oscar on their marriage, next door to Oscar and Sarah's home. The street is named after their daughter, who had died back in Wilmington, Vermont—the second of that name. Two daughters were still held in memory by this street name. Charles and Emma have been married twenty years. She is a prominent figure in Oakland, as we noted before. She was the first to put up Christmas decorations in the town. She is an active suffragette and has entertained Susan B. Anthony in her home.

Emma has little illusion by now about her husband's unreliability. Oscar has been dead for nineteen years and they have already weathered a major storm. In 1873, Charles had borrowed $50,000 against property in the estate "of a dead man," as Jack Mason describes it. I assume he is referring to the deceased Oscar Shafter. The following year he gave La Societe Francaise de Aspargus a second mortgage on the same property as security for a $250,000 loan. With interest rates as high as ten percent, Charles' debt quickly escalated to half a million dollars by 1879. In a desperate move, Charles announced in the newspaper that he was going to sell off 10,000 acres.

Too late. The society would not wait for the subdivision. At this point the sheriff steps in and is about to advertise a series of sales in the Marin Journal, which fortunately never takes place because Emma takes charge and enters into her own agreement with the society. A trust is established under G. Henshaw, which will collect the rents on the ranches, pay the taxes and see to it that the Societé Francaise is reimbursed. If and when the property is disencumbered, it will revert to Emma rather than Charles. The trust does well and in 1881, the debts are paid off, the trust is dissolved and the property reverts to Emma, who—if you can believe it— deeds the property back to Charles "and his heirs and assigns forever." The Shafter Empire is turning into the Shafter Soap Opera, full of twists and unhappy turns.

Nothing, of course, is forever. Particularly ownership of Point Reyes land. The marriage itself doesn't last. Charles is on to new schemes. He buys a San Francisco Newspaper, the *Wasp*, and hires the waspish Ambrose Bierce (dubbed Bitter Bierce for his stinging critiques and editorials) as editor. As president of the Spring Water Company, Charles buys columns of advertising space. In his position as publisher, a role which he keeps secret from the public, he pockets the profits. It will be two years before Ambrose Bierce discovers his scheme and forces him to sell out under threat of making the scandal public.

Emma is no doubt becoming increasingly disillusioned and bitter and in 1890, the marriage ends. She finds her own quarters, and in 1903 buys two lots from her cousin Julia to build a summer cottage at the corner of Bruce and Forres in Inverness. It burns down in 1907. Charles Webb Howard dies the following year at his home on Laurel Place in San Rafael at the age of 77. This is when Emma receives the news that she has inherited nothing. And as my mother would say, "this is where we came in."

When Dominic arrives at the Pierce Ranch, he is immediately put to work milking cows and ferrying butter across the bay to the village of Hamlet for shipment to San Francisco. In 1899, when he leases the 1400 acre ranch in Olema, it is part of the Oaks ranch belonging to Payne Shafter, who is now in residence there.

POINT REYES 1900–1902

AT THE START OF THE NEW CENTURY, TRAINS PASS REGULARLY through Point Reyes, including the "Hunters Special," which brings hunters through from San Francisco to Tomales, via Point Reyes Station to hunt wildfowl. There is a stop on the bay at Hamlet, where schooners carry goods back and forth to the Pierce Point Ranch pier at White Gulch. This was the run that Dominic Grossi had done on a regular basis when he was employed there.

The Inverness Stage waits in Point Reyes Station to transport passengers to the resort community that Julia Shafter Hamilton is developing there, advertising it as a relaxing vacation spot for San Franciscans. From there they can hire boats to take them to secluded spots along the bay's shore. A scattering of Coast Miwok people are still living in places around the bay, working as fisherman or farm laborers.

A herring fleet at Marshall supplies herring to markets in San Francisco and Europe. Farming activities and logging in the Tomales Bay watershed, however, are washing tons of silt into the bay. Fisherman and homeowners are continually extending their piers farther out into the bay to allow boat access. A 1,150 foot pier at the Booth Canning Company provides a place for the herring fisherman to unload their fish. Oyster beds on Tomales Bay are another source of commercial income.

When Dominic sets up his new life on the ranch in Olema in 1899, he is surrounded by successful Ticinesi like the Dolcinis, Martinellis and many others. He and Teresa are married on December 30, 1901. The first years of their life together cannot have been easy. They forge ahead, fueled by their dreams and their mutual memories of desperate lives in an increasingly poverty-stricken Ticino. Dominic had promised to help his parents by sending money back when he could— their consolation for the loss of a son; the consolation of parents of emigrants to America from all over the world, which usually comes with an unfulfilled promise of return. Those who go ...

As for Teresa, she has left only siblings behind. Both of her parents are dead and her stepmother, Caterina, had emigrated with her son Celeste, now Charles. Her sisters Sofia and Judit are still in Brione. Judit will stay and marry into the Gnesa family there. Sofia will leave Brione in years to come. A wave of people from Teresa's corner of the Versazca valley came over on the ship, La Gascogne, out of Le Havre, a year before, including Giuseppe Buzzini, Massimo Pinana and Agostino Gnesa. The Pinanas were already an old and large family in the time of Father Galli. Now, one by one, the children of Gaudenzio and Innocente Pinana, like so many others, are making their way to the New World. One will be a long-time worker for Jim Grossi—Ed's Dad—on the farm in Marin. Giuseppe and Massimo had given Santa Barbara as their destination when they embarked. They arrive, respectively, with $20 and $17 in their pockets. Massimo's sister Elvezia had emigrated with Caterina and Charles a few years before, also heading to a brother in Santa Barbara, which seems to have been a destination of many of the early emigrants from Brione. Elvezia becomes a further connection in our story by marrying Fulgenzio P. Morisoli of Monte Carasso.

It is as if a bit of Ticino has lifted up and moved itself to California. Some of these may have been the same people Teresa knew over there, but they are happier people, filled with energy. Working hard, yes, but with food to eat. There are many other Ticinesi she is meeting here for the first time. There is Dominic.

Dominic is a dapper man, when she meets him, sporting a lush black mustache, dark eyes—alert and intelligent. He is a natty dresser, usually appearing in more formal attire than others in a photograph. From the beginning, from poverty to riches, he is a gentleman farmer. Although short in stature, his presence is commanding. He has exactly what is needed for success in America: a canny and competent self-confidence. Determination. He is a shrewd businessman and is matched by a similar quality in his new wife. Above all, they are hard-workers, accustomed to putting in long hours. And like all immigrants before and after them, they are adventurous and courageous. No one would have made that difficult journey across the Atlantic and the American continent without these qualities.

When Dominic and Teresa's first child Eda is born in 1902, Emma and Charles Howard are on the threshold of their divorce and Julia is in her home in Inverness, optimistically planning creative ways to retrieve the family fortune. The Dominic Grossi dynasty has begun.

Novato, Marin County 1903
A RANCH OF ONE'S OWN

IN 1903, DOMINIC AND TERESA TAKE THEIR NEXT BIG STEP. They are starting a family and want a larger space to raise their children. Dominic has shown himself a canny farmer and, through thrift and hard work—nothing new to a Ticinesi— his success is on the rise, just as the Shafters' is on the wane. He and Teresa lease a ranch in Novato and set about in earnest to raise their family.

Novato lies due east from Inverness, on the other side of the coastal mountains that form the eastern border of Point Reyes. While it is drier than the Point Reyes landscape, which holds the sea fog in its palm through much of the year, Novato has a similar topography of rolling hills. It also has a lake and two mountains. To the north is Burdell Mountain and to the southwest, Big Rock Ridge. Stafford Lake lies to the west. Novato Creek originates on Burdell Mountain and flows seventeen miles into San Pablo Bay to the southeast. It was the site of several Coast Miwok villages, including Olompali, where Chief Marin often took refuge in his periodic escapes from life at the San Rafael Mission. Olompali was a sacred place to the Southern Miwok people. Archaeological evidence suggests that they were living in the area as early as 6,000 BC. According to Miwok descendants, Francis Drake was brought here during his brief visit to claim the lands for the British Crown. Cattle from the San Rafael Mission grazed in the area, as mission lands extended nine leagues to the north of the mission.

Like so much of California, Novato began as a land grant. In 1839 the Mexican government granted the 8,876-acre (35.92 km^2) Rancho Novato to Fernando Feliz. The rancho was named after a local Miwok leader, probably given the name of Saint Novatus (an obscure second century saint) at his baptism. To this were later added four additional land grants in the area: Rancho Corte Madera de Novato to John Martin in 1839, Rancho San Jose to Ignacio Pacheco in 1840, Rancho Olompali awarded in 1843 to Camilo Ynitia, son of a Coast Miwok chief, and Rancho Nicasio, by far the largest at 56,621 acres (229.1 km^2), awarded to Pablo de la Guerra and John B.R. Cooper in 1844.

Many of the people in our story have passed through this landscape. That adventurous Scot, James Black, married the widow of Ignacio Pacheco. Pacheco is often credited with being the first to plant grape vines in the region. In return for his services as the head of the customs house in Monterey, the Mexican government granted him a rancho in Sonoma, which he later traded for 6,680 acres in Marin County. Today the Pacheco Ranch and Winery covers roughly 70 acres of the original land grant.

Mt. Burdell takes its name from our friend the dentist, Galen Burdell, who married James Black's only daughter, Mary, and applied himself and his daughter's fortune to establishing the town of Point Reyes Station to welcome James Shafter's (and associates) North Pacific Coast Railroad. We may recall, regrettably, that Mary's mother, first wife of James Black, died in Burdell's dentist chair.

Remember that Galen and Mary Burdell were also the proud owners of 20,000 acres, ranging from Tomales Bay to San Pablo Bay, including large portions of Novato and Nicasio. In later years, Galen took pride in his soil reclamation project on San Pablo Bay, his fine fruit orchards, and his fifty acres of thirty varieties of grapes. Galen and Mary's son James made extensive renovations on their Olompali property, transforming it into a palatial country estate, including a 26-room mansion, complete with a Victorian formal garden. The property was later sold to a man named Court Harrington, who sold the property to the University of San Francisco as a Jesuit retreat. In the 1960s, it did a brief stint as the home of the Grateful Dead and became the site of a hippie commune in 1967. Later, the house burned down due to faulty electrical wiring and in 1977, the property was bought by the state and is now a state park, visible from highway 101, which runs north from San Francisco.

One of Novato's early leading citizens was an Irishman named John Redmond who followed a similar pattern to his countryman Timoteo, née Timothy Murphy, who was born in Ireland in 1900 and came to California by way of Peru. Burdell too had come by way of South America—his original destination being Brazil. At 26, John Redmond went to South America to work for merchants Warlington & Templeman. Several years later, Redmond moved to San Francisco when they opened up a branch there. In 1850, he started his own mercantile business and three years later, he married Joanna Walsh and started a family. They had seven children, of whom five survived. Perhaps this moved them to consider a life of ranching in the healthy air of Marin.

In 1864, the Redmonds bought a 640-acre ranch on Hicks Valley Road that had once been part of the Corte Madera de Novato and Rancho Nicasio Mexican land grants. He earned a reputation as one of the outstanding ranchers in the area. Given the success of dairy farmers in Marin County, he too established a dairy ranch and had a portion under cultivation. He also raised peacocks, golden pheasants, game chickens and imported Southdown sheep. Two streams flowed near the Redmond home, amply supplying them with water. In 1888, he was appointed Postmaster of Black Point—the Novato Post Office.

In 1893, following the death of John Redmond, his daughter Bertha married a neighboring rancher from Limerick County, Ireland named James Ryan and the couple took over the management of the ranch. Fifteen years later, Dan Ryan decided to move his family to Santa Clara. The timing was just right for Dominic and Teresa of Olema and they leased the ranch in 1903. They would operate a dairy there for fourteen years and raise a family to run it. Eventually, the North Marin Water District would build a dam and create the present Stafford Lake in an effort to provide water to their growing community. The lake would supply 20% of its water, supplementing the water that was supplied by the Russian River to the north. (Stafford Lake now covers the site of the Redmond Ranch home.)

The first child born to Teresa and Dominic on the Novato ranch is Elsie. Sadly, this new life begins on a tragic note for Dominic and Teresa. Elsie dies a year later, having fallen into a pool of water and drowned. But life goes on, and by the next year, 1905, another daughter—Lillian—is born.

Novato, Marin ~ 1910–1915

A GROWING FAMILY

By 1910, TERESA AND DOMINIC HAVE FIVE CHILDREN, the beginnings of a labor force. After Eda and Lillian, came their first son, Domingo Salvatore in 1907, then Mary Bertha in 1909 and Virginia Elizabeth in 1910. Teresa's step-mother Caterina is living with her son Charles in Petaluma. She has been married for a year to a man named Frank Mooney who works for the railroad. Her son Charles is now 20 and works in a shoe factory in Petaluma. Her sister Sofia, still in Brione, is making her plans to travel to California in the following year.

James Joseph Grossi, Farmer Ed's father—is born on Groundhog Day—February 2nd, 1912.

Pop's Story Continued

THE LAKE KIDS

I WAS BORN AS ONE OF THE LAKE KIDS—Stafford Lake*—at that ranch. That was the old Redmond Ranch. And that was 93 years ago. (Pause.) I'm still here. (Laughter). We were ten in the family, ten children. Five girls and five boys. We all milked cows, girls as well as boys. In fact the girls were better milkers than the boys, fortunately. We worked the soil, morning until night. My mother was cooking for ten kids. She had her hands full.

We used to go to a little school down there where the water district has a plant now. We used to walk to school, a little over a mile. It was called the Burdell School because the property that's there now, about 1100 acres, was owned by a fellow

* James Grossi calls himself a "lake kid" in retrospect, but the man-made Stafford Lake wasn't created until 1955.

named Burdell, Jim Burdell. The school was on his property.

Dewey: Jim Burdell was a grandson of James Black. In the 1860s and 70s, he owned a lot of this property around here.

Yes, he had his name on this one too.

There was the Azevedo family that lived just west of the lake up there. They had nine children, and they all went to school with us. And then there's the Lemos family, the Portuguese people. They went to the little school. And the Cordas went there too. There were always between 15 and 20 students. It was a one room school, not much bigger than 24x24. We all had one teacher.

My folks always talked Swiss-Italian at home. Right up to the end. On the first day of school, we didn't talk any English, but that's where we learned it. The teacher didn't speak Italian. My first teacher used to come from Nicasio, over the back of the hill, and go all the way to Burdell School. Ellen Redding.

Dewey: That's an old name from Nicasio. It's a big family over there.

Nicasio pioneer William C. Redding originally came to Calforina for the Gold Rush and lived first in Millerton, just south of Marshall on Tomales Bay, where his son Joseph was born. He moved to Nicasio in the early 1870s. As an adult, Joseph lived in a house on the square with his wife and children.

I've always been bad at geography and trying to visualize places in relation to one another. I had no idea how far or near Nicasio was from Pop's Ranch. Or for that matter, quite where the school was. I made a mental note to rendezvous later with a map. I not only found a map, but I found an old interview with the Grossi's school teacher, Ellen Redding, as part of a Marin Oral History project. Here is a brief glimpse of the gallant woman who rode on horseback over that mountain we eyed on our tour of the ranch with MALT.

EM (Ellen Redding McNeill): *I went to San Francisco Teachers' Normal School. I lived with an Aunt over in San Francisco. And then I graduated in 1918 and I got my first school over in Novato, or no, it was the Burdell School, a one-room school house.*

CE (Carla Ehat—interviewer): *When did you start, in the fall?*

EM: *In July, July 1918.*

CE: *Were you terribly nervous about that experience, looking back upon it?*

EM: *I think maybe I was, yes. I only had, like eight children, one in each grade, maybe skipped a grade. Mostly all one family.*

CE: *Any of those children's names you recall?*

EM: *Oh yes. I see them once in a while.*

CE: *Tell us their names if you would.*

EM: *The Grossi family.*

CE: *Was discipline a hard problem?*

EM: *No discipline whatsoever. And I rode horseback over the hill. We lived on one side of the hill and the school was on the opposite side of the hill and I rode horseback over the hill and I had saddlebags in which I took my papers. Corrected my papers at night. Put them in one side and my lunch in the other and my riding skirt on over my dress.*

CE: *Riding skirt over your dress?*

EM: *Yes. Slipped my riding skirt off and I was all dressed for class.*

CE: *You were always a lady. Is that school still there?*

EM: *No, it burnt down I believe, years later.*

✳ ✳ ✳ ✳

Grossi Farms ~ The Present

THE INVITATION

"DO YOU LIKE MUSIC SEÑORA?"

"Of course I do Lazaro."

"What kind of music do you like?"

"Classical music," I say without thinking. I'm in the midst of loading a bin with zucchinis. I look up. Lazaro is looking *pensativo*. Does he know what classical music is? I'm not sure if the words are the same in Spanish. *Musica classica?* Perhaps it is, because he is looking disappointed.

"Do you like *bandas?*"

"Yes, I like *bandas*, Lazaro." Of course I have no idea what kind of *banda* he is talking about. A hard rock band would send me into an air raid shelter. But a Mexican *banda*, although the brass can be a little grating in the small villages—especially during the wee hours of a fiesta—is fun.

"Do you like to dance?"

The zucchinis are forgotten. I'm looking carefully at Lazaro now, taking in his every word. I realize that he is looking a little nervous. I do like to dance, so I say honestly "Yes." He smiles.

"There is a very good *banda* coming to town. For a fiesta. Would you like to go?"

Is Lazaro asking me on a *date?* I am at a loss for words. I'm definitely old enough to be his mother. Would he invite his mother to a *dance?* Yet I am also touched and flattered. He is waiting intensely. I can feel that.

"Well . . . Lazaro . . . You know at my age, I don't really go to those things. Although I really appreciate the invitation . . ." There, I've said it. He nods and turns to pick up his task of sorting for a few moments and then quietly leaves. I'm wondering if the other fellows know about this invitation. Whether they encouraged or discouraged him. Whether they tease him. Lazaro has a wife and children in Mexico City. He has shown me the pictures. How does a young man like that survive up here, living alone. Perhaps he has invited me because it is a way to go to a fiesta with someone and be safe. Go with your mother. Then I begin calculating whether I am old enough to be his grandmother. Happily I'm not, although I might qualify as a great aunt.

Marin ~ 1917

GROWING UP

IN 1917, WHILE WAR WAS RAGING IN EUROPE, the Ticinesi ranchers in Marin were expanding their families and their lands. They were a new breed of people on this landscape. Not like the native people, living off the abundance of native plants, animals, fish and fowl. Nor like the adventurers from Europe and Mexico, who laid claim to vast ranchos bestowed by the distant king of Spain or the Mexican government. Nor like the missionaries and soldiers who grazed cattle on the land with indigenous labor. Certainly these new landholders were not like so many of the boisterous 49ers pursuing their dreams of wealth in gold or the habitués of San Francisco's bordellos and gaming houses. Theirs was a different kind of gold, gained by pure hard work and determination. Large families took the place of indigenous workers. As Pop Grossi tells us, the boys and girls worked side by side.

In the fifty years from 1860 to 1910, the population of Marin County has risen from roughly 3,000 people to 25,000—an eight-fold increase that does not include the spike in numbers caused by the Gold Rush. Some of it is due to the influx of people who fled the devastation of the earthquake in 1906. The county is increasingly becoming two different worlds, as a more sophisticated population develops along the eastern corridor that is now highway 101, including Sausalito, Tiburon, Mill Valley—the heart of the former Huimen lands. To the west are still the wide open grasslands that were formerly the Shafter Dairy Empire and the forested enclave of Inverness.

This is a banner year for the Buzzini-Grossi family. While Joe Corda and Dominic Grossi are negotiating for the Valencia Ranch in Novato (which they had been leasing), Teresa's younger sister is planning an August wedding in Salinas. Sofia had arrived from Brione in 1911. At age 35, she is marrying Giovanni, now John, Ferrini. John comes from one of the old families of Frasco, a village close to Sonogno and Brione. He emigrated in 1893 and is now 42. They will raise their family in San Ardo, in Monterey county to the south of the Golden Gate, and live the rest of their lives there.

There is no trace of Caterina Buzzini who was married to Frank Mooney and living in Petaluma in 1910. Irish as the name may sound, Frank Mooney is an Italian immigrant and has likely Anglicized his name. Caterina's son Charles, née Celeste, will be called up for the draft in the following year to fight overseas in the infantry. He is married and living in the Los Angeles area. He and his wife Martha have three children now and he hopes that having a family to support will gain him a deferment. He applies for one on that basis in 1918.

Meanwhile, by 1910, the Ticino families whom we have met are doing exceptionally well. Many have picked up the remnants of the Shafters' thriving dairy industry and transformed it into the family businesses of many dairymen— especially Ticinesi, Portuguese and Irish—who are taking advantage of large families for their labor. This is certainly true of Dominic, who now has nine little Grossis as a labor force. The youngest son, George, will be born in 1921.

Giuseppe Corda, who came over from Vogorno in 1886, is head of a large family in the San Antonio valley. Here he is known simply as Joe. He and his wife Adelaide have five children and a household full of people. For a man who arrived in Hicks Valley with 50 cents in his pocket, he is doing very well. In 1917, he goes into partnership with Dominic to buy the old Valencia Ranch in Novato. Joe Corda's three sons—Alfred, Henry and Frank—will extend the Corda legacy in the years to come, just as the sons and daughters of Dominic and other Ticinesi will do in Marin and Sonoma Counties.

We last saw William Spaletta walking out of his remote village, at the western edge of the Val Campo, bidding good-bye to neighbors, familiar sights; the deep forests and meadows of his valley. Was it feeling for those forests, or a practical job opportunity that drew him first farther north, to Humboldt County, where some of the finest stands of redwoods are found, including the one we have been following, seeded in the time of Monica and Augustine. William is living in Union City (later named Arcata) with his wife Barbara and their nine children. Their youngest, Augusta, is a year and a half. Their eldest daughter Guiditta is 16 and their oldest son, Charles, is 14. Charles will one day marry Dominic and Teresa's eldest daughter, Eda.

Lorenzo, now Lawrence Martinelli—who is really the "senior emigrant" among those we have been following—was among the most adventurous, joining up with the Fremont Expedition, which brought him to San Rafael in 1846. This arrival is a peak moment in the history of the Pathfinder, as Fremont was known. He intersects at this point with a location we have been following. The Mission San Rafael, now virtually abandoned after its secularization by Mexico, becomes the base of operations for the famous Bear Flag Revolt. From the San Rafael website history page: "In 1846 The Bear Flag Revolt rocked sleepy San Rafael. General John C. Fremont captured the Mission and used it as headquarters for the United States military forces. He used the Chapel as a stable and the old Mission continued to deteriorate." In a brash move, Fremont had shown defiance of Mexican authority by capturing the garrison at Sonoma and its Commandant, our old friend Mariano Vallejo. Fremont had run up a home-made flag to indicate that Alta California was now officially an American possession. Although this event took place prior to news that the United States had officially won the Mexican-American War, Vallejo seemed to recognize the inevitably that the reign of the Californios had come to an end.

The famous Bear Flag, which was later adopted as the state flag of California, was designed and made by Mary Todd Lincoln's nephew, William Todd. "The flag arrived at Todd's residence half completed, with the instructions to paint a Bartlett pear as the primary motif, to symbolize California's rich agricultural traditions. Todd misread the note as "bear," resulting in the basis for the modern California flag.

The event is important to Lorenzo Martinelli simply because he likes what he sees of San Rafael and decides to remain there. That is, long enough to earn money selling goods to gold miners after the discovery at Sutter's Mill. With his profits, he will buy a 160 acre ranch in Nicasio—on Camilo Ynitia's rancho and the old stomping ground of Timothy Murphy.

◆ ◆ ◆

A name that will sail around Marin with prominence and enter into the Grossi lineage is Giacomini. Near the Grandi store in Point Reyes Station is Toby's Feed Barn. It is a lively center of life in that community today.

From Gordola, in the Val Versazca, has come Celestina Domenghini. She arrived in 1907 on the ship Californie from Le Havre. She was 18 years old. Five years prior to that, a young man named Tobias C.B. Giacomini had arrived from Villa de Chiavena, Italy. It is only twenty-eight miles, as the crow flies (two and a half hours of mountain driving) from Gordola, Switzerland to Chiavenna, Italy. But, like Teresa and Dominic, Tobias and Celestina will meet in California. As far as we know, Tobias is not directly related to the Giacominis who had come earlier, like Julio Giacomini who was living with Salvatore and Louis Grandi in 1870. But it seems likely that not too far back one of the Giacominis from Brontallo, near Menzonio in the Val Maggia, was among the Ticinesi who stayed on in Italy, not far across the border in Lombardy.

By the time that Dominic Grossi and Joe Corda are completing the purchase of the Valencia Ranch in Novato, Celestina, now Celeste, is married to Tobias C.B. Giacomini and is about to become pregnant with her fourth child, Tobias Junior. They are raising their two sons—Bertram, age 5 and Waldo, age 4—and their year old daughter, Esther on their forty acre chicken farm on Washington Street in Petaluma.

You may remember that from Cevio, up in the Val Maggia, had come three of the earliest emigrants from Ticino: Carlo Martinoia and the brothers Pietro and Michael Dolcini. Word spread quickly through the valley of the success of people like the Grandi brothers and the Dolcini brothers. Carlo Martinoia emigrated in the 1850s and as Charles Martin, had gone on to own one of the largest ranches in Marin. In 1862, he bought a ranch in the Chileno valley and sent for his sweetheart, Katerina Traversi back in Cevio. Charles Martin and Caterina Traversi had 7 children. He became a leading citizen of Marin and a prosperous banker, serving in his life as head of Petaluma National Bank, the Marin Bank of San Rafael, the Hill Bank of Petaluma and the Swiss-American Bank of San Francisco. The second youngest of his children, Anita, married one of the hired hands—none other than her countryman Pietro Dolcini. Like Salvatore Grandi, Martinoia was a helping hand for the young men who were coming over from Ticino—finding them jobs and loaning them money. As a wedding present, he purchased a ranch in Nicasio—the Dolcini Ranch. He will leave his ranch to his daughter Anita

DOMINIC, TERESA AND THEIR TEN CHILDREN

Dolcini and move on down south to San Diego. When he died in 1905, his estate was worth $1,000,000.

In 1917, Peter and Anita Dolcini have five children. Their oldest son Arnold and son Albino have purchased a ranch in Hicks Valley, across from the schoolhouse. Their daughter Anita is born in 1916. That ranch will be sold in 1918. "We had a wonderful childhood," Anita claims. "I was always happy. I never felt denied anything. We had a whole ranch to run around on and we did. My brother and I explored every inch of that place and across the road, up into the forest because there were columbines growing there and brown bells and there were salamanders. But we also had a place on the ranch where I grew up that we called the Indian Trail..."

In 1908, Fridolino Lafranchi and Giocondo Cerini traveled from the village of Maggia, like Lorenzo Martinelli before them. Fridolino was 17—that ripe age for setting out for the New World. He found work at his uncle's dairy ranch at Red Hill and then, like Tobias Giacomini, had a go at chicken ranching in Petaluma, when his brother Alphonso came over from Ticino to join him. In 1919, Fred La Franchi married into the Dolcini family in Nicasio Valley. Fred and his wife Zelma, like Dominic and other Ticinesi, began by renting a Nicasio dairy, which they would eventually buy in 1930.

Fortune, however, continues to look away from Julia Shafter Hamilton. Julia is still in Inverness. She has finally found a buyer for Glen Ranch, south of Olema but the outbreak of war is just one more setback to her plans for turning a profit on her lands.

By 1921, the Grossi labor force is now complete. Parents and ten children start out their new chapter on their portion of the old Valencia Ranch in this year. James is now 9 and has three younger brothers—Henry, Alfred and George (just born this year)—and a younger sister, Helen, two years old.

POP'S STORY CONTINUES ~ 1917

WE CAME UP HERE IN 1917. My Dad bought this ranch from the Black family. They had this place and the Corda place across the street. About 2300 acres. Mr. Corda and my Dad bought the places together. This property and the neighbors' property were all one ranch. The Corda people wanted to buy half the farm and my mother wanted to buy the other half. So we made a division in 1920.

When we came up here, that old house had a big porch around the front and there were Portuguese people who were living here at the time. Mendoza.* There was a little yard and the cow would come up there into the orchards. We had a redwood grove and we hired men in the winter time to make split posts, seven foot posts for fencing. Then we could build all the fences we needed.

There was just the old house, all torn up, to live in with ten kids. The barns were hardly fit to use and needed a lot of repair because the ranch had been leased out to tenants and they had let everything go. It was just kind of a mess, so we had to start making fences to keep the cattle where they belonged. We had a lot of building to do. All the buildings you see now we and my Dad built. Corral work and all that stuff. We had to develop springs to get water and we got one spring way up on that mountain two miles from the house. And you got to maintain that, you know. There's another spring over here, so there's constant work on the dairy. If you want to keep going, you've got to keep working.

We worked the soil, morning until night. We'd get up in the morning and milk the cows at three o'clock. We'd clean up the barn and get ready to go to school. We had to be at school at 9 o'clock, so we had to move! We came back from school at three thirty, four o'clock. Then we had to go milk our cows, do our chores, and go to sleep around nine o'clock, after dinner. When you look back, you can hardly believe you went through that, but we all went through it together. It wasn't like one was suffering and the other was leading the life of Riley. We were all in the same boat.

Novato, before 1940, was on the other side of the highway. The main drag used to go through Novato and there were ranch fields on this side of the highway. Where Phoenix store is now it was all hay fields; all agriculture. There was a little dairy there by the bridge across from the Catholic church; a fella had a few cows to milk there. Everything where the Grant Ave is now, on this side of the highway, was all grain fields. And then from there into the main hills of west Novato, they were all pear orchards and chicken ranches. Two and three and four, five acres.

We always had 125, 150 cows to milk all by hand. They were brown swiss and then we switched to the Guernsey cattle. We used to sell the skim milk here. We'd make our cream, ship it to Petaluma, and then take the skim off and sell it to the chicken people around Novato. We used to deliver from a little old Model T truck. We always had a 50 gallon barrel tank that we used to dump the cans in, take our cans back and leave them the skim milk. It was a lot of hard work. If you got an outsider came in, it would be hard for him to take to it. But we were born with it and it didn't bother us.

* Not the Point Reyes Mendozas.

We'd start milking cows when we were 6, 7. You had a little milk stool that you moved from one cow to another cow and you'd do it all again the next day. When I was 13 years old, I still remember this one time we milked the cows out in the corrals. Took the bucket and stool and the cows out into the corral. They were all gentle. So we milked the cows by hand and took the milk up to the dairy house where it receives all the milk into the main can. We used to make cream for butter and skim milk for the hogs. We used to have 250, 300 hogs in those days. The skim went to the hogs and the cream went to Petaluma to the Western Dairyman's Co-op.

We changed from Swiss cattle to Guernsey because the Borden company, at that time, were looking for the color in the milk. With the Guernseys, they had a yellow color in the bottle and it was always more saleable to the public. It wasn't like blue milk, skim milk, when it came.

ED: You got your money from the butter fat. You were paid by the butter fat content in your milk. So you wanted Jerseys and Guernseys because they had more. The Guernseys have a genetic defect and the milk comes out a golden color, more than the Jerseys or the brown swiss. Those were the days before the homogenized milk when you had to shake it up to mix the cream in. Our cousin Scilacci over in Petaluma was one of the last ones to raise Guernseys. Now it's about 90% Holstein and the rest are Jerseys.

POP: There's still one dairy up there by Petaluma that milks goats. Somebody told me the coyotes got in on them and scattered goats all over. We never had goats or sheep here. Just cows and pigs and chickens.

Years ago, in the early '20s, everyone was producing Grade B milk. But the milk that you could drink is not Grade B, it's Grade A. So as the demand for drinking milk came on, there were more distributors that wanted milk. We shipped to the Borden company for 42 years. They wanted more milk. Of course we had seven dairies, so every time they wanted more milk, we had another ranch to develop more milk. We were selling Borden Company, for example, six thousand gallons of milk a day. That was a lot of milk in those years.

When we sold to Borden, we had to take the milk all the way to San Rafael at night time and not before nine o'clock so one of us had to lose his sleep cause he had to get up at 3 a.m. We'd take the milk down in 10 gallon cans, put it on the tray, wait for our cans to get washed and get home by 11:00. We did that for 42 years.

Then you had to milk in ten gallon cans. Now you've got a milk tank in the dairy house. You milk the cows and it goes right into refrigeration; into the tank and then another truck comes along and picks it up and you don't worry about it.

We didn't get electricity here until 1928. We waited a long time for it. They brought it along the valley, but then they stopped here. There was a problem because the cheese factory and all those dairies there had no electricity. PG&E wanted to cut across to Nicasio and Point Reyes, so they wanted to turn off here. The people in the Hicks Valley area were complaining. "Why didn't you hold them up so they'd come up our way?"

We had two or three teams of horses for plowing, before the tractor came along. Then we kept one or two cattle horses. My mother used to go into Novato for

470

groceries, but we always had a garden and still do. Beef and cabbage, lettuce, corn from the garden.

Things changed when they built the dam and put in the lake. You had to follow the state regulations. Anything above the dam, you have to keep your creeks clean and you can't leave no dead animal die in the creek. You have all that to contend with. You have to make sure that the Water Quality people approve what you do above the lake. My Dad sold 200 acres to the water district.

The Ryan ranch was where the lake is now. That's where I was born.

* * * *

Humboldt County, California ~ Summer 1917

PO·PO·LEEN

"I have not troubled about the Great Wars," said Treebeard; "they mostly concern Elves and Men . . . . I do not like worrying about the future. I am not altogether on anybody's side, because nobody is altogether on my side, if you understand me: nobody cares for the woods as I care for them.

— R.R. TOLKIEN

IN THE GREAT FOREST TO THE NORTH, THE TREE IS ASCENDING. It is now more than halfway into its own second millennium. Such a generous tree, sheltering birds and a myriad of small creatures as its upper branches grow dense and matted with ferns. In this summer month the dense fogs that roll in from the sea deliver moisture that the tree gathers in its tips and preserves like a well. Humans are like ants moving around its ankles, but it provides for them too, and in return the tree, like all of its neighbors, is venerated by them. In size, the human is to the tree as a caterpillar is to a human. Each is busy doing its work.

The redwood tree is known among the Yurok people as Keehi. It is blessed by the Creator as the heart of the Yurok people. Even when a tree falls, and is made into a house, it is still respected. Still considered living. The old old trees are called Po-Po-Leen, which means Ancient Ones, Great Ones. The same word is used for elders in the community, who share a wisdom of age with the trees. The old old people are like the old old trees. They can give you a lot. They need to be respected.

The people respect the redwoods and in return the redwoods give them shelter, wood for their dance and ceremonial houses; the female house for the women, where they pass on their teachings and rules for life; the sweat house for the men, where daily they cleanse and center themselves. Wood for their canoes, which can carry them over distances. Only certain families are allowed to build canoes, a work that can take up to seven years. The canoes will weigh up to 1200 pounds, yet they are carefully designed in a way that will allow one person to navigate the boat. The fashioning of the canoe is undertaken with great care and with prayers. It is treated, like the redwood from which it is made, as a living being.

The semblance of body parts are carved into the boat: Heart, lungs, and out of respect, and to make the boat a pure, clean boat, they give the boat two kidneys. In our culture, those feelings, those prayers that the maker put into it, resonate out of that canoe forever."

— Yurok descendant SKIP LOWRY, Forest Ranger, from OMSI
Film, *Popo-Leen: The Yuroks and the Redwood Tree**

A FAMILY PICNIC

WILLIAM SPALETTA SITS COMFORTABLY WITH HIS BACK AGAINST *the vast trunk of his favorite tree. He remembers doing this for the first time, alone, over twenty years ago. Like the trees in the forest near Cimalmotto, this forest had given him comfort and peace in a strange land. He had entered then with awe. The trees were nothing like the trees he knew and they frightened him a little that first time. Until he had found this particular tree and sat like a child in its protection.*

Now his wife Barbara sits dozing beside him and he watches his children playing among the gentle giants. That's what Barbara calls them. They always come here on their holidays, if it isn't raining. His younger children think of it as a fairy world and make up imaginary scenes that they play out together. His youngest, Augusta, is asleep in his lap. Everything in the world is big to her now and the trees hold little interest. William relaxes into the peace of it. Even with the challenge of nine children to support, his life is better here. His oldest children, Guiditta and Charles, will soon be leaving the family to go out into their own lives. He savors these last years that his family is still complete.

The latest news out of Europe is the great battle being fought in Belgium at a place called Paschendale. If the stories are to be believed, thousands are dying in that single battle.** Although Switzerland remains neutral, it lies right in the midst of the warring countries and thousands of his countrymen have been called up to defend its borders. Here, at least, he has only his wife and family to think about. Making ends meet as the Americans say. The tree, to William, is like America: Huge, protective, independent.

✳ ✳ ✳ ✳

---

* You can watch this on the web at http://www.nps.gov/redw/ photosmultimedia/omsi-video.htm
** Half a million of the combatants would die there.

Point Reyes ~ The Present

A RIDE WITH SALLY

SALLY AND I EASE INTO THE SOUTHWARD STREAM of Highway 101, *caught up in the manic hurry, the urgent pressure forward that is typical of freeways and modern life in general. Sally is driving and the afternoon is beautiful. Our flexible cerebri have a wonderful capacity to blot out the flying steel herd of cars that presses around us at 70, 80, 90 miles an hour. Then it is suddenly gone, as if we had crossed the threshold of a dimension. Or Harry-Potter-like, had reached Diagon Alley where magic folk slip out of the mundane world of Muggles. This is San Antonio Road, our favorite route for a country drive.*

We both sigh and sit back to absorb the green intimacy of trees. Soon they open onto vistas of rolling ochre hills, responding to the late afternoon alchemy of a light that turns straw into gold. We pass a one room schoolhouse with a banner proclaiming "Now Enrolling." As we reach the crest of the hill, hidden pockets of a ranch below us open out into view; gently sloping hillsides dotted with vineyards, olive trees, cows and sheep. Stands of live oak grow along the hillsides, with their gnarled tenacity before the winds and rains of winter and the dry hot summers. Over it all, the blue California skies are shot through with reflected light from the golden landscape.

We turn right on Hicks Valley Road and a wide landscape of rolling hills stretches out before us, enfolding us in its quiet. Its slower rhythms. Its older memory of wild grasses and drought-resistant shrubs that the eons of time have meticulously shaped to meet us in this moment, just so, to salute something old and deep in our own souls like the welcome of the prodigal son.

At the end of Hicks Valley Road, we turn westward on the Marshall-Petaluma Road. Its gentle rise reveals some of the most beautiful landscape yet—-now alive with the lights and shadows of early evening, drifting across it as far as the eye can see.

"I will lift mine eyes unto the hills" says the Psalmist and verily Sally and I are finding in that simple act some of the salvivic nourishment and aid to our spirits that he promised. "This is just what I needed," Sally declares, after a particularly busy and trying week. I nod as my eyes continue to pore gratefully over the landscape.

Is the country ride that so appeals to us, part of nature's mentoring of us in our profession of seeking happiness, the truly human gift? "Follow beauty," Nature teaches her children, as she paints wings and carapaces, flowers and trees, and the bodies of the tiniest insects. Fragrance, texture, taste . . . All of nature's wooing that it is our profession to follow.

"How about oysters at Tony's?" Sally suggests. We have turned onto a road that runs along Tomales Bay and we enter the town of Marshall, a small strip of houses, restaurants and oyster bars. We take a seat at Tony's where we can look out on the narrow bay at the small boats and the silhouetted peninsula beyond. A delicious meal of barbecued oysters from the bay and red snapper from Bodega Bay to the north provides the perfect benediction to our peaceful adventure. Squinting into the setting sun, with its profligate squandering of gold light, the land across the bay is

little more than a smoky mist that lies like a sulking dragon between us and the Pacific. I follow the dark profile outlined in the sun's glare as it dips south toward Point Reyes. Somewhere through that mist, I am looking at Dominic Grossi's ranch.

Point Reyes ~ 1939

A NEW CHAPTER

WHEN CHARLES HOWARD DIED IN 1908, management of the O.L. Shafter company fell to a man named Charles Slack, who worked out of the Alaska Commercial Building in San Francisco. An on-site overseer was hired to collect the rents and keep an eye on operations and revenues. In general, the ranches fared poorly under this arrangement and over time, so did the shareholders. The tenant ranchers were eyeing the moment when they could become their own landlords; own their own ranches. When the depression came along and prices fell, they saw their chance. In the thirties, shareholders were receiving no dividends from the property but had to pay assessments for food for the cattle and the costs of exterminating tuberculosis among the herd.

Fortune seemed to smile on the newcomers to these Point Reyes lands and continue to thwart the old. The estate was finally liquidated just before World War II, which would, ironically, bring prosperity to the dairy industry. There was an investor ready to step in and make his own killing on the Point Reyes land, like the Shafters before him and the land barons of the past. On July 6, 1939, Leonard David of San Francisco paid Oscar's heirs $150,000 for their ranches. He immediately sold the land off in parcels for prices ranging up to $50,000. Dominic Grossi's moment had come. Already a landowner in Novato, he now became a landowner in Point Reyes, looking ahead to the future of his sons and daughters.

POP'S STORY CONTINUES: THE RANCHES

WE WERE ALL RAISED HERE ON THE NOVATO RANCH, the ten kids. But my mother and father always wanted to put us some place where we could go out on our own

In 1928, we bought the place next door where my brother George is now. Then in 1932, we bought the ranch at the corner here—because we all worked together. Everybody's interest was going toward what he purchased in property. My Dad was pretty thrifty, you know, and we were like a bunch of workhorses. Then we bought a ranch in Tomales—in Marshall. And then we bought the ranches in Point Reyes. There were three ranches there. That was 2800 acres. It was depression time, and you always bought land when the prices were down.

We ended up with seven ranches and they were run by seven of us. Two of the daughters—my sisters—married ranchers and the other one wasn't a rancher. He worked in the freight yards. They were all good ranches. There was no competition between the brothers on the ranches. You had enough to take care of on your own.

Ed remembers hearing how Dominic's sons felt when he announced one day that he had purchased ranches in Point Reyes for them. They dutifully went out to look at the land, peering through damp, dense fog at their new possessions. They didn't like it much, compared to the clear skies to the east in Novato. They returned home and told their father so. He didn't speak to them for days. Ungrateful wretches!

But the deed was done and the elder sons—Domingo and Alfred—eventually took up their new responsibilities on the Point Reyes dairy ranches. They soon learned what so many ranchers had learned before them: The moist climate of Point Reyes, preserving fairly even year-round temperatures, provided grassland for grazing that was unparalleled anywhere. Henry would take over the ranch in Marshall on Tomales Bay. Over time, they would all prosper.

The Spaletta-Grossi union took place when William Spaletta's son Charles married Dominic's eldest daughter, Eda. In 1936, Dominic bought a ranch for them at the base of Red Hill, on the Point Reyes-Petaluma Road.

In 1939, Domingo Grossi Jr. was 32, Henry was 26, and Alfred was 16. They were about to become the next generation of dairy ranchers on the Point Reyes Peninsula. James, "Pop," would inherit the home ranch in Novato, where Ed was born. George would have the ranch nearby.

In 1942, Virginia Grossi married Thomas Gallagher and in the same year, Mary wed David Rogers, both would become prominent Point Reyes ranchers.

POP GROSSI: When my folks passed away, they had seven ranches, but they had ten kids so what do you do? Whoever wasn't on a ranch got compensated with money. One married a man with a lot of money, so there was no worry. Another married a man with two ranches, so there was no worry there. So we were all pretty well set up as a family. From where we were to where we are today. It was always understood that this would be my ranch. No one feels that they took a dime from the other one, and that was a good feeling to be in.

Domingo was the second oldest. He was the first one out there. Then I think they sent Alfred out there so Domingo could keep track of him. (If you knew Alfred you'd understand that.) This ranch ended up being the headquarters. Dad had a feed mill here. Mixed all of the grain for all of the ranches and at one point, back a long time ago, Dad used to buy all the hay in the valley, when they started importing hay from the central valley and then he would have it delivered to all the ranches so it was pretty much all run from here.

JIM JR.: My grandfather, Dominic, was still The Boss right up until the end. I was 11 years old when he passed away but he had enough foresight to basically not have any of the brothers and sisters as partners with each other. So they all owned their own ranches. That forestalled the problem. Today there are a lot of ranches with too many people having ownership, who can't agree on what to do. It's coming. But my grandfather put it off for a couple of generations by separating everybody, so there weren't any problems in that generation.

It took me a while to untangle the ten branches of Dominic's family tree, but now that I have, I can lay it out for you in true Family Tree style. In summary, Dominic bought three of the former Shafter Ranches on Point Reyes. The Shafters had designated their tenant ranches with the letters of the alphabet—A through Z.

Dominic bought the M and H ranches, 2900 acres, from Leonard David in 1940 for a reported $53,000. The Marvelous Marin Realty Company who handled the deal, (along with Lang Realty) must have seemed marvelous indeed to Dominic and Teresa, who had just picked up two fine ranches at bargain-basement prices, as well as to Leonard David, who made a good profit on a quick turn-around—buying all of the ranches for $150,000 and then quickly selling seven of them for around $350,000. The very profit that had eluded Julia for years, as well as the share-holder of the O.L. Shafter Estate, was suddenly showering on the Marvelous Marin Realty Company, Lang Realty and Leonard David.

Dominic sent out his oldest son Domingo to run M Ranch and his son Alfred to operate H Ranch. He sent his daughter Virginia along to cook for Alfred.

On the nearly two thousand acre M Ranch, Domingo moved into the old two-story house and set to work bringing the deteriorating dairy up to scratch. It had originally belonged to Oscar Shafter, but those gallant days when Oscar joined his vaqueros, dashing across his new land were long gone. Oscar had been dead since 1873, over sixty-five years, and we know of the problems that plagued the Shafter Estate in later years. Domingo's first project was to bring it up to the standards of a Grade A dairy as soon as possible.

Alfred Grossi's 1,148 acre H Ranch had a wide expanse of grassland, overlooking Abbott's Lagoon and the Pacific. The structures were built on a flat swale in the eastern portion of the land. The ranch had access to Schooner Bay and Abbott's Lagoon. Feral goats ranged on the hills near the lagoon. This ranch, which had also belonged to Oscar, had the biggest herd of all the Shafter ranches at one point. It was a prime location.

Like Domingo, Alfred at first continued with the production of cream on the ranch, but worked to convert it to a Grade A dairy.

In 1946, Dominic divided off a 398 acre parcel of M Ranch for his daughter Mary and her husband David Rogers. This portion of M Ranch became the Rogers Ranch.

Dominic's daughter Virginia married Thomas Gallagher and they bought C Ranch in 1946. The 1,062 acre ranch was mostly grassland, bounded on the east by Drake's Bay and the west, by the Pacific Ocean, rimmed with coastal dunes.

Thomas was the son of John Gallagher, who owned neighboring F Ranch—a 1,656 acre ranch that had once functioned virtually as a town on Point Reyes. It was the oldest of the ranches, site of the Post Office and the center of commerce and trading, with its access to the schooner landing.

When the Shafters divided up their Point Reyes land in 1869, between Oscar, James and Emma's husband Charles Howard, C Ranch was part of the property

THE FAMILY OF DOMINIC & TERESA GROSSI

DOMENICO GROSSI
Born 1874
Monte Carasso
Ticino, Switzerland

TERESINA BUZZINI
Born 1878
Brione
Ticino, Switzerland

EDA GROSSI	LILLIAN GROSSI	DOMINGO GROSSI	MARY GROSSI	VIRGINIA GROSSI
(1902–1933)	(1905–1999)	(1907–1998)	(1909–1991)	(1910–1992)
married	married	married	married	married
CHARLES SPALETTA	GEORGE MCWHORTER	EDITH POMO	DAVID ROGERS	THOMAS GALLAGHER
Red Hill Ranch		M Ranch	M Ranch	C Ranch
(purchased by Dominic)		(formerly owned by Oscar Shafter)	(formerly owned by Oscar Shafter)	(formerly owned by Charles & Emma Shafter Howard)
MARIN COUNTY		MARIN COUNTY	MARIN COUNTY	MARIN COUNTY

JAMES GROSSI	HENRY GROSSI	ALFRED GROSSI	HELEN GROSSI	GEORGE GROSSI
(1912–2010)	(1913–1998)	(1916–2004)	(1918–1998)	(1921–)
married	married	married	married	married
ROSE HALTER	LYDIA MAZZUCCHI	FLORENCE NOSECCHI	JOHN BIANCHI	ANNETTE HALTER
Home Ranch	Dairy Ranch	H Ranch	Dairy Ranch	Home Ranch
		(formerly owned by Charles & Emma Shafter Howard)	(formerly owned by Charles & Emma Shafter Howard)	(formerly owned by Charles & Emma Shafter Howard)
Novato	Marshall		Valley Ford	Novato
MARIN COUNTY	SONOMA COUNTY	MARIN COUNTY	SONOMA COUNTY	MARIN COUNTY

that went to Howard. The ranch complex was built on a wide flat area in the center of the property, with a two-story house from 1889 in the typical style of Shafter/ Howard ranch dwellings. The buildings had remained in good condition due to the excellent care of owners.

In 1955, Thomas and Virginia Gallagher leased C Ranch to Virginia's nephew Jim Spaletta, who developed his own Grade A Dairy business. Jim was the son of the oldest Grossi daughter Eda and Charles Spaletta, who had been given the Red Hill Ranch when they married in 1936. Jim Spaletta eventually moved to Valley Ford and turned the ranch operation over to his nephew and business partner Ernie Spaletta. The Gallaghers sold the property to the Federal government in 1964 and Spaletta continued to operate it under a special use permit.

Here is a list of the ranches owned by Grossi family members. Two of the ranches were owned by the spouses of Grossi daughters: The Bianchi Ranch in

HISTORICAL ALPHABET DESIGNATIONS OF THE
SHAFTER-HOWARD POINT REYES RANCHES
(Dewey Livingston)

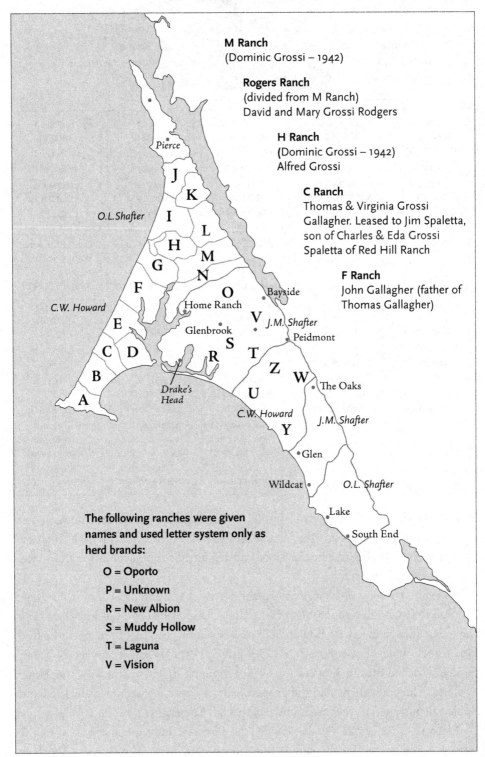

M Ranch
(Dominic Grossi – 1942)

Rogers Ranch
(divided from M Ranch)
David and Mary Grossi Rodgers

H Ranch
(Dominic Grossi – 1942)
Alfred Grossi

C Ranch
Thomas & Virginia Grossi
Gallagher. Leased to Jim Spaletta,
son of Charles & Eda Grossi
Spaletta of Red Hill Ranch

F Ranch
John Gallagher (father of
Thomas Gallagher)

**The following ranches were given
names and used letter system only as
herd brands:**

O = Oporto

P = Unknown

R = New Albion

S = Muddy Hollow

T = Laguna

V = Vision

Courtesy of the Jack Mason Museum, Point Reyes

Valley Ford and the C Ranch, owned by the Gallaghers. The other seven ranches were run as part of a single Grossi Family operation.

> **M Ranch** [1,192 acres*] – Domingo Grossi
>
> **H Ranch** [1,148 acres] – Alfred Grossi
>
> **C Ranch** [1,062 acres] – Thomas and Virginia Grossi Gallagher
>
> **Red Hill Ranch** – William and Eda Grossi Spaletta
>
> **Marshall Ranch** – Henry Grossi
>
> Home Ranch (Novato) – Jim Grossi
>
> Home Ranch (Novato) – George Grossi
>
> **Valley Ford Dairy** – John and Helen Grossi Bianchi
>
> **Rogers Ranch** [398 acres] – David and Mary Grossi Rogers

(Note: those in parentheses were not purchased by Dominic but by his daughters' spouses. Dominic had bestowed money in place of land on them, which likely went toward their ranching operations.)

In one generation, Dominic and Teresa have gone from near poverty-level lives in Ticino, on small bits of harsh land, to a small empire of ranch land in Marin and Sonoma Counties. The hard work of the Ten Little Grossis has paid off, to be followed by more hard work on their own ranches. Dominic has gotten them started, providing land and setting them up on ranches, but they have to run them and make them pay. Mary and David Rogers, for example, will lease their ranch until they can afford to buy it.

But the real contribution of the Ticinesi farmers is yet to be made, and it is the next generation that will take that step.

Sebastopol, California ~ June 2, 1942

CHARLES NÉE CELESTE

CHARLES LOOKED OUT THE WINDOW, which was coated with a fine layer of dust. A slight wind had come up and he watched a single page of newspaper slide along the street. It gathered speed and a corner of it lifted into the air. Then it became limp and slid in another direction. Lay still. Lifted again. Slightly gathered speed as if for a take-off as a gust of wind snatched at it. The front half nosed upward. But the gust passed and the paper fell listlessly back onto the street, with its occasional small movements, this way and that. He wondered what page it was. One of the insert pages. Sports? Classifieds? Continued-from-page-ones? He already knew what would be on page one: How different America had been on December 7th of last year after Pearl Harbor. Not so much for himself but for the others. Confident citizens born in the USA who thought themselves immune to upheaval. Not so for him. His life was like that newspaper, full of sudden starts and

---

* Before the split of 398 acres for the Rogers Ranch.

turnings. Aborted lift-offs, half-hearted risings. An inherent aimlessness.

Charles had been born into a family where he wasn't much welcome, being the child of a quick marriage after the death of his father's first wife. Then came the death of his stepfather. Not to mention the hard times, the hunger, that made tempers flare in his small village. He had only vague memories of a dreary stone place. The sense that the place was a hostile being of some sort and the villagers, ever vigilant of its next attack. And "the times"—the other hostile being against which the villagers muttered daily imprecations. His mother telling him one day that everything was going to change. Forgetting that everything had always changed in his six years of life in Brione. But better, she said. Things would definitely be better. They would leave behind those hostile presences that haunted them in Ticino. New world. New life.

At first he believed it. Men had come from Sonogno and Frasco and they had seemed very merry. There was a holiday feeling in the air that morning that chased the hostile beings away—Bad Place and Bad Times—and they rode on that feeling like a wave that carried them down the valley, to Gorgola, to Bellinzona. Oh it was a great adventure and The Place suddenly seemed beautiful. As if one might come to miss it. Then up up up—a stagecoach ride that took them to a crest of mountains—a final good-bye to Switzerland—then down, down into France. He had sighed at the swelling sense of it. The train ride too was a first for him and the joyful sense of adventure continued. The port. The sight of ships. He had always been a quiet boy and he said nothing in response. But even a quiet boy likes the sight of ships. It all ended quickly after that. Interminable hours waiting in lines for grown-up things he didn't understand. Boredom. Fatigue. Hunger. For this was different from a holiday in a significant way: there was no feasting. His mother said they had to be careful. To make their food last. But it would be better in the New Place—a friendly being that waited on the other side of the sea. America.

The novelty of being on a ship wore off as soon as they were herded into a dark space below decks. After that was a blur. A sickly one. A smelly and noisy one. He became distrustful of the new and friendly Being on the other side. He sank back into himself and became more quiet.

Change. Constant. No time to evaluate whether it was hostile or friendly at all. It was more like the wind outside the window. A thing that pushed you here and there, gave you a push and a sense of taking off into the blue and then dropping you somewhere. Spinning you around. Sending you off in an unexpected direction. That was all he had ever known. The hopeful lift-offs that had never taken him anywhere.

He looked back at the form in front of him. This was a déjà vu moment because he had done all this before—twenty-five years ago in Los Angeles. Fill out a draft registration form. Just when it looked like his own life was taking off in marriage and a family. Another new place—San Pedro. Life would be good there with his wife and three children. He was a naturalized citizen in a country that was now officially at war. Bitter irony. It had frightened him then, but he had been granted an exemption. The country needed farmers. They needed food.

Now here he was again. Fifty-two years old. Only a week ago there had been a big scare in Los Angeles and he was almost sorry to have missed it. Angelinos thought they were being attacked by Japanese planes. Perhaps the newspaper page was carrying that story—a few feet this way, a few feet that, up and down the street. The shock of Pearl Harbor and the aftermath of fear had not worn off. Japanese had been rounded up and interred. As a foreigner himself, he felt sorry for them. Italians were not much welcomed either and he was at pains to explain that he was Swiss and Switzerland was a neutral country.

The thing that had first stopped him on the simple form and sent his thoughts backward was the line that asked for the name of a person who would always know his address. He had had to think about that.

In his very careful writing, he finally wrote Amosi Angeli's name. Amosi understood. Amosi was from a place called Camaiore in Italy, so they spoke Italian together.

"You know the leaning tower of Pisa?"

"Certo!"

"Camiore is only about 20 miles away, if you can fly like a bird."

Amosi had been through the same experience at nine years old. He knew the dark deck of a ship. But it had been worse for him. He came over with his mother a year after his father. When they reached the immigration office at Ellis Island, he had not passed the medical test and he was sent directly into the hospital with his parents. The whole time they were there, they were afraid of being deported, which was often the fate of those who received the dreaded chalk mark on their backs.

Amosi's father became the proprietor of a hotel in Point Reyes Station. He was a gifted woodworker. Amosi learned to make butter and worked at a creamery. He married a nice Italian girl and had four girls, the youngest named after his father—Clemente. They moved to Nicasio, not far from Point Reyes. Hardly a move at all.

Amosi was eleven years younger than Charles. Would they send him to fight his own people? It was a strange world. Anything was possible.

Point Reyes ~ 1946

THE RETREAT CENTER

IN SAN FRANCISCO, SWAMI ASHOKANANDA—formerly Yogesh Chandra Datta of Durgapur—had in mind the needs not only of the Vedanta Society as a whole but, more urgently, of the monastery. There was a need to build further upon what Swami Vivekananda had begun. The monks (whose number, Swami knew, would grow) were confined to the top floors of the Temple. Their only breath of fresh air was the small roof garden—an unhealthy situation not only physically but psychologically. The retreat property should be closer to the city, more accessible than Shanti Ashrama. While Swami Vivekananda was in America holding classes and delivering lectures, one of Swami Abhedananda's students, Miss Minnie C. Boock, offered, as a gift for the work, a tract of land of 160 acres lying eighteen miles southeast of Mt. Hamilton, the site of the well-known Lick Observatory. It was a lovely spot but so far removed from the center in San Francisco, and frequently *plagued with water problems. They needed a site that would be close by and provide a year-round climate that could be endured without strain.*

At first, the Swami Ashokananda's vision was modest: a place of some twenty acres—enough land to ensure privacy, but not so much as to be a burden. In order to find such a place, he and Ediben (Swami's driver, along with a monk from the Vedanta Center, Mr. Brown) would take off on search-excursions in the East Bay, down the peninsula, and in Marin County. Property was available, but nothing was suitable. Then he had the bright idea of asking Miss Irude Martini, a member of the Society who was in the real estate business in San Rafael, to search for a piece of land in Marin County, which seemed the most suitable area in respect to beauty and accessibility.

Aware that Swami Vivekananda had spent a few weeks in the vicinity of Camp Taylor, Swami Ashokananda leaned in that direction—west, toward the Coast Range and the ocean.

After presenting many pieces of property, which Swami Ashokananda explored and for one reason or another rejected, Miss Martini at last came up with a very large piece in the vicinity of Camp Taylor. It was near the tiny town of Olema, separated from the Pacific Ocean by a ridge of the forested Coast Range. The property was only seven or so miles from the place where Swami Vivekananda had camped. Its entrance was a long avenue bordered by towering hundred-year-old cypress and eucalyptus, from the latter of which hung long strips of bark in untidy festoons.

On a rainy day in April of 1946, Ediben drove Swami and Mr. Brown down that entrance avenue. "The vista," Ediben recalled, "was magnificent, even in the rain. Suddenly Swami, who was sitting in the front seat, turned to Mr. Brown in the back and said, 'This is it, Mr. Brown. This is it!'"

"This" was the property of James McMillan Shafter—The Oaks—that had become the estate of his son, Payne Shafter, although the house was not included in the sale at this point. In 1925, when Payne was 78 years old, he sold 2,000 of his acres to a Los Angeles syndicate for $75,000. (His wife and daughters had earlier left him to live in the Bay Area.)

The syndicate had great plans for the property (as Yogi Berra would say, this is déjà vu all over again): Acre and a half villa sites, tennis courts, a polo field, golf course and several hundred thousand dollars worth of roads from Olema to the ocean. Of course they were neither the first nor the last to propose such grandiose schemes. The results were the same. The depression, after all, was right around the corner.

Payne kept the manor house and a few acres for himself. From that point on, Payne spent his summers in Olema and his winters at 751 51st Street in Oakland, where his daughters could "keep an eye on him" as Point Reyes historian Jack Mason put it. He died in 1934 at the age of 87.

Leo M. Harvey and Louis Evans purchased the property in 1946. They were the owners of the property when Miss Irude Martini recommended it to the Vedanta Society and Ediban drove Yogesh P. Datta, now Swami Ashokanda, down the long graceful, tree-lined entrance planned by James so long ago. The land was about to become what neither the syndicate nor any of the Shafters, even Julia, had imagined in their best attempts to promote Point Reyes property. A Vedanta Retreat Center.

Swami Ashokananda had found his Society's dream place—like Rafael Garcia, James Berry, and James Shafter—and for a little while, Dominic Grossi, who had rented a part of it to start his family. The Vedanta Society purchased the property on July 18, 1946 for $166,000.* The retreat center remains today.

OLIVES?

OLIVES? IN MARIN? THAT WAS THE QUESTION MANY ASKED when Nan Tucker McEvoy first proposed her idea. Even agricultural officials warned her against it.

I hadn't forgotten that tantalizing glimpse of olive trees on the drive to Marshall with my friend Sally for dinner at Tony's. I asked Ed about it later. "That's Nan McEvoy's olive ranch," he said. "She produces olive oil there." When I told Sally, she said "Let's go sometime!"

It was a hazy day when Sally and I made our visit to the McEvoy Ranch. Today, as then, it appeared like a Mediterranean mirage. The rows and rows of olive trees brought back my memories of traveling through Umbria and Tuscany with my friend Virginia. We do associate those trees with ancient Mediterranean lands and their people. Homer wrote of olive trees and Pliny the elder devoted almost an entire book of his *Natural History* to the olive and olive oil production. He tells us that an olive tree was planted in the Roman forum to provide shade. But here they are! They've traveled west like countless other migrants, from the Old World to the New.

In a May 2007 interview for *Marin Magazine*, Mimi Towle asked her about this unusual choice:

> **Why olive oil?** Because it didn't involve any animals, and wine had already been done. I wanted to do something in Marin County that hadn't been done before. I have a great passion for food and had been taking cooking classes in Italy. I would lug olive oil home in these five-gallon cans and I thought, "Why not make my own rather than carrying it through customs?" Everyone told me it would never work, so we brought an expert out from Tuscany to assess the ranch, and luckily, Marin County's soil and microclimate are perfect for growing Tuscan olives.

---

* The property bought by the Vedanta Society in 1946 did not include the manor house which Payne had left to his daughters Helen and Mary. The Vedanta Society bought the house in the late 1960s after the elderly Shafter sisters sold it to Bill and Louise Watt.

What first attracted you to the ranch? I really wanted a wonderful place in the country for my grandchildren. Marin County was perfect because it's so close to my home in San Francisco, yet once we cross the bridge, we have wide-open land for the dogs and children to run as fast and far as they can go. And the hills—I love the rolling hills.

Nan McEvoy would make the same choices on her farm that many other Marin farmers were making. Like Penny Livingstone Stark, she understood the importance of soil and of sustainable agriculture. "In 1994 we made the decision to go organic . . . which means that the olive trees are grown without any chemical pesticides or herbicides. We bring in sheep to graze on spring grass, so that we don't use mowers, which need fuel. And we also plant cover crops that keep the soil healthy."

McEvoy Olive Ranch came at the end of a long and distinguished life for Nan McEvoy. She was a founding member of the original Peace Corps, served on John D. Rockefeller's Population Council, and then returned from Washington to head up the family business, the *San Francisco Chronicle*, which had expanded to include the KRON TV channel and Chronicle Publishing.

The roots of this olive farm and more directly of the newspaper, go back to two brothers—one born in the same year as Daniel Burnham in Hendersonville, New York (one of our "New York Nobodies") and the other in 1849. Charles and Michael (M.H.) de Young were the sons of Cornelia and Miechel de Young who had emigrated from the Netherlands and France. They moved from St. Louis to San Francisco and the brothers became active in the rough and tumble days of the city. Oscar and James Shafter were pursuing their distinguished careers. Oscar was on the Supreme Court when the young men began publishing the *Daily Dramatic Chronicle*, mostly gossip and light news in 1865, which paved the way for their publication of *The San Francisco Chronicle* in 1869.

This was still the Wild West and disputes were often settled with a revolver. Judge James McMillan Shafter, remember, barely managed to overcome a gun-toting assailant in city hall!

In 1879, a dispute broke out between Charles de Young and a candidate for mayor, Isaac Kalloch. Opposing his election, Charles de Young accused Kalloch of having an affair and in response, Kalloch accused Charles' mother of running a brothel. Charles responded by shooting Kalloch, who survived, gained the sympathy vote from the electorate and became the next mayor of San Francisco. But by then the grievances ran deep and in 1880, Isaac Kalloch's son walked into the Chronicle building and shot and killed Charles de Young. He was only 34 years old.

In a way, the de Young story is the story of San Francisco itself, as we have seen it unfold through the pen of Oscar Shafter, from rough to refined. M.H. de Young takes over the *Chronicle* and hires our friend Daniel Burnham of Chicago to design a new Chronicle Building. M.H. nearly suffers the fate of his brother in another dispute, this one with the sugar king, Adolph Spreckels, who enters the new Chronicle building and shoots Michael twice. De Young survives his wounds. By then, one writer notes, it was becoming clear to the city fathers and its chief publicist "that the environment and the image of San Francisco was not that of a civilized community that would attract growth and investment." De Young conceived the idea of holding a great exposition in Golden Gate Park on his own extensive property in western San Francisco, patterned after the Chicago Exposition of 1893. What began as the Exposition's Fine Arts building became the de Young Museum, which is still a premier museum in San Francisco today.

Nan McEvoy was the grand-daughter of M.H. de Young and part of the large de Young family that owned the *Chronicle* until it was sold to the Hearst Corporation in 1999. From the heart of San Francisco life and politics, Nan McEvoy moved to the peaceful life of an olive farm in Marin, now under the guidance of her son Nion, the long-time Editor-in-Chief of Chronicle books.

The haze has lifted as Sally and I load up our McEvoy Virgin Olive Oil. Nan McEvoy is still alive at this time but she will pass away in 2014 at the age of 95. Her farm in Marin still thrives.

* * * *

Grossi Farms ~ October

THE BIRTHDAY SONG

THE GUYS ARE AT IT AGAIN. "Tell us! What do you want for your birthday?"

"My birthday is still a long way off."

"No es verdad. Lunes es Octubre."

I am amazed that they have remembered. And it is true: Monday it will be October. I suddenly have an inspiration and turn around to face them, sorting tomatoes behind me. "I know exactly what I want for my birthday!" I tell them in Spanish. They stop sorting. Mexicans have a lot of niceties they say like, "Mi casa es su casa"—My house is your house. The phrase is always appended to someone's address. "I live at 45 First Street. Mi casa es su casa." Or for variation, "there you have your house." Even someone you meet while standing in a grocery line will say that. If everyone took this seriously, there would be no room for anyone in their own houses. Or perhaps everyone would just accept the invitation and go visit someone else. Then there would be no problem because no one would be home to visit.

I was wondering if "What do you want for your birthday" was just another little nicety. But the guys were eyeing me with great interest. What did I want for my birthday.

"Un cancione!" I declared happily. A song! It was the perfect solution. They looked puzzled.

"Your voices are so beautiful. I love to hear you sing in the fields. You can give me a song for my birthday." They looked doubtful. Suddenly shy. I could understand that since I feel the same way. I love to sing if it is not on demand. Maybe this sounded too much like a performance.

They asked me the same question a week later and I gave them the same answer. They didn't look too enthusiastic about it.

The third week, on Friday, was my birthday. Susie always makes a big fuss about birthdays for her employees, whom she treats as members of her own family. There was pizza and a beautiful cake with my name on it. Susie can put Martha Stewart to shame when she entertains.

Tables had been set up on the deck and people took breaks from work to come and join the celebration. This included the nursery and farm employees. I stood by the table where Alfonso, Otún, Adrian and Lazaro were sitting. I teased them. "Are you going to sing for me?" They still didn't look enthused and I quickly changed the subject. There was quiet suddenly and all the fellows looked at each other. Alfonso looked at his watch and nodded to Otún, who surreptitiously clicked on one of those little radios that are always hooked in their pockets.

I heard my name and then a song started up. He turned up the volume and at first I didn't get it. The song was on a Spanish station and when I caught the words I could hardly believe it. They knew I was taking a big trip after the season ended in a week. I can't recite the Spanish, but it went something like "You are going away. We will miss you. Would that you could carry us with you in your *maleta*. (Your suitcase.)" But once I got the idea of it, I stared at Otún, and then the others. When the song ended I asked Otún, "Was that for me?" "Yes," he said. "We called it in to play at exactly 1:00."

What a birthday present!

PART VIII

A NEW ERA

Throughout the Cenozoic the Earth evolved independently of the human.
In the emerging Ecozoic period almost nothing will happen
that will not in some manner be related to the human.
Not, however, that we will control the inner workings of the planet.
We cannot make a blade of grass.
But there is liable not to be a blade of grass
if it is not accepted, protected, and fostered by the human.

— THOMAS BERRY

As the twilight began to fall, I sat down on the mossy instep of a spruce....
One bird, a thrush, embroidered the silence with cheery notes, making
the solitude familiar and sweet, while the solemn monotone of the stream
sifting through the woods seemed like the very voice of God, humanized,
terrestrialized, and entering one's heart as to a home prepared for it. Go
where we will, all the world over, we seem to have been there before.

— JOHN MUIR

Washington, D.C. ~ 1961

ZENA MENDOZA SPEAKS OUT

I WAS NOT BORN IN THIS COUNTRY. I was born in Europe. But since I was a child I wanted to come to America, to the land where there was respect for human dignity, the land of the free . . . where the minorities would not be trampled on, where there would be no dictators.

Point Reyes is where my children were born and my grandchildren were raised. My grandson, after he came from the service, that is where he is living. The other grandson that is married and who has a baby—I have a little great-granddaughter— has his family there. My other two grandsons, their choice is dairying, the farm. Now I am faced with the possibility of losing everything that I have worked for. The strangest thing is that I never was approached. Everything was done underhanded. . . . Nobody ever came to me to ask, "Do you want to sell your property for a park?"

If my ranches would be taken for defense, well, you have to sacrifice, but it is for the benefit of all, for the benefit of my family as well as for the others. But for recreation, what kind of recreation did I have when I was a youngster? Work and save so my children would have a sense of security and heritage that I felt belonged to them. Now every inch of my land is supposed to disappear.

— Zena Cabral, widow of Joseph V. Mendoza before
a Congressional Committee, Washington, DC 1961*

From now on, the story of the Point Reyes ranchers is Everyman's story for the latter twentieth century—certainly in California and for many other parts of the West. The West was won, yes, but it turned out to be much more than anyone imagined, certainly as Lewis and Clarke discovered and, indirectly, Thomas Jefferson. Story upon story came back from people like John Fremont, Kit Carson, the Army Corps of Engineers, about this wild, vast, beautiful landscape west of the Rockies. But how could people sitting in their comfortable homes in New York, New Jersey, Massachusetts, imagine the scale of the Grand Canyon, the vast desert landscapes, the gigantic grandeur of California's redwood forests? It took wave after wave of pioneer families, writing letters home or returning in person to begin to grasp the scale of the new landscapes of America. Above all, it took good writers and artists who could capture the scenes for the uninitiated eye. Greatest among these was John Muir, who received much of his literary inspiration from the nature writings of Ralph Waldo Emerson. He would sit under the stars in the West, reading Emerson and being uplifted with a wild joy at sights like Yosemite. John Talmadge writes of this in *Meeting the Tree of Life: The Teacher's Path:* "On his long, solitary excursions into the backcountry—these were the days before topographic

* Quoted by Dewey Livingston in *Ranching on the Point Reyes Peninsula.*

maps and down sleeping bags—Muir would take only a tin cup, a handful of tea, a loaf of bread, and a copy of Emerson. At night he would build a fire and read, wrapped in his overcoat, under the enormous stars." It is thanks largely to him that places like Yosemite were preserved.

Yosemite, California ~ 1871

EMERSON, MUIR AND THE TREES

Our age is retrospective. . . . It writes biographies, histories, and criticism. The foregoing generations beheld God and nature face to face; we, through their eyes. Why should not we also enjoy an original relation to the universe? . . . The sun shines to-day also. . . . There are new lands, new men, new thoughts. Let us demand our own works and laws and worship.

— Ralph Waldo Emerson
Nature

[From *The Life and Letters of John Muir* by William Frederic Badè]

Emerson, Agassiz, Gray*—these men influenced me more than any others. Yes, the most of my years were spent on the wild side of the continent, invisible, in the forests and mountains. These men were the first to find me and hail me as a brother.

First of all, and greatest of all, came Emerson. I was then living in Yosemite Valley as a convenient and grand vestibule of the Sierra from which I could make excursions into the adjacent mountains. I had not much money and was then running a mill that I had built to saw fallen timber for cottages. . . .

He came to the mill on horseback attended by Mr. Thayer and inquired for me. I had a study attached to the gable of the mill, overhanging the stream, into which I invited him, but it was not easy of access, being reached only by a series of sloping planks roughened by slats like a hen ladder; but he bravely climbed up and I showed him my collection of plants and sketches drawn from the surrounding mountains which seemed to interest him greatly, and he asked many questions . . .

He came again and again, and I saw him every day while he remained in the valley, and on leaving I was invited to accompany him as far as the Mariposa Grove of Big Trees. I said, "I'll go, Mr. Emerson, if you will promise to camp with me in the Grove. I'll build a glorious campfire, and the great brown boles of the giant Sequoias will be most impressively lighted up, and the night will be glorious." At this he became enthusiastic like a boy, his sweet perennial smile became still deeper and sweeter, and he said, "Yes, yes, we will camp out, camp out"; and so next day we left Yosemite and rode twenty five miles through the Sierra forests, the noblest on the face of the earth, and he kept me talking all the time, but said little himself. . . .

Early in the afternoon, when we reached Clark's Station, I was surprised to see

---

* Asa Gray and Louis Agassiz were prominent naturalists of the time. Gray was called the Father of American Botany and Agassiz was aided by Muir in developing his theories of glaciation.

the party dismount. And when I asked if we were not going up into the grove to camp they said: "No; it would never do to lie out in the night air. Mr. Emerson might take cold; and you know, Mr. Muir, that would be a dreadful thing."

In vain I urged, that only in homes and hotels were colds caught, that nobody ever was known to take cold camping in these woods, that there was not a single cough or sneeze in all the Sierra. Then I pictured the big climate changing, inspiring fire I would make, praised the beauty and fragrance of Sequoia flame, told how the great trees would stand about us transfigured in purple light, while the stars looked between the great domes; ending by urging them to come on and make an immortal Emerson night of it. But the house habit was not to be overcome, nor the strange dread of pure night air, though it is only cooled day air with a little dew in it. . . .

In the morning we rode up the trail through a noble forest of pine and fir into the famous Mariposa [Sequoia] Grove, and stayed an hour or two, mostly in ordinary tourist fashion—looking at the biggest giants, measuring them with a tape line, riding through prostrate fire-bored trunks etc., though Mr. Emerson was alone occasionally, sauntering about as if under a spell. As we walked through a fine group, he quoted, "There were giants in those days," recognizing the antiquity of the race. To commemorate his visit, Mr. Galen Clark, the guardian of the grove, selected the finest of the unnamed trees and requested him to give it a name. He named it Samoset, after the New England sachem, as the best that occurred to him.

The poor bit of measured time was soon spent, and while the saddles were being adjusted I again urged Emerson to stay. "You are yourself a Sequoia," I said. "Stop and get acquainted with your big brethren." But he was past his prime, and was now a child in the hands of his affectionate but sadly civilized friends, who seemed as full of old-fashioned conformity as of bold intellectual independence. It was the afternoon of the day and the afternoon of his life, and his course was now westward down all the mountains into the sunset. The party mounted and rode away in wondrous contentment apparently, tracing the trail through ceanothus and dogwood bushes, around the bases of the big trees, up the slope of the sequoia basin, and over the divide. I followed to the edge of the grove. Emerson lingered in the rear of the train, and when he reached the top of the ridge, after all the rest of the party were over and out of sight, he turned his horse, took off his hat and waved me a last good-bye.

Ralph Waldo Emerson was born in that momentous year of 1803, when Thomas Jefferson was president and the Louisiana Purchase was about to spark the western movement of the young nation. In 1871, Emerson was 68 to Muir's 38. Muir was still in his prime and had been living a vigorous life in the Sierras, while Emerson was living "the life of the mind in Boston." It was keenly disappointing to Muir that Emerson could not fulfill his dream of sharing a fire at night in the beauty of the great trees and the starry sky. Nevertheless for Emerson, Muir was the living quintessence of his thoughts and writings on nature. He was the man who went out to greet God and nature face to face. For Muir, Emerson's writings touched on his ineffable experience of nature's grandeur and inspired his own efforts to articulate that experience, which would later become so valuable. Their encounter was a hidden but priceless moment in the history of the land.

Emerson's giving of the name "Samoset" to one of the great trees in the Mariposa Grove is another little noted but meaningful event. Samoset was the first native American to approach the pilgrims of Plymouth Colony. It is the reverse of the meeting of the members of the San Carlos expedition and the Huimen Miwoks. Samoset went to *them*: courageously strode among them to their great surprise on a March day in 1621 and spoke to them in English, which he had learned from an earlier arrival of Englishmen among the Wampanoags in Maine. In the naming of the tree, Emerson was making the deep connection between tree, native and newcomer. This is a rare bonding that was often torn asunder, as by those newcomers, the cattlemen who killed off the last of Ishi's tribe in Northern California—a story so poignantly told by Theodora Kroeber in *Ishi: The Last Yahi*.*

John Muir's dream of having Emerson as a camping companion in Yosemite was fulfilled in a different and much more significant way decades later from an unexpected quarter: The President of the United States, Theodore Roosevelt. This encounter in 1903 was to have a profound influence on the future of the American West. Here is Teddy Roosevelt's own description of it.

[From "John Muir: An Appreciation" by Theodore Roosevelt in *Outlook*, January 16, 1915]

. . . *Ordinarily, the man who loves the woods and mountains, the trees, the flowers, and the wild things, has in him some indefinable quality of charm, which appeals even to those sons of civilization who care for little outside of paved streets and brick walls. John Muir was a fine illustration of this rule. He was by birth a Scotchman - a tall and spare man, with the poise and ease natural to him who has lived much alone under conditions of labor and hazard. He was a dauntless soul, and also one brimming over with friendliness and kindliness.*

He was emphatically a good citizen. Not only are his books delightful, not only is he the author to whom all men turn when they think of the Sierras and northern glaciers, and the giant trees of the California slope, but he was also - what few nature lovers are - a man able to influence contemporary thought and action on the subjects to which he had devoted his life. He was a great factor in influencing the thought of California and the thought of the entire country so as to secure the preservation of those great natural phenomena - wonderful canyons, giant trees, slopes of flower-spangled hillsides - which make California a veritable Garden of the Lord.

It was my good fortune to know John Muir. He had written me, even before I met him personally, expressing his regret that when Emerson came to see the Yosemite, his (Emerson's) friends would not allow him to accept John Muir's invitation to

---

* I also highly recommend the documentary produced in 1992, *Ishi: The Last Yahi*, which contains original footage of Ishi himself, as well as a feature film based on the same story.

spend two or three days camping with him, so as to see the giant grandeur of the place under surroundings more congenial than those of a hotel piazza or a seat on a coach.

I had answered him that if ever I got in his neighborhood I should claim from him the treatment that he had wished to accord Emerson. Later, when as President I visited the Yosemite, John Muir fulfilled the promise he had at that time made to me. He met me with a couple of pack mules, as well as with riding mules for himself and myself, and a first-class packer and cook, and I spent a delightful three days and two nights with him.

The first night we camped in a grove of giant sequoias. It was clear weather, and we lay in the open, the enormous cinnamon-colored trunks rising about us like the columns of a vaster and more beautiful cathedral than was ever conceived by any human architect. . .

As one source put it, Muir's three-night camping trip with President Theodore Roosevelt in 1903 could be considered the most significant camping trip in conservation history. (PBS. *National Parks*). He was able to persuade Roosevelt to return Yosemite Valley and the Mariposa Grove to federal protection as part of Yosemite National Park. On that same trip west, Roosevelt visited the Grand Canyon and asked for its protection as well. During his term as president, Theodore Roosevelt created five national parks (doubling the previously existing number); signed the landmark Antiquities Act and used its special provisions to unilaterally create 18 national monuments, including the Grand Canyon; set aside 51 federal bird sanctuaries, four national game refuges, and more than 100 million acres' worth of national forests.

But as Zena Mendoza reminds us, this was not all good news to ranchers.

◆ ◆ ◆

The Lombards who had drifted up into the alpine valleys of Ticino were seeking a place to live independently and in peace, secluded from the constantly changing machinations of the political powers of Europe. They had not always been successful in this, and the political events of 1853 had driven most of their young from their secluded villages to find a better life. The Ticinesi arrived in Marin and put down roots to stay, like their fellow immigrants. Yes, they had become the People Who Stayed and they had forged new communities in their new land. They were not going to let go easily, but events in the larger society were about to overtake them and their decisions would be crucial. The idea of the federal government coming in and arbitrarily taking their land was anaethema to them.

Manifest Destiny was having its unintended consequences, no more intensely felt than in the midst of the land battles fought by farmers and ranchers. Radical change has taken place since the mass emigration of the people from Ticino that began in earnest after 1870, in the last second of the Earth Calendar. A nano-moment in the long calendar year. Dominic and Teresa take up their lives in

America and raise their families in a period that develops at a dizzying pace. Zena Mendoza's plea to congress in 1961 expresses this poignantly. She is giving voice to the wrenching changes that are overtaking the Point Reyes ranchers and their families. They are not alone in this. If Zena Mendoza gives voice to the problem, many of the Ticinesi farmers and ranchers we have met will take up the challenge and be at the front edge of the solutions.

CROSSING THE GOLDEN GATE

WIND. THE WORD SLID THROUGH HIS MIND LIKE A PRAYER. All other thoughts were sifted out by his concentration on the moment. But "wind" was never far away. It was like a living thing. Sometimes monstrous. Wind. He spoke to it beseechingly. Please. . .

But the danger was part of it. He knew that there would never again be something as splendid, as privileged in his life as these moments. These years. It was like the war. Living on the knife-edge of danger, you never feel so alive. You are ready to die in the next instant. Not really for the freedom of Europe or even for your country. But for those buddies in your unit, right there on the knife edge with you. This wasn't for his country and there was no killing to do. It was for a bridge. It was for building something extraordinary. And again, it was danger and daring shared by a tight fraternity of brothers whose lives depended on one another. He was not one of a million soldiers in the trenches, but one of a hundred, privileged with a view of God's magnificent landscape that no one ever saw. Sunrise and sunsets where the sea, the sky, the hills, the lowlands, the city all melded into one living thing and through it all, as no where else, blew the wind. Potentially a deadly foe.

Please. . .

Still the wind blew and his fragile vehicle swayed with every in and out breath of the gale as it inched along, 752 feet above the Golden Gate.

The crossing had been made many times.

We may remember that in 1783, six years after the visit of Father Santa Maria from the San Carlos, Juluio and Olomojoia were the first two Coast Miwoks to make the crossing from their Huimen village of Livangula to the Mission Dolores. The crossing made by Huicmuse/Chief Marin with his wife Mottiqui in 1801 was for him the first of many such crossings.

The name Golden Gate, which refers to the narrow opening from the Bay to the Pacific was first applied by John C. Fremont. The mile-wide strait had not then been spanned by a bridge.

Now, a heroic crossing was being made at a windy and perilous height. It was the summer of 1935 and the building of the bridge had reached the last and most treacherous phase: suspending the bridge cables. This had required closing the shipping lanes so that the first strands could be dragged across the Gate by Coast Guard vessels, whose movements through the hazardous waters were being directed by radio operators. Following this, a mid-span work platform had to be lowered across the gap. But the platform had become stuck on the initial strands. Two bridgemen had volunteered to crawl across the swaying span to free the platform.

Every moment on the bridge was an act of skill and courage. This one is nearly unimaginable. Yet two men volunteered, braving wind gusts up to 45 miles per hour over 742 feet above a thrashing sea.

Once that heroic task succeeded, the workers began the arduous and delicate process of bundling and draping the huge 7,650 foot cables, which would support the bridge, over the steel towers. Each cable was made up of over twenty-seven thousand individual wires, each the size of a large pencil lead. The wires were put into 61 bundles and each of those bundles would have over a million pounds of force on it. Over 80,000 miles of steel wire had been forged for the project in Pennsylvania and shipped to the site.

The unimaginable feats continued as a network of spinning wheel carriages was put in place to transport the 27,572 miles of wires across the span, six wires at a time. 3000 wooden palettes were used to create a catwalk over the bay. I doubt even a cat would have been crazy enough to walk it, but from this swaying platform, men could supervise the last stage of the compacting of the bundles: By hand and with the aid of hydraulic machinery the thousands of wires were bonded together and wrapped into a tight bundle of steel thread, then painted to create a water tight seal. Workers had to place individual wires by hand into a geometric pattern. The final result was a cable exactly three feet in diameter.

During one record-breaking 8 hour shift, a thousand miles of wire were spun over the gate. Men rode the enormous steel supports lifted by giant cranes to help guide them into position. Twisted webs of steel rods were laid across the width of the bridge, welded together and then covered in tons of concrete, delivered by narrow gauge locomotives. Giant leveling machines ground the surface into a smooth roadway. The suspension of the cables was completed in only 191 days. From these two cables, the roadway beneath would be suspended from vertical cables spaced exactly 50 feet apart.

Contrary to everyone's expectation, and in spite of the daunting obstacles, the bridge was ready to open two months early.

Santa Rosa ~ 1923

MADMEN AND DREAMERS

IT WAS A SURPRISE TO ME THAT THE PUBLIC MEETING at which the need for a bridge connecting the city of San Francisco with Marin was held in Santa Rosa— far north in Sonoma County. It is even north of Mr. Fields. (We are the southern-most point of the Santa Rosa postal region.) It was January 1923. Legislation was drafted here directing the building of the bridge, which was later introduced to the California legislature and signed by Governor Richardson on May 25th of the same year.

This was only the official beginning. Many trace its beginnings to the middle of the 19th century when the Gold Rush of 1849 transformed the village of Yerba Buena, population 400, in one year into a city of thirty-five thousand fortune seekers, now called San Francisco. Among the unlucky who came for riches and ended in bankruptcy was a merchant-turned-lunatic who declared himself *Norton I, Emperor of the United States and Protector of Mexico*. Norton I was received with tolerant good humor by the locals. He printed his own money which was accepted by some of the restaurant owners and others, allowing him to "rule" with modest dignity. In 1869, the self-made emperor issued a proclamation in the Oakland Daily News ordering that a suspension bridge be built from San Francisco to Yerba Buena Island, "from thence to the mountain range of Sausalito." He directed that it be of "sufficient strength and size for a railroad." Responding to the emperor's decree or otherwise, three years later the Central Pacific Railroad tycoon, Charles Crocker, (one of the Big Four) reported to the Marin County Board of Supervisors that his engineers had prepared drawings and estimates for a suspension bridge across the Golden Gate. He later abandoned the idea in favor of putting his train on huge steam barges.

Emperor Norton may have been a certified madman, but anyone who put forth the idea of building a bridge across the treacherous span of the Golden Gate teetered on that reputation. It was popularly known as the Bridge That Couldn't Be Built. Constant foggy weather, frequent 60 mile-an-hour winds, a powerful ocean current surging through the canyon below, and a longer span than any bridge in the world had crossed: 1.2 miles. Not to mention how much this crazy idea would *cost*.

Enter another madman: Joseph Strauss. Strauss was born in Cincinnati, Ohio to an artistic family with German roots. His mother was a pianist and his father, a writer and painter. He was a talented and imaginative young man, who graduated from the University of Cincinnati as class poet and class president after completing his studies. He could easily have been dismissed as a small man with big dreams. He stood, after all, only 5'3" tall. After his try-out for the football team, he ended up in the infirmary, staring at the Cincinnati-Covington Bridge, America's first suspension bridge. His senior thesis was based on the outlandish proposal to build an international railroad spanning the Bering Strait between Alaska and

Russia. "Before a crowded house, a bewildered faculty, and a distinguished group of visitors and speakers, this modest, soft-spoken young graduate unfolded his Utopian dream." Though Strauss's plan was unorthodox, his earnestness won over the skeptical audience.

After his graduation, Strauss applied his artistic abilities in the business world by going to work as a draftsman for the Lassig Bridge and Iron Works Company in Chicago. Seven years later, he became a principal assistant engineer to the Chicago engineering firm of Ralph Modjeski. There he developed his trademark design for the "bascule" or moveable, drawbridge. In 1904, he started his own company with this design, Strauss Bascule Bridge Company, building some 400 of these bridges across the United States. But Strauss had a bigger dream. He wanted to build "the biggest thing of its kind that a man could build." He was the ideal dreamer-madman to make the Emperor Norton's Proclamation a fact.

In 1919, Strauss was approached by Michael O'Shaughnessy, the San Francisco city engineer, about a project to bridge the Golden Gate. The die was cast. He would become both the project's driver and its nemesis. Considering the vested interests that opposed the project, it is a wonder that it ever went forward. The Navy argued that sabotage or a ship collision could block one of its most important harbors. The Department of War feared that the bridge could interfere with ship traffic. Not surprisingly, the most powerful local protest came from the Southern Pacific Railroad, which saw the bridge as competition with its ferry fleet. It filed a lawsuit against the project which resulted in a mass boycott of the ferry service. Unions were insistent that their local workers be employed in its construction. Then there was the fact that permission would have to be granted to build on the Federal lands on both ends of the span. Again, for some reason I haven't determined, the Santa Rosa Chamber of Commerce—miles to the north in Sonoma County—was charged with the task of considering the necessary steps to proceed with construction of the bridge.

The suspension of the cables was completed in only 191 days. The finished result was twin cables exactly three feet in diameter. From these, the roadway would be suspended with vertical cables, like the strings of a harp. The last ceremonial gold rivet was driven into place by Iron Horse Stanley, the same man who drove the very first rivet into the bridge four years earlier.

On opening day, May 27, 1937, an estimated 15,000 pedestrians an hour passed the turnstiles in a steady stream each paying 25 cents to cross. Skating, on stilts, some on bicycles, some running, one on horseback. On the second day, cars were allowed to cross for the first time. Flyovers, marching bands and parade floats announced the triumph, pride and joy of a city that had been reduced to rubble just thirty years before and had barely come through the Great Depression. This was the official resurrection of their city and of their spirit.

◆ ◆ ◆

More and more, we are seeing that a collective is developing in the city with a character and will of its own. The future of San Francisco, and of Marin across the Bay, will no longer be made by the sheer force and character of the madmen and dreamers who created the bridge, or the men of wealth and power who created the railroads, or even by men of dedication and insight like Oscar Shafter. It is The People who step up to the plate now to make extraordinary things happen. A little known detail about the completion of the Golden Gate Bridge is the crucial role that they played.

The Southern Pacific Railway owned the ferry system and was making money hand over fist. Not surprisingly, they were powerfully opposed to the bridge and brought lawsuits against the project. But the people boycotted the ferries and forced them to back down from their lawsuits against the bridge.

The price tag for the bridge was projected as a whopping 35 million dollars. Where could such money be found on the heels of a depression? The civic leaders put the fate of the bridge in the hands of the people.

Here is a description of those events by Celia Kupersmith, former CEO and general manager of the Golden Gate Bridge Highway and Transportation District, speaking on a Golden Gate Bridge documentary*:

> There's an attitude in San Francisco that developed after the earthquake of 1906 that said "We've been knocked back but we are never going to fall. We are never going to stop and we are always going to be out on the edge." This was a chance to do something that people said couldn't be done. And that's usually what San Francisco does best.
>
> What happened is that they went to the voters in all of the counties from San Francisco north to the Oregon border and asked "Would you be willing to put a lien against your personal property—your farm, your vineyard, your home, your business—for security against the bonds to fund the bridge? If something happens— we build the bridge and it falls down as some say it will, and we still owe money— we're going to come back to you, your house, or farm, to pay off the bonds." And the people said YES! I can't believe that today. That people would literally put that kind of faith in an idea.

The Bay Area civic pride exhibited by the people inspired institutions to make contributions of their own. Financial institutions were ready to invest in San Francisco's future. Bank of America founder A.P. Gianini felt that as a result of the Depression, jobs were necessary and he offered a five million dollar line of credit to go ahead and begin construction of the bridge.

The costs of the bridge were completely paid off by 1971 and the residents of the Bay Area no longer had a lien on their property to pay for the construction of the bridge.

---

* "Modern Marvels: Golden Gate Bridge" produced for the History Channel

BOOM TIME

THE BRIDGE CHANGED EVERYTHING. AS IT WAS MEANT TO DO. The North Pacific Railroad had mostly facilitated the movement of products from Sonoma and Marin, especially timber and dairy products, but the bridge moved *people* as well as goods: People in large numbers. It was now "thinkable" to live in Marin and work in San Francisco. It was thinkable to take weekend trips there or, for the wealthy, to have weekend homes and commute from the other direction, as Julia Shafter Hamilton had planned all along.

In the heyday of the Shafters, the western side of Marin County was the busy and thriving place. Sleepy little places of today, like Nicasio, Olema and Tomales, were campaigning to displace San Rafael as the county seat. The bridge changed that, picking up the development fever that was sweeping through the whole state. The eastern part of the county was swiftly emerging into a metropolitan area with a suburban lifestyle.

The next big step after a railroad and a bridge for facilitating transportation and moving people about was the freeway system. The California Bureau of Highways was created in 1895, when the huge state was only connected (if connected at all) by horse trails and wagon roads. California's world-famous scenic Highway 1 was begun following a bond issue in 1910. During the Great Depression, New Deal funds contributed to the project. In 1926, U.S. Route 101, part of a national highway system maintained by the states, was inaugurated. It paved large sections of the trail walked by Father Serra and Father Palou. A major expansion of the state highway system, however, did not take place until a 1933 mandate by the California state legislature. After 18 years of construction, Highway 1—a paved two-lane road along the coast of the state—was completed and opened on June 17, 1937, only two weeks after the week-long celebration of the completion of the bridge. Highway 1 and Highway 101 both converged in San Francisco, so the opening of the Golden Gate Bridge was like the gates of a dam thrown open through which gushing waters passed.

This surge would be felt in the hearts of developers as a straight shot to an economic boom and personal wealth. It was the beginning of California's big economic bubble. By the 1950s, state highway planners conceived of big plans for Route One, which was still a beautiful, winding and—in places like the Big Sur Coast—precipitous highway. This, of course, was its major appeal; access to the remarkable coastal beauties of California—Calafia's paradise.

How often has it happened that the roads to paradise are the very thing that destroys it? The irony threatened to apply to West Marin, because the plan was to widen the two-lane "parkway" into a four lane highway. New freeways would be carved through the hills from Novato and San Rafael to Point Reyes Station. Marin was about to hit the cutting board and be chopped to pieces all the way to Point Reyes. As John Hart put it in his prologue to *Farming on the Edge*, "A county planning study listed other possible corridors and concluded zestfully that 'major traffic facilities' would someday have to be built in all of them.'' In 1971, a Marin County official echoed this sentiment by saying that in 1990, Tomales would probably look like Malibu. There were plans for shopping centers, a commercial district and housing developments to support a population of 125,000 people.

Well . . . what happened?

A lot of little battles is what happened, and some surprising alliances.

What happened is that a new generation of Ticinesi descendants—and Portuguese and Irish and others—stepped up to the plate and made a tectonic shift of their own. What few people in the larger world realized during that time is that in many ways, the farms, not the cities, were ground zero for forging the future. How is this possible? Two reasons: food and love of the land. Remember that a major tenet of the New Age in the '60s, which captivated the minds of that generation, was a return to Nature; to the land; to organic foods; to holistic thinking. It is as if two opposite ends of a spectrum circled round and met in the back. Not two opposite ends of a pole but a loop.

The ranchers were the key and theirs was the battleground. Speculators arrived on the scene, ready to pay big money for the large tracts of ranchland, which would eventually be sold off in small parcels at enormous profits. Theirs was the tough choice. Like people all over the United States, as a postwar boom finally showed itself, there was a big opportunity here for ranchers to become materially much better off. Money in the bank for children's education, for retirement, for traveling, for the little luxuries of modern life. Farming was still a hard labor and in no way quick money. But here was quick money at the door. Perhaps the greater pressure on the ranchers came from the sense that forces were in play that would inevitably destroy the agricultural base of the county. In that case, what choice did they have?

In the face of this inevitability, some sold but others were deeply attached to their ranches and held out against the offers to buy. But they still worried about the future of the agricultural industry, which requires not only land, but the businesses to furnish the equipment and services essential to ranching.

The first blow came in 1959 when the federal government announced the plan to buy up some 50,000 acres of the coastline for a park. The battle over this raged for three years and in the end, arguably, the government won. But from another perspective, it was the rancher's gain: The first step that would ultimately lead them toward the preservation of their land.

The next step would be taken by the unexpected alliance of ranchers and environmentalists, joining forces to save their rare and beautiful—and productive—landscape. They are the new players in the ongoing drama of land in Marin. The result will be MALT, and one of its founders is Farmer Ed's brother Ralph.

RALPH GROSSI:
THE MARIN AGRICULTURAL LAND TRUST

We had this idea and nobody had done it before.

BENEATH OUR STORIES OF MARIN'S CHANGING HISTORY is the single story of
the land. Every person we have met has interacted significantly with the headlands,
hills, grasslands and valleys of this landscape; impacted it and been impacted by
it. Miwoks roamed over it for thousands of years, surviving on its bountiful gifts.
Spanish missionaries laid claim to it on behalf of Spain and Christianity. European
and Mexican citizens made fortunes through Spanish and Mexican land grants.
The Shafter brothers brought a code of law to land ownership and in the process,
enriched themselves and developed a thriving dairy industry. Immigrants from
Ticino, Italy, the Azores, England and Ireland worked the land and eventually
became its new owners.

The mighty force of the industrial, post-war era was now bringing a new
challenge to the region: Would development reshape the landscape into highways,
malls, and tourist strips? Development of the land was Julia Shafter's dream for
the saving of her ranches. But I am guessing that even Julia and Emma would have
blanched at these new prospects. I am certain that Oscar would.

To understand what happens next in our story of Marin, it is necessary to
understand the meaning of a "conservation easement," which will prove so essential
to the new era. Here is a description of it from the Land Trust Alliance.

The sensibility to the American landscape and awareness of the pressing need
to preserve its natural treasures continued to spread from the time of John Muir,

---

CONSERVATION EASEMENTS

The most traditional tool for conserving private land, a "conservation easement" (also known as a conservation restriction) is a legal agreement between a landowner and a land trust or government agency that permanently
limits uses of the land in order to protect its conservation values. It allows
landowners to continue to own and use their land, and they can also sell it
or pass it on to heirs.

When you donate a conservation easement to a land trust, you give up
some of the rights associated with the land. For example, you might give
up the right to build additional structures, while retaining the right to grow
crops. Future owners also will be bound by the easement's terms. The land
trust is responsible for making sure the easement's terms are followed. This
is managed through "stewardship" by the land trust.

Ralph Waldo Emerson and Theodore Roosevelt. Two decades after their meeting, as Dominic Grossi was starting his new life in America, a young architect in Boston named Charles Eliot established the first land trust in Boston. Eliot proposed the creation of a unique statewide nonprofit organization – a corporation governed by a board of voluntary trustees who would be empowered by the state legislature to hold land free of taxes for the public to enjoy "just as a Public Library holds books and an Art Museum holds pictures." It was a unique idea but it was about to take hold.

Like Theodore Judah—three decades before, passing out his pamphlets in San Francisco with his proposition to build a transcontinental railroad—Charles Eliot passes out a circular in Boston called "The Preservation of Beautiful and Historical Places." It lays down the special reasons why "places of historical interest or remarkable beauty should be withdrawn from private ownership, preserved from harm, and opened to the public." Each is emblematic of their eras. Also like Judah, Eliot succeeds in enlisting a distinguished group of citizens to support his proposal. Out of this comes the Trustees of Reservations, still in existence today with an impressive record of valuable sites preserved and a legacy of similar land trusts around the country.

The problems of the Point Reyes ranchers, however, were unique. So were their solutions. Land Trusts were saving "beautiful and historic places" but what about agriculture? It is at this juncture that the stories of Dominic's family and the landscape of Marin merge in the person of Farmer Ed's brother, Ralph Grossi.

I paid my second visit to the Farm in Marin (that is really a ranch) to hear the story of MALT first hand from him.

RALPH: *We had this idea and nobody had done it before. I had been the Chairman of the Farm Bureau Land Use Committee in the late 70s and we had been working on land issues with the county in the area of zoning, which is really one of the tough issues. If you over-regulate you are diminishing the value of the property for the owners and if you under-regulate, you are giving away public goods. It is that fine balance, and it's always contentious. A couple of us were working together on it— Gary Giacomini and Jerry Friedman. Gary Giacomini was then a county supervisor and Jerry Friedman was a key person as chairman of the planning commission. Jerry was from the Friedman Bag Company and lived in Inverness.*

Sometime in 1978, Jerry sent me an article about a concept in Maryland where they were trying to transfer development rights: the farmer would give up his right to develop but could transfer it to another farm that could be developed to increase the density. It struck me as a really interesting idea—that you could separate the development portion from the rest of the land, like mineral rights or water rights. You could sell it to somebody else. It sat there for about a year or so and we kept talking about it.

In early 1979, Phyllis Faber and Ellen Strauss came to me. I had just been elected president of the Farm Bureau. Phyllis was a conservationist and Ellen Strauss and her husband were Marshall ranchers also looking for a way to conserve the

PROTECTED FARMLAND

MARIN AGRICULTURAL LAND TRUST

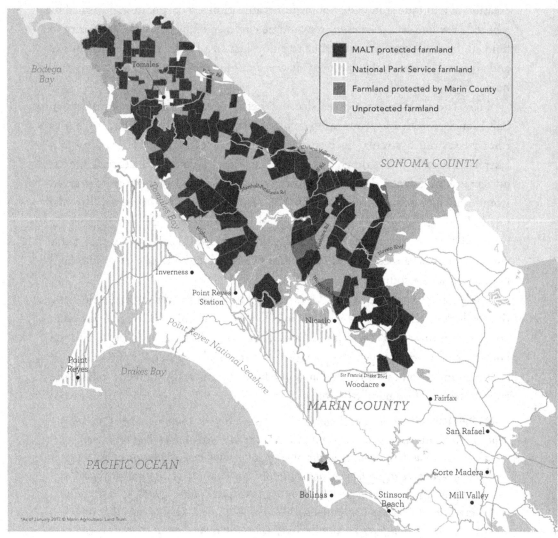

© 2017 Marin Agricultural Land Trust. Mapped by ArcGIS software
granted by the ESRI Conservation Program.

land. They said they liked this idea of a Land Trust where ranchers could donate their easement, which effectively would be donating their development rights to a nonprofit organization. An easement is a legal restriction that is recorded with the deed that prohibits subdivision. It's different from an access easement. Legally, it is a document that you sign when you sell your development rights. So MALT buys an easement and records it with your deed. It becomes part of the permanent record at the county records office.

Phyllis and Ellen had been talking with the Trust for Public Land* and thought that this idea of a Land Trust would be great because then ranchers could donate this easement to a nonprofit group like the Trust for Public Lands—or to start a new one locally that could accept these easements—and take a tax deduction. But my own thought was that ranchers in Marin weren't looking for tax deductions. It's not that profitable here. There were very few ranchers who were going to be excited about the idea of giving away their future development rights for a tax deduction. My comment at that point was—"That idea is a nonstarter. What we have to have is a program where they get paid for that easement. We're right here close to the city and the suburbs and the land is valuable." So that's what we began to work on.

We asked the Trust for Public Lands to come in and give us some examples. We got excited enough to think that we might be able to raise some money to buy the easements to permanently protect the land. So we went ahead and incorporated MALT—the Marin Agricultural Land Trust. Fortuitously, that was about the same time that the Buck Trust was being debated in Marin. The Beryl Buck Trust was a huge part of all of this.

In the early 1970s, a woman named Beryl Buck passed away and left her estate, her land, to the San Francisco Foundation to be held in trust to the benefit of the people of Marin County. Basically setting up a kind of an endowment to be used for good things in Marin County. Her family contested it, obviously because she hadn't left it to them. The case took 6 or 8 years to work its way through the courts.

In the end, the San Francisco Foundation finally was awarded the land to start the Beryl Buck Trust. During that period of time a number of other things happened: There was the energy crisis and the technology boom.

Well it turned out that this land was down near Bakersfield and it had oil under it. But it was heavy oil that previously didn't have that great a value because they couldn't extract it. The technology was developed during the period of time that the Beryl Buck Trust was being contested in the courts, so by the time it was resolved, this piece of property was worth a couple hundred million dollars. The San Francisco Foundation received in the neighborhood of 250 to 300 million dollars.

For a period of time they started making grants to needy groups in Marin but then the San Francisco Foundation determined that it was too big an amount for one county (Marin) so they took the matter to court and tried to change the terms of the Trust.

The Marin County Board of Supervisors, led by Gary Giacomini, fought and won and the court took the trust away from the San Francisco Foundation and gave it to the Marin Community Foundation. One third of the total went to the Beryl Buck Center for Aging, right up here on the side of Mt. Olompali, those white buildings up there. That's a major research facility on the aging process—Alzheimers and other age-related diseases. Now it's a world class research facility, funded in part by money from this trust. (This was on the Black-Burdell property; the original land grant.) The Marin Community Foundation ended up with a lot of money, and of

---

* The Trust for Public Land was founded in San Francisco in 1972 for the purpose of using emerging real estate, legal, and financial techniques to conserve land for human use and public benefit.

course the stock market was taking off so the money was growing. I think today there may be around $500 million dollars in that Trust.

About 1979 or 80, they had to start spending the earnings from it—about 5% of it every year. MALT came along just at the right time because we went immediately to them. The Farm Bureau made the initial application to what was still the San Francisco Foundation. But by the time MALT was officially established, the money had gone to the Marin Community Foundation and the recipient was changed from the Farm Bureau to the Marin Agricultural Land Trust. The timing couldn't have been better. It gave MALT start-up money to hire an executive director.

So for more than 20 years the Marin Community Foundation was a steady funder of the core operation of MALT. It was a big boost to be able to have full-time staff to work on this all the time. We were able to make the case that saving the farmlands of Marin County was certainly a benefit to the people of Marin County.

I had named a land use committee of the Farm Bureau that was made up of one of each of the major family members in West Marin: Willie LaFranchi, Rod Martinelli, Earl Dolcini and Jerry Corda. They became the core of the initial Board of Directors. When we wrote the by-laws of MALT, we said that at least half the board members had to be agriculturalists. The policy has to be dominated by agriculture. So wonderful people like Martinelli and Dolcini and LaFranchi were on that initial Board of Directors. They were all pretty skeptical of the idea at first because it was a pretty big stretch. I mean who would pay us land-owners to keep on farming? It took some education. It took a while—four or five years—to get it going.

By 1985, MALT was able to get some money from state bond issues to match up with what the Buck Fund had available. Through the Coastal Conservancy and through the State Department of Conservation, it began to put some projects together. It wasn't until much later that private funds, donations from individuals, started coming in to help buy easements. Once it became clear that this was going to be successful, remarkably successful, donations started coming in. MALT is now without question the leading farmland preservation group in the country. MALT was the first land trust to focus on agriculture and preserving farmland.

Marin, New York, Washington ~ 1980 to 2003

ONWARD AND OUTWARD

IN HARD TIMES, JUST SURVIVING THROUGH ANOTHER DAY is a desperate personal challenge. Certainly the farmers and ranchers of Marin must have felt that way when their futures were threatened. But Zena Mendoza stepped out of her personal world to communicate with Congress. And wonder of wonders, ranchers had allied themselves with environmentalists to defeat the swallowing up of their land by suburban development. This had required tough decisions, sacrifices, compromises for the families of the land. The descendants of Ticinesi immigrants who had started with only a few dollars and a lowly ranch job, were now owners of their own ranches, yet the future of agriculture in the region was itself in peril. Many of the Ticinesi, Portuguese, and Irish families of those immigrants had become important community voices in envisioning the changing future of agriculture. Members of the current generation of Grossi, Dolcini, Martinelli, Giacomini, and Lafranchi families had forged ahead with the novel idea of an agricultural land trust, supported by other families who built up the ranching industry in Marin; especially in Point Reyes. But their impact was being felt beyond Marin. Even beyond California.

ENTER MRS. ROCKEFELLER

As it turns out, the Marin Ranchers were not the only people thinking about an Agricultural Land Trust. There were people on the east coast and in Washington D.C. thinking along the same lines. One person in particular was closely following the events from the other side of the continent: Peggy Rockefeller, wife of David Rockefeller.

RALPH: *In the mid-80s the Nature Conservancy had been growing rapidly and one of the board members of the Nature Conservancy was Mrs. David Rockefeller—Peggy Rockefeller—a passionate farmer. A wonderful lady. Her husband was head of Chase-Manhattan Bank. A lot of good things happened in the Hudson Valley, in part because of the Rockefeller Family. Mrs. Rockefeller was on the Nature Conservancy Board and she went to the Conservancy and said, "I think you ought to add preserving farming, agriculture, to your mission." This is late 70s. But they turned her down. Well you don't turn down Peggy Rockefeller. She said, "Well, we'll start our own." She got together with the then president of the Nature Conservancy, who was also, fortuitously, retiring from that position. A remarkable man named Pat Noonan. A MacArthur fellow in fact, for the work he's done in conservation.*

Peggy Rockefeller got together with Pat and a man named Bill Riley who later became EPA Administrator in the Bush Administration and Doug Wheeler, who later became Resources Secretary in California under Pete Wilson. This was the core group that got together and started forming the American Farmland Trust. That's when they heard about MALT. They invited me to come back and be part of the initial working group, so I joined the board. We started that in 1980. Its purpose was to promote farmland protection around the country. They borrowed from the Nature Conservancy plan and the National Trust for Historic Preservation that was doing easements for historic reasons. There were bits and pieces in place and the idea was to pull this together for agriculture, with headquarters in Washington.

When the first president, Doug Wheeler, resigned to become president of the Sierra Club, they asked me if I would come back for three or four years to take over the position. I very naively thought I could do that and run the family dairy at the same time, shuttling back and forth. After three years it was pretty clear that wasn't going to work. I was here two or three times a month on long weekends to help with the dairy. In late '87, we decided to sell the milking herd and just convert it to a beef cattle operation, which is a lot easier to manage and my Dad was still in good health at the time. It was a little more appropriate use of the ranch. So instead of staying there three or four years, I ended up staying there for 23 years. As AFT began to evolve, it became clear to me that my role there was to help set the stage for organizations like MALT or in some states, county agriculture agencies or state agencies—sometimes a public group, sometimes a private group—to create the right policy framework and eventually get some money in the pipeline. Some federal dollars for matching.

I honestly believe that our staff were the foremost experts because they were following all of these initiatives around the country. We had a couple of people who really became the gurus of farmland preservation and how to set these programs up, how to promote them in your community and get public support.

Thanks largely to the work of the American Farmland Trust, agricultural easements have become a widely popular technique for the express purpose of protecting farmland. Farmers and ranchers appreciate their non-regulatory and landowner compensation features.

AFT also developed their *Keeping Farmers on the Land* campaign to address the threat to urban edge farms which face sprawling development and difficult market conditions. The goal is to save family farms by building community support for agriculture, improving market opportunities and ensuring access to land for the next generation.* In the last quarter century, it is estimated that about 1,100,000 farmland acres nationwide have been put under easements at an approximate cost of $2.3 billion.

ON THE FUTURE OF AGRICULTURE

My original purpose in interviewing Ralph Grossi was to get an understanding of how MALT had started. Now the conversation had opened up from local to national, and that led me to ask questions about what Ralph thought, after his twenty-three years in Washington, about the future of agriculture. It wasn't just in Marin that agricultural lands and businesses were under siege, but throughout the country. As Ed often repeated, "Whatever happens, people need to eat."

RALPH: *It's not just that we're saving land in Marin and around the country. It really is saving agriculture. Agriculture is evolving rapidly.*

Back in 1980 we said—If we could save the land then our proximity to the many affluent customers in Marin and San Francisco would have to work to our benefit as farmers in this region. The question is, how would that play out? We're farmers, all within fifty miles of a couple million people, so why wouldn't that be an advantage? Conceptually, we always felt that if we saved the land, agriculture would evolve to

---

* See more details at www.farmland.org

take advantage of its strategic position here (Marin, Sonoma). Its closeness to the consumer. I think that's what's happening now with the emergence of the artisanal cheese businesses in the area, organic dairies—many dairies are converting to organic production because the area is well-suited to organic production—grass-fed beef and organic vegetables . . . Just a lot of interesting things . . . Some wine vineyards. It's beginning to happen. It's what we hoped would happen.

I believe Local may be more powerful than Organic in some respects. There's the good feeling that if you are buying, you are helping preserve the local farms. People are beginning to recognize that agriculture—farms—are more than just food. Farms are Open Space. Farms are watersheds. Farms are wildlife habitat. Marindale—the Home Ranch for the Grossi family—produces beef right now and grapes. But it also produces the scenic vista, the water quality for Stafford Lake watershed (20% of the watershed is our ranch); wildlife habitat—the deer and the hawks, all of the animals out here. So the way we manage our ranch has a direct effect on the quality of water that the city of Novato gets. All of those are "farm products." We produce them every day. They are not something we have a tangible market for, where we can say "We're going to sell you so much wildlife habitat today" but in effect, that's what MALT has done. By MALT buying the easement, they have insured that these products will keep being produced.

SR: What do you think the future is for farming. You've seen it locally and you've seen it nationally. What moment are we in in regard to that? Now and looking into the future?

RG: Before we get into that, I think it's important to just mention that at least some of us feel a huge responsibility for not screwing it up. To keep this going. MALT is certainly a big part of that. But that doesn't guarantee anything in terms of the next generation. It guarantees that the land will be available but it doesn't mean that it will be farmed, and farmed properly unless we create the right conditions, atmosphere, culture and markets to make it appealing to the next generation. I have three daughters and they all love this ranch, but they are all making their own careers in very different worlds; one in San Francisco, one in Washington and one in Budapest. One in the corporate world, moving up the ladder at the GAP, one is a biochemist who is working in the technology field and the other one is a school teacher, traveling the world teaching in English schools in other countries. I expect that one or more will end up back here at the ranch someday. But probably not until later in life.

So for us, we're thinking now about how we make this available to the right young person to have access . . . We're not interested in selling, but to the right young person, we would offer a long-term lease so that they could start an agricultural business here. In fact, we have a new tenant who is running cattle and marketing grass-fed beef. I hope he does well in that because that's an opportunity here.

In some families, there is an obvious successor. My cousin next door, George, has a young son Dominic, who is a fine dairyman. He's now president of the Farm Bureau. So we see some families are making that transition and in others some question about who will take over in the next generation.

In the Giacomini family, the girls are making some of the finest blue cheese in the country and distributing it all over the country. So there are some examples of the new generation stepping in, but it's always an individual situation.

We don't know what the critical mass is to support an industry, particularly such a diverse industry as agriculture, but certainly if very many more dairies go out of business, it will be hard to maintain the infrastructure—the feed mills and the hay dealers and the milk processing plants and those kinds of things that are important to the dairy industry for example. The beef, sheep, pork—the livestock meat industry—is already struggling. We only have one processing plant in the whole North Bay area, so there has been a lot of concern about trying to get another processing facility here. Those are important discussions that have to take place. Markets have been picking up for specialty products—meat products, etcetera—so hopefully someone will make the investment to provide more processing facilities. When you get into organic vegetables and some of these other areas, it tends to be more of an individual process; more self-contained.

MALT keeps the land available, but it has also helped some families get through the generation transfer challenge by providing liquidity. When the landowners get paid, often multiple family members who own these ranches, it provides some cash, some liquidity, so that certain family members can move on and not be part of the operation any more if they don't want to; or let others stay who want to stay. That's a pretty big deal because most of these ranch families don't have liquidity. They have land. This maybe buys us the time for agriculture to develop from what it was when we knew it to what it is going to be in the 21ˢᵗ century.

I'm very optimistic about the future of agriculture because of the macro-economic issues. Between 2000 and 2050, the world population is going to grow by 50%. From 6 billion people to at least 9 billion people. That's the conservative estimate for 2050. We already passed 7 billion last year, so it's actually happening faster than expected. But even if you stick to the 9 billion projection for 2050, that is 50% more mouths on the globe to be fed in the next 38 years.

In addition to that, in the emerging nations, people have more wealth than they used to. Those economies are doing better. They are moving into the middle class. Their diets change pretty rapidly when they move up the ladder. They want more meat, protein, more dairy products. But that takes more grain to feed animals; to feed pork and chickens and dairy cows. The conservative projection is that between 2000 and 2050 we have to double food production on the globe. That's a well-accepted figure, so that's a big macro-issue.

There is a lot of demand in the pipe-line coming in the years ahead. So broadly speaking, this should be very good for agriculture. We're already seeing it on the commodity markets. Corn is now $8 a bushel, where it had been between $1.50 and $3 for thirty years. Up until just a few years ago. We're already seeing that demand equation change and that doesn't count the use of grain for ethanol—which may be a very short thing, so I don't count it.

So we have this big demand increase, people moving up the ladder in terms of nutrition, quality of food, etcetera, higher level protein. But that doesn't mean that everybody's a winner. It means there will be winners and losers. In our area, the losers are traditional dairy farmers. The winners are dairy farmers who can switch to specialty produces like the artisanal cheeses, or organic milk production. Something that has more of a local market appeal.

In Kansas or Iowa or Illinois, the winners are the corn and soybeans producers, and they're doing very well. This is my personal feeling, but I think there's enough evidence to support it—that we're in a fairly long period boom for agriculture. I didn't grow up in a boom period. I grew up in a period where there was constant over-supply and depressed prices. That's simply not the case anymore. That doesn't even factor whatever the consequences of climate change are on agriculture, which could add another component.

On the whole, we see a lot of young people who didn't grow up in agriculture, coming into agriculture today. It's a very good sign. There has been an explosion of small farms. They are not self-sufficient; they're supported by off-farm income. But the reality is that a lot of agriculture has been supported by off-farm income. For many years, government helped support a lot of agriculture. In the last 20 to 25 years, on small farms throughout the country, one member is doing the farming and one has an off-farm job. Part of the reason for having an off-farm job is to get health Insurance. So there are indirect support structures in agriculture and I don't think that will change.

THOSE WHO STAY

AS HISTORIAN GIORGIO CHEDA OBSERVED, the emigrants who went from Ticino to California found a very different life than those who went to Australia. They formed their own colonies here, marrying into other emigrant Ticino families, as Dominic Grossi of Monte Carasso married Teresa Buzzini of Brione. Once settled in Point Reyes, or elsewhere in Marin like Nicasio and Novato, they were no longer the people who went, but the people who stayed. The Grossis, Dolcinis, Martinellis, Cordas, LaFranchis, Giacominis . . . They are all still there, generations later. Tobias C.B. Giacomini may have come over from Villa di Chiavenna in Italy, but he married a Ticino woman from Gordola, Celeste Dominighini, and their son Waldo married a Giacomini woman from Brontallo in the Val Maggia, reuniting the separated Giacomini clans.

What are they doing? How have they been able to stay? This is the last question I put to Ralph Grossi on that afternoon on the Novato ranch—the "Farm in Marin."

SR: *As you go down the generations, what's happening to the next generations and their attitudes?*

RALPH: *Point Reyes is now producing specialty produce.*
The Lafranchis built a cheese plant right over that ridge.
Bob Giacomini has built the Point Reyes blue cheese plant and his daughters run that now. So the girls have come back into the business.
The next generation of the Mendoza family are now organic dairymen—both the son and the daughter. Gerrad?? Mendoza and JoLynn McClellan, grandchildren of Joe Mendoza. They each just started an organic dairy out on the Point Reyes peninsula.
By next April, all of the dairies on the Point Reyes peninsula will be producing organic milk. They're producing over 15,000 gallons a day on the peninsula, in the park. That's over 100,000 pounds of organic milk a day produced by a Spaletta, Grossi, Evans (of our family), two Mendozas, their cousins the Nunes dairy, Kehoe and McClure.
Rich Grossi, son of Domingo, has the M Ranch now. He raises beef.
The Spalettas oldest son, James, has the dairy out there. And his son Ernie and grandson, Ernest are also in the business. Four generations—from Eda. Five including Dominic.
David Evans, his mother is my cousin, [daughter of Dominic's son Alfred Grossi of H Ranch] has started this wonderful Marin Sun Farms. It's grown beyond his own ranch now and he contracts with other ranchers in the area to help him produce enough for his market.

Point Reyes Station ~ September 8, 2005

TOBY'S FEED BARN

FIVE HUNDRED PEOPLE ARE PACKED INTO TOBY'S FEED BARN. Bags of grain are piled along one side and birds flutter in the high rafters. A warm wave of chatter and laughter eddies through the cavernous barn that is the sound of community. The railroad line is long gone. The Miwok, the Garcias, and the Shafters are names from a distant past. But there are names you will still recognize here.

As you enter the town on Sir Francis Drake Boulevard you will pass Cheda Chevrolet and Garage owned by Louis Cheda's great-grandson, Adolph "Sonny" Cheda with his son Gary. (Louis had been one of the early arrivals from Maggia, sailing around the Horn in 1864 with Peter Campigli.) Becker's Deli*, on the main street, was owned by Sonny's cousin Vernon Cheda. Across the street from Toby's Feed Barn is the Grandi Building. It has gone through a few incarnations but the name can still be seen on the largest building in town. The original Grandi store did not survive the 1906 earthquake. Louis Grandi's son Reno built a larger and very successful establishment. Louis's daughter Lydia married Alfred John Bianchi, another successful Marin dairyman whose sister Corinne, married John Pelosi. You may remember that their son Paul married the woman who would become the first female Speaker of the House, Nancy Pelosi.

Salvatore Grandi's competitor and former employee, Pietro-Peter Scilacci's Point Reyes Emporium survived the earthquake. Vernon Cheda's aunt married Wilford Scilacci, Pietro's son Wilford "Bill" Scilacci took over the store in 1922 and renamed it the Palace Market.

And then there is Toby Giacomini's son, Chris Giacomini—grandson of Tobias and Celeste Giacomini—who runs Toby's Feed Barn now. Toby's Feed Barn is the agricultural and cultural center of the town. It is also a store selling items from T-shirts to gourmet foods. On Saturdays there is a Farmer's Market here. Regularly, there are speakers of national renown and people come from all over Point Reyes and beyond to attend the events. These five hundred people have come to hear Wendell Berry—poet, farmer, and voice of the land.

Warren Weber steps forward to greet everyone and to introduce their guest. Weber is a member of the board of the Marin Agricultural Land Trust. The event, like many here, is being sponsored by MALT. A complete century has passed since Julia and Emma laid out their own vision for the future of farming in Point Reyes. I can't help but feel that although their personal lives spiraled downward toward personal and financial failure, they would be proud to hear that something of that vision is still flourishing and the battle for the agricultural presence and the natural preservation of their region is still being worthily fought.

"Fifteen years ago MALT had 19 ranches and 15,000 acres under easement. Today 57 ranches and 38,000 acres are protected, which is exactly one-third of all privately held ag land—a remarkable achievement. Fifteen years ago, Marin

---

* Now Whale of a Deli

Organic (MO) didn't exist. We had then perhaps 80 acres farmed organically by four producers. Through our Ag Commissioner's stellar program, today there are 13,000 acres and 47 farms certified organic in Marin. These statistics are the bare bones of an amazing agrarian renaissance going on under our feet.

"In his foreward to *Farming on the Edge*, Wendell Berry applauded us for "dissolving our opposing interests in the spirit of community." And he suggested we could do even more by promoting our local farm products. I'm happy to say we are now doing that as fast as we can. The Point Reyes Farmers' Market, at Toby's Feed Barn on Saturdays, is but one example. School lunch programs serving 4,000 children per week, local organic food delivered to elder centers, to a hospital, to low-income folks in San Rafael's Canal District, are others. Twenty tons of free organic food have been distributed to those institutions by Marin Organic, along with purchased produce. Additionally, MO, MALT, and UC sponsor numerous workshops for ranchers and the public.

"Today, all of us together—farmers, ranchers, environmentalists, consumers, public and private advocates—are doing something unique here, and a little differently from 15 years ago. Now we are focusing less on development, more on agricultural productivity; less on outside forces and more on locally produced food and the regional consumer; and less on landscape as open-space, and more on its biodiversity, its productivity, its community-strengthening attributes. We are figuring out, step by step, case by case, how our, at times, sadly mechanistic and confrontational culture fine-tunes the balance between people and the rest of nature, between feeding ourselves and protecting biodiversity, between using natural resources and cherishing them.

"As some of us know firsthand, there remains a lot of potential conflict in balancing this equation. But the process is well worth the prize: a community sustained by the nature it loves. And that's why we are here tonight, to stimulate the dialogue and learn from each other. Thank you."

INVERNESS

THE NEST IS AS WIDE AS YOUR OUTSTRETCHED ARMS. High up in the bishop pine tree atop Inverness Ridge, it has the best ocean view for miles around. You can see clear to China—or so it seems. In one direction, you will have the last view of the setting sun as its disappearing light sheds a golden path across the sea. In the other direction, the tidal waters of Tomales Bay. Inverness spreads out below you, tiny, insubstantial houses, ant-like nameless people. This nest has been built upon by generations of osprey. There are larger, older nests in other places—like Ohio, where bald eagles added to their nest every year for more than three decades until it finally weighed two tons and toppled its host tree.

It is May and the two chicks are wide awake to the world, their orange eyes gleaming as they watch for the looming shadow that means food. Through a thin fog she appears, sailing toward them with a large fish in her talons. Bringing lunch.

Below the Point Reyes lighthouse and on the small Farallones islands, the Common Murres are gathering in their large numbers, packed tightly together along the beach, hundreds of them. They have been gathering here since long before the arrival of humans, back into prehistoric times. If groups of geese are a gaggle, what is a crowd of Common Murre? A loomery. When the first Boston sealers arrived in 1807, a loomery estimated at 400,000 birds bred on the Farallones. Like small penguins, they stand upright and can inhabit precipitous places along the cliffs. Like the penguin, they produce one large pear-shaped egg, which they hold beneath their webbed feet. A cloud of chattering noise rises up from their numbers.

On the sunny eastern slope of Inverness Ridge come the sweeter sounds of the Nuttal's white crowned sparrow. The blue-eyed grass and indigo douglas iris have come and gone, along with the delicate trillium bloom in the fields and meadows as early as February.

Coastal brush of coyote bush, blackberry bramble, sword fern and poison oak provide perfect cover for the stealthy bobcats that are occasionally seen near Abbott's lagoon and Muddy Hollow. Mountain lions move invisibly through more remote areas. Delicate gray foxes with pointed noses prowl through the brush. Until the arrival of humans, this was a landscape presided over by the grizzly bear. Captain Richardson often left his home in Sausalito to hunt in these wild places. His friend Charles Lauff, who hunted with him, reported in 1847 that they had killed a large brown grizzly and entering Tennessee Valley they had seen the bones of hundreds of elk and deer that had been killed for their hides. Richardson had told him that there were over a hundred bear and lion in the ravine. This was in the area that is now Mill Valley, where my friend Sally has her condo adjacent to CVS Pharmacy and Whole Foods Market. Fortunately the Whole Foods there are less dangerous than those that Lauff and Richardson faced. Of course they didn't have the traffic problem. Joaquin Miller, in 1900, describes a time when bears were as common in California as cows are now.

Over the dunes and headland of Abbott's Lagoon the bright orange poppies flare out; tidytips, goldfields and lupine carpet the meadows. Hillsides are covered in mustard, and along the beaches, the beach pea, strawberry and evening primrose are in bloom. Sun yellow buttercups and blue-eyed grass.

This is the town that James McMillan Shafter founded in 1889 and named after the family's roots in Scotland. Ironically, its founding was part of a last ditch effort on James part to climb out of his indebtedness. Here too is where Julia Shafter Hamilton fought her futile battles. A while back, my friend Annaneia Poder and I visited Lotte Stein here, a fellow CIIS student who got her master's degree as an 85 year old widow! Lotte and her husband were part of the Jungian circle in Zurich for a while and she has led a varied and interesting life. She says that there is a community of intellectuals in Inverness whom she enjoys sharing time and conversation with. No, she has never heard of Julia Shafter. She drives me by the Jack Mason museum/library but alas, it closed on the weekends. They are all folded up in there, I know, in their yellowing histories, their parchment photos. Rafael Garcia, Antonio Osio, Oscar, James, Charles Howard, Jack Hamilton, Emma, Julia, Payne and down through the line of people—not so many of them—who have shaped the history of Point Reyes. I will return another time.

The narrow road divides at one point, and there is an arrow for the Pierce Point ranch in one direction—probably the same road traveled by Dominic with Jack Hamilton on that Christmas Day—and another for Mt. Vision. We drive up to the ridge of Mt. Vision, site of a famous fire here in 1995, which destroyed 48 homes and twelve thousand acres of Point Reyes National Seashore. In the early years, Julia's home had been destroyed by fire, was rebuilt, then lived in by her daughter Bertha, whose house also burned to the ground. But the whale swims on at his steady pace, heading northwest toward Alaska at eight centimeters per year. I am startled by the beauty of the sudden panorama that opens up. We are standing among lovely bishop pines on the ridge of the whale's back. From this height, the Pacific opens up before us in its deep blue, gleaming with sunlight. I am speechless before the grandeur of it and filled with gratitude for the efforts to preserve it.

We could, after all, be standing at the edge of the 18th hole of an exclusive golf course or on the noisy deck of a mall restaurant or a parking lot.

Spread out below are the lowlands that are now part of Point Reyes National Seashore. To the south, Limantour Beach and Drakes Estero. To the north, Abbott's Lagoon. Although I can't see them, I know that bordering that lagoon, north through the pine forest from me, are Dominic's H Ranch and M Ranch. And his tribe still flourishes there.

WORKING FROM THE HEART:
THE LEGACY OF A POINT REYES FARMING FAMILY

(from *Edible Marin and Wine Country Magazine* online)
By Kirsten Jones Neff

The rain has finally given way to another unstoppable California spring as I weave my way through the Inverness pine forests and emerge into a wide-open Point Reyes countryside. The grass has made a dramatic deep green appearance across the rolling hills and the sky looks painted on in large swaths of cobalt blue. A hawk watches from a signpost, unimpressed by my speed as I wind west toward a white farmhouse tucked into the pastoral landscape above the narrow inlet that is Abbotts Lagoon. Miles and miles of fenced grassland, ducks floating lazily on an amber stock pond, clusters of yellow mustard and the endless reach of the Pacific Ocean beyond—this is the paradise that frames the historic H Ranch in the Point Reyes peninsula. My own young family's table has been blessed with meat and eggs produced on this neck of land off the far western edge of Marin County, and today I am here to meet some of the people responsible for this local legacy.

Dolores Evans grew up on the H Ranch and then raised her own two children, David Evans and Julie Evans Rossotti, on the ranch. Both Julie and David are now fourth generation Point Reyes farmers. When I arrive, Julie, a bright-eyed woman in her mid-30s, greets me at the gate. Julie and her husband Tony Rossotti own and operate Rossotti Ranch in Petaluma, but they keep a portion of their herd of grass-fed African Boer goats on the certified organic acreage of Julie's childhood home. "I'm sorry my mom's going to be a little late for the interview," Julie apologizes, pointing south toward the barn and a maze of paddocks. Over the dark heads of several dozen cattle I see Dolores, shouting and herding her charges. "She wants to get the vaccinations done before she has her other shoulder replaced next month." "Her other shoulder?" I think to myself. "She's really only got one good arm right now," Julie tells me as I stare with admiration at her mother's strength and dexterity.

When Dolores finally takes a lunch break, we sit on a warm, wind-protected bench to talk about the cow and calf operation she and her husband, Dan, who grew up in nearby Marshall, California, have run for 35 years. Looking out over the land she knows like the back of her hand, she reminisces about growing up on the peninsula before it became a national park. As close as they were to large population centers, hers was an adventurous childhood, with very few restrictions. Her family harvested their own protein and fiber, hunting and tending a robust vegetable garden. "I'd follow my father around and he'd teach me to do everything," Dolores says. "We'd hunt. Everything you shot—you were taught to use it." Her father was Alfred Grossi, a son of Domenico and Teresa (née Buzzini) Grossi, who first arrived in West Marin in the late 1800s. Alfred and his wife, Florence, inherited H Ranch from Domenico and Teresa, and ran it as a dairy before Dolores and Dan took over and transitioned to beef cattle in the 1970s.

In 1962, President Kennedy had signed a bill creating the Point Reyes National Seashore, encompassing the H Ranch and others in the area. The federal government's stated mission was to protect the peninsula from development, but what would happen to the families who owned the land? How would they be compensated for the land, not to mention the loss of livelihood for those who made their living by ranching? Over the next decade, various deals were negotiated with the ranch owners in which the government bought their land and then leased it back to the former owners as long as they agreed to preserve it as "pastoral" working farmland.

Julie, who grew up in the '70s, also recalls a remote life on the peninsula, except for the steady stream of beach and lighthouse tourists. Back then the Point Reyes ranching families lived truly "off-the-grid"—before "off-the-grid" became a lifestyle choice. "You name it, we canned it when I was a kid," Julie says. "My mother and grandmother would preserve anything they could get their hands on." On canning days they could be found in the cozy H Ranch kitchen, preserving everything from blackberries to Brussels sprouts. These days the "fruits" of this family wisdom can be found any Sunday at the Marin Civic Center Farmers' Market at both Julie's Point Reyes Preserves booth or her brother David's Marin Sun Farms booth where he sells Marin Sun Farms Preserves.

Dolores, now in her 60s, with a bad shoulder and a bum knee, still seems to have more energy and stamina than many 40 year olds. She is a living reminder that producing food is hard work. She is also one of the fortunate people on this planet who love their home and vocation, including the job requirements that have her hauling and tossing hay bales—the unfortunate undoing of her shoulders. As she speaks, she gazes out toward her cattle—on her lunch break, but always observing. The current H Ranch cow and calf operation involves about 300 head of cattle, an innovative cross of Angus, Herefords and Gelbviehs. As her daughter says, Dolores "knows every single one by its face," tending them as if they were children, monitoring their health by the look in their eyes and the texture of their coat. "I watch," Dolores tells me in her concise, matter-of-fact way. "I am always watching."

✳ ✳ ✳ ✳

The Golden Gate ~ November 7, 2007

COSCO BUSAN

THE FOG COMES IN SOFTLY, SOMETIME DURING THE NIGHT. It swathes the city, prowling its heights. Embracing and erasing it. From Mt. Tamalpais, you could see it move like a living thing, rolling over hilltops, pouring into valleys, hiding ships and skycrapers, huge trees, and small animals thankful for its cover but wary of hidden predators. Swiftly it surges into bay and riverbeds. The lively descendent of Yerba Buena and all the life it spawned might never have existed.

Beneath the surface of the bay, marine creatures go about their business as they have for millions of years, heedless of the fog in their changeless dark. Above them, scoters drift on the surface of the waves and the gulls ready themselves for their dawn raids on waves and ships and dockyards.

It is still dark when the Bar Pilot boards the red and white vessel and chugs through the mist-laden darkness to Berth 55 in the Oakland Estuary. Bar Pilots have been guiding vessels through treacherous waters of the bay for over a hundred years. The pilot is one of 60 who shepherds some 10,000 ships a year through their arrivals and departures. His movements are agile and experienced as his fingers feel their way up the hundred foot ladder of the Cosco Busan above heaving waters. It is 6:20 am. Almost an hour until sunrise, when they are due to depart. Voices in Chinese drift toward him as he nears the top. The Chinese captain and the officer of the watch greet him in English. When he inspects the bridge, he finds state-of-the-art equipment, including two radar displays to penetrate fog and darkness. The Cosco Busan is a Chinese container ship chartered out of Seoul. The vessel has just changed ownership, and the 21 Chinese officers and crew are making their first voyage with the ship. It is only six years old.

By seven o'clock the invisible city across the bay is beginning to stir. The low mournful call of the foghorns sweeps through the air and the muffled sounds of the other waking cities along the perimeter of the shore come in whispers. Soft plashes as the gulls and pelicans swoop on their morning meals and sea lions slide clumsily into the water. Work goes on, in one of the busiest cities in the world. The streetcars hum, the cable cars clang, silent elevators lift a fleet of workers to their airborn heights in the upper offices of skyscrapers. The fish markets open in Chinatown, the financial markets prepare to open on Montgomery Street and the homeless begin to stir in doorways and under makeshift cardboard covers.

By 7:30, the fog has thinned, if not lifted. Visibility is one mile, and the Bar Pilot radios the vessel traffic service that he is headed for the Delta Echo span on the San Francisco side of the Bay Bridge. The 900 foot ship has left Oakland's inner harbor to set out on its long trip across the Pacific. Dwarfed by its enormous bulk, the 78 foot tug Revolution chugs along beside it. The Bar Pilot's first challenge is to get his ship around the dredge Njord, which is anchored in the estuary. As the ship approaches Yerba Buena Island, the fog curtain closes around them and shrouds the next few critical moments aboard the Cosco Busan in a mystery that may never be fully revealed. How is it that with a veteran pilot of 26 years and state-of-the-art electronics, the ship veers left instead of right? Shortly after, the vessel traffic service calls the Bar Pilot to say that he is off course, heading parallel to the bridge and needs to make a right turn. At the same time, a shout comes from the watch and the danger bell rings as the pilot takes the ship on a sharp right. The action saves the boat from a direct collision with the bridge. But the Cosco Busan now wears a gash one-hundred seventy feet long and four feet deep.

Quiet as the fog is the thick black oil that purls like water through the gills of a fish, into the bay, carried on the tides, spreading to the beaches, coating the sands, the kelp, the living and the dead . . . Everything it touches. 58,000 gallons of oil will soon bring fishing to a standstill, and catalyze the efforts of scores of agencies, environmentalists, marine biologists.

Water moves. The tides are ceaseless. The heart of the earth, sending water into bays and estuaries, lagoons and coves. Pulling it back. Sending it out again. Receiving along its arteries all of the water sent by the heavens to the mountains and hillsides where it is borne downward by gravity through streams and creeks and rivers and floods to join the rhythm of the sea. This is the first story. The circulation of water. And it is written on tablets as old and fragile as a veined leaf. As expressive of information as a silicon chip yet with the added chapter at the beginning called Life and Endless Replication and the chapter at the end called Beauty.

Water moves and carries things everywhere. It is the original transport. Put a message in a bottle in Southampton and it will be read in China or Louisiana or . . . Who knows? Not all ancient peoples had the wheel but if they were anywhere near water, they had boats. People too became corpuscles flowing through the streams of the world.

Water moves, and within the water, more sluggish and toxic, move the black braids and globules of oil from the Cosco Busan. On the incoming tide, it flows into the eelgrass fields of Alameda to the east. It coalesces into small continents that drift into the Berkeley Marina and spread across the Inner Richmond Harbor. Other strands join to enter the Oakland Inner Harbor. A broad necklace of oil surrounds Angel Island and virtually takes it hostage. The Angel Island State Park is shut down. Like eyes and mouths closing, like the raised drawbridges of old, the Bay Area closes off its treasures to the toxic invader but still it presses inward toward the *wildlife refuges and bird sanctuaries, into the fishing grounds and the oyster beds. The wealth of Marin's jewels—Tiburon and Belvedere and Sausalito—cannot keep it from their beaches. The cormorants in Ft. Baker cove are drenched in it. Sleek boats in marinas, are coated with oil as it spreads through Raccoon Strait, following Sutter's route, to the north of Angel Island, past Paradise Beach into San Pablo Bay.*

On the outgoing tide, it travels westward through the Golden Gate and is carried on the rips and currents, north and south, but mostly north. It passes the Marin Headlands, leaving its heaviest concentrations on Rodeo Beach. It will reach Stinson Beach and the entrance to Bolinas Lagoon, where the residents are taking every measure they can think of to protect their idyllic landscape. Booms have been set up and residents are being trained as volunteers to clean up oil. Across a park service sign that warns against picking up oiled birds or entering contaminated areas appears a rueful and spontaneous caption: WE STILL HAVE NOT REACHED ENLIGHTENMENT.

By Sunday, it will reach the southern tip of Point Reyes.

The stench was overwhelming. The sight was terrible. Pitiful. Yet something else was in the air too. It could not be smelled or seen but each one felt it. A sense of hope. Of possibility. A camaraderie born out of the unexpected. The idea that there was something one could do. That people *together* could do. This was new. Perhaps it is what people felt at barn-raisings in the old days. Or when everyone pitched in at harvest time, "bringing in the sheaves."

Careful fingers probed delicate throats, even cleaned tiny teeth. Bird's teeth! One was passing a tube from the esophagus of a gull into its stomach. Another was preparing the special slurry of Ensure and fish that would be passed down the tube. Nearby, triage was going on just as in any emergency room. Body temperature and blood were being taken to determine if a bird was dehydrated or anemic. Once they were fed and stabilized, they were passed to a series of baths. Other volunteer hands delicately massaged little bodies after Dawn dishwashing liquid had been pressure-washed into the feathers. Each was passed from tub to tub, bathed, rinsed, probed for any lingering signs of oil until the water came out clear and the bird was declared clean. Extra care in hot tubs for those that needed it. Then swaddled in a towel and carried off for drying, where they can begin to preen their feathers, reconnecting the interlocking fibers that form their natural wetsuits.

Each bird takes about an hour to care for. Seven hundred have arrived so far at the San Francisco Bay Oiled Wildlife Care center in Cordelia, near Fairfield in Solano County. By the end of the month, over a thousand birds will have been in care at the center. Close to 800 washed by the volunteers. Close to 600 died or were euthanized. Over 300 were released. Close to 2000 found dead in the field. They have done this work in California, Alaska, Norway, Spain and South Africa, where they helped to rehabilitate 21,000 African penguins.

Hair salons donated human hair to make hair mats, determined to be effective at sopping up oil. There were calls for pantyhose donations because these were used to hold the human hair to make the mats. Photos and documents were being called for and gathered by Save the Bay to provide essential information to government agencies working on the spill and to keep the larger community up-to-date. Hotlines, websites, training programs in beach clean-up for volunteers, notifications and numbers to call and things to do, community by community.

When the EPA offered HAZMAT training for volunteers in Golden Gate Park an estimated 600-700 people showed up, more than the room could fit. But by 11 pm, 570 volunteers left with their official certification badges and additional sessions were held at the County Fairgrounds on Wednesday and on Saturday. At a training session held in Berkeley on the 14th, the session filled up with 400 people but a few hundred others who lined up didn't make it in, so additional training sessions were scheduled. Sessions were held on Thursday and Saturday in Half Moon Bay to the South. Anticipating a high tide on Thanksgiving Day, volunteers joined a beach clean-up in Bolinas and Ocean Beach. Over 1600 people participated in these volunteer sessions and many more volunteered in areas that didn't require certification. Efforts were coordinated by such seasoned organizations as Save the Bay, Bay Keeper, Golden Gate Audobon, Golden Gate National Parks Conservancy, the California Coastal Commission, the Marine Mammal Center and the Surfrider Foundation.

I tell the Cosco Busan story because it underlines both sides of the Ecozoic Era, to use Thomas Berry's term. "In the emerging Ecozoic period almost nothing will happen that will not in some manner be related to the human. Not, however, that we will control the inner workings of the planet. We cannot make a blade of grass. But there is liable not to be a blade of grass if it is not accepted, protected, and fostered by the human."

In this new epoch, the earth is seen as an interconnected system, like the roots of the redwoods in the great forests to the north that feed an support one another. Humans are both the most protective and the most destructive elements on the planet, but we have advanced our understandings to such an extent that individuals and organizations can mobilize quickly when disaster strikes. It is a delicate balance of course.

The eager-for-war and the pasture-loving Winnili are among us—they are all of us really. In our daily lives, we fight these little battles and protect what we can. Ordinary people leading ordinary lives paused, listened to the news of the Cosco Busan, left what they were doing to protect their bay and its creatures. San Franciscans. People from Marin, Sonoma and counties to the north and south, rallying to the cause as they did the building of the Golden Gate Bridge or the Marin Agricultural Land Trust or the protection of the Steelhead Trout that run mysteriously (i.e. unseen by me) down Copeland Creek. But there is one difference in this case: The Internet.

FROM ZUNA SURFER WEBSITE TO 2000+ SURFERS

Good afternoon—
Is there a good contact number for East Bay efforts? I must work 9-5 on the weekdays—but I have time on the weekends! I see that there is a training session this coming Saturday—I want to know if there is a number for the meeting that I can call.

Thank you!
Sonja
p.s. kudos for putting up this site! (aside from the impressive efforts otherwise!!)

Is there going to be a group working in Bolinas on Saturday morning? I'd love to help out somewhere in Marin, have certification, scoop, towels & bags. Liz

Hi,
I have been out of the area and am due back Fri. I would love to help on Sat. or Sun. I live in Petaluma. Please contact me if I can be of help in Marin or Sonoma coast. Thanks so much. This is tragic!!!

As a 31 year bay swimmer, I am so upset about this for all the wildlife! Love to help out. Kathie Hewko 707 ***-****.

Clean Up Ocean Beach with the John Butler Trio!
Sunday, December 2
10:00 a.m.- 12:00 p.m.,
Free concert immediately following cleanup!
In partnership with Surfrider Foundation, Rock the Earth, Music Matters, and Clif Bar

FROM SFGATE.COM:

"You see the migratory shorebirds coming to the bay at this time of year," said Jack Dumbacher, chair of ornithology and mammalogy at the California Academy of Sciences.

The birds go to the mudflats and tidal marsh, seeking mussels, worms and little crustaceans and the rich plant life. Growing salmon and Dungeness crab, and many other species of aquatic life, use the edges of the bay as nurseries.

Dunlins, sanderlings, marbled godwits and whimbrels are feeding heavily at this time of year. "These birds feed on animals that live below the surface of the water and mud. When they ingest their prey, they will ingest the oil as well," Dumbacher said.

The oil has made its way to Hayward south of the San Mateo Bridge, where the state Fish and Game Department has shut down its water structures that circulate bay water into new marshes restored from former salt ponds.

As a precaution, the U.S. Fish and Wildlife Service is considering doing the same at its restored wetlands in the southern end of the bay, said John Bradley, deputy manager of the San Francisco Bay National Wildlife Refuge.

The petroleum material will enter the sediment where the herring will be spawning, McCosker said.

"It's not only tragic for the poor herring that come into the bay to spawn," he said, "but also for everything that depends on the herring - the seals, sea lions, birds and bigger fish."

The tiny salt marsh harvest mouse, the most endangered animal around the bay, weighing the same as a modern quarter, may not be so much at risk as other marsh creatures. The mouse stays in the middle to upper wetlands, said Howard Shellhammer, a professor of biology at San Jose State University who studied the effects of a 1988 leak of 400,000 gallons into Shell Marsh near Martinez.

"The impact on small mammals is very much like that on small birds," Shellhammer said. "The oil wets down the fur and increases heat loss. Because they're very small, heat loss may lead to death."

Zeke Grader, executive director of Pacific Coast Federation of Fishermen's Associations, the group that represents the commercial side of fishing, said he's already spoken to people at Fish and Wildlife about doing a more thorough assessment of damage to the bay's natural resources than was done after the Cape Mohican spill.

"We're concerned particularly about the juvenile crab and herring but also keeping an eye on the salmon migration as well as some of the other critters that use the bay, such as California halibut and English sole," he said.

Surely, in the long history of the Earth Calendar, it has not happened that a species like ours—bipedal, sporting an opposable thumb and brandishing a powerful neocortex—would collectively give such thought to the tiny salt marsh harvest mouse.

* * * *

Redwood Forest, Humboldt County California ~ The Present

LAURELIN

Then did fair boughs thrust overhead in all directions, and golden buds swelled from all the twigs and lesser branches, and from these burst leaves of a rich green whose edges shone. . . . "O, this is a very fair tree indeed, and must have a name unto itself," and Kémi said: "Let it be called Laurelin, for the brightness of its blossom and the music of its dew."

— R.R. TOLKIEN

THE TREE SIGHED ALONG ITS GREAT LENGTH, *creating nothing more than the slightest shiver in its highest branches. Or was it wind? A long awaited rain had finally come to soil parched by seasons of drought. Over the centuries, Laurelin has watched the slow withering of other trees in this same forest as they weaken and then suffer further insult from insects and fungus. But Laurelin had an ingenious system for such bad times, perfected over millions of years. If one of its parts began to dry and wither, it could draw water up from another and send it to the rescue of the ailing part, much as a human body can. The drought might have hurt it more if it stood its ground alone above its shallow root system, which could reach no deeper than six to twelve feet in search of water. There are other kinds of trees that have roots as deep as a tree is tall. That wouldn't be practical for this redwood and its family. So they depend upon one another; a vast interconnected underground network offering mutual support.*

Within its arms, Laurelin holds worlds within worlds. Small forests, thickets of huckleberries, elderberry, salmonberry; crustaceans from the deep sea, and its own tree progeny that are the duplicates of itself growing up perpendicular to its generative limbs. It holds deep mats of ferns, many feet thick, and there it watches over the salamanders, the small pink earthworms, the tiny copepods of sea and streams that have found new homes among its boughs. Other miniature trees have risen in that aerial soil—hemlock, oak, bay laurel and fir. Each new thing has been a surprise to it. Like finding a new friend.

The ancient redwood has been a natural refuge. A lofty Eden.

Now comes the greatest surprise of all. Over sixteen hundred years old, three-hundred sixty-eight feet tall and still growing, a man is about to enter its hidden paradise. His name is Steve Sillett.

♦ ♦ ♦

The man tied his arrow to a fishing line and then used his hunting bow to shoot it high up into the lower crown of the tree. He attached one end of the rope to a smaller, nearby tree and then took hold of the other end to climb to the lower crown. He wore a helmet and soft-soled shoes (spikes, he knew, could damage a tree) and a harness, attached to ropes looped over parts of the tree as he rose. He grasped a thick, strong and soft main rope to make his ascent. Once he reached the lower crown, he detached himself from the rope and moved from branch to branch.

His body touched the tree only lightly, moving sideways at times or diagonally. Unhurried. Studying what he saw with a scientist's intent. Yet cautious. It was like climbing a thirty-five story building without a scaffold. Buildings did not have giant pieces of dead wood that could be dislodged by his movement or by the tree itself. Wood the size of an SUV. The tree around him moves and breathes like the living being it is. Once in the upper crown, he sits on a mat of ferns eating the crisp tart huckleberries that grow on a bush there. Smelling the sea, looking across a green world in the highest canopy on earth.

♦ ♦ ♦

"You perceive time more clearly in redwoods. You see time's illusory qualities. When you get up into the crown of a redwood, you stop thinking about your life, you stop planning your future missions. You start feeling the limits of your perceptions of the world as a member of the human species. When you feel one of these trees moving, you get a sense of it as an individual . . . It's a being. It's a 'person,' from a plant's point of view. Plants are very different from animals, but they begin life with a sperm and an egg, the same way we do. This organism has stood on this spot for as many as two thousand years. Trees can't move, so they have to figure out how to deal with all of the things that can come and hurt them. This tree has burned at least once. The fire must have continued inside some of these caves for a long time—the caves were smoldering orange holes in the tree for weeks. Redwoods don't care if they burn. After the fire, the tree went, `Wooaah,' and it just grew back."

— STEPHEN SILLETT PhD*

SPIDER-MAN

Sillett is the principal explorer of the redwood-forest canopy, the three-dimensional labyrinth that exists in the air above the forest floor. . . . No scientist had been there before. The tallest redwoods were regarded as inaccessible towers, shrouded in foliage and almost impossible to climb, since the lowest branches on a redwood can be twenty-five stories above the ground. . . . The general opinion among biologists at the time . . . was that the redwood canopy was a so-called "redwood desert" that contained not much more than the branches of redwood trees. Instead, Sillett discovered a lost world above Northern California.

— RICHARD PRESTON
"Climbing the Redwoods"

STEPHEN SILLETT IS AN ASSOCIATE PROFESSOR OF BOTANY at Humboldt State University in Arcata, where William Spaletta had lived almost a century before. What he discovered in the redwood canopy was stunning, and Sillett, with his colleagues and students, has been gathering data about this uniquely flourishing ecosystem.

When William Spaletta arrived in the United States, the redwood forest of Northern California covered roughly two millions acres of virgin, old-growth trees. The burgeoning human population and demand for construction resulted in aggressive clear-cutting, speeded up by the introduction of power saws and Caterpillar tractors. It is estimated that ninety-six percent of the forest was cut down, possibly including trees bigger and older than any presently found. Since then, new approaches to logging and agreements made with the timber companies who owned these forests have protected the old-growth trees. Today the companies only harvest young redwood trees, mostly under eighty years old whose crowns are devoid of life.

In one grove of redwoods, Sillett believes there are trees dating back to the time of Caesar. The trees can live for two thousand to three thousand years. The age of the tallest ones cannot be exactly determined of course, only estimated. Laurelin may be older than I have suggested here, in a fictionalized account of the tree's life.

* From "Climbing the Redwoods" by Richard Preston in *The New Yorker*.

But Laurelin exists, as I have described it, based on Steve Sillett's own description of climbing into its canopy. It is very likely to have been alive in the time of Monica and Augustine.

The tallest tree in the world, so far discovered, is Hyperion, in the same redwood forest region: 379.7 feet (115.72m). It was measured by Steve Sillett in 2006, when he climbed to the top and dropped a tape straight to the ground. (The event was filmed by National Geographic.) In that same year, other discoveries were made of trees of record heights: "Helios," named after the Greek God of the sun, 374 feet (114 m); "Icarus" 371 feet (113.14 m); and "Daedalus," 363.5 feet (110.76 m).

✻ ✻ ✻ ✻

ED AND SUSIE GROSSI

Grossi Farms

THE FARMER TAKES A WIFE

Ed Grossi and Susie Sweet met doing things they loved most, although in both cases it was an avocation. Ed was working on his organic vegetable farm, moonlighting on the side doing landscape jobs. Susie was working as a flight attendant for United Airlines, moonlighting doing landscaping jobs. With Ed. Susie was renting Ralph Grossi's house in Novato with another flight attendant, down the street from Pop Grossi's place. Ralph and his family were in Washington, D.C. while he was working as head of the American Farmland Trust. Susie had been Flying the Friendly Skies with United all over the world. She was now doing her favorite runs to the Orient. But some part of her—the part that grew up on a Nebraska farm—was loving the sight of cows and horses. A farm in Marin.

When I started work on their Sonoma farm, Ed and Susie had been married for two years—a second marriage for them both. Together with some friends, they started Sweet Lane Nursery.

Susie's story is important here because it summarizes in so many ways the farming tradition that became the heart of America after Lewis and Clark completed their expedition and the settling of the country began in earnest. It brings together several threads of our story, because Susie's mother was an Oglala Sioux Indian and her father the descendant of an American immigrant from Europe and a mail order bride. Like the communities in Point Reyes, the towns in Nebraska were the legacy of the Union Pacific Railroad—fondly known as the UP—which brought settlers west and, very importantly, created the transport system that got livestock to markets.

So here is the last portrait in our gallery: Susan Sweet Grossi.

SUSIE'S STORY

MY DAD WAS A FARMER. ALFRED SWEET. *His father, Alfred Senior, was French. His original name was Bouvier, but he took the name of his sponsors in Ellis Island. His mother was English. A mail order bride. Alfred Senior had ridden the Union Pacific train to what was then the end of the line, in Clarks, Nebraska on the Platte River. (That's on the Lewis and Clark trail.) He went there for what was called the land grab and staked out three hundred and fifty acres three miles north of the Platte River. Then he ordered his bride, Sarah Sharman, from a British catalogue and she too arrived in Clark's on the UP. They raised twelve children. My father was the baby. His father passed away when he was two years old. The older boys came home and ran the farm. Joe and Al Sweet, the youngest, quit school in 8th grade when their turn came to run the farm.*

527

Through the years, the ranch was added on to. The home ranch became a section. 640 acres. As each boy got married, they bought their own places. In the beginning they raised corn, alfalfa, wheat and corn-fed cattle, shipped to Omaha on the UP. The big stock yard that developed in those years was in Omaha. All the cattle from Texas, Oklahoma, Kansas and the cattle from up north were either driven to the stockyard or to the nearest branch of the UP. Omaha Beef and Cattle Company was probably the largest slaughter-house, meat-packing and sale barn in the US.

My father went into the military, the army corps of engineers, during WWII. There was a law then that only one member of a farm family could serve, because the farms were feeding the soldiers. They kept my Dad stateside, building roads and highways in the Everglades in Florida. When he returned, he met my mother who was teaching school on the Oglala Sioux reservation where she was born.

The Oglala Sioux reservation was in the Sandhills of Nebraska. You can't grow anything in sand hills. They had been moved there from the Platte River area to make room for settlers like my grandfather and my Dad. Before that, their hunting grounds had stretched from Omaha to the Colorado Rockies. Her mother died of some disease when she was ten, so I never met my grandmother. Her father lived into his 80s and I can remember him. He called himself the Old Codger from the Hills and that's how we thought of him. We never called him grandpa. He lived in a little shack up in the sandhills. He was pretty much an alcoholic who chewed tobacco and smoked a pipe. Raised watermelons, probably to make watermelon wine. He was crippled up with arthritis but he died of skin cancer when I was about six. He was probably born around 1870. The reservation was just a shack here and a shack there, with a long distance in between. It was centered a long way away in Oglala. By then, they had all disbanded. My mother took the name of the Christian family that took her to school—Goerl. Missionaries were taking children into Christian families. After her mother died, she left the reservation, probably with her Dad's blessing. She never wanted to talk about those years. As far as she was concerned, her life began with the Goerls. She was happy to be taken in by them.

She married my Dad when she was 20 and she had already been teaching two years. She had graduated from high school with a teaching credential. She came to be a teacher in a small one room school two miles from my Dad's ranch and lived with a family nearby. She taught Kindergarten through 8th grade. One evening the family she stayed with took her to a community dance in town on Saturday night. Town being Clarks, population 200 when I was growing up. Dad had just gotten off the train, coming home from the military, and stopped off at the dance, because he knew his brothers and sisters would be there and could give him a ride home in their horse and buggy. Mom said he was in uniform and looked handsome. She was a pretty lady too. Tall. Dark-eyed and dark-hair. They started dating and six months later, they were married.

Dad went to the banker in town and asked if he knew anybody who needed someone to work their farm. The banker knew of a couple who had all girls and were willing to lease the farm with an option to buy. He split his crop with the owner, which was his payment. Sharecropping. The farm was 350 acres. Land-grant size. He raised corn, wheat, alfalfa and fed-cows. That means that they corn feed their cows and when the calves are born, they keep the females for breeding, turn the males into steers and fatten them up on the corn they had already raised, then ship them off for beef cattle. A beef cow operation. Not cattle ranching which is just a cow-calf operation; raising calves to sell. The heifers are kept to breed. The beef cow operation gets a cow fattened up to be sold for meat. Ed's father had a Holstein dairy cow operation there in Marin. Strictly milk, but the little bull calves were sold off for veal, which is meat from a milk-fed calf. They had so much land, that they used the back ranch for a cow-calf operation. They had black angus cattle. The calves were raised to about 400 pounds and sold off. The females were kept for breeding.

On Dad and Mother's farm, the main source of income was the corn and alfalfa, but every inch of land was used for something. The ground near the creek was wet and used as pasture land. The rest that was tillable was used for crops. When I was a child, Dad ran about two hundred cattle. But when I was in eighth grade, he bought a large place, doubling his acreage, and he moved us into the house which was bigger than ours. He put in feed lots and probably fed out about a thousand cows a year. They were sold off when they reached about a thousand pounds.

Mom and Dad had three boys and two girls. Sally is the oldest, nine months older than me. Nine months after me was Eddie. Ten months later, Jessie, and ten months later, Jack. After the birth of Jack, Mom had her tubes tied and they excommunicated her from the Catholic church. They did that in those days.

My earliest memories are of laughing, playing and getting into trouble. As Mr. Douglas at the hardware store in town used to say, "Here comes Mrs. Sweet and her tribe of Indians." To me it was a joke. I never noticed anything different about us. I wasn't aware of any hostilities until the Ku Klux Klan came and burned a cross on our ranch. My Dad went out with a shot gun and called out to them by name because he recognized their boots. That was enough to scare them off.

My Dad was a great guy. Kind, generous, a great sense of humor. He was an excellent farmer and the hardest worker I know. He wasn't afraid to try new things. He was one of the first farmers in the area to get a loan from the bank to level the land and ditch irrigate the crops rather than dry farm. That was around 1950. Dad never used pesticides. He recycled the manure. When the chemical dealers—the fertilizer salesmen—came he'd say get the dog off the leash Susie. Around 1964, the government demanded that all marijuana be destroyed with chemical sprays. To us it was just a weed—loco weed—that grew in rope ditches but it cost Dad about $10,000 a year to eradicate it. By then we had two sections, 1280 acres, mostly in corn. In addition to the home ranch, which he worked.

Dad got up at 4:30 and Mom made a big breakfast. He'd load up a feed wagon to feed all of the cattle. Then get on the tractor to prepare, seed, cultivate, or "hill it" for irrigation. Then the ditches were dug, filled with water. Irrigation was done then with a siphon tube. One end was in the irrigation ditch and the other into the row of corn. It had been plowed on a slant to run downward, so we'd go to the end of the row, about a mile away, to check it. We'd do that morning to night, all summer long. Dad would get us up early and he had us work in teams, dividing us up according to who worked well together. So Jack and I worked as a team and

Sally and Eddie worked as a team. He put us on our horses, with a bridle but usually bareback, because it was just too hot for the horses otherwise. We'd take care of the pumps all day to be filling up the hoops. I was probably around 3 or 4 when I started. For us, it was a fun game. And we each got a quarter a week. A quarter went a long way on Saturday night at La Howitzes candy store. You can get a lot of penny candy for a quarter!

When we were older, we were driving tractors, helping with the hay, planting the corn, cultivating the corn. By then, we got a salary. A dollar an hour I think. And we had savings accounts. We went into town on Saturday nights and the bank was always open then. All these farmers would bring their kids in to put their money into their savings accounts. It was a good lesson to learn. We all had our farm animals too—4H—that you took to the fair. That went into the bank too. We always had a goal. After 8th grade, we went to the town school so the goal was always to buy an old car or pickup. You could get a special license at that age to drive from farm to school.

Dad also had hired hands, usually from the Polish community to the north—a poor community called Krakow. If they started working for him in 8th grade, and they continued to work summers through high school, he had a contract with them that if they kept up their grades to qualify, he would help them with college. As far as I know, there were 14 kids that he helped to get through college. Most of the guys were the honorary pall bearers at his funeral. I wish I could have had a recorder in the hearse because I was told that they all had stories to tell of Dad. They all went on to become excellent farmers, mostly around Krakow.

The home ranch went to my Uncle Joe, who had never married. My Aunt Ethel had never married, so she stayed on that farm too and is still there. She's 92 and still lives on the home place. The others all got ranches close by, just the way my Dad did.

The Sweets in that area were probably the most successful of families. Uncle Frank had a section. Uncle George went into carpentry so just bought 50 acres for raising vegetables. He went around building these exquisite barns. George was a painter. One built the barns, the other painted them! All the girls in Dad's family became school teachers. My Aunt Ethel was the first one in the family to get a PhD in education at the University of Nebraska. It took a long time of course. She was probably in her late 40s. She taught upper levels in the Lincoln School District. My brother Jack farms the home place and the home place of my grandfather. His son Jessie works with him. Frank's two girls married into farming.

The biggest change now I notice is the deterioration of places that used to be show places. The kids didn't want to stay and work that hard. They went off to college and learned that they could make more money with less work. 9 to 5 rather than sunrise to sunset. And they could buy nice cars and other things. What farmers get for their product now is basically nothing, because we no longer export in the quantities we did in the past. Farm equipment now is astronomical to buy. A tractor can cost 200 grand. And that doesn't include the harrower and the disk. A combine to harvest corn—huge, computerized—costs a fortune. Dad could buy used equipment and he could fix his own equipment. You can't do this with modern, technological equipment.

When I was growing up, farm subsidies came in. Dad thought that was just a way to support a farmer who didn't know how to farm in the first place. Yes, they had an over-production of corn. But there were plenty of countries that needed it. Why couldn't we have found a country who could use it? On a flat Nebraska plain, a stockpile of corn rose up like a mountain. Corn the government had bought.

There were always bad seasons of course. Like the tornado with golf ball size hail, when we lost a whole crop. But my father was diversified. He didn't put his eggs in one basket; JUST corn. JUST cattle. JUST alfalfa. And when the corn crops were bad, he planted potatoes. When the potato crop failed, he did something else, but while he raised them, he made money.

We never lacked for food on the table. We didn't have a whole lot of money but I never felt poor. We played a lot and worked really hard, but we were always rewarded for the work. I remember learning a lot and being happy. Dad always gave us praise for the good work we did, which gave us confidence growing up. The girls did the same work as the boys. We all had certain jobs we had to do. I went into the garden in the morning with Mom to pick food for the noon meal for 14 or 15 people. I had to help her chop the heads off the chickens to cook. Sally had to stay in the house and clean. I begged Dad to let me go outside and work because I didn't like the inside work.

Dad found work for me and took me with him to the sale barn to buy animals. I used to sit there with all these guys. I was the only little girl in the place and they all made a fuss over me. The women in town had baked pies for the men which I got to share. He taught me how to put my hand up and bid. He made me go ahead with it and I got some pretty bad animals for a while.

SUSIE GROSSI WITH MR. LA HOWITZ'S SCALES

Dad was good at teaching his kids. Once I stole a penny piece of bubble gum at La Howitz 5-and-10. Mr. La Howitz told my Dad so Dad brought me back in and said to Mr. LaHowitz, "here's the little thief. Tell her what you want her to do." I remember shaking in my boots while he showed me the broom and the dust pan and the dustbin. All the family was sitting in the car waiting for me. Everybody else was going home. I was inside Mr. LaHowitz's store getting the floor swept, crying my eyes out. My Dad took me back there the next morning and I had to work two weeks—two weeks!—for that penny bubblegum that I stole. But when Mr. La Howitz died, he left this in his will for me. Let me get it down here for you. It's Mr. LaHowitz's scale that he weighed out the penny candy in. He actually left it in his will for me. I can never get rid of it. It just reminds me that I'm never again to take the penny candy. Mrs. LaHowitz felt sorry for me and would slip me candy at the end of the day. Mr. La Howitz came to my graduation. And you know, it was a good experience for me. I came to see what it would be like to work in town and it gave me ideas about my future.

Farm families were great about having social events. There was the band concert in town on Saturday night. Sometimes the Polish community would come down and play Polka music. Then there was a Swedish community about six miles away and they would have Swede days with entertainment. Then there was another Czech town where they would have Czech days. They were like mini-festivals. Then there were dances on the river too. There was a place on the Platte River that they used for roller skating and then they would freeze it for ice skating in the winter. That's where they used to have dances too. Uncle Tom, the carpenter's son, would come and pick me up and take me, with his other friends, to dances on the river at the Platte River Dance Hall. There was a hamburger drive-thru where we'd get a burger and cherry coke. When we'd come home, the house looked dark as if they were all asleep, but when we drove in, the pole light would start flashing on and off: Dad making sure we knew he was waiting for us to come in. Maybe that's why I took so long to get married! 'Cause Dad put the fear of God into those boys! He was a classic flicker-of-the-pole-light. If you didn't come in then, the kitchen light would come on and if the kitchen light came on, you knew he was coming. He was on his way!

My Dad was strict. I got spanked sometimes but there was always a reason. I remember every spanking I got and what I did and I know I deserved it. It was always for something big. One of them was because we snuck up behind two cows near the water tank and tied their tails together. They took off running and one cow lost her tail. We got the cow in the barn and called the vet and the vet came out and treated the cow. So then he made my brothers and I sit in the barn with scissors and a big needle—the kind that sewed up the bags of wool sheared off the sheep—and gunny sacks. We had to make a coat for the cow. Since we took her tail away, she had no protection against the flies. It took us two days to get that coat done. We had to keep the cow in the barn, put fresh bedding down and keep the poop out of there, absolutely keep the poop out of there. And for the rest of the year, our job every morning was to go and put the coat on the cow.

The other really big thing I remember we got spanked for was once, when they had rounded up the bulls in the fall, to shift them to new pastures. We crawled up on the side of the fence and we've got pockets full of stones and we're throwing them at the bulls, making them madder and madder. I think the reason we got spanked so hard on that one is that he was afraid of what could have happened to us.

The Platte was three miles away and its tributaries ran through the property. On Friday nights in August, Mom would pack a picnic of fried chicken and potato salad for us and we would go down by the Platte to play in the water. They say the Platte River is an inch deep and a mile wide, but there are also holes and quick sand.

Mom was a very strong force in my life because I saw her work so hard. She was a quiet, elegant lady. Never needed much or spent money on herself. Raising children *was a stressful experience for her. In the early days, there was no electricity and a wringer washer. We had a wood burning stove and no plumbing. But Dad went to town and bought her a big tub that he rigged up on the porch and plumbed so that she could give us all a bath at one time. My mom had lots of clothes lines strung through the house with clothes and diapers. It was a two room house, with all the kids in one room.*

It was very isolated so it was a big deal if a car came. Us kids would run like little idiots to see who it was. She taught us girls how to sew and how to iron. I liked ironing so I would do it in the evenings and she would pay me a quarter for so many pieces. She was happy not to do it. I also got paid a quarter a week by my Dad for washing the separator in the milking barn. My sister Sally hated it because she couldn't stand the smell. I'd take the pieces out in the yard with a bucket of soapy water and a bucket of rinse.

I was into making money. Dad paid us a penny a sunflower to chop the sunflowers out of the corn field. So we'd go up and down the rows of corn and haul them out and put the sunflowers in a pile. He pretended that he counted every one of them but I don't think he did.

The small farmers who were struggling have been bought out by big corporations like Kellogg. Dad believed that when the corporate people came in, they would ruin the land. That they would come in with chemicals and modified seeds without knowing what the outcome would be. Dad didn't believe that genetically altered seeds should enter the food supply.

All my siblings remained on the ranches but the next generation is starting to move to the city.

FARMER ED'S NEWS

ED AND SUSIE HAD GIVEN ME THE NEWS WHEN I CAME BY the farm in the Spring to visit Mr. Fields for a few days and air him out after the winter. It hit me hard—less for myself than for the many customers, the farm workers and the hundreds of children who had come to look forward to their October field trip to Grossis.

The farm was losing money. It had been for several years and the nursery, which was flourishing, had basically been subsidizing it. In recent years, as I was all too aware, weather had not worked in our favor and it looked like a real climate change was taking place. Where the farm once opened in June with its strawberries and had tomatoes and crane melons by August, rains were coming in May that delayed the planting season. Summers were more overcast and there were not enough hot days to ripen the tomatoes and other vegetables. Each year I had worked there, the farm stand had opened later. Last year, we didn't open until September 1ˢᵗ and the tomatoes still weren't ripe. "This will be our last season," Ed said. "Besides, I'm getting older. I'm tired," he said honestly. Ed had been working two jobs now for a few years—running the nursery with Susie during the week, plowing after work and overseeing the farm. He was still the main contact with the supermarkets, although I had been able to take on some of this for him. Managers get used to working with the farm owner. People knew and loved Ed and he was still the face of Grossi Farms. But it was an inhuman pace for even a younger man used to hard work. Ed was now pushing 60. "I'm ready to get a few weekends off," he said. "We may continue the Pumpkin season in October and have the schools come. Would you be up for that?"

I said I would and they assured me that my home in Mr. Fields was there for me any time. By now, Susie and Eddie were like family.

In September, I made up an announcement to be posted about the closing of the farm. We had flyers for the customers but mostly I broke the news to them one by one. They were devastated. It was like being at a funeral that would never end. For all of Ed's resigned tone, I knew this had to be a real loss for him—a farmer to the bone. He was luckier than some other farmers with the same problem because he had the nursery business to support him. But deep down, his true home was on a tractor—"moving dirt" as he put it. He still found occasion to do that—preparing the soil and planting pumpkins as well as a winter crop of oats, which could be sold for feed in the spring. He was back to haymaking.

If there was one thing I had learned from Dominic and from Pop Grossi, farmers know how to adapt to change. It is what a farmer's life is all about.

✳ ✳ ✳ ✳

Sonoma Coast: Kashaya Pomo village of Metini ~ 1962

DREAM DANCE

SCENE: *In the background, the grass is a brilliant green, lush after the season of rains, in a clear light before the season of mists. A wall made of brush, maybe six feet high, in a circle, with openings to the east and the west. And in the center, the women dancing.*

Four women, big, strong, with thick arms and solid bodies that seem made of earth themselves. Earth to earth, yet lightly they dance. Graceful, serious, sure. Their feet are hidden under the long dresses as if they were secretly tapping out a message from the Creator. Above their broad shoulders, brown hair falls in waves, underneath a wreath of flowers. From their fingers stream ribbons, black and the pale color of tule. The colors of their baskets. Thick arms wave them back and forth, like waves of water flowing in the air. Or up and down in quick movements like rain or tall rushes bending in a storm. In their mouths, each is blowing on a double-reed whistle which sighs above the split elderberry clapper rattles of the two singers. Their white long dresses are in the style of American frontier women. Black and white designs have been appliquéd on the bodice. Dream designs. As the dance itself has been dreamed.

ESSIE PARRISH: *We believe songs are delightful to Yukabe and our songs are prayers to please him. "Bole" is a Patwin word for Spirit. Maru means Dreamer. The Bole Maru religion is under the leadership of prophets who communicate in dreams or trance with the spirit world. Through the revelation of dreams, each local dreamer gets her supernatural authority.*

Maru means to dream something [with the Great Creator]. Indians always dreamed but our Maru is new. The Creator gives the dreams to a Maru Dreamer. [A yuncta.] I am a Yuncta. The details of each dance are controlled by the local dreamer. This dance is the Choso Weya Ko'o—The Hand Power Dance.

The dancers movements with the colored ribbons are important. It is the color of the ribbons that make them valuable. Like the colors of the magnesite beads and our feather baskets. The ribbons that flow from their hands represent the powers of the dreamer's right hand. It is this power which locates pain and draws it out in doctoring.

The four dancers circle round the fire and then do a quick step, spinning in circles. The dances ends, like all Bole Maru dances, with a short ceremony performed by the dancers and musicians called the Itay Lau.

In 1872, when the men failed to take leadership in the religious activities, the women assumed control. Special dances were developed and danced only by them.

I am a Yuncta. A prophetess of the Creator. And when he places a Yuncta upon the earth to be a witness for him, to represent him, he places within that Yuncta all the mysteries of life.

Every little thing is recorded within me and I could know all things if I take the time to search what is within me. Someday the whole world will know about me and the tradition of my people.

Dreamers have to do everything their dreams tell them. They don't rest well at night. They stay awake most of the time, until they have done all that their dreams directed. Then they feel relief. The Creator said—You have to dance, hold a big feast and tell the people about your dreams.

We have no writing. No education, like the white people. The creator sends dreamers and prophets. The keepers of the Indian custom. The Dreamer gives each dancer the responsibility of keeping one religious article on her cloth banner. The article itself may be made of cloth or wood or some other material. If the article becomes lost or destroyed, its pattern is preserved by the designs on the banner. The cloth banners appliquéd with dream designs express our beliefs.

Since the dances' designs and paraphernalia come from the dream, they are constantly changing [to reflect current cultural influences]. The dreamers receive designs for their regalia then sew them on cloth. This sets them on the right path. But once they have put designs on the cloth, they must dance in them to get protection.

— From the 1962 documentary "Dream Dances of the Kashia Pomo" filmed by the University of California.

Grossi Farms ~ Late October

THE LAST CLASS

THE DAILY ARRIVAL OF SCHOOL BUSES IS OVER. The rush is mid-month, peaking in the third week. On Halloween Day, if it is during the week, the schools have their own celebrations. This year Halloween is on a Tuesday and nothing is scheduled after the Friday before. The weather is touch and go then too—November's frosty chill breathing down on us and the first of the winter rains.

I received a call on Friday asking if we could do a class on Halloween Day. I was surprised, since our classes seemed finished on that Friday and we rarely got requests so late in the month. "Sure," I said. "What time and how many children."

"Eleven would be good. Would that work?"

"Sure. It's good to allow 45 minutes or an hour for the tour, the hayride, and the hay maze. How many children?"

"Eight."

"What age?"

"Well the youngest is 7 and the oldest is 15."

I paused a moment to take that in.

"What's the name of your school?"

"Kashaya."

"Could you spell that?"

"K-A-S-H-A-Y-A. Is there a place we can eat our lunch there?"

"They can sit on the hay bales and eat their lunch by the maze."

"That would be great. It's a two hour drive back and they will be hungry."

"TWO HOURS?" Why would anyone come to Grossi Farms from two hours away?

"Yes. It's a long drive from Stewart's Point."

"Well we will be looking forward to seeing you all."

Our last class was coming from two hours away. Amazing. Terry the Herb Lady was passing by just then. Terry grows herbs at the edge of the farm and has developed a wonderful line of products that she sells in the farm stand and at farmers' markets. I told her with amazement of the conversation I had just had.

"Ah, those would be the Kashaya Pomo up there on Stewart Point. I know that area. My grandfather was in the timber business up there."

"You mean these are Pomo Indians? This is the reservation school?"

"That's right."

When Alison, my latest assistant from Sonoma State arrived, I gave her the news and her eyes grew as big as saucers. This was the first time Alison had shown much interest in her work. She did what was asked of her but never showed particular enthusiasm. Of course now that we no longer had vegetables and just waited for classes or the occasional pumpkin customer, the farm stand was not a lively place except when the school busses arrived. Then it was chaos.

"Pomo Indians! I'm writing a paper on California Indians. I think I'm part

Indian myself. This is just GREAT. Wow!" Enthusiasm just poured from her like a fountain that had been dammed up by boredom, I suppose. The conversation led to dreams, she had studied Pomo dreamers, and I shared the fact that I was a dream worker. More enthusiasm. "I've been taking a great course in dreams at Sonoma State. I've been keeping a notebook of my dreams. I'll bring it to show you tomorrow."

The last day of the farm and the last class arrived on a chill gray Novemberish day, but Alison and I were warmed by the thought of our visitors, driving those two hours toward us through the morning. A small bus with Kashaya Pomo School lettered on the side, drove in at close to 11. A small group of children stepped out of assorted age and size, but clearly Native American. I greeted them and led them to the place at the edge of the orchard where Farmer Ed gave his talk on Grossi Farms and organic farming. Delfino sat waiting on the tractor in front of the hay wagon. I went to talk one of the women who had come with them. I was familiar with Native American reticence and knew to approach with reserved friendliness. I asked if she would like any water after her long ride. She shook her head. It seemed wrong to give voice to all of the questions in my mind, but later I was able to talk more openly to the Anglo school teacher. She lived on the reservation and had great respect for the Pomo people. Alison plied her with several questions and asked if the teacher thought she could visit the reservation. The teacher told her who to contact to ask.

We were joined by a woman in her late 30s, I guessed, who was the mother of a lively and handsome little boy of about 9. She explained to me that at the moment they did not have a chief. A leader. Such people, she said, were "shown" to them. Sometimes in dreams. She nodded toward the boy. Some say it will be him. We are watching."

We were sad to see them go. Like bidding good-bye to old, long-anticipated friends. But there was also the fact—so very clear now—that this had been the last class. The season was over. Grossi Farms was over.

Grossi Farms ~ 2005

GOOD-BYES: THOSE WHO GO

AT CLOSING TIME, ALFONSO IS THERE WITH ME. I have sent Alison on home. It looks like it might rain and I don't expect any more customers on this last day. We say little. We don't kid. We share a companionable silence. This is usually the moment when all pitch in so gallantly to put my vegetables away, even though it's not their job. I look around and shrug my shoulders. "Not much to put away." Alfonso nods, as I push the handcart into the stand and fill it with the few light boxes. Lazaro and Angel have returned and they just watch me. It's as if they had lost some coinage in no longer being able to perform this small task for me, There's no reason now for them to stay but they can't leave either. I call to them over my shoulder as I load the boxes in the reefer, trying to return to our usual banter.

"*Adios, Niños Heroes!*" I say. This is a joke between us. The Niños Heroes are young soldier heroes of the Battle of Chapultepec in the Mexican-American War. There is a monument to them in Mexico City. When I see them marching back toward the stand from their Cantina Lunchroom with their smooth Mexican swagger, I often say "*Aqui vienen mis Niños Heroes.*" Here come my Boy Heroes.

"*Hasta la vista,*" Alfonso responds. (I've only ever heard gringos use this phrase.)

"*Hasta pronto,*" I call out from the dark interior. "See you soon." Not that I will.

"*Hasta luego,*" comes the reply, as they move toward their vans and trucks. I latch the reefer door and insert its huge round electrical plug in its outlet to turn it on for the night.

I pick up the cash box and my backpack and head back toward the nursery office and Mr. Fields.

"*Señora!*"

I turn to look back. It's Lazaro with his earnest look.

"*Que sueñe con los angelitos.*"

"*Igualmente, Lazaro.*"

May you dream with the little angels.

You too Lazaro.

Grossi Farms ~ A Sunday Morning

JOHANN SEBASTIAN, AUGUSTINUS AURELIUS
AND MR. FIELDS

The Chicago Symphony Orchestra and Chorus have joined me in Mr. Fields this morning, along with an old and dear friend, Herr Bach—Johann Sebastian. Amid the pungent scent of eucalyptus and the fragrant smoke drifting this way from Ed's Sunday morning trash burn, the glorious voices lift their praises into the bright morning air accompanied by birds, lyrical in their own living celebration of the day. To think that I can share with them the grandeur of *St. Matthew's Passion*—even without electricity!—seems wonderful and miraculous.

And here I am too with St. Augustine, in far off Italy of another time, but touching me as intimately with his praise of God and creation as J. Bach from a millennium later and half a millennium before this day.

Is this not a wonder?

As I listen, the work and its composer is as present to me now as Daedalus was for Homer, Aeneas was for Virgil, Cicero was for Augustine, and Augustine was for Petrarch—though they lived centuries apart. As present as Emerson was, on the still quiet nights of John Muir in Yellowstone.

I feel that I have been granted a great happiness, in spite of what some might see as a great poverty. At the moment, my particular life is the sun rising over Sonoma Mountain, the sublime music of Bach made possible for me by a gift from my brother and his wife of an iPod and a portable, battery-operated sound system which will play it for me. I have these new friends, Augustine and Paul the Deacon and others made possible for me by a short walk to Sonoma State University across the street and a $10 community membership access to the beautiful unversity library in the Jean and Charles Schulz Information Center. From the college store, I buy pen, paper and any other thing I need to study and write.

We have never had such a banquet of possibilities for making a simple and good life with all we most love. The choosing process is the essence of it all and there is where we founder. We are being sold *everything* on the banquet table. Made to feel embarrassed if we have left behind a delicacy. Told that we will starve without it. Yet if we eat all the hors d'oeuvres, all the entrees, all the desserts, what will we have tasted? What will we have savored? No wonder there are so many remedies on the market for indigestion. No wonder we have become literally insatiable.

I find for myself that the key to a savory meal is the hunger that precedes it, as the key to beautiful music is the silence out of which it comes. So the main ingredient of my pleasure, my happiness, is a spacious void between things; an emptiness in which I may be, for its duration, content and not voracious. Voracious hunger is never filled or satisfied but becomes addiction. Love of silence sharpens the ear to sound.

Above all, my happiness comes from nature: the sound, the sight, the smell of living things in a living world. Unlike artificial objects, they remain fresh and new, as if they had just come into being. Into this world, I can selectively bring my man-made treasures, artistic and practical. Bach, Augustine, my one plate, one pan, one cup, two spoons and an extra fork. Perfect.

EPILOGUE

San Francisco ~ 1992

GRACE

THERE ARE FORTY FOUR STEPS TO GRACE. I start up them at the corner of Bush and Jones Streets, half a block from my residence at the Mary Elizabeth Inn for Women in Transition on Bush Street. We all laugh at that: Who *isn't* in transition? MEI, as we call it, was the brain child of Lizzie Glide, who saw a need in San Francisco for a protected place for single women coming to the city for employment, schooling and other reasons. I have twisted the chronoscope back a bit to my own arrival in San Francisco to attend graduate school. I am one of those women Lizzie was thinking of—a single woman coming to the city for schooling. She built it in 1914 and donated it to the United Methodist Church. United Methodist Women are running it today. Lizzie is more well-known for her building of Glide Memorial Church in San Francisco, which she founded fifteen years later. Glide is located in the heart of the Tenderloin, serving the poorest of the poor in the city under its charismatic and sometimes controversial leader Cecil Williams.

I always say to friends that I live suspended between Heaven and Hell. I can walk two blocks down and be among the x-rated movies stores, hookers, drug pushers and panhandlers of the Tenderloin, or walk two blocks up—forty-four steps to ease the steepness of the incline—and emerge on Nob Hill opposite Grace Cathedral. That's San Francisco for you: A seven square mile city where you can go from the poorest of the poor to the richest in a few energetic steps (since most of it is uphill or down).

While living at the Mary Elizabeth Inn, I walked down each day through the Tenderloin to Market Street to catch the 7 or 71 bus to Haight-Ashbury, where the California Institute of Integral Studies was located at the time. That walk was both invigorating and humbling: Nodding shyly to the streetwalkers, the derelicts, the street people who were mostly Viet Nam veterans, shattered physically or mentally or both. The bus ride was edifying in its own way. I called it the Leather and Studs run. A mixed lot of passengers heading to or from the Haight—vampire-styled, beringed, beleathered, and fluorescent coiffed. I once lost $20 in a shell game on the 71. I sometimes learned more on the way *to* school than *in* school.

On Wednesday nights, chaplain Penny Sarvis of Network Ministries came to offer a worship service in the small chapel at the Inn. Network Ministries, founded by Glenda and Scott Hope, offers services for the homeless and residents of the Tenderloin and runs a safe house for women escaping prostitution. MEI was just on her beat.

I was intrigued by the fact that this trim, intelligent forty-some woman was a chaplain in the Tenderloin and I asked her about her work there. I wanted to go with her sometime on her "rounds." She invited me to go one day to a hotel that was a key part of her ministry. It was a terminus. A dead-end place where hospitals sent poor AIDS patients who wouldn't recover, or social services sent drug addicts who *might* recover. A step down from a flophouse, which had the advantage of being only temporary.

There was a sluggish gloom over the place, but Penny entered with her quiet good spirit and put the coffee pot on to brew. Then we walked through the narrow halls as she greeted people, asked how they were and introduced me. A young blonde man named Andy invited us into his room. Every inch of wall was covered by some graphic, mostly from magazines. The small room looked like a psychedelic bad trip. Andy had AIDS, so perhaps this was a way of keeping the world alive around him as it was escaping within. This was before effective treatment had been found for the disease.

A few weeks later, I received a call from Penny asking me if I would be willing to do a dream for Andy. She knew that I had a small dream group at the Inn at the time. Andy was having bad dreams and was very frightened. All of his friends had died of AIDS and he was the last one left. I always welcome the opportunity, the privilege really, of doing dreams with people of all ages and backgrounds. They teach me. So I readily agreed.

The next day I walked down to the Tenderloin in the late afternoon to meet Andy at the local Wendy's. We sat in a booth in the back and I listened to his dream over a coke. Only it was not a dream. I recognized that right away. As wild and varied as night dreams are, they still have a recognizable character and I can follow my usual approach in trying to get at their meaning or message with the dreamers.

This dream was what I call an After Death Experience—not so different from what we hear of Near Death Experiences or NDEs. He is walking down a hall and sees in a room on his right a coffin, and people around it weeping. They are people close to him in real life and he realizes that the coffin is his own. He is startled by this and wants to let them know he is there, but he can't communicate. He continues down the hall and finds himself in a beautiful green meadow. In the distance, a waterfall, toward which he walks. I had heard similar imagery on the few occasions that someone—always someone approaching death—had shared a similar "dream." There is a different quality to these.

C.S. Lewis has such a scene in his book *The Last Battle*, which is his final book in the Narnia series. I assured Andy that he had been given a great gift in the dream; a glimpse of what lay beyond his death, so that he needn't be frightened and could reassure others. His face held a radiant light at this point—right there as night descended on Wendy's in the Tenderloin. I might have been frightened walking through this grim neighborhood in the dark, but Andy had given *me* a great gift with his dream and I was free of fear, full of quiet joy, as I made the steep walk up Jones to Bush Street.

The climb to Grace is equally steep but ends in a very different reality. In this direction, Jones Street leads up to Nob Hill, the peak of San Francisco. We meet our four New York nobodies here in their huge Somebody incarnations. Grace Cathedral sits on property owned by Charles. The cathedral is the descendant of little Grace Church, built on Powell Street in 1849 and replaced by a larger brick church by the time of the Earthquake when it was destroyed. The Crocker family donated their ruined property on Nob Hill to the Episcopal Diocese to erect a full-size cathedral. Now here it sits in imposing grandeur on the very nob of the city with its imposing French Gothic architecture, bell tower and replica of the Ghiberti doors—the Gates of Paradise—which once graced the Florence Baptisty.[*]

To my right is the Scarlet Huntington Hotel, named after our friend Collis and built after his death. It is across the street from the the location of the original Huntington Mansion where he lived. It is now the site of Huntington Park. A block beyond that is the Mark Hopkins Hotel, one of the not-to-be-missed landmarks of San Francisco, renowned for the "view from the Top of the Mark." I visited it once in rather unusual circumstances. I had met Australian anthropologist Diana James at a conference in Ontario, California. She was there with Lee and Leah, members of the aboriginal Pitjantjatjara Tribe of Australia. They were coming to San Francisco to do an interview on New Dimensions Radio and Diana asked me if I could arrange a meeting with Brian Swimme, one of my professors at CIIS. I agreed to that and also to honor a special request from Lee to go somewhere high enough up to have a good view of the city. Well, that would be the Top of the Mark surely, so that was arranged too

We arrived by taxi at the site of the Nob Hill hotel. Lee and Leah were dressed simply in western street clothes. But there was an unmistakable air of the wide open spaces of the Australian bush about them and the distinct aboriginal features of their heritage. Lee was a tall, dark, robust man with an impressive, imposing presence. And then there was the fact that he was carrying a bow. I can't recall now why this huge bow traveled up and down the elevator at CIIS, to many curious glances, and now accompanied us up the posh elevator of the luxurious Mark Hopkins Hotel. We seemed more likely candidates for a safari than the Top of the Mark.

The elevator doors opened directly onto the restaurant, which was full of people dining at elegant tables, taking in the spectacular view of the city and listening to the soft jazz being played by a combo of black musicians. When Lee stepped off the elevator, shouldering the huge bow, he made instant eye contact with the lead musician of the band and they both raised a hand and called "Hello Brother" across the crowded room. It was an amazing moment. Cups and forks halted in mid-air as the diners took in this curious visitation. I took a deep breath and went on about the business of taking Lee and Leah and Diana from window to window ("excuse us, excuse us. We're here for the view . . .").

Just beyond the Mark Hopkins is Stanford Court, on the site of Amasa Leland

[*] The present doors on the Florence Baptistry are copies of the original doors, which are preserved in the Museo dell'Opera del Duomo in Florence.

Stanford's mansion. Our New York Nobodies who never met one another during their modest days in the Empire State, became close and prosperous neighbors on their San Francisco peak. Nice to know you can borrow a cup of sugar from a millionaire on any side of you.

Directly across California Street from Grace is an equally grand, although very different building. I didn't notice it until the first time I exited the cathedral on that side and there it stood before me: San Francisco's Masonic Temple. It has the coveted address of 1111 California Street. In counterpoint to Grace Cathedral's French Gothic Architecture, steeped in British and European history, the Masonic Temple is an icon of mid-century modernist architecture. By its own description "It is a testament to simple lines, open spaces, and heavy materials, and was designed to be a 'beacon of light for all Masons.'"

When I caught that first glimpse of it from Grace, I was stunned. I crossed the street to have a better look. Through the glass entrance was the largest mural I had ever seen, other than the murals in Mexico City's Zocalo. It rose two stories and covered the entire wall of the entry area, about fifty feet. In the very center of it rose a large human figure in silhouette. No details to it except a white apron in the shape of an envelope. I was looking at the Master Architect: the Magister Comicini. Daedalus. The builders of Dido's Carthage. Of the church of San Bernardo in Monte Carasso or the Church of the Holy Virgin in Brione. Or those churches in the high Pyrenees with their mysterious "virgin of the grail." St. Reparatus. The walls of Troy. The Temples of Rome. An icon of stoneworkers everywhere, including those who left Ticino each winter to work on churches in Italy and Europe.

On one side of the Master Architect were two figures with hands extended toward him, described by the artist as the landfarers, balanced by two figures on the other side described as the seafarers. Those who go. By land and by sea. But here, they are those who came, in particular masons who helped develop California; people in all forms of industry. There are ships, like the San Carlos. A Mission. The 49ers. The pioneers in covered wagons. Dairy farmers. Ranchers. The Golden Gate Bridge. The tools of every trade are there.

Emile Norman was the self-taught designer of this master work. He incorporated thousands of pieces of natural material, native to the area, such as seashells, grass, soil, foliage, thinly sliced vegetable matter, bits of metal and 180 different colors of stained glass.

In one way or another, all of the portraits in this book can be seen here. There is even a beehive, as iconic to the masons as it was to the Minoans. Tiny workers about their business of building their complex hives, making their golden honey, nourishing the gods, like Zeus on Mt. Ida and modern-day honey lovers from Winnie-the-Pooh to humans across the planet; the farmer's best friend as the pollinator of crops.

Surmounting the mural at its lofty height is the All-seeing Eye, as a reminder that all works are being watched over by the Great Architect of the Universe—an image that goes back to the ancient Egyptians as the right eye of Horus: the Sun.

The two buildings, so very different from one another, have one subtle element in common with one another: Daedalus. In the early Masonic guilds, Daedalus was celebrated as the prototype of the Master Architect. He was also remembered as the creator of the Labyrinth, which figures so prominently in the myth of Theseus and the Minotaur, still depicted in Roman times in mosaic pavements and appearing first in the Christian church of St. Reparatus in North Africa in the fourth century.

The Labyrinth is what brings me up the forty-four steps to Grace. Rev. Lauren Artress, Canon of Special Ministries, has hired me for a short time as her Labyrinth assistant and I am on my way to work. Lauren had conceived the idea of reproducing the medieval labyrinth from Chartres Cathedral on the floor of Grace Cathedral. It had fallen into disuse at Chartres, but in Lauren's mind, it provided the perfect western form of meditation, as it had once been in medieval times. A walking meditation that suited the temperament and life-style of busy westerners. One had been created on the outside of the church in terrazzo, where anyone at any time could walk it. We also had a temporary indoor labyrinth in canvas, which we could lay out on the cathedral floor one evening a week, also open to anyone who wished to walk it.

My project was to oversee the creation of a permanent labyrinth floor tapestry, which could remain on the floor at all times. As Rev. Artress had already discovered, this was not an easy task. It required the application of the sacred geometry of the ancients based on cosmic rather than material proportions. In the end, she had turned to Keith Critchlow, a leading expert in sacred architecture and sacred geometry in England.

Lauren Artress had awakened a sleeping dragon in the human psyche. After articles appeared in *Walking Magazine* and *The New York Times* on her Labyrinth Project, she was deluged by communications from all over the world and requests for information on how to create one. Overwhelmed by this response, she got a grant to hire an assistant for a short period and I was the lucky recipient of the job.[*]

Forty-four steps . . .

---

[*] I highly recommend Lauren Artress's book *Walking a Sacred Path*, which recounts her story of the labyrinth project and provides details of the history and use of the labyrinth. Her story also appears in Terry Lazlo-Gopadze's *The Spirit of a Woman*.

LABYRINTH

*We all inhabit this spiral; an inner odyssey in which we take our turn as the
warrior whose taste for the fight dissolves into a need for the ancient quiet.*

— MARK NEPO
Seven Thousand Ways to Listen

THERE IS THE SINGLE WINSOME SOUND OF A FLUTE FIRST, *rising
up into the high dome of the cathedral. The sound of a tenor sax, slow and haunting,
circles slowly round the other end of this great stone edifice. After a silent pause,
crystalline voices rise together in a medieval madrigal. Tinted light from the stain-
glass windows hovers over the stone floor and the large white canvas with the
intricate figure of a labyrinth painted on it. A replica of the labyrinth at Chartres
Cathedral that was created there around the year 1200. The group is Musica Divina
and they play every Wednesday for the Labyrinth walk, when we lay down the
canvas labyrinth.*

*I have walked it many times, since I began work as Lauren's labyrinth assistant a
few months ago. Each walk is a unique journey but today's is particularly special for
me. My dear friend and mentor, Jack Cross, is walking ahead of me, at a thoughtful
pace, pausing often to listen. I see his head turn back to see what a musician is
doing and I know how keenly attuned he is to each sound. He is in the city for just
a few days from New York and this moment is the peak of our visit together. Jack is
a physician in Virginia but he is also a composer of lovely music that has threaded
through my entire adult life. I came to California because of them in 1966. Jack, his
wife Barbara—my high school history teacher—and their three children. I lived with
them then in Julian, in the mountains of San Diego County. Jack's medical office
was in Santa Ysabel, on land that had previously been owned by Carlos Martinoia,
also known as Charles Martin, after he moved from Marin. Jack was composing a
ballet during that period. Lying awake in the guest house, listening to the soaring
music of his Steinway blend with the wind as it soughed through the pines, I could
imagine that I was back in Valldemosa on Majorca, listening to the music of Chopin
on the island where Father Serra was born.*

*For the last decade, Jack has been composing his opera, "Knossos, the House
of the Double Axe." Ariadne dances on the labyrinth in his work and I can feel her
presence as we walk this mysterious path, created for her by Daedalus. I recently
read that in the center of the Chartres Labyrinth, there may once have been a
plaque depicting the minotaur. But no one has taken this seriously. Especially in
a Christian church. For centuries, the six-petaled rose at the center has been a
symbol of the Virgin Mary, and her presence in this beautiful cathedral sheds a more
immediate grace. But the value of the labyrinth is not in any thought, doctrine or
personage. It is a path almost as old as time and as we walk it, accompanied by
the prayerful sounds of the Musica Divina musicians, we are beyond time and the
journey is incalculable.*

As it has always been.

EPHEMERA

To Madame Brillon, of Passy, Paris
From Benjamin Franklin
1776

You may remember, my dear friend, that when we lately spent that happy day in the delightful garden and sweet society of the Moulin Joly, I stopped a little in one of our walks, and stayed some time behind the company. We had been shown numberless skeletons of a kind of little fly, called an ephemera, whose successive generations, we were told, were bred and expired within the day. I happened to see a living company of them on a leaf, who appeared to be engaged in conversation.

You know I understand all the inferior animal tongues. My too great application to the study of them is the best excuse I can give for the little progress I have made in your charming language. I listened through curiosity to the discourse of these little creatures. . . . They were disputing warmly on the merit of two foreign musicians, one a cousin, the other a moscheto; in which dispute they spent their time, seemingly as regardless of the shortness of life as if they had been sure of living a month. Happy people! thought I; you are certainly under a wise, just, and mild government, since you have no public grievances to complain of, nor any subject of contention but the perfections and imperfections of foreign music. I turned my head from them to an old gray-headed one, who was single on another leaf, and talking to himself. Being amused with his soliloquy, I put it down in writing, in hopes it will likewise amuse her to whom I am so much indebted for the most pleasing of all amusements, her delicious company and heavenly harmony.

"It was," said he, "the opinion of learned philosophers of our race, who lived and flourished long before my time, that this vast world, the Moulin Joly, could not itself subsist more than eighteen hours; and I think there was some foundation for that opinion, since, by the apparent motion of the great luminary that gives life to all nature, and which in my time has evidently declined considerably towards the ocean at the end of our earth, it must then finish its course, be extinguished in the waters that surround us, and leave the world in cold and darkness, necessarily producing universal death and destruction.

"I have lived seven of those hours, a great age, being no less than four hundred and twenty minutes of time. How very few of us continue so long! I have seen generations born, flourish, and expire. My present friends are the children and grandchildren of the friends of my youth, who are now, also, no more! And I must soon follow them; for, by the course of nature, though still in health, I cannot expect to live above seven or eight minutes longer. What now avails all my toil and labor in amassing honey-dew on this leaf, which I cannot live to enjoy! What the political struggles I have been engaged in for the good of my compatriot inhabitants of this bush, or my philosophical studies for the benefit of our race in general! for in politics what can laws do without morals?

"Our present race of ephemera will in a course of minutes become corrupt, like those of other and older bushes, and consequently as wretched. And in philosophy

how small our progress! Alas! art is long, and life is short! My friends would comfort me with the idea of a name they say I shall leave behind me; and they tell me I have lived long enough to nature and to glory. But what will fame be to an ephemera who no longer exists? And what will become of all history in the eighteenth hour, when the world itself, even the whole Moulin Joly, shall come to its end and be buried in universal ruin?"

"To me, after all my eager pursuits, no solid pleasures now remain, but the reflection of a long life spent in meaning well, the sensible conversation of a few good lady ephemeræ, and now and then a kind smile and a tune from the ever amiable Brillante."

And here, too, one learns that the world, though made, is yet being made; that this is still the morning of creation; that mountains long conceived are now being born, channels traced for coming rivers, basins hollowed for lakes; that moraine soil is being ground and outspread for coming plants,—coarse boulders and gravel for forests, finer soil for grasses and flowers,—while the finest part of the grist, seen hastening out to sea in the draining streams, is being stored away In darkness and builded particle on particle, cementing and crystallizing, to make the mountains and valleys and plains of other predestined landscapes, to be followed by still others in endless rhythm and beauty.

— JOHN MUIR

GANDALF: A thing is going to happen which has not happened since the Elder Days: the trees are going to wake up and find that they are strong.

— R.R. TOLKIEN

SELECTED SOURCES FOR FURTHER READING AND VIEWING

It is my hope that some part of this book piqued your interest and you would like to discover more. These sources are for the general reader and have been arranged in the order that the relevant material appears in the book. (Websites last accessed in July 2017).

PART 1: BEGINNINGS

THE EARTH CALENDAR

Dragons of Eden, Carl Sagan. (1977)

Longitude, Dava Sobel. (1995)

Earth Song, Charles Camp. (1952)

The Universe Story, Brian Swimme, Thomas Berry. (1992)

The Journey of the Universe, Brian Thomas Swimme, Mary Evelyn Tucker. DVD. (2011)

SUMMER 1776

On Wings of Gold, T. Anthony Quinn. (1998)

Walking in Ticino Switzerland, Kev Reynolds. (1992)

1776, David McCullough. (2005)

One Day in History July 4, 1776, Rodney Carlisle. (2006)

John Adams, David McCullough. (2001)

Jefferson: Writings, Thomas Jefferson. (1905)

Autobiography of Benjamin Franklin, Benjamin Franklin. (1888)

CALIFORNIA 1775

Benjamin Franklin, Walter Isaacson. (2003)

"John Adams," HBO mini-series produced by Tom Hanks. (2008)

Lands of Promise and Despair: Chronicles of Early California 1535-1846, Rose Marie Beebe, Robert Senkewicz. (2001)

A World Transformed: First-hand Accounts of California Before the Gold Rush, Joshua Paddison. (1998)

Life and Apostolic Labors of the Venerable Father Junípero Serra, Francisco Palou. (1913)

Chief Marin, Betty Goerke. (2007)

Discovering Native People at Point Reyes, Betty Goerke. (2012)

Kule Loklo and the Coast Miwok Indians, Sylvia Barker Thalman. (1982)

The Coast Miwok Indians of the Point Reyes Area, Sylvia Barker Thalman. Excellent introductory pamphlet with illustrations for young people.

Interviews With Tom Smith and Maria Copa: Isabel Kelly's *Ethnographic Notes on the Coast Miwok Indians of Marin and Southern Sonoma Counties*, ed. Mary E. Collier. (1991)

Ishi in Two Worlds, Theodora Kroeber, Karl Kroeber. (2002)

"Ishi: The Last Yahi," available as DVD. (1994)

"Pedro Fages and Miguel Costansó, "Two Early Letters From San Diego in 1769," *Journal of San Diego History*, Spring 1975. Account of San Carlos voyage.

PART 2: EARLY MIGRATIONS

THE EARTH CALENDAR

Flame Trees of Thika, Elspeth Huxley. (1959) This is a classic memoir of Africa , beautifully adapted as a TV series in 1981.

Out in the Midday Sun: My Kenya, Elspeth Huxley. (1985) A sequel to *The Flame Trees of Thika*.

Noah's Flood: The New Scientific Discoveries About the Event That Changed History, William Ryan, Walter Pittman. (2000) An engrossing book by two distinguished geophysicists who use the latest scientific techniques to explore the possibility that the great flood of the Biblical account and the Sumerian Gilgamesh epic were actual events.

PANGAEA

Animate Earth: Science, Intuition and Gaia, Stephan Harding. Foreword by Lynn Margulis. (2009)

Gaia: A New Look at Life on Earth, James Lovelock. (1979)

THE MEDITERRANEAN SEA

The Odyssey, Homer. Andrew Lang translation. (1888)

Minotaur: Sir Arthur Evans and the Archaeology of the Minoan Myth, J Alexander MacGillivray. (2000)

The Civilization of Ancient Crete, R.F. Willetts. (1977)

Art and Religion in Thera, Nanno Marinatos. (1984) An excellent book with plates and graphics by the daughter of the archaeologist who discovered Akrotiri on Thera.

Atlantis: The Evidence," (2010). BBC Documentary that compares Minoan Akrotiri with Plato on Atlantis.

Secrets of the Dead: Sinking Atlantis. (2008). Excellent PBS Documentary on recent scientific discoveries around the Thera eruption.

Exodus Decoded (2005) is a documentary that explores the theory that the Minoan catastrophe is related to events of the Biblical Exodus.

"The Minoans—DNA and all," Mathilda's Anthropology Blog. DNA findings on origin of the Minoans. (2008)

The Maze and the Warrior, Craig Wright. (2001)

The Unending Mystery, David McCullough. (2004)

Walking a Sacred Path, Lauren Artress. (1995)

Rediscovering the Labyrinth: A Walking Meditation, Lauren Artress and Grace Cathedral. (2001) Available on DVD.

The Aeneid, Virgil. John Dryden translation. (1834)

The New American Bible. (1970)

The Iliad, Robert Fitzgerald translation. (1974)

The Gold of Troy, Robert Payne. (1959)

Greek Treasure, Irving Stone. (1975) A Novel about the Schliemann's, later made into a movie.

In Search of the Trojan War, Michael Wood. (1985) Michael Wood also hosts the BBC series of this name, available on DVD and online. (2005)

NORTH AFRICA TO THE LOMBARDS

"The Martyrdom of Saints Perpetua and Felicitas" The prison diary of Perpetua from Carthage ca. 203 AD. www.pbs.org/wgbh/pages/frontline/shows/religion/maps/primary/perpetua.html.

Confessions of St. Augustine, John K. Ryan (trans.). (trans. 1960)

St. Augustine, Gary Wills. (2005)

St. Augustine, Edward Cutts. (1914)

The Confession of Augustine, Jean-Francois Lyotard. (1998) A post-modern philosopher on Augustine. (Stanford's "Cultural Memory in the Present" series).

The Christian Centuries: From Christ to Dante, Robert Payne. (1966)

Tunisian Mosaics, Aïcha Ben Abed. (2006)

ROME ~ NOW AND THEN

The Passion of the Western Mind: Understanding the Ideas That Have Shaped Our World View, Richard Tarnas. (1991). I highly recommend this book as a background to the early history in many of our portraits, particularly the shift from Pagan to Christian Europe.

Ancient Rome, Robert Payne. (1970)

SPQR: A History of Ancient Rome, Mary Beard. (2015)

"The Roman Empire," 7-pt. documentary. Available on YouTube and DVD. (2014)

"Virtual Tour of Ancient Rome" 320 A.D., Google Earth. (2009)

"Clickable Map of the Forum," online at http://www.vroma.org/~forum/forum.html . Excellent resource for scholars or the casual cyber wanderer of ancient Rome.

The Rise and Fall of Alexandria: Birthplace of the Modern World. Justin Pollard, Howard Reid. (2007)

Hypatia of Alexandria, Maria Dzielska, F. Lyra. (1995)

"The Letter of Paula and Eustochium to Marcella, about The Holy Places (386 A.D.)" at "A Celebration of Women Writers" webpage: http://digital.library.upenn.edu/women/paula/letter/letter.html. A remarkable document that records Paula's pilgrimage to the Holy Places in Scriptures. She provides an especially rich description of Jerusalem at the time as a place of great diversity with pilgrims arriving from throughout the empire.

THE LOMBARDS

History of the Lombards, Paul the Deacon. (trans. 1974)

Charlemagne: From the Hammer to the Cross, Richard Winston. (1954)

TARIQ

The Arab Conquest of Spain: 710-797, Roger Collins. (1989)

Men of Salt: Crossing the Sahara on the Caravan of White Gold, Michael Benanav. (2006)

Islam: Empire of Faith, (2009). PBS Documentary series available online and DVD

The Lost Libraries of Timbuktu, BBC Documentary. (2010) Fascinating. Available as DVD or online

"Where Camel Meets Canoe: Discovering Timbuktu's Ancient Past," Douglas Park. Published in *Past Horizons*: Vol: 8, March 2009.

The House of Wisdom: How Arabic Science Saved Ancient Knowledge and Gave Us the Renaissance, Jim Al-Khalili (2011)

The Search for the Tassili Frescoes: Rock Painting in the Sahara, Henri Lhote. (1959)

PART 3: PUSHING UPWARD

MAGISTER COMACINI

The Decline and Fall of the Roman Empire, Edward Gibbon. (1777). If you wish to dig in deep and read English prose from another century, this work is a timeless classic.

The Secret History, Procopius. (trans. 1674)

Le Morte d'Arthur, Thomas Mallory, Ed. John Matthews. (2000)

The Virgin and the Grail, Joseph Goering. (2005)

CHACO CANYON

The Mystery of Chaco Canyon, narrated by Robert Redford. DVD. Solstice Project. (2003)

The Book of the Hopi, Frank Waters with Oswald White Bear Fredericks. (1963)

The Chaco Meridian, Stephen H. Lekson. (1999)

"The Chaco Meridian," J.Q. Jacobs. (2008) http://www.jqjacobs.net/southwest/chaco_meridian.html Archaeology site well worth visiting.

Cahokia: Ancient America's Great City on the Mississippi, by Timothy R. Pauketat, one of the leading archaeologists of the site.

Cahokia: City of the Sun. A short, somewhat fanciful video but a good introduction to Cahokia. https://www.youtube.com/watch?v=GAXBA2Pt9wE

Cahokia: America's Lost City. A full length BBC documentary. https://www.youtube.com/watch?v=pgJV_xqJh1k

CREATION STORIES

The Maidu Indian Myths and Stories of Hanc'ibyjim, William Shipley. (1991)

"Malki Museum/Founding and History," http://www.malkimuseum.org/founding.htm (2007)

14TH CENTURY

"The Little Ice Age in Europe," (2009) http://www2.sunysuffolk.edu/mandias/lia/little_ice_age.html

The Great Mortality: An Intimate History of the Black Death, the Most Devastating Plague of All Time, John Kelly. (2005)

"Francesco Petrarch and Laura de Noves," http://petrarch.petersadlon.com/petrarch.html An excellent website that includes a large collection of his works. (2007)

Petrarch, the First Modern Scholar and Man of Letters: A Selection from His Correspondence with Boccaccio and Other Friends, Francesco Petrarca. (1898)

The Decameron," Boccaccio (trans. 1903). Online at "The Decameron Web," Brown University. http://www.brown.edu/Departments/Italian_Studies/dweb/

Cicero: On Old Age, On Friendship, On Divination (Loeb Classical Library No. 154), Cicero. W.A. Falconer trans. (1923)

The Materials and Techniques of Medieval Painting, Daniel V. Thompson. (1956)

A History of Painting in Italy, Umbria, Florence and Siena, from the second to the sixteenth century. Joseph Archer Crowe et al. (1972)

Petrarch: his life and times, Henry C. Hollway-Calthrop. (1907)

PART 4: THE WAY WEST

Neither Dog nor Wolf: On Forgotten Roads with an Indian elder, Kent Nerburn. (1994) Excellent book that presents the native perspective on the emigrant settling of America through the voice of a wise and eloquent Sioux elder.

The Emigrants, Vilhelm Moberg. (1951). A fine classic novel of emigration, following migrants from Sweden.

The Story of Majorca and Minorca, Clements R. Markham. (1908)

The Missions and Missionaries of California, v.2, Upper California, Zephyrin Engelhardt. (1929)

Lands of Promise and Despair: Chronicles of Early California 1535-1846, Rose Marie Beebe, Robert M. Senkewicz. (2001)

Chief Marin, Betty Goerke. (2007)

Contested Eden: California Before the Gold Rush, Ramón A. Gutiérrez, Richard J. Orsi. (1998)

Sixty Years in California: A History of Events and Life in California, William Heath Davis. (1889). A first-hand account of life in California under the Mexican regime and through its transition to a State of the Union.

The Western Gate: A San Francisco Reader, ed. Joseph Henry Jackson. (1952)

Eldorado: The California Gold Rush, Dale L. Walker. (2003)

PART 5: POINT REYES

Broken Shore: The Marin Peninsula in California History, Arthur Quinn. (1987)

Assembling California, John McPhee. (1993)

Natural History of the Point Reyes Peninsula, Jules G. Evens. (1988)

Geology of the San Francisco Bay Region, Doris Sloane. (2006)

Dairy Farming in the Olema Valley: A History of the Dairy and Beef Ranches of the Olema Valley and Lagunitas Canyon, Dewey Livingston. (1995) Dewey Livingston was historian for the Golden Gate Recreation Area, Point Reyes National Seashore.

Point Reyes Peninsula, Carola DeRooy, Dewey Livingston. (2008)

Point Reyes, Gayle Baker. (2004)

Point Reyes: The Complete Guide to the National Seashore and Surrounding Area, Jessica Lage. (2004)

Point Reyes: The Solemn Land, Jack Mason. (1970)

THE SHAFTERS

The Life, Diary and Letters of Oscar Lovell Shafter, edited for Emma Shafter Howard by Flora Haines Loughead. (1915). Available online.

Early Marin, Jack Mason, Helen Van Cleave. (1971)

The History of Marin County, California, J.P. Monro-Fraser. (1880). A remarkably rich compendium of detailed physical, historical and biographical descriptions of 19th century Marin. Available online.

Narrow Gauge to the Redwoods: The Story of the North Pacific Coast Railroad and San Francisco Bay Paddle-wheel Ferries by Ables Bray. (1981)

FOUR SOMEBODIES AND A RAILROAD

High Road to Promontory -- Building the Central Pacific (now the Southern Pacific) across the High Sierra, George Kraus. Palo Alto: American West Publishing Company. (1969)

The Associates: Four Capitalists Who Created California, Richard Rayner. (2009)

EAST MEETS WEST

A Heart Poured Out: A Story of Swami Ashkananda (Yogesh Chandra Datta), Sister Gargi (Marie Louise Burke). (2003)

MAKING WAVES ~ BOLINAS, POINT REYES

Marconi: The Man Who Networked the World, Mark Raboy. (2016). Long and detailed biography of the man who has been called the Steve Jobs of the last century.

"Commonweal." The website for the healing and retreat center, video interview archives and regenerative garden at commonweal. org

"Symphony of the Soil." (2013) An excellent documentary available on DVD.

Dirt: The Movie. (2009) at www.dirtthemovie. org You will never look at "dirt" the same way.

Phenomenon of Man, Pierre Teilhard de Chardin. (1959)

Finding Beauty in a Broken World, Terry Tempest Williams. (2008)

Rediscovering the Labyrinth: A Walking Meditation, Lauren Artress and Grace Cathedral. (2001) Available on DVD.

Dream of the Earth, Thomas Berry (1988)

The Sixth Extinction, Elizabeth Kolbert. (2014)

PART 6: ENDINGS AND BEGINNINGS

THE NEW CENTURY

I vecchi e la montagna (The old people and the mountain), ed. by Franco Binda. Published in 1983 by Armando Dadò.

This Date in San Francisco. John Ralston. (2011)

Fremont Older and the 1916 San Francisco Bombing. John Ralston. (2013)

Vivekananda: A Biography, Swami Nikhilananda. (1953)

Disaster: The Great San Francisco Earthquake and Fire of 1906, Dan Kurzman. (2001)

The Great Earthquake and Firestorms of 1906: How San Francisco Nearly Destroyed Itself, Phillip L. Fradkin. (2006)

PART 7: A FARM IN MARIN

TICINO

"Economic crisis and fools gold: Interview." (2009) Ticino historian Georgio Cheda discusses the roots of the mass nineteenth century migration from Ticino http://www.swissinfo.ch/eng/economic-crisis-and-fools-gold--interview/994310 .

"We shall not stay long." A rich website with articles on the 19th century emigration from Ticino. http://www.swissinfo.ch/eng/in-depth/-we-shall-not-stay-long-

"Dale Bechtel interview with Ticino historian Giorgio Cheda on Italian-Swiss Migrations."

http://www.swissinfo.ch/eng/migrations-interview--part-five/7135364

SAN FRANCISCO BAY TO SAUSALITO

"An introduction to the San Francisco Estuary," Andrew Cohen. www.savethebay.org (1991)

"Marine Mammals of the Bay Area," at www.SFBayWildlife.info

"Dr. Sylvia Earle," (2014) a 15-minute documentary about Sylvia Earle, one of the pioneers of ocean exploration and of women in science; a hero of mine! https://www.youtube.com/watch?v=_7JFlWdNxOU . Also a TED talk at www.ted.com

POINT REYES STATION, 1892

Lives of a Cell: Notes of a Biology Watcher, Lewis Thomas. (1974) A delightful classic by an eminent biologist, physician and former president of the Memorial Sloane-Kettering Cancer Center.

Two Years Before the Mast, Richard Henry Dana Jr. (1842) Classic first-hand account of this era

"Popo-Leen: The Yuroks and the Redwood Tree," OMSI Film.

PART 8: A NEW ERA

Ranching on the Point Reyes Peninsula, Dewey Livingston. "Zena Mendoza Speaks Out." (1994)

EMERSON, MUIR AND THE TREES

A Passion for Nature: The Life of John Muir, Donald Worster. (2008)

The Life and Letters of John Muir, John Muir, ed. Frederic Badè. (1924)

Biography of John Muir. https://www.youtube.com/watch?v=-CDzhIvugw8. (2010)

John Muir in the New World. DVD. (2011)

The Essential Writings of Ralph Waldo Emerson (with an introduction by Mary Oliver). (2000)

CROSSING THE GOLDEN GATE

The Gate: The True Story of the Design and Construction of the Golden Gate Bridge, John Van Der Zee. (1986)

"Modern Marvel: Golden Gate Bridge." (2006). History Channel video.

"Marin Agricultural Land Trust," www.malt.org .

Farming on the Edge: Saving Family Farms in Marin County, California, John Hart. Foreword by Wendell Barry.

"Climbing the Redwoods," Richard Preston in *The New Yorker,* February 15, 2006.

POINT REYES

"The Legacy of a Point Reyes Farming Family," Kirsten Jones Neff. *Edible Marin and Wine Country Magazine* online. (2011)

Dream Dances of the Kashia Pomo—The Bole-Maru Religion—Women's Dances." Filmed and produced in 1963 by the University of California Extension Media Center.

EPILOGUE

"From Benjamin Franklin to Madame Brillon: 'The Ephemera,' 20 September 1778" in *Lin Yutang on the Wisdom of America,* Lin Yutang. (1950, 2007). Online at https://founders.archives.gov/documents/Franklin/01-27-02-0408

ACKNOWLEDGMENTS

A book of this length and scope would not be possible without the time and space for deep thought and extensive research. For this, I give thanks first and foremost to Mr. Fields and our hosts Ed and Susie Grossi, and to our former host Laurie-Ann Barbour. Also to those wonderful people who provided refuge for this work: J.J. Wilson, for her "writerly house" and extensive book collection, which provided inspiration for several of these portraits; Gertrud Lackschewitz, who opened her home to me time and again and provided delicious meals throughout. Bo and Ari Dickinson offered welcome refuge in Bishopville, South Carolina and many summers were spent in Camden, South Carolina at the lovely home of Anthony and Judy Hawkesworth. Diana Eck, and Howie and Peggy Fly provided wonderful refuges for me in Ovando, Montana.

I am deeply indebted to material support provided by James and Kara Cross and Phillip and Lynda LaBerge, especially through the early inchoate phase of this project!

For decades of support and precious friendship that feeds the creative soul, I thank Barbara and Jack Cross and all of their family; Virginia Igonda and her family; my *comadre* Yolanda Hay and her family in Mexico; Anne Mery, Katie Law, Sally Mahé, Terry Gopadze, Anita Doyle, Howie and Peggy Fly, Wayne and Rose Tyson, Margaret Edwards, Dorrie Adessa, Alice Nolan, Josefina Burgos, and many other dear friends too numerous to name here. You know who you are!

This book would never have seen the light of day without the full-hearted encouragement and help of Brian Swimme and input from Richard Tarnas. I am especially grateful to Sally Mahé and Paulette Millichap for believing in it and carrying it forward to reality. I thank Carl Brune, the peerless book designer, for his talent and his patience. Barbara Cross, Sue Tideman and Paula Hammett were generous and invaluable in reading early drafts of the work. Katherine Dickinson offered research assistance at a critical moment. I thank Beverly Grossi and Ralph Grossi for help in producing the family photo.

I am grateful for the generous contributions and guidance of experts in various fields. Tony Quinn helped me track down Grossi genealogies and provided detailed pictures of life in Ticino. Tarek Radwan told me about the remarkable rock art of Tassili N'Ajjer. I am grateful to Carola DeRooy, Point Reyes archivist, and Dewey Livingston, Point Reyes historian, for reviewing the Point Reyes portions of the manuscript. Anthropologist Betty Goerke provided invaluable information on Chief Marin and kindly reviewed those sections. I am indebted to San Francisco historian John Ralston for reviewing the San Francisco sections. Celia Kupersmith, former CEO of the Golden Gate Bridge, Highway and Transportation District gave input and Charlie Siebenthal, President of the Northwestern Pacific Railroad Historical Society, reviewed relevant material on the North Pacific Coast Railroad. Any errors are mine alone.

Lastly, I thank Domenico Grossi for inspiring this work and siring many of its characters! I recently came across these lines in a novel by Scott Turow that said it beautifully: "[He] had been overwhelmed by how much harder life would have been for the old man's twenty-three children and grandchildren were it not for the blessing of his bravery in making the journey here. The example of a heroism that spread itself over so many lives . . ."

PATRON'S CIRCLE

Special thanks to those who contributed to the
Tri-S Foundation Kickstarter Campaign in support of the work.

Katie Ackerly

Susan Babcock

Sarah Brightwood

Barbara B. Cross

James and Kara Cross

Linda Barry Esposito

Cheryl Genet

Herman Greene

Terry and Lee Gopadze

Sally Mahé

Ben and Jeanne Meleca

Anne Mery

Christopher Ritchlin

Brian Thomas Swimme

Alice Harroff Waters

Revay Wilson

Robin R. Wilson

This book is dedicated to the memory of James Allerton Cross (1933–2017)

CPSIA information can be obtained
at www.ICGtesting.com
Printed in the USA
FSOW04n0506270917
39062FS